PROCESSING
of
THERMOPLASTIC MATERIALS

Edited by

ERNEST C. BERNHARDT, Dr. Ing.

Polychemicals Department

E. I. du Pont de Nemours & Co., Inc.

PLASTICS ENGINEERING SERIES

REINHOLD PUBLISHING CORPORATION
NEW YORK
CHAPMAN & HALL, LTD., LONDON

PRINTED IN THE UNITED STATES OF AMERICA

THE GUINN CO., INC.
New York 14, N. Y.

CONTRIBUTORS

J. T. Bergen, M.S.
Research & Development Center
Armstrong Cork Company
Lancaster, Pennsylvania

E. C. Bernhardt, Dr. Ing.
Polychemicals Department
E. I. du Pont de Nemours & Co., Inc.
Wilmington, Delaware

C. E. Beyer, B.S.
The Dow Chemical Company
Midland, Michigan

J. F. Carley, Ph.D.
Modern Plastics Magazine
Breskin Publications, Inc.
New York, New York

F. M. Cash, B.S.
Polychemicals Department
E. I. du Pont de Nemours & Co., Inc.
Wilmington, Delaware

R. B. Dahl, B.S.
The Dow Chemical Company
Midland, Michigan

W. H. Darnell, Ph.D.
Polychemicals Department
E. I. du Pont de Nemours & Co., Inc.
Wilmington, Delaware

T. M. Hearst, B.S.
Tennessee Eastman Company
Division of Eastman Kodak Company
Kingsport, Tennessee

G. P. Kovach, Dipl.-Ing.
Foster-Grant Company, Inc.
Leominster, Massachusetts

D. I. Marshall, Ph.D.
Union Carbide Plastics Company
Division of Union Carbide Corporation
Bound Brook, New Jersey

J. M. McKelvey, Ph.D.
Department of Chemical Engineering
Washington University
St. Louis, Missouri

A. B. Metzner, Sc.D.
Department of Chemical Engineering
University of Delaware
Newark, Delaware

J. W. Mighton, B.S.
The Dow Chemical Company
Midland, Michigan

W. D. Mohr*, Sc.D.
Department of Chemical Engineering
Massachusetts Institute of Technology
Cambridge, Massachusetts

J. B. Paton, B.S.
Polychemicals Department
E. I. du Pont de Nemours & Co., Inc.
Wilmington, Delaware

N. Platzer, Ph.D.
Plastics Division
Monsanto Chemical Company
Springfield, Massachusetts

B. P. Rouse, Jr., Ph.D.
Tennessee Eastman Company
Division of Eastman Kodak Company
Kingsport, Tennessee

P. H. Squires, Ph.D.
Polychemicals Department
E. I. du Pont de Nemours & Co., Inc.
Wilmington, Delaware

G. B. Thayer, B.S.
The Dow Chemical Company
Midland, Michigan

R. F. Westover, M.S.E.
Bell Telephone Laboratories, Inc.
Murray Hill, New Jersey

* Present address: Polychemicals Department, E. I. du Pont de Nemours & Co., Inc., Wilmington, Delaware

THE PLASTICS ENGINEERING SERIES
OF THE
SOCIETY OF PLASTICS ENGINEERS, INC.

The Society of Plastics Engineers, founded in 1941, is an international organization representing the plastics engineering profession. Its broad purpose is to promote scientific and engineering knowledge related to plastics. Since its inception, the Society has fostered the interchange of technical information through its technical conferences, the *SPE Journal*, and the work of professional activity committees.

In its dedication to the task of disseminating scientific information, the Society of Plastics Engineers has encouraged members of the profession to contribute to this series of books on the various aspects of plastics engineering. The first of these, "Quality Control for Plastics Engineers" was published in 1957. "Processing of Thermoplastic Materials" represents the second contribution. Additional volumes are currently being planned to broaden the scope of the Plastics Engineering Series.

PREFACE

The technical problems encountered in extrusion, injection molding, calendering, and other thermoplastics processing operations are closely interrelated. The purpose of this book is to emphasize the scientific foundation which underlies an engineering approach to the processing of thermoplastic materials.

In such a relatively new area, one should expect some of the gaps in fundamental understanding which are evident in this volume. One of the purposes of this book is to direct attention to the need for further engineering studies in thermoplastics processing.

The specialists whose contributions are presented here should be regarded as individually responsible for their chapters. The editor wishes to express his particular appreciation to the authors and to Jules W. Lindau, III, who, as Technical Administrator of the Society of Plastics Engineers, Inc., lent the motivation which initiated this project. Sponsorship by the Society of Plastic Engineers, Inc., offered a rallying point around which the contributions from such widespread sources could be joined together. The editor is indebted to the many firms in the plastics industry that supported this volume through their contributions of information and data, much of which was especially correlated and had not been published previously. Particular acknowledgments are also due those companies which made possible the contributions by authors who are members of their staffs.

Without the excellent *esprit de corps* of all contributors, and their devotion to their work, and without the cooperation of the many associates who supported this publication through their valuable suggestions and constructive criticism, this book could not have been published.

Wilmington, Delaware   ERNEST C. BERNHARDT
November, 1958

CONTENTS

SECTION III: PROCESSING PROPERTIES

INTRODUCTION

E. C. Bernhardt, Dr. Ing.

Polychemicals Department
E. I. du Pont de Nemours & Co., Inc.

There is no accepted and generally recognized definition of "plastics engineering." It is commonly agreed, however, that this term designates and includes the following major areas:

(1) *Compounding of Plastic Materials*—the modification of plastic materials via chemical changes or by means of additives in order to alter the properties of the plastic and to make it especially suitable for specific end-use applications.

(2) *Polymer Processing*—the design and operation of various processes for molding, forming, and otherwise altering plastic materials in order to increase their utility.

(3) *Design of Plastic Parts*—the engineering of component parts, considering the pertinent properties of the materials used and the end-use application of the part.

(4) *General Plastics Engineering*—miscellaneous engineering studies such as quality control, cost studies, market studies, end-use and application studies, testing procedures, etc., as applied specifically to the plastics industry.

This book deals with a specific area of *Polymer Processing*.

Within the past two decades there has been a phenomenal increase in the consumption of polymeric materials. Although natural polymers such as rubber, cotton, and silk have served mankind for many centuries and continue to be essential industrial products, synthetic polymers are now approaching them in importance and have opened large new areas of application. In recent years these polymers, in the form of synthetic rubbers, fibers, plastics, and surface coatings, have become extremely important items of commerce and have accounted for a large part of the spectacular growth of the American chemical industry.

1

The manufacture of most synthetic polymers is a technically complex operation and is, at the same time, economically feasible only on a very large scale. This high degree of technical complexity and large scale of investment required for an industrial installation has stimulated the growth of a particularly high quality of research and engineering in the manufacture of polymers.

Polymer processing, on the other hand, presents conditions which, until recently, were entirely different from those encountered in polymer synthesis. Most polymer processing operations were technically simple and required only modest investments, which made it economically feasible to carry them out on a very small scale. In the late 1930's, *e.g.*, a typical 2-in. extruder for processing about 30 lb/hr of resin represented an investment, including associated equipment, of not much over $4,000. Under these circumstances it was relatively simple and it involved little risk to develop and improve the equipment through empirical methods.

In the last decade, however, the techniques and equipment have been refined, and the size and capacity of processing machines have increased to the point where the construction of plastics processing plants requires considerably larger investments. Large extruders such as those used in modern paper-coating equipment can process up to 1,000 lb of polymer per hour and, with their auxiliaries, may involve an investment of up to $250,000. Some large molding machines and calenders require even greater capital expenditures. A high percentage of the polymers used today is processed on machines of this size.

The cost of carrying out experimental development work on these large-scale operations is so high that a more certain and scientific approach to the design of this equipment is required. For this reason, resin suppliers, machinery builders, and processors are increasingly concerned with the application of basic engineering theory in the design of commercial polymer-processing equipment.

Polymer processing has been defined[*] previously, as follows:

> *"Polymer processing is an engineering specialty concerned with operations carried out on polymeric materials or systems to increase their utility. These operations produce one or more of the following effects: chemical reaction, flow, or a permanent change in a physical property. Specifically excluded are the chemical reactions involved in the manufacture of resins."*

This field comprises two major areas—(1) processing of thermoplastic materials and (2) processing of thermosetting materials.

Processing operations on thermoplastic materials generally do not

[*] Bernhardt, E. C., and McKelvey, J. M., "Polymer Processing—A New Engineering Specialty," *Modern Plastics*, **35**, 154 (July, 1958).

involve major chemical changes. It is possible to analyze most thermoplastics processes and to predict the performance of thermoplastics processing equipment, provided the viscous and thermal properties of the resin being treated are known, and the operation of the equipment is understood.

The analysis of thermosetting processing operations, on the other hand, requires, in addition to the above, an understanding of the kinetics of the polymerization reactions and their effects on the viscous and thermal properties of the resin as it goes through the curing process. This field is therefore technically vastly more complex. A text dealing with the processing of thermosetting materials would demand separate consideration of the problems involved with each resin, and would require a basically different organization from the present volume.

In view of the above considerations, this book is confined in its coverage to the thermoplastics area of polymer processing. It does not consider any chemical changes which may accompany these processing operations, nor does it cover processes which involve major chemical transformations and reactions.

The present volume contains three major sections:

The *Fundamentals Section* describes the basic theories of flow behavior, heat transfer, and mixing on which the design of thermoplastics processing equipment is founded.

The *Applications Section* covers the design of the major categories of processing equipment and demonstrates how equations may be derived which describe the behavior of plastic materials in a given piece of equipment.

The *Processing Properties Section* presents a compilation of the viscous and thermal properties of thermoplastics needed for the design of processing equipment. These data are presented in forms which are believed to be most suitable for direct application in the equations presented in the preceding sections.

The goal of the engineer concerned with thermoplastics processing operations is to calculate and predict the performance of polymer processing equipment, working from the design and operating variables and from the physical and chemical properties of the material being handled. It is the hope of the contributors that this book may lead the reader closer to the achievement of this goal.

Section I

Fundamentals

1. FLOW BEHAVIOR OF THERMOPLASTICS

A. B. Metzner, Sc. D.

Department of Chemical Engineering
University of Delaware

BASIC MATERIAL PROPERTIES

Idealized Materials

Idealized materials represent a necessary starting point in consideration of the flow of polymeric materials, since the nonideal behavior of these substances is usually defined and best visualized in terms of deviations from these ideals. Furthermore, many of the concepts developed for the idealized materials prove to be of value in interpreting the behavior of real polymers. Solids as well as liquids must be considered, at least briefly, since polymeric melts and solutions display some of the properties commonly associated with both of these states.

Ideal (Elastic) Solid. The ideal solid is defined by Hooke's law:

$$d\tau = E \frac{dL}{L_o} \tag{1}$$

or

$$\tau_T = E \frac{L - L_o}{L_o} = E \gamma_T \tag{2}$$

Thus the fractional elongation γ_T (i.e., the strain) is directly proportional to the imposed tensile stress τ_T. The constant of proportionality E is frequently termed Young's modulus, or, more directly, the modulus of elasticity of the solid.

Hooke's law serves to define the response (elongation) of an ideal solid to a tensile stress τ_T, by use of the modulus of elasticity E which may be considered a true physical property of the material. One may analogously define the behavior of an elastic solid which has a shearing stress imposed on it by use of a shear modulus of elasticity, commonly termed simply the

6

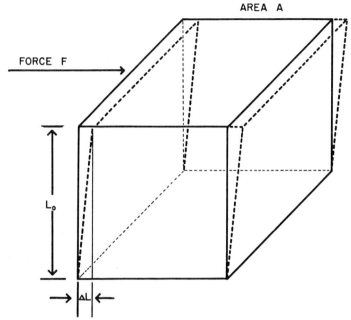

FIG. 1.1. Deformation of an elastic solid by a shearing stress.

"shear modulus" of the material, as follows:

$$F/A = G \frac{\Delta L}{L_o} \tag{3}$$

or

$$\tau = F/A = G\gamma_s \tag{4}$$

where τ is the shearing stress exerted on the material (Fig. 1.1), and γ_s is the deformation of the material (or shearing strain) caused by this shearing stress. The shear modulus G is directly related to the tensile modulus E, although in general the two are not numerically identical.[1, p. 15]

Within any range of stresses in which a real solid behaves in an elastically ideal manner, upon removal of either the tensile or shearing stress, the solid returns precisely to its initial shape immediately.

The characteristics of an ideal solid in tension are thus seen to be identical with those of an ideally elastic coil spring. Since the behavior of the solid in shear is directly related to its tensile behavior, rheologists sometimes use a coil spring as a mechanical model descriptive of the shear behavior of elastic materials. It is not intended to imply thereby that the molecules of the solid are necessarily in a coiled configuration but simply that they be-

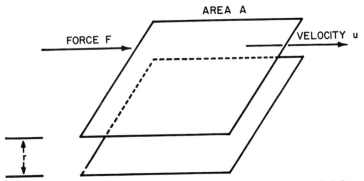

Fɪɢ. 1.2. Diagram depicting idealized fluid shear between two parallel flat plates. (Reproduced from Ref. 59 by permission of copyright owner).

have in such a way as to cause the bulk material to behave much as a spring would.

The chief characteristics of an elastic solid may be summarized as being: (1) the direct proportionality between stress and strain and (2) the instantaneous change in shape of the object when the stress is changed.

An ideal coiled spring may be considered to be a mechanical model having the same behavior as an elastic solid.

Ideal or Newtonian Fluid. Figure 1.2 illustrates the behavior of an ideal fluid under the influence of a shearing stress $\tau = (F/A)$. In this experiment it is visualized that the fluid fills the space between the two parallel plates of area A. On imposition of even a very small force F, the upper plate does not simply move instantaneously to a new location as in the case of the upper surface of the solid cube depicted by Fig. 1.1. Instead, when the shearing force is imposed on a plate bounding the fluid, this plate will be found to move relative to another at a constant velocity u as long as the force remains constant. (Of course, the ideal experiment depicted in Fig. 1.2 would have to be considerably modified in practice to avoid fluid spillage and to maintain the areas opposite one another indefinitely.) Furthermore, the fluid exhibits no tendency whatever to return to its original shape when the shearing stress is finally removed.

Since even a nonwetting liquid adheres sufficiently to a confining wall to prevent relative motion between the two except under very unusual circumstances (see p. 41), the liquid next to the lower plate in Fig. 1.2 has zero velocity, while that which is in immediate contact with the upper plate will have velocity u in the direction of the force. Since the shearing force is transmitted uniformly through the liquid to the lower plate, each layer of the fluid within the space of height r will slip relative to the next, setting up, in this way, a uniform change in velocity with distance. Mathematically, the relationship between this shearing stress and the resulting change in velocity with distance may be given by either of two equations, since u/r is constant (hence equal to du/dr):

$$\tau = F/A = \frac{\mu_M}{g_c} \frac{u}{r} = \mu_F \frac{u}{r} \tag{5}$$

$$\tau = \frac{\mu_M}{g_c} du/dr = \mu_F \, du/dr \tag{6}$$

where du/dr is the velocity gradient or shearing rate of the fluid, and μ denotes the coefficient of viscosity of the fluid. As in the case of the elastic moduli relating stress to strain in the elastic solid, the viscosity of the ideal Newtonian fluid may be considered to be a true physical property of the material.

Equations (5 and 6) may also be written in another manner, to emphasize their relationship to Eqs. (3 and 4).[1, p. 24] In the case of the ideal Newtonian fluid, the strain (i.e., the distortion of the initially rectangular volume of fluid) progresses uniformly with time. In time dt, the distortion of the element is equal to the distance which the upper plane has traveled:

$$dL = (u)(dt) \tag{7}$$

The differential strain $d\gamma_s$, given by dL/L (or dL/r in this case), is therefore

$$d\gamma_s = \frac{dL}{r} = \frac{u}{r} \, dt \tag{8}$$

or

$$\frac{d\gamma_s}{dt} = \frac{u}{r} = \frac{du}{dr} \tag{9}$$

Thus it is seen that the velocity gradient du/dr is equal to the rate of strain $d\gamma_s/dt$. Therefore, for an ideal Newtonian fluid,

$$\frac{d\gamma_s}{dt} = \frac{\tau}{\mu_F} \tag{10}$$

as compared to

$$\gamma_s = \tau \times \frac{1}{G} \tag{11}$$

for an ideal elastic solid. Noting that both μ and G are constants at a given temperature, it is instructive to compare the behavior of the fluid and the solid under a given shearing force: In the solid the total strain or deformation produced is a constant, while in the Newtonian liquid the rate of strain is constant and the total shearing strain may increase without limit at a given stress.

Newtonian behavior is common to all gases and to liquids of reasonably low molecular weight,[59] at least within experimental accuracy.*

Simple Viscoelastic Fluids. Perhaps the simplest approach mathematically to non-Newtonian behavior is to assume that materials exist which have the characteristics of both a Newtonian fluid [Eqs. (5 and 10)] and an ideal elastic solid [Eqs. (3 and 11)]. There are many alternate ways in which this combination may be affected, but only few merit consideration.

The physical visualization of the structure of these fluids is aided somewhat by considering them to be made up of mechanical elements which impart the actual flow behavior observed. Unfortunately, there is at best only a vague relationship between the mechanical models and the true reasons for the actual physical properties of the fluid. However, even this limited visualization is of some value. In order to simplify further this visualization, the behavior of the material in simple tension, rather than in shear, will be considered. While no particular difficulty is encountered in devising other mechanical models which would impart the same behavior in shear, such a detailed study of the mechanical models probably is not worth while.

Three mechanical models are required:

(1) The Newtonian liquid is represented by a dashpot consisting of a container filled with a viscous Newtonian fluid. A piston moves through this fluid under the influence of stresses exerted on the model at point P in Fig. 1.3a. Provided this system is ideally designed so that all turbulence, gravitational, inertial, and end effects are negligible, the force P exerts a stress τ on the fluid, which then shears at a constant rate. If P (and hence τ) is doubled, the shearing rate of the fluid and rate of rise of the piston are also doubled. If the pull P is suddenly stopped, the piston stops just as suddenly and has no tendency whatever to return to its original position in the container. Thus it is seen that this model possesses all the essential

---

* Reiner[91, 92] discusses qualitatively the peculiar behavior of gases in a special apparatus. This effect is consistent with the assumption of the existence of a "cross-viscosity" which would lead to stresses normal to the direction of flow, in addition to usual Newtonian stresses along the direction of flow required for the movement of Newtonian fluids. While these stresses are entirely negligible in most flow applications dealing with otherwise Newtonian fluids, their existence, if proved, could account for the peculiar behavior of fluids under special conditions. This suggests that possibly *all* fluids possess non-Newtonian characteristics, although many materials (such as gases) approximate Newtonian behavior extremely closely under usual experimental conditions.

features of pure Newtonian behavior: the linear shear-stress–shear-rate relationship required by Eqs. (5 and 10) and no "memory" or preferred configuration of the system exists.

(2) An ideal elastic spring is used to represent the elastic solid, as shown in Fig. 1.3b. Again, inertial effects are assumed to be absent.

In this case, when the stress P is applied, the spring elongates instantly to its new equilibrium position, the extension being directly proportional to P, as required by Eqs. (3 and 11). When the stress is released, the spring returns instantly to its original position, thus exhibiting perfect "memory" for its preferred configuration.

(3) A St. Venant body, which may be represented by a block resting on a plane surface, is required to designate some few types of fluid properties. The block (Fig. 1.3c) is assumed to possess no inertia; its static and kinetic friction coefficients are also assumed to be equal. This system has the characteristic of not moving (deforming) at all until some finite "yield" stress is applied. However, it will move (shear) at all rates between zero and infinity when a stress of this magnitude is applied, i.e., it cannot sustain

(a) NEWTONIAN DASH POT

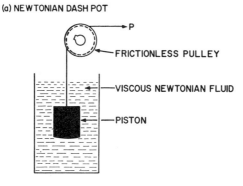

(b) ELASTIC SPRING

(c) ST. VENANT BODY

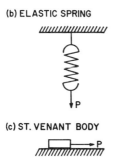

FIG. 1.3. Mechanical models used to visualize rheological behavior of real materials.

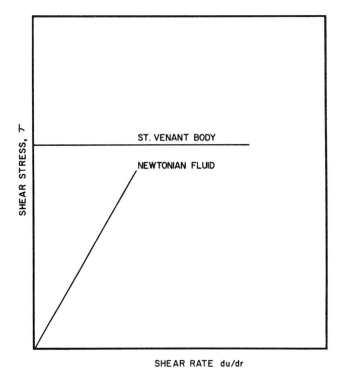

SHEAR RATE du/dr

Fɪɢ. 1.4. Comparison of the shear stress-shear rate relationship of a St. Venant body with that of a Newtonian fluid.

stresses greater than the stress corresponding to this yield value. This is brought out more clearly in Fig. 1.4, which compares the shearing-stress–shearing-rate relationships for a St. Venant body with those of a Newtonian fluid.

On the basis of these three mechanical components, we are now ready to discuss the behavior of several types of more complex fluids.

Maxwell Body. The Maxwell body is defined as an ideal spring and dashpot in series, as in Fig. 1.5a. When a force per unit area of τ is applied, the spring immediately elongates, and the same stress τ is carried back into the dashpot, the piston of which accordingly moves at a uniform rate as long as τ is held constant. The total deformation therefore is equal to the sum of the individual deformations of the spring and the dashpot. Similarly, the total *rate* of deformation is given by

$$\frac{d\gamma_{\text{total}}}{dt} = \frac{d\gamma_1}{dt} + \frac{d\gamma_2}{dt} \tag{12}$$

where γ_1, the deformation of the spring, is given by Eq. (11), and $d\gamma_2/dt$

is given by Eq. (10). Since the elastic shear modulus of the spring G and the Newtonian viscosity μ_F are both constants, substitution gives

$$\frac{d\gamma_{\text{total}}}{dt} = \frac{1}{G}\frac{d\tau}{dt} + \frac{\tau}{\mu_F}$$

(13)

If one strains or deforms the material suddenly to a fixed point, and then restrains it in such a way as to retain this deformed shape, $d\gamma_{\text{total}}/dt$ will

(a) MAXWELL BODY

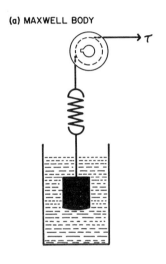

(b) VOIGT OR KELVIN BODY

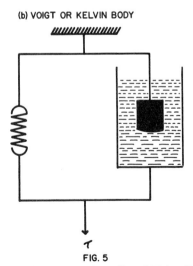

FIG. 5

Fig. 1.5. Rheological models: Maxwell and Voigt (Kelvin) bodies.

be zero during this retention. Rearrangement of Eq. (13) gives

$$\frac{d\tau}{\tau} = -\frac{G}{\mu_F} dt \qquad (14)$$

Integrating, one obtains

$$\tau = \tau_o e^{-Gt/\mu_F} \qquad (15)$$

where τ_o is the stress at the instant the deformation first ceased. That is, the stress τ falls to $1/e$ (37 per cent) of its original value in a time such that

$$\frac{Gt}{\mu_F} = 1 \qquad (16)$$

or

$$t_{\text{relax}} = \frac{\mu_F}{G} \qquad (17)$$

The group μ_F/G has the dimensions of time and is termed the "relaxation time" of the material. This is a quantity which will be referred to later and, as such, represents one of the chief results of this consideration of quantitative behavior of Maxwell bodies.

If, instead of deforming or straining the object by a given amount, one applies a constant stress τ, the term $d\tau/dt$ in Eq. (13) is equal to zero and one obtains

$$\frac{d\gamma_s}{dt} = \frac{1}{\mu_F} \tau$$

which is idential to Eq. (10) for a Newtonian fluid. The reason for this is that the spring immediately elongates to its final extension in the instant that the stress is initially applied. After this time, the motion of the entire system depends only on the behavior of the Newtonian dashpot. A situation in which just the reverse is true may also develop: If alternating stresses of a sufficiently high frequency are applied to the Maxwell body, the dashpot will not have time to move appreciably, and the entire body will behave as if only the spring were present, i.e., perfectly elastically.

The final point of interest concerning a Maxwell body is its behavior on complete release of a stress. The spring will immediately retract to its unstressed length; the dashpot, however, will simply stop. As a result, the body as a whole will remain deformed by an amount equal to the movement of the piston in the dashpot.

Voigt or Kelvin Body. This body may be visualized as consisting of a spring and dashpot in parallel (Fig. 1.5b) rather than in series as in a Maxwell body. When a constant stress is applied, the body distorts rapidly initially, since most of the stress is taken up by the dashpot until the spring has been strained appreciably. As time continues, the rate of strain decreases and eventually reaches zero as the spring takes up the entire stress. Thus, while a Maxwell body had more of the characteristics of a liquid in that it would strain or shear indefinitely when a constant stress was applied, the Voigt or Kelvin body behaves somewhat like a solid in that its strains remain finite; in fact, the only difference between the Voigt model and a pure elastic solid is that a finite time is required for it to be strained. Similarly, on release of the stress, the Voigt model returns perfectly (although slowly) to its original configuration.

Miscellaneous Models. To mention just two of the many other combinations that have been proposed to represent the behavior of various real materials, Bingham bodies may be represented by a dashpot and a St. Venant body in series,* and the Poynting and Thompson body consists of a spring in parallel with the Maxwell body. These are discussed in detail by Reiner[90] and by Alfrey.[1] In fact, Alfrey also discusses the behavior of many of these systems if the complication of inertia is introduced, although his mathematical discussion is not so complete as that of Reiner. For more complete mathematical descriptions of the Maxwell body than was presented here, the reader is referred to an older publication by Reiner,[90] which is free of the several typographical errors in Reiner's more recent treatise.[92] Recently Noll[73] has developed a three-dimensional extension of the Maxwell element, but the resulting equations do not appear to predict flow curves which are in accordance with experimental facts, although the general changes are correct.

Flow Behavior of Real Materials

Classification of Fluids on the Basis of Their Steady-State Behavior. Consideration of steady-state behavior is not particularly confining, since flow through tubes, through dies of constant cross-sectional area, and in viscometers all represent steady-state processes, except in regions in which end effects are not negligible, provided only that the flow conditions (temperature, pressure, and flow rate) are all constant or nearly so. Thus, the steady-state behavior represents a convenient starting place from which to analyze flow behavior in a reasonably simple manner. Then the time-dependent effects may be superimposed on this knowledge in the form of simple additions to a well-established basis.

Figures 1.6 and 1.7 represent graphically the definitions of various types

* Reiner[92] denotes a Bingham body by a dashpot, a St. Venant body, and a spring in series. Fluids approaching Bingham behavior do not, however, usually show any signs of appreciable elasticity. Hence inclusion of the spring appears to detract from the already limited utility which this model may possess.

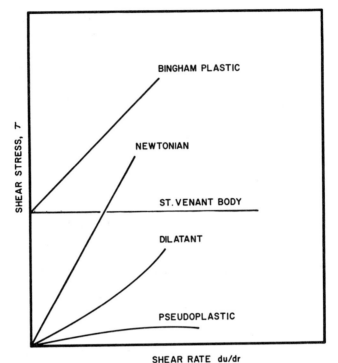

FIG. 1.6. Flow curves—arithmetic coordinates.

of steady-state flow behavior. These definitions are in terms of the relationship between shear stress and shear rate which is exhibited by the fluid in question—ideally in a viscometer such as depicted by the experiment illustrated in Fig. 1.2.*

Figure 1.6 depicts the various shear-stress–shear-rate relationships on the traditional arithmetic coordinates. This figure is presented since the many individuals who commonly read the rheological but not the engineering literature may be familiar only with this form. However, for engineering purposes this representation is not particularly useful, for the following reasons:

(1) The representation is misleading in that the accuracy with which the data are represented is variable across the graph: An enormous percentage error in data points at low shear rates does not show up as clearly (in terms of a deviation from the smooth curve) as a small percentage error does at high shear rates. This is especially important in processing of non-New-

* Methods of obtaining the true shear-stress–shear-rate relationships from data obtained with less ideal but practical and useful viscometers will be discussed under Practical Methods of Measurement of Fluid Properties, p. 61.

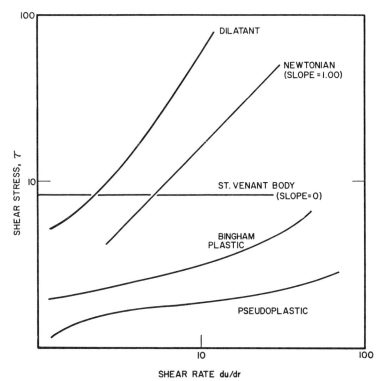

FIG. 1.7. Flow curves—Logarithmic coordinates.

tonians such as polymers, since extremely wide ranges of shear rate must usually be considered, a hundredfold range being not uncommon.

(2) Comparisons between Newtonian and non-Newtonian behavior are difficult to make. In particular, the question "Exactly how non-Newtonian is a given fluid?" is very difficult to answer.

(3) That class of non-Newtonian behavior which is most important industrially—the pseudoplastic—shows up as a poorly defined curve. On the other hand, a straight line is usually obtained over rather wide shear-rate ranges when the same data are plotted on logarithmic coordinates as in Fig. 1.7.

The degree of departure from Newtonian behavior may be obtained quantitatively from the logarithmic shear-stress–shear-rate plot given in Fig. 1.7. Taking logarithms of the equation describing Newtonian behavior [Eq. (6)], one obtains

$$\log \tau = \log\left(\mu_F \frac{d\mu}{dr}\right) \tag{18}$$

Noting that the logarithm of a product of terms is equal to the sum of the logarithms of the individual terms, this may be written

$$\log \tau = \log \frac{du}{dr} + \log \mu_F \tag{19}$$

The equation of a straight line, viz.,

$$y = nx + b \tag{20}$$

is identical to Eq. (19) if one defines:

$$y = \log \tau \qquad x = \log \frac{du}{dr}$$

$$n = 1.00 \qquad b = \log \mu_F$$

Thus the shear-stress–shear-rate relationship* of a Newtonian fluid becomes a straight line with a slope of unity (slope $= n$) on logarithmic coordinates. The degree or extent of non-Newtonian behavior is simply represented by the amount by which the slope of the logarithmic flow curve for a given non-Newtonian fluid differs from unity. For pseudoplastic and Bingham plastic non-Newtonians, the slope of the logarithmic flow curves must be between zero (for a fluid having the properties of a St. Venant body) and unity; the flow curves of dilatant fluids exhibit slopes which may vary between unity and infinity. Since the slope of the logarithmic flow curves provides a quantitative description of both the degree and kind of non-Newtonian behavior, it has been termed the "flow-behavior index" of the fluid[59, 63] and may be considered to be a true physical property of the fluid. It frequently happens that this flow-behavior index is a constant over a rather wide range of shear rates, although this is not necessarily so, and care must always be exercised in application of experimental data to new design problems to be sure that the flow-behavior index of the fluid was determined over the actual range of shear rates in which it is to be used. This qualification is really just the same as must be applied to all other physical properties: since almost all vary with the quality they describe, they must be carefully defined. For example specific heat and thermal conductivity both vary with temperature, hence the temperature range over which a given value is useful must always be noted.

The term b in the equation for a straight line [Eq. (20)] represents the intercept on the y-axis when $x = 0$. Since $\log du/dr$ is equal to zero when $du/dr = 1.00$, the viscosity of the fluid μ_F may be read off the y-axis at $du/dr = 1.00$. Thus the more viscous the Newtonian fluid, the further up it will fall on Fig. 1.7.

---

* The shear-stress–shear-rate relationship of a fluid is also called its flow curve. (See, e.g., Ref. 59.)

A similar argument may be applied to non-Newtonian fluids: The "thickest" or "most viscous" fluids appear furthest up on the logarithmic shear-stress–shear-rate diagram. Since the non-Newtonian flow curves may not be straight lines, this means, however, that a given fluid may be more viscous than another in one range of shear rates and less viscous in another shear-rate region. These factors may be brought out additionally by considering the behavior of the "apparent" viscosity of the non-Newtonian fluids.

The viscosity of a material is defined* by Eq. (6) as

$$\mu_F = \frac{\tau}{du/dr} \tag{6}$$

For Newtonian fluids this is a true constant (at a given temperature). For non-Newtonians, this ratio of shear stress to shear rate is no longer constant at a given temperature but varies with the shear stress (or the shear rate). Nevertheless, it is still a useful concept in many applications. Figure 1.8 is a

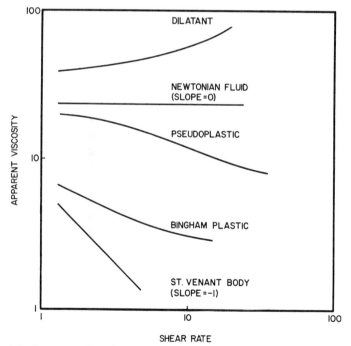

SHEAR RATE

Fig. 1.8. Apparent viscosity as a function of shear rate for fluids of Fig. 1.7.

* The fact that Eq. (6) and *not* a variety of integrated relationships gives the fundamental definition of viscosity is frequently unrecognized. (See, e.g., Ref. 123.) This is one of the primary reasons for much of the confusion in this otherwise simple area.

replot of the curves of Fig. 1.7, in which the shear stress at any point was divided by the corresponding shear rate to give an "apparent" viscosity (as the varying ratio of shear stress to shear rate of non-Newtonians is termed). As may be seen from the figure, the comparative rates of change of apparent viscosity with shear rate may be different for different fluids, resulting in one material being most viscous in one range of shear rates and less viscous in another. The same may be true even if the various fluids of interest are all of one given type, e.g., pseudoplastics.

The slopes of the curves in Figs. 1.7 and 1.8 are directly related, as may be shown by the following argument:

$$\text{Slope of Fig. 1.8} = \frac{d(\log \mu_a)}{d \log du/dr}$$

$$= \frac{d\left(\log \tau \Big/ \frac{du}{dr}\right)}{d\left(\log \frac{du}{dr}\right)}$$

$$= \frac{d\left(\log \tau - \log \frac{du}{dr}\right)}{d\left(\log \frac{du}{dr}\right)}$$

But $(d \log \tau/d \log (du/dr)) = n$ — the flow-behavior index of the fluid, which is equal to the slope of the curves of Fig. 1.7

$$\therefore \text{slope}_{\text{Fig.1.8}} = \text{slope}_{\text{Fig.1.7}} - 1$$

$$= n - 1.$$

This conclusion, that the slopes of Fig. 1.8 are simply equal to those of Fig. 1.7 minus unity, may be verified by comparing the values of the slopes listed beside several of the curves on the figures.

The discussion so far has been rather general in that it applied to all types of fluid behavior. Before leaving it, the relative importance of the various types of fluids may be indicated. It has been pointed out[59, 62] that true Bingham plastic behavior is exhibited at best by only very few fluids and quite possibly by none at all.[1] Otto[74] has shown that, when one considers the wide range of shear rates covered by diagrams such as Figs. 1.7 and 1.8, even a true Bingham plastic flow curve can be closely approximated by either a Newtonian fluid (at high shear rate) or a St. Venant body (at low shear rates), leaving only a relatively small intermediate region in which the Bingham plastic possesses properties which are at all unique. The discussion of Bingham plastics was primarily introduced in this book only for reasons of historical interest* and completeness, since the mathematical simplicity of the Bingham plastic fluid continues to stimulate theoretical studies which, in view of the above comments, have necessarily limited practical utility (e.g., Refs. 44 and 87 may be cited). For the same reasons, no discussion of the so-called "generalized non-Newtonian fluids"[90] has been presented, their unique features being rarely, if ever, found in real fluids.

The importance of dilatant behavior has been discussed elsewhere in some detail,[59] the extensive recent data of Metzner and Whitlock[64] and Whitlock[125] generally supporting and emphasizing earlier theories. It suffices to point out here the dilatant behavior is almost always closely associated with suspensions of high solids contents. Thus dilatant behavior will be seldom encountered in thermoplastics processing.† Therefore, while the later discussion of flow and viscometry of pseudoplastic fluids is also generally applicable to dilatant behavior, no special further mention of dilatancy will be made.

In summary, pseudoplastic and Newtonian behavior in steady flow are of primary importance in thermoplastics processing. The flow curves of these types of fluids (Figs. 1.6–1.8) have been presented in some detail.

Time-Dependent Effects. Some fluids—particularly some slurries and certain polymer solutions—are found to give reproducible flow curves such as shown in Figs. 1.7 or 1.8 only after they have been vigorously agitated or otherwise sheared strongly, prior to measurement of the flow curves. In the absence of such prior mixing, the shear stress, at constant shear rate, is found to increase or decrease with time, asymptotically approaching the steady-state value. Fluids which show an increase in shear stress (hence in apparent viscosity) with time are termed "rheopectic"; those which show decreases, "thixotropic."[59]

Thixotropy, assumed to be much more important than rheopexy (which is found to occur only infrequently), has been the subject of considerable study, much of which is presented in Green's book.[32] The works of more recent investigators, which have been briefly reviewed elsewhere,[59] indicate that the magnitude of uncorrected experimental errors in most thixotropy studies invalidates almost any quantitative conclusions which were drawn. Little further discussion of these effects will be made, since:

(1) A critical analysis of the methods used to study thixotropy has indicated that many "examples" of thixotropic behavior were actually due to

---

* Reiner has pointed out on several occasions[90, 92] that modern rheology really began with Bingham's analysis of systems which approach what now is termed "Bingham plastic" behavior.

† An important exception to this statement may occur in extrusion of granules which are slightly lubricated, as in processing of vinyl chloride plastisols.

experimental error rather than to the true presence of any time-dependent effect.

(2) In many process applications the material being processed is sufficiently sheared in a pump, feeder, or other auxiliary piece of equipment (preceding the equipment which is being precisely designed) to degrade the fluid to its final time-independent properties, thereby enabling their use in the precise design. This is perhaps less true in the plastics industry than in other areas of chemical engineering, but nevertheless contributes somewhat to the unimportance of thixotropy (and rheopexy) in most process applications.

(3) Time-dependent effects are largely (but not necessarily entirely) confined to end effects in steady-flow equipment. With polymers the end effect is probably largely due to the energy requirements of the elastic distortion of the material, and any superimposed thixotropy might well leave the over-all effect relatively unchanged.

As indicated above, in addition to thixotropy and rheopexy, the viscoelastic character of polymers creates unusual entrance and exit effects. This will be further discussed under Entrance Effects, p. 48.

Actual Behavior of Polymers, Melts and Solutions: Steady-State Behavior. *Factors Determining the Shape of the Flow Curve.* The non-Newtonian behavior of polymer melts and solutions in steady flow or shear is directly attributable to the following two characteristics of the molecular structure of these materials:

(1) The asymmetric shape (great length as compared to the radial dimensions) of the molecules themselves results in an orientation of the particles when a velocity gradient is imposed on the polymer molecules.[47, 59] Thus, in steady flow inside a tube, e.g., the higher velocities near the center line of the tube will tend to move any end of a long molecule which appears in this region downstream at a higher velocity than the other end, which is slightly nearer the wall and therefore in a region of slightly lower velocity. As a result of this orientation, the molecules become progressively more perfectly aligned as the velocity, hence velocity gradient (or shear rate), of the fluid is increased. Relatively complete orientation will be achieved only when the rate of orientation by this flow mechanism becomes sufficiently great to offset the disrupting effect of random molecular (Brownian) motion. Thus, at extremely low shear rates, the balance would obviously be in favor of the disrupting forces, no alignment would occur, and the material would behave as a Newtonian fluid. Conversely, at extremely high shear rates, where the disrupting effects of Brownian motion are negligible in comparison with high rates of orientation owing to shear, further changes in shear rates could not affect the degree of orientation appreciably, and the material would again approach Newtonian behavior, at least insofar as its flow curve is concerned.

While the above argument shows clearly why asymmetric particles become aligned during flow, it does not indicate whether the viscosity of the aligned particles at high shear rates will be different from that of the disaligned ones encountered at extremely low shear rates, and therefore whether or not the alignment alone would be sufficient cause for non-Newtonian behavior at intermediate shear rates, as depicted by the pseudoplastic curves of Figs. 1.7 and 1.8. To determine this, one must consider the underlying causes of viscosity in a fluid, i.e., the mechanisms by which momentum is transferred from the fast- to the slow-moving elements of fluid. In the case of gases, the undirected (Brownian) motion of the small molecules causes those in faster moving laminae occasionally to move laterally into regions of lower velocity where they lose their excess (directed) velocity by collision with the slower-moving molecules. In a liquid the free volume* is much too small to enable even a small molecule which moves laterally to penetrate the slower-moving layer completely.[45] † As a result, momentum is interchanged not by direct collision but rather by means of a mechanism in which the faster-moving molecule "drags" the slower one along, owing to the attractive forces between them.[45] The molecules, in many cases, will be separated again before this momentum interchange is complete.

In the case of polymer molecules aligned completely by high rates of shear, the transfer of momentum from fast- to slow-moving laminae must necessarily take place virtually entirely by means of the imperfect "drag" process pictured above, since the probability that a "hole" of sufficient size to accomodate the long molecule is available must be extremely small. As a result, the viscosity at high shear rates will be extremely small—more nearly comparable to what might be expected of a liquid composed of ordinary rather than polymer molecules. On the other hand, at low shear rates where no appreciable alignment has taken place, one end of a given polymer molecule may frequently find itself in a region of high velocity, while the other end may concomitantly be in a region of low velocity. Thus momentum may be transferred away from the region of high velocity by means of a mechanism which is, perhaps, even more efficient than momentum transfer in gases: The excess energy transfered to the end of the molecule which is in the high-velocity region is simply transmitted to the other end of the same molecule, where it is lost by direct collision with other slower-moving molecules. Therefore, in the region of low shear rates, the viscosity of the polymer is extremely high.

The greater the flexibility of the polymer molecule itself, the less pro-

* This term denotes the volume or space between the molecules themselves.

† While this statement is true in most cases, it will be statistically possible for a few molecules to penetrate between those in adjacent layers. The probability that this might happen frequently is low, however.

nounced would the above effect be,[36] since even at low shear rates parts of the molecules would align readily. For all molecules, increases in temperature would tend to make complete alignment more difficult because of the greatly increased Brownian motion of the molecules; hence the differences between the Newtonian viscosities at low and high shear rates would be less, and the inception of non-Newtonian behavior would be delayed to still higher shear rates. Both of these effects would tend to decrease the rate of change of viscosity with shear rate—i.e., the flow-behavior index increases or the degree of non-Newtonian behavior (pseudoplasticity) decreases with increases in temperature.*

Bondi[9] has presented a quantitative treatment of orientation based on the flow equation of Eyring. However, the use of this equation, discussed on page 28, has been criticized by other rheologists.

(2) The size of the flowing elements—if they are groups of molecules rather than single particles—would be decreased progressively by increases in shear stress or shear rate. The restoring tendencies in this case are due to intermolecular forces; the effects of shear rate and temperature on particle size are similar to those on alignment, hence the same type of Newtonian-pseudoplastic-Newtonian behavior is again observed as one moves progressively from low to high shearing rates. The rheological literature has generally assumed that where alignment of molecules is possible it is the more important factor in determining flow behavior, relegating the importance of size of flow elements to situations in which the polymer molecules are nearly equidimensional and to slurries of solids in liquids. No direct observation of the true relative importance of the two mechanisms seems to have been made.

Since the assumption of viscoelastic behavior (i.e., that the material behaves as one or more bodies of the Maxwell, Vogit-Kelvin, or similar types, or combinations of these) has proved useful in study of small distortions of solid polymers, attempts have been made to apply the same structural models to interpret the steady flow of polymers. These have been summarized by Pao[76] and by Eirich.[24]

In this case the only assumptions made about molecular structure during shear are that the molecules can slip past one another—contributing thereby a viscosity term to the flow behavior—and that, in addition, the shearing stresses distort the molecules elastically. Pao has pointed out that it is really quite obvious from the earlier discussion of Maxwell elements that

---

* This would be the sole effect if temperature were changed at constant volume. Since practically all industrial temperature changes are, instead, carried out at constant pressure, there is an additional effect owing to the decreased density of the fluid at high temperatures. These density decreases increase the separation of the molecules in the liquid and hence decrease their intermolecular forces and the viscosity at all shear rates.

it is impossible to predict the observed variation of apparent viscosity with shear rate in steady flow for a fluid with only one relaxation time (i.e., for a fluid consisting of only one Maxwell element), although many of the authors whose work he reviews, as well as Eirich, claim this to be possible.*

In view of the mathematical difficulty of dealing with an entire spectrum of elements in parallel, the progress achieved by applying this method of approach to the study of flow behavior has, to date, been of limited utility. Pao carried his approach, the most complex to date, far enough to compare the calculated flow curve with an experimental one, and also calculated the flow rate of the material through a round tube at an unspecified shear stress. The scatter of the experimental data precludes a detailed comparison of the flow curves, but the differences, while not gross, are still appreciable: In spite of the minimization of errors by the integration used to obtain the predicted flow rate in a tube, the theory predicts a flow rate which is over 25 per cent higher than the measured one. Since this best result to date was for a fluid which was appreciably but not highly non-Newtonian (flow-behavior index of approximately 0.6), it is apparent that further work is needed to put this approach on a design basis. Accordingly, this author's present recommendation concerning this method of attack is for the interested reader to watch the literature closely for further work by Pao and the other authors discussed by him.

In addition to the type of approach used by Pao, several mathematical rheologists have attempted to develop flow equations without reference to basic molecular properties. (See, e.g., Rivlin and Ericksen.[97]) This approach yields little insight toward the reasons for observed behavior of polymers, and, since the design results obtained to date have been very limited, the approach cannot be recommended.

In summary, this section has discussed how the shape of the flow curve is determined by the size, orientation, and elasticity of the elements of the flowing fluid. While a knowledge of these factors is of definite engineering utility in predicting the direction and approximate magnitude of contemplated processing changes, specific quantitative relationships based on molecular properties are not yet well developed.

Flow Curves—Illustrative Examples. In the works of Philippoff and his associates one finds the best available viscometric data over wide ranges of shear rates.[14, 78, 81] Figure 1.9 shows the actual shear-stress-shear-rate curves condensed from publications by Brodnyan, Gaskins, and Philippoff[14] and Philippoff and Gaskins.[81] The two central curves show the expected effect of consecutive additions of polymer to a solvent: The viscosity of the solution increases and non-Newtonian behavior of the pesudoplastic type (flow-behavior index less than unity) may occur. As predicted by the

* For a detailed account of the opposing point of view, see J. G. Oldroyd (in Ref. 24).

theory of the preceding section, the solution behavior becomes Newtonian at both extremes of low and high shear rate. As the concentration of the polymer solution is increased, the fluid becomes increasingly non-Newtonian at any intermediate shear rate, and the range of shear rates within which non-Newtonian behavior occurs progressively increases. However, the shear rate at which the solution again approaches Newtonian behavior at high shear stresses remains nearly constant. These effects are in perfect agreement with the predictions of the previous theoretical section, as the following discussion will show.

Since solution of the polymer molecules results in their association with those of the solvent, the percentage of "free" or relatively unassociated solvent in the solution decreases with increases in polymer concentration. As a result, the apparent viscosity at any given shear rate increases with concentration, since both the mass and the force fields* surrounding a large flowing polymer unit are greater than those of the free solvent. The extent to which particle alignment and decreases in particle size occur (owing to the presence of the shearing stresses) depends primarily on the magnitude of the stress, hence, in a given solution, non-Newtonian behavior always begins to occur at approximately the same shearing stress, independent of the solution concentration. The slight dependency on concentration shown in Fig. 1.9 is probably due to changes in size of the flow unit with increases in concentration. In a concentrated polymer solution not only will there be no free solvent but, furthermore, each polymer molecule will be incompletely solvated. As a result, all the solvent molecules associated with a given polymer molecule are held more firmly (there are none available to be held only weakly), and changes in size of the flowing particle or unit do not occur under the influence of weak shearing stresses. By contrast, Newtonian behavior at high shear rates occurs when the rate of alignment owing to the velocity gradient becomes sufficiently great to maintain relatively complete alignment in spite of the disrupting effect of Brownian motion. This should depend on the magnitude of the velocity gradient (shear rate) alone, as borne out by Fig. 1.9.

The curves for polymer melts, rather than solutions, would be expected to show exactly the same over-all shape or flow behavior. Figure 1.9 shows this to be the case as nearly as one can tell. Unfortunately, the difficulty of obtaining good data on high-polymer melts is such as to prevent coverage of the same wide range of shear rates. In fact, as will be discussed in detail later in the section on extrudate shape and roughness, the inordinately high stresses in polymer melts flowing at high shear rates may cause mechanical breakdown of the polymer and fracture of the filaments being sheared.

---

* That is, the factors influencing the momentum transfer, hence the viscosity, of the solution.

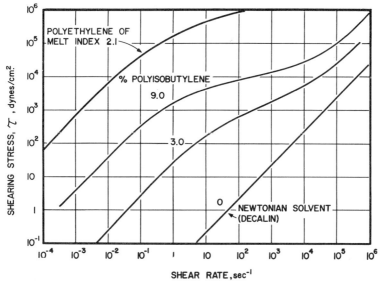

FIG. 1.9. Flow curves of a polymer melt compared with the flow curves of polymer solutions. Upper curve: Polymer melt at 125°C. Lower curves: Polymer solutions (0%, 3% and 9% polymer) at 25°C. (Data of Brodnyan, Gaskins and Philippoff[14] and of Philippoff and Gaskins[81], reproduced with permission of copyright owner)

One extremely important point which must be emphasized concerns the broad ranges of the shear rate over which the data of Fig. 1.9 were obtained: Most authors are very pleased to obtain data which extend over one or two decades of shear rate, and there are still many individuals who falsely believe that a single point is generally useful. In this light, the 6-to-9 decade shear-rate ranges of the data in Fig. 1.9 are truly phenomenal.

The S-shaped flow curves of Fig. 1.9—which show Newtonian behavior only at extremely low and high shear rates—may be concluded to be typical of both polymer melts and solutions. Polymer pastes, on the other hand, frequently exhibit dilatancy at high shear rates. In this case the curves are similar to those of Fig. 1.9 except that, at high shear rates, the slope of the curve (i.e., the flow-behavior index) may appear to increase indefinitely toward infinity rather than to increase only to a value of unity. If the concentration of the paste is high,[74] as is the usual case, the point at which the slope increases above unity may occur at shear rates as low as 10–100 sec^{-1}, and could, of course, conceivably occur at still lower shear rates.

Quantitative Flow-Curve Description by Theoretical and Empirical Equations. The qualitative aspects of the preceding sections are of major importance in trouble shooting and in prediction of the general magnitude and direction of fluid-property variations due to variations or changes in processing conditions. Many attempts to describe these properties quantitatively appear in the literature.[32, 47, 69, 70, 89, 90, 102, 105] Most of the many approaches attempted may be eliminated, because they either do not adequately represent the flow characteristics of real fluids, are too complex to permit their practical usage, or both. As a result, only two quantitative relationships are felt to be worth discussing in some detail.

(1) The Eyring-Powell[86] relation between shear stress and shear rate

$$\tau = \mu \frac{du}{dr} + \frac{1}{B} \sinh^{-1}\left(\frac{du/dr}{A_{EP}}\right) \tag{21}$$

is in terms of three experimentally determined constants μ, B, and A_{EP}. At low shear rates, $\sinh^{-1}(x)$ approaches (x), hence the equation predicts

$$\tau = \left[\mu + \frac{1}{A_{EP}B}\right]\frac{du}{dr} \tag{22}$$

i.e., it predicts a region of Newtonian behavior at low shear rates, this Newtonian viscosity being equal to the quantity inside the square brackets of Eq. (22). At intermediate shear rates Eq. (21) predicts pseudoplastic non-Newtonian behavior, in accordance with the qualitative facts as presented in Fig. 1.9. At high shear rates the second term in Eq. (21) becomes negligible as compared to the first, and hence the predicted shear-stress–shear-rate relationship is again linear, i.e., Newtonian behavior is predicted. Since the equation was based on theoretical concepts,[86, 89] and since its general behavior is in qualitative agreement with fact over extremely wide shear-rate ranges, it is immediately obvious that this equation should possess considerable utility.

However, the practical utilization of Eq. (21) has been quite limited; three reasons for this follow:

(a) The quantitative "fit" of the equation to experimental data is not as unique or as perfect as the above qualitative discussion might indicate. In fact, the simpler "power law" to be discussed on the next pages has been found to fit rheological data on several fluids better over perhaps a thousandfold range of shear rates than Eq. (21).[62] Thus, while the Eyring-Powell equation may be better than most in terms of representing approximately the general behavior of fluids over an infinite range of shear rates, its utility in representing the same fluid behavior with great accuracy over the narrower ranges of shear rate, of interest in a given practical problem, is much less. This argument should not be construed to indicate that the Eyring-Powell equation fits experimental data poorly, since this is not the case. However, while it does fit experimental data very well, other and simpler equations appear to be as good or possibly superior for use in a majority of applications.

(b) The theoretical concepts upon which the equation is based have been pointed out to be unsound,[1, 68] hence its claimed utility in giving a detailed mechanistic picture of the flow process is, at best, only partially valid. This, together with the difficulty of obtaining only one set of constants which will represent the flow data,[15] tends to negate any academic advantages over use of purely empirical equations.

(c) In many applications it is desirable to use an equation which is explicit in shear rate rather than in shear stress. For example, integration of Eq. (21) for the comparatively simple problem of flow inside a round tube leads to considerable mathematical complexities. However, a convenient graphical representation of the results obtained by numerical integration is available.[15]

In summary, even though Eq. (21) represents the simplest theoretical attempt to derive a generally useful relation between shear stress and shear rate for non-Newtonian systems, the results are somewhat limited in their practical utility, partly because of the complex form of the equation. Furthermore, in view of the theoretical objections to its development, the pursuit of improvements of Eq. (21), such as the 5- or 6-constant modification of Ree and Eyring,[89] cannot be strongly recommended. The utility and therefore the recommended uses of Eq. (21) are believed to be as follows:

(a) In purposes of extraordinary extrapolations of data, the fact that the equation has the right general form may be useful. It should be noted, however, that data are needed over a very considerable range of shear rates in order to determine the constants A_{EP}, B, and μ with sufficient precision for such extrapolations.

(b) The most useful empirical equation—Eq. (23)—does not fit experimental data precisely in regions of sharp curvature—as at a shear rate about 2×10^4 sec^{-1} on the 9 per cent curve of Fig. 1.9. Thus, if one finds oneself consistently dealing with practical applications in a region of extremely sharp curvature of the logarithmic flow curves, the use of Eq. (21) may be justified. However, most polymer melts and solutions do not show excessively strong curvature [that of Fig. 1.9 is probably not great enough to warrant use of Eq. (21), at least at the present state of the art].

(2) The so-called "power-law" equation

$$\tau = K \left(\frac{du}{dr} \right)^n \tag{23}$$

relates shear stress and shear rate through *two* experimental constants, the flow-behavior index n and the consistency index K.[59, 62] Since two constants are the minimum number which may be used to define the flow curve of non-Newtonian materials,[59] and since Eq. (23) may be solved explicitly for either shear stress (as shown) or shear rate, it is evident that Eq. (23) portrays non-Newtonian behavior in as simple a mathematical form as is probably possible. In view of this simplicity of Eq. (23), the accuracy with which it may be used to portray experimental data is phenomenal. Furthermore, this accuracy is easily determined, since, on a logarithmic plot of shear stress vs. shear rate, Eq. (23) is represented by a straight line of slope equal to the exponent n, and deviations from the equation are directly evident. In terms of apparent viscosity the equation may be written[59]

$$\mu_a = \frac{\tau}{du/dr}$$

$$= \frac{K}{(du/dr)^{1-n}} \tag{24}$$

$$= K(du/dr)^{n-1}$$

Therefore, a logarithmic plot of apparent viscosity vs. shear rate will be a straight line with a slope equal to $n - 1$ in a region in which Eq. (23) is obeyed. References to the earlier theoretical discussion and to experimental data (Fig. 1.9, also Refs. 14, 62, and 89) show that while Eqs. (23) and (24) must necessarily break down when extremely wide ranges of shear rate are considered, the equation almost always is valid over a tenfold range of shear rates and not infrequently represents data within experimental accuracy over a thousandfold or even a ten-thousandfold shear-rate range.* Theoretical objections to use of a purely empirical relation such as Eq. (23) may validly be rejected at the present time.[59]

The chief limitation of Eqs. (23) and (24) is their inability to portray correctly flow behavior at shear rates in which the fluid is approaching Newtonian behavior. Thus, extrapolation of data taken over a modest range of shear rates from the non-Newtonian into a Newtonian region may result in appreciable errors. Unfortunately, there is no ready solution to this problem, since the more complex theoretical equations also cannot be extrapolated if their constants are evaluated from such modest data. Accordingly, one cannot overemphasize the extreme importance of obtaining rheological data at shear rates corresponding to those to be used in process. If situations arise in which extrapolations to new shear rates are imperative, the only present recommendation possible is to compare the available data with those of Section III of this book, and to extrapolate by noting the similarity between the data presented there and those to be extrapolated.

Normal Stresses. Garner and co-workers[28, 29] and Weissenberg[119, 120] drew attention to the existence of normal stresses (as well as the usual tangential

---

* It is interesting to note, e.g., that the experimental data cited by Ree and Eyring[89] as conforming to their 6-constant equation are fitted within experimental error by Eq. (23), except for the one or two points obtained under the most extreme conditions (and therefore possibly in error).

stresses considered up to this point) in the flow and distortion of polymers and their solutions. In particular, the works of Weissenberg[120, 121] have led to particularly vivid demonstrations of manifestations due to such stresses. As a result, many authors refer to these normal stress manifestations by the term "Weissenberg effect." Some of these manifestations are as follows:

(1) The fluid has a tendency to climb up a shaft which is rotating in the liquid. Whereas a pure Newtonian liquid would tend to be thrown progressively further from a shaft rotating in a pool of the liquid (by centrifugal force) as the rotational speed of the shaft is increased, in many polymer melts and their solutions exactly the opposite effect occurs; at increasing rotational speeds, the fluid climbs progressively *farther* up the rotating shaft. Depending on the volume of the container used, it may be possible to empty it effectively—with no fluid remaining on the walls of the container. If, instead of using a rod one uses a short hollow tube which is open at both ends, the fluid will effectively be "pumped" up into the tube and spill over the top.

(2) Shearing of a sample of fluid between two parallel rotating plates (or between the cone and plate of a rotational viscometer) results in the development of stresses normal to the plates, in addition to the tangential shearing stresses developed. If one does not rigidly maintain the two plates a fixed distance apart, the effect of these normal stresses is to increase the axial separation of the plates, this being accompanied by contraction of the fluid in the radial direction. These normal stresses and their distribution have been quantitatively measured in several systems.[14, 33, 52, 54, 75, 79, 82, 83, 98]

A qualitative explanation[120, 121] for the effect is found in the elastic properties of polymers and their solutions: As one rotates a shaft in a liquid, e.g., if there is little or no slip between the shaft and adjacent liquid, a manifestation of elasticity would be the stretching, or "strangulation," of the liquid layers being strained, as one "winds up" the layers of fluid onto the shaft. This strangulation would tend to be relieved by the climbing of the liquid up the shaft, as is actually found to occur in practice. Furthermore, the liquid on the shaft should be in tension, if this explanation is a valid one. Weissenberg points out[121] that this may actually be confirmed with viscous materials such as polymer melts: If this liquid has climbed up a shaft and is cut vertically, one finds that the cut actually opens up. However, while elasticity qualitatively serves to describe the phenomena, it has been shown by Rivlin[95] and Reiner[92] that inelastic fluids may show similar effects provided that the presence of "cross-viscosity"* effects is assumed. Mooney

---

* The coefficient of cross viscosity is defined by Reiner[92] as a measure of stresses in a fluid which depend on the velocity gradients in all directions rather than only in one.

has pointed out[66] that even if cross-viscosity effects alone may be sufficient to account for the phenonema, these effects quite probably have their origin in the elastic nature of the fluid concerned, and that this was assumed by Rivlin in another paper.[96] In a later paper Mooney[67] mentions but does not discuss in detail inadequacies of the Rivlin (and Reiner) approach. Experimentally, Reiner[91] shows that, whatever the true cause of these effects, even air molecules appear to have measurable tendencies in this direction. These remarks serve therefore primarily to indicate the widespread importance of the so-called "Weissenberg effect" and its partly proved direct connection with elastic properties of the fluid. They also emphasize an argument presented in Reiner's books: It appears likely that only few materials are true Newtonian fluids. Many fluids are believed to be Newtonian only because their deviations from Newtonian behavior have not been measurable in commonly carried out experiments. Therefore, as processing conditions progressively become more extreme, many materials which now are believed to be Newtonian may actually have more complex flow behavior.

Almost all of the quantitative measurements of normal stresses have been published only during the last three or four years. Figure 1.10 shows the results of the most recent measurements on polymer solutions. These data enable one to discard the theory of Padden and DeWitt,[75] as well as their method of plotting reduced variables. However, as this theory was an extension of DeWitt's earlier work on flow curves which Pao[76] has already shown to be unrealistic, this only serves to confirm Pao's statements. Brodnyan, Gaskins, and Philippoff[14] also point out that the data are in agreement with the Greensmith-Rivlin[33] and Mooney[66] theories only at the lower end of the shear-rate range investigated. Thus, no complete and proved analysis of these effects appears to exist at the present time.

The following conclusions drawn from Fig. 1.10 may be useful as a guide to the general importance of normal stresses in polymer solutions:

(1) Normal stresses appear to be insignificant in magnitude when the shear rate is low enough for the fluid to exhibit Newtonian behavior in its shear-stress–shear-rate relationships.

(2) As the shear rate is increased to the point at which appreciable non-Newtonian character is displayed by the liquid (in shear), i.e., as the flow-behavior index drops to about 0.7 ± 0.2, the normal stresses increase to about the same level as the shearing stresses.

(3) By the time the point of inflection in the shear-stress–shear-rate flow curve is reached (corresponding to shear rates of about 500–5,000 $\sec^{-1}$ for the data of Fig. 1.10), the normal stresses have grown to about 10 times the value of the shearing stresses.

Undoubtedly, the above conclusions cannot be accepted as also being identically true for other systems and for polymer melts. However, quali-

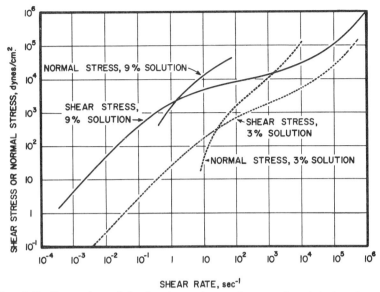

Fig. 1.10. Comparison of the shearing and normal stresses in polyisobutylene solutions. (Abridged from Ref. 14 with permission of copyright owner)

tatively, one might expect the elasticity and therefore the normal stresses to be greater for melts than for solutions. Since polymer melts are usually processed in the range of shear rates under which appreciable non-Newtonian behavior is observed, one clearly sees that the normal stresses under processing conditions are probably not negligible and may possibly far overshadow the shearing stresses in magnitude. Undoubtedly, these normal stresses are of significant and possibly controlling (if yet unknown) importance in problems such as changes of shape of an extrudate after it leaves the die. Approximate calculations also show that if the normal stresses are as great as the shearing stresses in polymer melts, they should not be neglected when determining the hoop tensions, hence the thickness required of structural members, as the added outward pressure may be appreciable. Few data have been published on normal stresses in polymer melts but the one study available[85] strongly supports the above conclusions as to the importance and possible magnitude of normal stresses.

Unsteady-State Behavior. Except for the study of unsteady-state response of polymers to small stresses and strains (in which case the polymer is usually treated as an ideal Maxwell body), very little work has been done on this question. As the problem of small stresses is not of interest here, discussion of these theories is not felt to be useful, and the entire subject will be considered only in the light of a practical application in the section on entrance effects, p. 48.

Effects of Pressure

Effects of Pressure on Flow Properties. Since the viscosity of a liquid depends on the magnitude of the intermolecular forces effecting the momentum transfer (pp. 22–27), and since these are extremely dependent on intermolecular distances,[31, 45] compression of a liquid should result in large increases in viscosity, some of which are readily correlated.[35] For many liquids the change is not great, since little change in density occurs unless enormous pressures are used. For example, the viscosities of ethyl ether and acetone at 4,000 atm are only 6.3 and 3.9 times as high as at atmospheric pressure.[11, 17] However, the possible effects are enormous: The viscosity of isobutanol at 12,000 atm is 790 times that of the atmospheric value at the same temperature,[17] and that of some silicone fluids is increased by a factor of 10^7 by pressures of less than 10,000 atm.[12] Many of the data on ordinary liquids have been summarized by Hersey and Hopkins.[37]

Since the compressibility of many polymers at processing temperatures is much greater than that of ordinary liquids* at room temperature (corresponding to the above examples), the viscosity changes will be correspondingly greater, resulting perhaps, in some cases, in an order-of-magnitude effect. Thus the possibility exists that a material which appears to be workable at ordinary pressures may become almost perfectly rigid at high extrusion pressures. In some cases this could conceivably result in decreases in extrusion (or other processing) rates, rather than in increases, when the pressure is increased.

No experimental data on polymers over a wide range of pressures appear to be available.† Accordingly, the above must remain merely as a caution not to extrapolate flow curves obtained at relatively low pressures to higher ones without taking ample precautions in terms of safety factors.

Volume Viscosity. Just as fluids resist shearing forces through the usual viscous effects, so must they also resist changes in volume. For example, oscillatory volumetric compressions must be damped[92] just as free oscillations causing fluid shear (such as waves) are found to be damped. This "volume viscosity" is also termed the "second coefficient of viscosity."

Reiner[92] describes some calculations of this second coefficient in materials such as concrete and asphalt. Davies and Jones[18] report the ratio of the second to the normal coefficient as being equal to 10 for glycerol and 200

---

* Comparing data in Refs. 118 and 45, one sees that the change in volume of polyethylene compressed by a pressure of 10,000 atm at 100°C is over twice that of carbon bisulfide.

† A recent paper[56] discusses this problem but unfortunately does not separate changes in apparent viscosity due to varying shear rate from pressure-induced changes. While one can conclude that the true effects of pressure alone must be much smaller than reported by these investigators, their actual magnitude remains unknown.

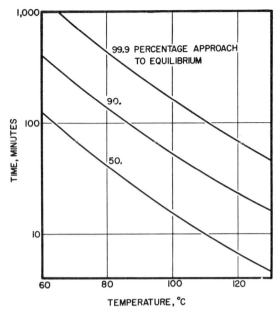

F‍IG. 1.11. Effect of temperature on the time required to approach equilibrium by isothermal expansion on contraction. (Data of Spencer and Boyer[104], reproduced with permission of copyright owner)

for glucose. No quantitative values are yet available for polymers, but Spencer and Boyer[104] have measured the time required for the volume of polystyrene to change when its temperature is suddenly changed, and found that up to 15 hours were required in some cases. Since the temperature change is accomplished in a few minutes, the long time is largely a manifestation of the high value of the volume viscosity. Figure 1.11 is taken from their data. The conditions under which it is valid are not entirely clear, hence its reproduction here is purely to show the general magnitudes of time involved. They calculated the activation energy of this effect to be about 12 kcal/gm mole; i.e., its temperature dependence is about the same as that of the first or shear viscosity.

Undoubtedly, this volume viscosity is important in determining dimensional changes in plastics processing, and emphasizes the time which may be required for relief from compressive stresses, as may be necessary for dimensional stability. It appears quite possible that further investigation will show this viscosity coefficient to be an "apparent," or non-Newtonian, one also.

P-V-T Properties of Polymers. An equation-of-state for liquids, similar to the perfect gas law as used for gases, would enable correlation of volume changes (with temperature and pressure), thermodynamic properties

such as work of compression,* internal energy changes, etc. The simplest
gaseous equation-of-state which does not assume perfect gas behavior, viz.,
van der Waals' equation, may be written as follows (for 1 gm mole of material):

$$(p + a/V^2)(V - b) = RT \qquad (25)$$

Since this equation also approximates liquid-phase behavior, Spencer and
Gilmore[106] have proposed a slightly simplified version for use with polymers:

$$(p + \pi_i)(V - \omega) = R'T \qquad (26)$$

in which π_i, the internal pressure, is assumed to be independent of volume
as a further approximation. The following table gives values of the constants
as determined by Spencer and Gilmore.

	R'	ω, ml/gm	π_i, psi
Polystyrene	11.6	0.822	27,000
Polymethyl methacrylate	12.05	(0.734)	31,300
Ethyl cellulose	19.95	(0.720)	34,800
Cellulose acetate butyrate	22.18	(0.688)	41,300
Polyethylene	43.0	(0.875)	47,600

(Values in parentheses are only approximate.)

Data to check the validity of the equation were taken only in the 175–
196°C. temperature region, hence extrapolations must be cautious. Partly
because of the neglect of V in the internal-pressure term of Eq. (26), and
partly because of the difficulty of obtaining true equalibrium data at low
temperatures, Spencer and Gilmore report that the value of π_i must be
changed to 50,500 for polystyrene as room temperatures are approached.
Toor and Eagleton[112] obtained a value of 22,000 for polystyrene in comparison
to the above values, over the temperature range from 140–260°C. but
the correctness of this value depends on the validity of specific heat data
required in their calculations of π_i. In addition to the above contributions,
Boyer and Spencer,[10] in 1944, summarized all the specific volume-temperature
data then available.

The "hybrid" units used in the above table have considerable convenience, enabling the expression of p in psi, V in ml/gm, and T in °K. The
value of R' is in units of psi $\times$ (ml/gm) $\times$ 1/°K. The value should be
theoretically obtainable from the universal gas constant, if one knew the

---

* The thermodynamically calculated theoretical work of compression will usually
be smaller than the true work, by an amount depending on the rate of compression
and the volume viscosity of the material. While this difference may be negligible in
most ordinary liquids and gases, this is not likely to be true in polymers under many
conditions. No calculations of this difference are yet possible, because of the absence
of data on the volume viscosities of polymer melts.

molecular weight of the polymer. This does not turn out to be the case, but, curiously enough, use of the molecular weight of one mer (or of the monomer, if the polymer is formed by addition) predicts values of R' which are, at least occasionally, very close to those determined experimentally.

C. E. Weir[118] has published a remarkable study of polymer compressibilities. Instead of using the approximate Eq. (26), he chose to use a power series in temperature and pressure:

$$\frac{V}{V_o} = 1 + a_1 p + a_2 p^2 + a_3 p^3 + t(b_o + b_1 p + b_2 p^2 + b_3 p^3)$$
$$+ t^2(c_o + c_1 p + c_2 p^2 + c_3 p^3)$$

(27)

in which V = polymer specific volume at temperature t and pressure p

V_o = specific volume at atmospheric pressure and 0°C

t = temperature, °C

p = pressure, atm

The following table gives values of the constants for polyethylene and polyvinyl alcohol, studied at 80°C and at pressures as high as 10,000 atm. Other data were also obtained on samples of polymonochlorotrifluoroethylene ("Kel-F"*), polytetrafluoroethylene ("Teflon"*), a polyester ("Selectron"* 5003), polyvinyl fluoride, polyvinylidene fluoride, and a copolymer of ethylene and tetrafluoroethylene; the internal energy changes resulting by compression have also been calculated and presented by Weir. A further, apparently extensive, investigation has also been published by Kovacs.[42]

	Polyethylene	Polyvinyl Alcohol
V_o	1.0881	0.7674
a_1	-3.354×10^{-5}	-1.584×10^{-5}
a_2	3.511×10^{-9}	1.178×10^{-9}
a_3	-1.575×10^{-13}	-4.863×10^{-14}
b_o	-2.86×10^{-5}	3.01×10^{-4}
b_1	-2.66×10^{-7}	-3.92×10^{-8}
b_2	-5.92×10^{-11}	-1.09×10^{-14}
b_3	3.44×10^{-15}	1.68×10^{-16}
c_o	7.73×10^{-6}	3.18×10^{-8}
c_1	-3.85×10^{-9}	1.67×10^{-11}
c_2	6.70×10^{-13}	-1.41×10^{-5}
c_3	-3.58×10^{-17}	-5.38×10^{-20}

P-V-T studies are also reported in Ref. 57, but the investigators failed to obtain any equilibrium measurements. Thus their rather extensive experimental data are not quantitatively useful.

* Reg. U. S. patent office.

Effect of Temperature on Flow Properties

The effects of temperature are carefully analyzed and compiled in two recent publications.[6, 81] Two different approaches have been considered: (1) effect of temperature on shear rate at a given shear stress and (2) effect of temperature on shear stress at a given shear rate.

The second of these is also equivalent to considering the effect of temperature on the flow-behavior index K, or the apparent viscosity μ, all at constant shear rate, provided the power-law equation is obeyed over the temperature range as well as the shear-rate range considered [compare Eqs. (23) and (24)]. Since the primary purpose of this section is to provide for modifications of the design equations necessitated by temperature changes, we will not use the above approaches but will, instead, consider how temperature affects the applicability of Eq. (23).

Effect of Temperature on the Flow-Behavior Index. In view of the earlier theory that the flow behavior depends on the size and alignment of the effective flowing particles, one would expect non-Newtonian tendencies to be suppressed by increases in temperature—since the more rapid molecular motion at higher temperature would redisperse any aligned particles more rapidly. Higher temperatures would also tend to decrease the size of flow units even in the virtual absence of shear—simply by virtue of the desolvating action of increased Brownian motion. Therefore, the shearing stresses would have only a marginal role in effecting further decreases in particle size, hence in promoting non-Newtonian behavior. However, the magnitude of all these effects should be small, since mean molecular velocities range only as the square root of the absolute temperature.[31]

Experimental flow curves of polymer melts at various temperatures are given by Westover and Maxwell,[124] Philippoff and Gaskins,[81] Dexter,[19] and Bestul and Belcher,[6] among others. In addition, Philippoff and Gaskins have very well summarized all other available work. The following conclusions may be drawn from these data collectively:

(1) The shear rate at which non-Newtonian behavior first begins (i.e., a Newtonian flow curve is obtained at lower shear rates) increases appreciably with increasing temperature: for polyethylene (melt index 2.0, specific gravity 0.923) it increases from about 0.002 sec^{-1} to 0.08 sec^{-1} as temperature is increased from 112 to 250°C. For a plasticized polyvinyl butyral the corresponding numbers are 0.002 sec^{-1} at 119°C to 0.09 sec^{-1} at 155°C; for another polyethylene (melt index 2.1, specific gravity 0.914) the values are 0.005 sec^{-1} at 108°C and 0.04 sec^{-1} at 230°C. These data are too divergent to enable any generalizations except to say that a 100°C change in temperature will vary this shear rate by at least one order of magnitude. The data of Philippoff and Gaskins appear to be the only ones available over a wide enough range of shear rates to include both the Newtonian and non-Newtonian regions at all temperatures.

(2) Within the non-Newtonian flow region, the flow-behavior index increases slightly with increases in temperature, as summarized by the accompanying table.

Material	Shear rate, sec⁻¹	Flow-behavior index and corresponding temp., °C.	Increase in Flow-behavior index per 100°C temp. increase
Polyethylene (melt index 2.1)	0.01	0.84 at 108° and 1.00 at 230°	0.13
	100	0.32 at 108° and 0.49 at 230°	0.14
Polyethylene (melt index 2.0)	0.1	0.59 at 112° and 0.88 at 250°	0.21
	10	0.33 at 125° and 0.59 at 250°	0.21
Plasticized polyvinylbutyral	10	0.24 at 125° and 0.365 at 155°	0.42
"Vistanex" LM-S polyisobutylene	1,000	0.30 at 38° and 0.49 at 149°	0.17
X-672 GR-S rubber	100	0.17 at 38° and 0.25 at 93°	0.14

With the exception of the plasticized polyvinyl butyral, whose flow properties are extremely temperature sensitive, it is seen that the flow-behavior index increases only very slowly with increase in temperature. Therefore, a convenient, and usually good, approximation in design work is to assume constancy of the flow-behavior index, provided temperature does not change by more than about 30°C. If the flow-behavior index is evaluated near the middle of such a 30°C range, the end values would be within 20 per cent of this median value for all the polymers tabulated above, and within less than 15 per cent for all except the butyral.

However, if the temperature range to be covered is a large one—of the order of 100°C or more—the table also shows that constancy of the flow-behavior index would be a rather poor assumption to make if one wished to obtain a better than order-of-magnitude design within the non-Newtonian region. Philippoff and Gaskins[81] have pointed out that these changes in curve shape preclude the use of "reduced" coordinates, frequently recommended by other authors to superimpose all the curves for various temperatures, and that such recommendations are strictly valid only over limited temperature ranges.

Effect of Temperature on the Consistency Index. Philippoff and Gaskins[81] present an excellent summary of all work at low shear rates (Newtonian region) in which the effect of temperature on the Newtonian viscosity may be expressed by the usual exponential equation.

$$\mu_F(=K) = Ae^{E/RT} \tag{28}$$

$$\frac{d(\ln \mu_F)}{d(1/T)} = E/R \tag{29}$$

The plots of $\ln \mu_F$ vs. $1/T$ are excellent straight lines; values of the activation energy E are as follows, in order of increasing temperature dependency of the polymer:*

Polyethylene	11 –12.8 kcal/gm mole
Polyisobutylene	15.7–16.4 kcal/gm mole
GR-S rubber	20.8 kcal/gm mole
Polystyrene	22.0–23.0 kcal/gm mole
Polyvinyl butyral	25.9 kcal/gm mole
Polyvinyl chloride acetate	35.0 and 60.0 kcal/gm mole
Cellulose acetate	70.0 kcal/gm mole

Of greater practical interest is the dependence of the consistency index K on temperature at higher shear rates, i.e., in the non-Newtonian region. In this case it is arbitrary whether one considers the variation of K with temperature at constant shear rate or at constant shear stress, but different values will be obtained for the activation energy, that at constant shear rate being lower.[6] Since that at constant shear rate may be of somewhat greater practical interest, values for several materials are tabulated below. These have been calculated from the data of Philippoff and Gaskins[81] and Bestul and Belcher[6] at shear rates of practical interest and over whatever temperature-range data were available.

Material	Average temp., °C	Shear rate, sec⁻¹	Activation energy, kcal/gm mole
Polyethylene (melt index 2.1)	150	1,000	6.9
Polyethylene (melt index 2.1)	200	1,000	5.7
Polyethylene (melt index 2.1)	150	100	8.2
Polyethylene (melt index 2.1)	200	100	7.0
Plasticized polyvinyl butyral	147	100	13.6
"Vistanex" LM-S polyisobutylene	55	1,000	4.9
"Vistanex" LM-S polyisobutylene	120	1,000	5.5
"Vistanex" LM-S polyisobutylene	55	100	5.7
"Vistanex" LM-S polyisobutylene	120	100	6.7

While it is seen that the activation energy now varies with both temperature and shear-rate level, this restriction is not particularly serious when one considers that Eq. (28) is limited, in any case, to temperature regions in which the flow-behavior index remains reasonably constant. Thus, if one again chooses limits of $\pm 15°C$, the variation of activation energy for polyethylene and polyisobutylene is considerably less than ± 10 per cent.

Within the same temperature range the more empirical equation:

$$K = A'e^{-BT} \qquad (30)$$

---

* These values probably depend on polymer molecular weight, but the magnitude of such effects should be small. Fox and Flory[26] showed that above molecular weights of about 30,000 the melt viscosities in the Newtonian (low shear-rate region) are very nearly independent of molecular weight in polystyrene.

fits experimental data equally well. (Refer to Chap. 3.) Thus, choice of Eq. (28) or (30) may be made on the basis of mathematical convenience and will vary from problem to problem. Since polymers expand and contract more with temperature changes than do most liquids, use of an equation which takes this into account may be fruitful. da C. Andrade's[17] recommendation for Newtonian fluids might be generalized to

$$Kv^{1/3} = C_1 e^{C_2/vt} \tag{31}$$

where v is the specific volume of the fluid at temperature T and C_1 and C_2 are constants to be experimentally determined. No attempt to use Eq. (31) with polymers has yet been reported, however.

Hopkins[38] has shown how the temperature dependency of the (low shear rate) Newtonian viscosity may be estimated from other data-creep curves, dynamic moduli, etc.

MECHANICS OF FLOW IN TUBES OF SIMPLE GEOMETRY

Isothermal Flow in Round Tubes

Pressure Drop-Flow Rate Relationships. Rabinowitsch[88] and Mooney[65] have shown that in steady flow the relationship between the shear stress at the wall of a round tube, $D\Delta p/4L$, and the term $8V/D (8V/D = 32q/\pi D^3)$ *must* be independent of tube diameter in laminar, isothermal flow for all fluids for which:

(1) The shear-stress–shear-rate relationships are not time dependent. This qualification excludes fluids in which thixotropy and rheopexy[59] effects are measurable, and those which are degraded or broken down by flow through the equipment. These are not, however, significant limitations in almost all cases: thixotropic and rheopectic effects are present only infrequently, and, if present, may usually be assumed to be confined to a short inlet region, near the upstream end of the tube, especially if the material flowed through a number of connections or fittings prior to entering the tube.

Since polymer degradation in processing equipment undesirably affects product properties, the problem of degradation also tends to be absent in well-designed equipment.

(2) Slippage does not occur at the wall of the tube. In all normal fluid-flow problems the absence of slippage is a very valid assumption, and the fact that the velocity of the fluid which is immediately adjacent to the wall is zero has been experimentally indicated by investigators in the field of fluid mechanics. (See, e.g., Ferrell, Richardson, and Beatty.[25]) While some

qualitative evidence exists that in polymers slippage may occur,* slippage has been found to increase the over-all flow rate only 5 per cent in a tube coated to prevent wetting by the fluid,[99] thereby presenting a good and possibly maximum opportunity for the effect to occur. Mooney and Black[69] were unable to find any slip during extrusion of rubbers, although any 5 per cent effects would have been too small to detect under their more difficult experimental conditions. Furthermore, Mooney[65] and Mooney and Black[69] present equations for accounting for any slip which might occur. While these are of importance in flow of suspensions[32, 93] in which the solids may separate from the carrier liquid next to the wall (leaving a low-viscosity film in which most of the over-all velocity change occurs and therefore having an effect similar to that of true slip), in view of the absence of any appreciable proved effects attributable to slip in fluids other than suspensions, these equations will not be presented here.†

In addition to showing the existence of a unique functional relationship between τ_w (or $D\Delta p/4L$) and $8V/D$ (or $32q/\pi D^3$), the Rabinowitsch analysis developed on the basis of the same assumptions shows the true relationship between the volumetric flow rate q and the fluid shear rate at the wall. It may be expressed as

$$(-du/dr)_w = \frac{3n' + 1}{4n'} \frac{32q}{\pi D^3} \tag{32}$$

where

$$n' = \frac{d(\ln \tau_w)}{d\left(\ln\left(\dfrac{32q}{\pi D^3}\right)\right)} \tag{33}$$

Two consequences of these relationships are of interest:

(1) The true shear-stress–shear-rate flow curves may be obtained from pressure-drop–flow-rate data taken in a round tube, even for non-Newtonian fluids. Since n' is the slope of a logarithmic plot of τ_w vs. $32q/\pi D^3$ (at

---

* The evidence cited by Mooney and Black[69] is that extrusion operations may be carried out without scorching of the stock which is in contact with the hot metal surfaces of the extruder. However, minor scorching of the very thin film immediately adjacent to the surfaces would be very hard to detect. The fact that most fluids become less viscous when heated would further tend to promote flow near the surface and hence reduce even more the thickness of the extremely thin, slowly moving film. Therefore, while the qualitative absence of scorching proves that no stagnant layer of appreciable thickness exists, it is difficult to come to any firm conclusion as to the existence of slippage at the wall.

† Many early publications in rheology, especially in the engineering literature, claim problems due to slippage. However, in many cases the limitations of the experimental techniques used do not permit definite conclusions to be reached.

the given value of $32q/\pi D^3$ or τ_w of interest), simple graphical evaluation of the data is all that is required to convert the measurements into true shear-stress–shear-rate curves.

(2) If the data are to be used *solely* for design of equipment in which the fluid flows inside round tubes, the unique relationship of τ_w to $32q/\pi D^3$ may be used directly (and rigorously) for scale-up.

Alves, Boucher, and Pigford[2] made use of the unique relationship between $D\Delta p/4L$ and $32q/\pi D^3$ or $8V/D$ in correlating data on a wide variety of non-Newtonian suspensions and solutions. Since this method is essentially one of scaling up to the new conditions under consideration, it is very simple, direct, and accurate. Metzner[58] pointed out that this scale-up must obviously be at a constant value of V/D, not at a constant value of V, as has frequently been recommended. Furthermore, for all the fluids under consideration here, a single experimental determination in a model of convenient size theoretically enables the prediction of the pressure drop in any larger pipe at the same value of V/D. However, whenever measurements in several tubes of different diameters are possible, they should be carried out, to ensure the absence of complicating effects such as thixotropy and slip.

The derivative of Eq. (33) represents the slope of a line; hence it is rigorously permissible to write

$$\frac{D\Delta p}{4L} = \tau_w = K'\left(\frac{8V}{D}\right)^{n'} \tag{34}$$

If the derivative in Eq. (33), i.e., n', is a constant, the mathematical relationship between the $D\Delta p/4L$ and $8V/D$ in Eq. (33) is given by Eq. (34). If n' is not a constant but varies with τ_w, Eq. (34) represents the tangent to the curve at any chosen value of $D\Delta p/4L$ or $8V/D$.

The similarity between Eqs. (23) and (34) is obvious, the only important difference is that Eq. (23) is not useful for relating pressure drop to flow rate until it has been integrated, which, in turn, requires that the exponent n be constant over the entire range of shear rates in the pipe [from zero to $(-du/dr)_w$], unless laborious averaging procedures are used. Methods based on Eq. (23) are therefore approximations—although frequently of excellent engineering accuracy—while Eqs. (33) and (34) already relate ΔP to V and hence require no integration; they therefore present a theoretically rigorous relationship between pressure drop and flow rate. If n' varies from one value of τ_w to another, it is simply necessary to evaluate it at the point appropriate for the problem at hand. This advantage of Eq. (34) over Eq. (23) has been discussed in detail recently,[60] where the rigorous applicability of Eqs. (33) and (34) to various types of non-Newtonian fluids has been compared with other design methods.

If n', as experimentally determined, may be shown to be a constant over some range of $32q/\pi D^3$, the shear rate as given by Eq. (32) will be a simple multiple of the term $(32q/\pi D^3)$. That is to say that the shear-stress–shear-rate and the shear-stress vs. $32q/\pi D^3$ curves will be identical in shape but shifted with respect to one another along the $32q/\pi D^3$ axis by the factor of $(3n' + 1/4n')$. Since the two curves then have the same slope, comparison of Eqs. (23) and (34) shows that n' must be exactly equal to n. Equating Eq. (23) to Eq. (34) under these conditions gives[59]

$$K' = K \left(\frac{3n' + 1}{4n'}\right)^{n'} \tag{35}$$

If n' is changing with $32q/\pi D^3$, one may similarly show that

$$K' = K \left(\frac{3n' + 1}{4n'}\right)^{n} \left(\frac{32q}{\pi D^3}\right)^{n-n'} \tag{36}$$

Inspection shows Eq. (35) to be a special case of Eq. (36).

In the same way as K and n were defined to be consistency and flow-behavior indices, respectively, one sees that K' is simply another consistency index and n' another flow-behavior index. However, while n and n' may be used interchangeably for power-law fluids, Eq. (35) shows that K' and K are not identical even for power-law fluids except at the special condition of Newtonian behavior ($n = n' = 1.00$).

Metzner and Reed[63] have used the indices K' and n' to derive a generalized Reynolds number which is descriptive of non-Newtonians as well as Newtonians. This Reynolds number may be written as

$$N'_{Re} = \frac{D^{n'} V^{2-n'}}{\gamma} \rho \tag{37}$$

where*

$$\gamma = g_c K' 8^{n'-1} \tag{38}$$

For the special case of Newtonian behavior, $n' = 1.00$, $K' = \mu/g_c$, and Eq. (37) becomes $N'_{Re} = DV\rho/u_M$, showing that the conventional Newtonian Reynolds number represents one special case of Eq. (37).

Metzner and Reed[63] and Dodge and Metzner[23] have shown that the end of the stable laminar-flow region occurs at generalized Reynolds numbers of about 2,100 for most non-Newtonian systems, just as in the case of Newtonian behavior. In highly elastic non-Newtonian fluids however, the elastic forces apparently suppress turbulence sufficiently to permit the pressure

---

* The reader must take care to avoid being confused by the nomenclature: γ, as defined here, is totally unrelated to the strains of pp. 6–14, which were denoted by γ_s, γ_t, γ_1, γ_2, and γ_{total}.

drop–flow-rate relationships to continue to follow the laminar-region relationship closely to generalized Reynolds numbers which are several times greater than 2,100, although the exact values have not yet been worked out for elastic fluids. These authors also show that the many prior-art references to "premature" or "structural" turbulence are incorrect. Dodge and Metzner[23] and Metzner[61] have discussed in some detail the probable reasons for the incorrectness of these observations of prior-art workers in the field of turbulence in non-Newtonian systems.

In view of the conclusive evidence that stable turbulence in non-Newtonian systems does not occur at Reynolds numbers below 2,100 and in view also of the viscous nature of most polymer melts, it is extremely unlikely that turbulent flow will be of positive interest here. Instead, the interest of a plastics investigator will usually be limited to evaluating the generalized Reynolds number only to show that turbulence must be absent. Accordingly, no further discussion of the information on this subject[23, 59, 63] will be presented here.

If only shear-stress–shear-rate data (e.g., as obtained with rotational viscometers) are available, pipe-line design becomes somewhat more complex than when scaling up pressure-drop–flow-rate data directly by use of Eq. (34), but only slightly so if the fluid behaves the power-law, Eq. (23), over the most of the shear-rate range of interest. In this case n' and n are identical, K' may be calculated from K by means of Eq. (35), and the final pressure drop may be evaluated by means of Eq. (34) as before. This will be a trial-and-error calculation, although a simple one, since the correct value of shear rate at which n and K (hence K') are to be evaluated is not known beforehand. The procedure is as follows:

(1) Assuming a value for the shear rate of interest, one determines n and K from the flow curve of the fluid. If the logarithmic flow curve is not a perfect straight line, one must note that the straight-line approximation used when fixing the values of n and K should fit the data at all shear stresses (or shear rates) *up to* the chosen one, but not beyond. A good fit should be obtained over about a twofold range of shear stresses.

(2) Having n and K, one calculates K'.

(3) With the chosen value of flow rate (q) in question, Eq. (34) is used to determine the shear stress, hence the pressure drop in the equipment being designed.

(4) The predicted value of shearing stress should check with the one initially chosen for evaluation of n and K. If this is not the case, a new value of shear stress is chosen, and the calculations are repeated.

The trail-and-error calculation would be unnecessary if the fluid behaved as a true power-law material at all shear rates, since in this case the values of n and K would be fixed, regardless of the shear stress. While this is not

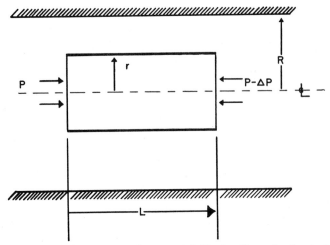

Fɪɢ. 1.12. Force balance on an element of fluid of radius r flowing inside a round tube.

the case with real materials, only few fluids deviate sufficiently from power-law behavior to make more than one recalculation necessary.

For the very few fluids for which n varies extremely rapidly with shear stress—dilatant suspensions of a polymer in a plasticizer being an example—the above method of approximating the true fluid properties with a power-law equation breaks down. In this case one has only one of two alternatives in making use of the shear-stress–shear-rate data. In the first place, one may try to fit the flow curve with other equations, such as that of Eyring and Powell (p. 28). Alternately, one may proceed by means of a graphical or numerical integration, as described in the following paragraphs.

By means of a force balance on a cylindrical element of fluid of radius r (Fig. 1.12) one may show that:

Forces pushing fluid element from left to right equal

$$\Delta p(\pi r^2)$$

Forces restraining free movement (shearing forces over the surface of the element) equal

$$\tau 2\pi r L$$

In these equations Δp represents the frictional pressure drop over a length of tube L.

Under steady flow conditions (no acceleration) in a horizontal tube,* the

* The assumption of horizontal tubes is one of convenience, not of necessity. Gravitational effects may be simply added later, although they are probably only seldom of significance in molten polymers.

two forces must be equal, and equating them gives

$$\tau = \frac{r\Delta p}{2L} \tag{39}$$

which clearly shows that the shearing forces on a fluid element vary from zero at the center line of the tube to a maximum value of $D\Delta p/4L$ at the wall.

Since some functional relationship must exist between shear stress and shear rate, one may write either

$$\frac{r\Delta p}{2L} = \varphi(-du/dr) \tag{40}$$

or

$$-du/dr = \varphi'\left(\frac{r\Delta p}{2L}\right) \tag{41}$$

where φ and φ' denote different and unknown functions.

The variation of the velocity across the cross section of tube may be obtained by integration of Eq. (41) from the wall to any point at radius r from the center line. Since, in the absence of slip, the fluid velocity is zero at $r = R$, one obtains

$$-\int_o^u du = \int_{r=R}^r \varphi'\left(\frac{r\Delta p}{2L}\right) dr \tag{42}$$

Integrating,

$$u = -\int_R^r \varphi'\left(\frac{r\Delta P}{2L}\right) dr \tag{43}$$

The integral in Eq. (43) represents the area under the curve of $\varphi'(r\Delta P/2L)$ (which is equal to $-du/dr$) vs. r, taken between $r = R$ and $r = r$. Graphical integration may be used as follows:

(1) If the pressure gradient $\Delta P/L$ is fixed, and one is interested in determining the corresponding flow rate q, one calculates the value of $r\Delta p/2L$ and at various values of r between $r = R$ and $r = 0$. From the flow curve for the fluid, one obtains the corresponding value of $-du/dr = (\varphi'(r\Delta p/2L))$ at each r, and then plots $-du/dr$ vs. r. The value of the velocity u at each chosen value of r is obtained by determining the area under the curve from radius $r = R$ to a radius equal to the chosen value. Repetition of this integration for a number of values of r results in a tabulation of u vs. r, i.e., of the velocity profile.

The bulk or volumetric flow rate q is equal to the summation of all the (local velocity $\times$ local area) products across the radius of the tube. Since the local areas are equal to $2\pi r \, dr$, one obtains

$$q = \int_{r=R}^{r=0} u2\pi r \, dr$$

or

$$q/2\pi = \int_{r=R}^{r=0} ur \, dr \qquad (44)$$

Equation (44) states that the term $q/2\pi$ may, in turn, be evaluated by determination of the area under the curve of ur plotted vs. r, evaluated between $r = R$ and $r = 0$. Accordingly, the final values of flow rate q is determined by two successive graphical integrations.

(2) If the value of the flow rate q desired is fixed, and one wishes to determine the corresponding value of the pressure drop Δp (or pressure gradient $\Delta p/L$), multiple calculations of the above type are involved. What must be done is that one assumes, using whatever background, experience, and intuition available, a value of the answer $\Delta P/L$, and proceeds (as outlined above) to calculate the corresponding value of q. Repetition of this procedure at one or two addition values of $\Delta p/L$ enables one to draw a curve relating q to the chosen values of $\Delta p/L$. Interpolation on such a curve finally enables establishment of the pressure gradient $\Delta p/L$ corresponding to the desired value of the flow rate q.

Entrance Effects. The velocity profile at the entrance to a tube, when the fluid flows into a tube from a large tube or a reservoir, is essentially flat; i.e., the velocity is constant across the radius of the tube. In an extremely thin region next to the wall, the velocity rapidly changes from this finite value to a value of zero at the wall. As the flow proceeds down the tube, a velocity profile is built up which becomes parabolic for Newtonian fluids. It is steeper than parabolic (i.e., approaches a conical shape) for dilatant materials ($n' > 1.00$) and it is flatter than parabolic for pseudoplastics ($n' < 1.00$). For Newtonian fluids the distance required to produce a well-developed parabolic velocity profile has been determined experimentally to be about equal to $0.05 \, N_{Re}$ diameters (Ref. 22 reviews such work in detail), although theoretical analyses predict an entrance length of only $0.029 \, N_{Re}$ diameters, in laminar flow.

For non-Newtonian pseudoplastics the L/D required to establish a well-developed profile is not this well established, but available data[22] indicate it to be within the range of 0.03 to 0.05 N'_{Re} diameters, or about the same as in the case of Newtonian fluids.

Within this entrance region the pressure gradient ($\Delta p/L$ or $-dp/dL$) will be greater than predicted by the equations for the case of well-developed velocity profiles (pressure-drop–flow-rate relationships pp. 41–48). This arises for several reasons. In the first place, the fact that most of the velocity profile is abnormally flat near the entrance to a tube means that higher-than-normal velocity gradients must occur near the wall, in order to fulfill the condition of a zero velocity at the wall. These higher-than-normal velocity gradients or shear rates in turn require high shear stresses or pressure gradients. Secondly, the kinetic energy of the fluid corresponding to any given flow rate q increases as the velocity profile becomes sharper (p. 52), hence additional work in the form of a higher pressure gradient is necessary in order to provide for the progressively increasing kinetic energy. However, except in viscometric measurements, this kinetic-energy requirement is usually small as compared to the excess pressure drop due to the abnormally high shear rates near the wall. Also, a significant fraction of the kinetic energy has usually been supplied in the region *just upstream* from the entrance to the tube, in accelerating the fluid to its entering velocity. A third reason for excess pressure losses near an inlet is that the molecules themselves must be deformed and aligned as a velocity gradient is imposed on them. This would be expected to occur in the entrance region which extends upstream as well as downstream from the geometric entrance to the tube itself. These molecular deformations require work to overcome both intra- and intermolecular forces, and should therefore be related to the elasticity of the fluid as through its elastic modulus.

No theoretical analysis of all these effects appears to be available,* hence one must resort to experimental determination of the total pressure loss due to entrance effects.** In general, the method of approach has been to use the procedure of classical hydrodynamics of plotting the pressure drop measured over a system containing *both* an entrance region and a straight tube vs. the L/D of the tube, for tubes of various lengths at a given flow rate. Extrapolation to a pressure drop of zero gives the entrance effect expressed in terms of tube diameters.

Experimental results[4, 51, 94, 117, 124] and theory combined suggest:

(1) The entrance effect should increase as the elasticity of the fluid increases. For example, comparative values at a shear rate of 10^4 sec^{-1} are

$L/D = 110$ for 2 per cent napalm in toluene (an *extremely* elastic fluid) and

$$L/D = 4.8 \text{ for polyethylene (a } slightly \text{ elastic melt)}$$

The napalm value was calculated from data presented by Weber and Bauer;[117] that for polyethylene was given by Bagley.[4]

(2) The entrance effect should be relatively independent of shear rate at

---

* However, the work of Smith[101] may represent an excellent starting point for further studies.

** Note added during proof: all of these effects except elasticity have been considered by Bogue, D. C. (Paper presented at the 1958 "Christmas Symposium," American Chemical Society).

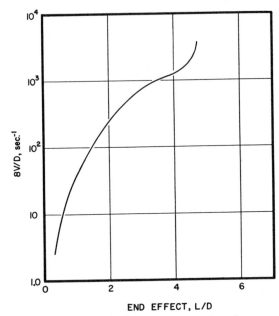

Fig. 1.13. Dependence of the end effect or pressure drop (expressed as equivalent diameters) on the polymer flowrate. (Data are for a polyethylene of melt index 70. at 190°C taken from Bagley[4] with permission of copyright owner)

shear rates which are sufficiently low to permit Newtonian behavior, since little polymer alignment or distortion is observed in this range. Within the non-Newtonian region, at somewhat higher shear rates, the entrance effect may increase rapidly with shear rate as polymer alignment progressively increases. These effects are brought out quantitatively in Fig. 1.13, taken from Bagley.[4] At extremely high shear rates, the effect should approach a constant as polymer alignment becomes complete. This is also found in Fig. 1.13, but it occurs at shear rates at which polymer alignment is not nearly complete. The reasons for the near-constancy of the end effect above shear rates of 10^3 are not entirely defined at present.

(3) The entrance effect L/D (or L/R) appears to be independent of tube diameter at least over modest (two- to fourfold) ranges.[4, 117]

(4) A substantial fraction, but by no means the entire entrance pressure loss, occurs just upstream from the entrance itself. Therefore, measurements on flow through sharp-edged orifices, as carried out by Westover and Maxwell,[124] may be used to portray the entrance effect approximately but not precisely.

(5) With dilatant fluids the entrance geometry is extremely important;[94] to date, no similar effect appears to be reported for pseudoplastics. The

entrance losses are very high for concentrated suspensions. Riggs[94] found the entrance pressure loss to be as great as 325 diameters. As might be expected for dilatant materials, the shear rate had no effect on the entrance pressure losses.

Velocity Profiles in Well-Developed Flow. Beyond the entrance region discussed in the previous section, the velocity profile does not change shape in isothermal flow through a round tube. The relationship between the local velocity at a point in the tube and the corresponding radial position is given by Eqs. (42) and (43). The right-hand part of Eq. (43) may be integrated graphically, but if the power law [Eqs (23)] predicts the fluid properties adequately, one may obtain the following analytical solution directly:[59]

$$\frac{u}{V} = \frac{1 + 3n}{1 + n}\left[1 - \left(\frac{r}{R}\right)^{(n+1)/n}\right] \tag{45}$$

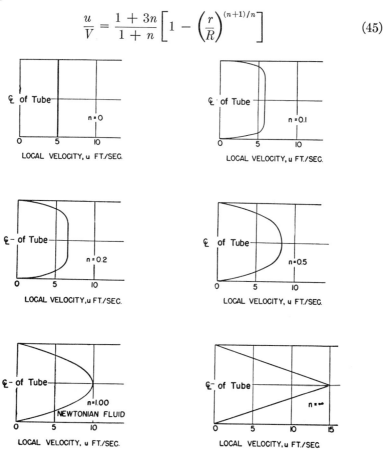

Fig. 1.14. Velocity profiles of power law fluids flowing inside round tubes in laminar flow. (Reproduced from Ref. 59 with permission of copyright owner)

Velocity profiles calculated by means of Eq. (45) are shown in Fig. 1.14; the results are self-explanatory.

Fluid Kinetic Energies. The kinetic energy of any moving stream in a round pipe is given by[46, 59]

$$\text{Kinetic energy} = \frac{1}{VR^2} \int_0^R \frac{u^3 r \, dr}{g_c} \tag{46}$$

For any fluid, the local values of u may be obtained as a function of r by graphical integration of Eq. (43), as outlined before. The kinetic energy (multiplied by VR^2), in turn, may be obtained by graphical integration of Eq. (46) by evaluating the area under a plot of $u^3 r/g_c$ vs. r, between $r = 0$ and $r = R$.

For the special case of power-law fluids, Dodge (in Ref. 59) has integrated Eq. (46) to give

$$\text{Kinetic energy, ft lb}_F/\text{lb}_M = \frac{V^2}{\alpha g_c} \tag{47}$$

where

$$\alpha = \frac{(4n + 2)(5n + 3)}{3(3n + 1)^2} \tag{48}$$

and n is the flow-behavior index. Equation (48) is shown graphically in Fig. 1.15.

Extrudate Shape and Roughness. In liquids of low viscosity, the

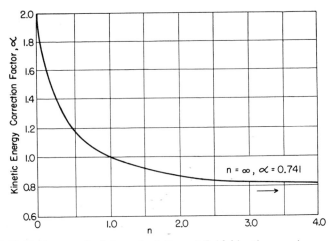

FIG. 1.15. Factor required for calculation of fluid kinetic energies according to Eq. (47) as a function of flow behavior index of power law fluids. (Reproduced from Ref. 59 with permission of copyright owner)

diameter of a jet of fluid (the extrudate) emerging from a vertical capillary tube is usually found to decrease with increasing distance from the tube owing to redistribution of fluid velocities and—if the jet moves downward—owing to the influence of gravitational effects. In the case of viscous oils and polymer melts, however, the opposite effect is noted: The jet rapidly swells to a diameter appreciably greater than the inside of the tube from which it emerges. Farther downstream the jet diameter is again found to decrease under the action of gravity if the fluid is not too viscous. These increases in diameter may be very large—Severs[100] reports ratios of jet to tube diameter as large as 2.8 for polystyrene at 175 to 200°C and at high flow rates.* The diameter increases observed were believed[100, 105] to be due to relaxation of the molecules which had been oriented and possibly distorted while flowing through the tube. It is not obvious why such orientations and distortions should be present to an appreciable extent under conditions corresponding to Newtonian behavior in shear, however, hence further experimental work, particularly on viscous Newtonian oils as used by Keefe,[40] appears to be desirable.

Even more important than the increases in diameter of the extrudate are the irregularities which have been observed to occur as the flow rates are increased. In several polymers the flow rates at which such irregularities first appear are very low; this phenomenon therefore severely limits the maximum permissible flow rate which may be used in industrial extrusion operations.

Nason[72] was apparently the first to point out the existence of these irregularities. The results of quantitative investigations by Severs,[100] Spencer and Dillon,[105] Tordella,[113, 114, 115] and Westover and Maxwell[124] are reviewed and compiled in a recent paper[61] in which it is noted that in some respects the phenomenon is similar to the familiar "tearing" of a dilatant fluid under high shear stresses, although the causes of this phenomenon are possibly different in suspensions and in polymer melts.

Figure 1.16, taken from a paper by Tordella,[113] vividly illustrates the importance of the observed irregularities. The basic causes of the effect are still in dispute, hence no recommendations for methods of controlling or reducing the magnitude of the irregularities are yet possible. In fact, the three most probable theories—none of which may definitely be refuted as yet—place the location of the causes for the irregularities in the entrance to the tube, inside the tube, and downstream from the tube, respectively. The recent review[61] of data on the subject has only enabled rejection of the most obviously incorrect theory: it may be conclusively shown that the irregularities are not due to fluid turbulence.

---

* Westover and Maxwell[124] show how this ratio rapidly increases with increasing flow rate at low flow rates. It then levels out as flow rates are increased further.

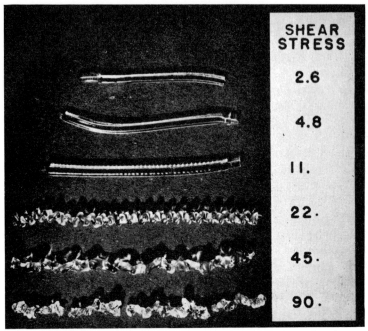

FIG. 1.16. Photograph of extrudate irregularities at various shearing stresses. (Data of Tordella[113], reproduced with permission of copyright owner)

Isothermal Flow Between Flat Plates and Through Rectangular Ducts

Flow Between Parallel Flat Plates. A force balance on the element of fluid in Fig. 1.17 gives, under conditions of steady flow,

$$p(2b \cdot 1) = \tau(1 \cdot L \cdot 2) + (p - \Delta p)(2b \cdot 1) \tag{49}$$

or

$$\tau = \Delta p b / L \tag{50}$$

For power-law fluids,

$$\tau = K\left(\frac{-du}{db}\right)^n$$

hence

$$\int_0^u - du = \left(\frac{1}{K}\frac{\Delta p}{L}\right)^{1/n} \int_B^b b^{1/n}\, db$$

and

$$u = \left(\frac{\Delta p}{KL}\right)^{1/n}\left(\frac{n}{n+1}\right)[B^{(n+1)/n} - b^{(n+1)/n}] \tag{51}$$

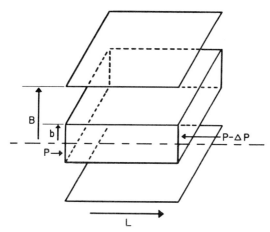

Fig. 1.17. Force balance diagram on a rectangular element of fluid (of thickness $2b$, of unit width and of length L) flowing between infinite parallel flat plates separated by a distance $2B$.

Equation (51) for the velocity distribution may, in turn, be integrated over the cross-sectional area of the tube to give the pressure-drop–flow-rate relationship

$$\frac{B\Delta p}{L} = K\left(\frac{2n+1}{2n}\frac{q'}{B^2}\right)^n \tag{52}*$$

in which the term $B\Delta p/L$ gives the wall shearing stress, and $(2n + 1/2n)$ (q'/B^2) is equal to the shearing rate at the wall. The term q' is equal to the volumetric flow rate per foot of channel width.

Eqs. (51) and (52) form the basis for design of sheeting dies; they also represent one special case of the equation for flow through annuli (p. 56) and for flow through rectangular tubes (p. 55).

Flow Through Rectangular Ducts. Beyer and Towsley[7] and Spencer[103] have treated flow in rectangular channels using 5- and 4-term series expressions for the shear-stress–shear-rate data. The resulting expressions appear to be impossible to solve for pressure drop explicitly and are stated to be limited to shear rates which are not more than one or two decades above the Newtonian (low shear rate) region. The reader is referred directly to the original articles for equations useful within the above limitations. No successful application of the power law to flow in rectangular ducts having a finite-aspect ratio appears to exist as yet.

* It must be noted that in Eq. (52) B is equal to *half* the clearance between the plates, i.e., that the distance between the plates is $2B$.

Flow Inside Annular Spaces

A force balance on the cylindrical element of fluid shown in Fig. 1.18 gives the following.

Forces pushing element of fluid toward the left:

$$(p - \Delta p)2\pi r \, dr + \tau 2\pi r L$$

Forces pushing element of fluid toward the right:

$$p2\pi r \, dr + 2\pi r L \tau + \frac{d}{dr} (2\pi r L \tau) \, dr$$

In these balances the directional convention used leaves the pressure drop Δp a positive quantity. The shearing stress will be negative at radii only slightly larger than R_i, since the lower side of the fluid element is retarded, not accelerated, by stresses in this region. Similarly, the shearing stress is taken as positive in the region near R_o.

Under steady flow conditions, and in the absence of external (e.g., gravitational) forces, the two forces must be equal, giving

$$d(\tau r) = \frac{\Delta p}{L} r \, dr \tag{53}$$

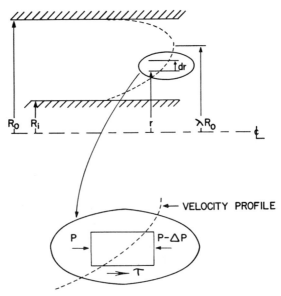

FIG. 1.18. Force balance on a cylindrical fluid element of radius r and thickness dr located within the annulus between tubes of radii of R_o and R_i.

Upon integration, one obtains

$$\tau = \frac{\Delta p r}{2L} + \frac{C}{r} \tag{54}$$

where C is a constant of integration.

As outlined briefly earlier, the shearing stress τ is taken as negative at radii only slightly larger than R_i and becomes positive as r approaches R_o. At the intermediate radius corresponding to a zero velocity gradient (and maximum velocity), the shearing stress must be zero. Designating this radius by the term λR_o, the constant of integration in Eq. (54) may be eliminated, giving[27]

$$\tau = \frac{\Delta p}{2L}\left(r - \frac{\lambda^2 R_o{}^2}{r}\right) \tag{55}$$

Equation (55) may, in turn, be integrated to obtain velocity profiles and pressure-drop–flow-rate relationships upon assumption of a specific shear-stress–shear-rate relationship. Since analytical solutions have not yet been obtainable for the important case of power-law fluids, Fredrickson and Bird[27] integrated Eq. (55) numerically. The results obtained were expressed in the form

$$\frac{R_o \Delta p}{2L} = K\left[\frac{2n+1}{n}\frac{q}{\pi R_o{}^3}\frac{1}{Y\left(1 - \dfrac{R_i}{R_o}\right)^{(2n+1)/n}}\right]^n \tag{56}$$

Y is given in Fig. 1.19 and Table 1.1 as a function of R_i/R_o and the flow behavior index n.

In order to use Eq. (56), one must be able to specify the fluid-property parameters K and n. This, in turn, requires a knowledge of the shear-stress range. The present author recommends the following trial-and-error procedure:

(1) Assumption of the probable value of shear stress is made, enabling determination of K and n from the flow curve.

(2) With these values of K and n, Eq. (56) is used to calculate $R_o \Delta P/2L$ at the flow rate q of interest. [This calculation requires the above value of n in determination of Y, as well as in Eq. (56)].

(3) The calculated value of $R_o \Delta P/2L$ is used to determine the shear stresses at the inner and outer cylinders, given by Eq. (55) as follows:

$$\tau_o = \frac{R_o \Delta P}{2L}(1 - \lambda^2) \tag{57}$$

$$\tau_i = \frac{R_o \Delta P}{2L}\left(\frac{R_i}{R_o}\right)\left(1 - \frac{\lambda^2 R_o{}^2}{R_i{}^2}\right) \tag{58}$$

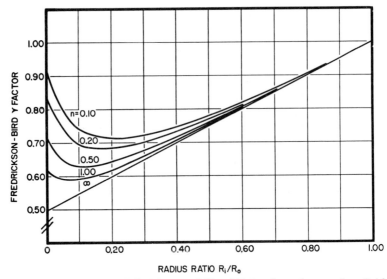

FIG. 1.19. Fredrickson-Bird Y factor of Eq. (56) for flow of power law fluids inside annular spaces. (Copyright 1958 by the American Chemical Society and reprinted with permission)

This calculation requires knowledge of λ, which may be obtained from Table 1.2 or Fig. 1.20, at the assumed value of n.

(4) If the shear stresses determined by means of Eqs. (57) and (58) do not check with the one assumed in picking K and n initially, a new value of

TABLE 1.1. NUMERICAL VALUES OF THE FREDRICKSON-BIRD Y FUNCTION

(Abridged from Ref. 27, copyright 1958 by the American
Chemical Society and used with permission.)

R_i/R_o	0.01	0.1	0.2	0.4	0.6	0.8	0.9
$n = 1.00$	0.6051	0.5908	0.6237	0.7094	0.8034	0.9008	0.9502
$n = 0.50$	0.6929	0.6270	0.6445	0.7179	0.8064	0.9015	0.9504
$n = 0.33$	0.7468	0.6547	0.6612	0.7246	0.8081	0.9022	0.9506
$n = 0.20$	0.8064	0.6924	0.6838	0.7342	0.8128	0.9032	0.9510
$n = 0.10$	0.8673	0.7367	0.7130	0.7462	0.8184	0.9054	0.9519

TABLE 1.2. RADIAL POSITION OF THE FLUID ELEMENT OF MAXIMUM VELOCITY

(Condensed from Ref. 27, copyright 1958 by the American
Chemical Society and used with permission.)

(The tabulation gives values of λ; the maximum velocity occurs at $r = \lambda R_o$.)

R_i/R_o	0.01	0.1	0.2	0.4	0.6	0.8	0.9
$n = 1.00$	0.3295	0.4637	0.5461	0.6770	0.7915	0.8981	0.9495
$n = 0.50$	0.2318	0.4192	0.5189	0.6655	0.7872	0.8972	0.9493
$n = 0.33$	0.1817	0.3932	0.5030	0.6587	0.7847	0.8967	0.9492
$n = 0.20$	0.1503	0.3712	0.4856	0.6509	0.7818	0.8960	0.9491
$n = 0.10$	0.1237	0.3442	0.4687	0.6429	0.7784	0.8953	0.9489

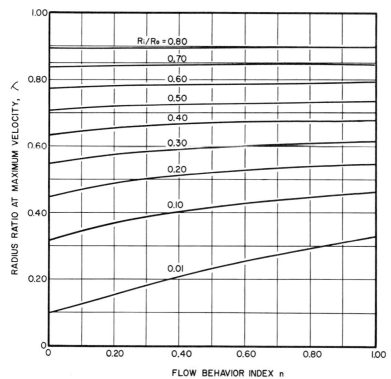

FIG. 1.20. Chart for determination of radial position at which the local velocity is a maximum (Eq. 58). (Reprinted from Ref. 27 with permission. Copyright 1958 by the American Chemical Society)

τ (hence of K and n) is taken, and the calculation is repeated. A little experience in initial choice of τ_o eliminates the need for a second calculation in most cases, however.

It may be noted that no trial and error is involved in calculating the flow rate q corresponding to a given pressure drop ΔP. In addition, it should also be noted that a rigorous calculation requires K and n to be constant over the entire range of shear stresses from τ_o (which is positive) through zero, to τ_i (which is negative). That this can never occur for non-Newtonian fluids is clear from the earlier discussion of non-Newtonian fluid behavior, hence the calculation will, at best, be an approximation.* The degree of approximation improves, in general, at increasing shear stresses τ_o, since the flow-behavior index then tends to be constant over a wider range of stresses up to this maximum value. It should also be noted that if the values of n

* In view of this fundamental difficulty, the recommendation of Ref. 27 to consider use of annular-flow data for viscometric calculations cannot be supported by the present author.

and K corresponding to τ_i and τ_o are appreciably different the one at τ_o should be used, since the average flow rate is more strongly influenced by shear stresses at the outer tube than at the inner one.

For earlier (and much less satisfactory) theoretical studies of annular flow, the reader is referred to the brief review given by Fredrickson and Bird.[27] No experimental data appear to be yet available to check any of the calculations.

Nonisothermal Flow—Round Tubes

The purpose of this section is not to discuss heat-transfer problems but to emphasize the possibly significant changes in polymer temperature even when flowing through a perfectly insulated tube. This arises from two causes:

(1) The high viscosity of many polymer melts leads to very significant frictional heat generation as the fluid flows through the tube. This rate of frictional heat generation (per unit volume of fluid) is equal to

$$(1/J)\ \tau(-du/dr),$$

hence varies from zero at the center line of a tube (where both τ and $-du/dr$ are zero) to a maximum rate at the wall.

(2) The high viscosity leads to a large pressure gradient, hence in long tubes the possibility of appreciable density decreases exists because of volumetric expansion of the polymer. This expansion consumes energy; while its magnitude per unit fluid volume must be independent of radial position in the tube, it consumes the most heat near the center line since the flow rate of fluid is greatest there.

While the differential equations describing this problem are obtainable quite readily, the several publications in this field,[8, 13, 30, 34, 110, 111] although mathematically extensive, do not solve the problem completely. Grigull[34] and Brinkman[13] assumed Newtonian behavior and neglected volumetric expansion; Bird[8] also neglected expansion but attempted to consider non-Newtonian behavior approximately.* Toor[110, 111] showed that expansion cannot be neglected but, in turn, assumed the rheological properties to be nontemperature dependent.† Gee and Lyon[30] attempted to solve a more general set of differential equations, and, after particularly extensive numerical calculations, did obtain a solution for one particular polymer;

---

* As an approximation, Bird assumed the temperature profile to be used in calculating local velocities to be that corresponding to a fluid whose rheological properties are independent of temperature.

† In this last respect his approximation to non-Newtonian behavior is not as good as that of Bird.

for one particular set of flow conditions the results are presented in some detail. However, the results are not quite as general as claimed, and no general tabulation of results which might be used by others for design purposes is given.*

In summary, it would appear that the approach used by Gee and Lyon may be generalized to develop dimensionless correlations applicable to most polymers under a variety of processing conditions. Until this is done—and the mathematical calculations required may be prohibitively extensive even with the use of high speed computers the reader is referred to the original articles for the approximate analyses available at present. The papers by Bird[8] and Toor[110, 111] should be particularly valuable in this respect, as they are complementary. All publications to date neglect the effect of pressure on flow properties, which may well be significant under the same conditions at which volumetric expansion must be considered.

PRACTICAL METHODS OF MEASURING FLUID PROPERTIES

Steady-State Flow Properties

Rotational Viscometers. Rotational viscometers are in many ways well suited for obtaining the true shear-stress–shear-rate relationships. However, these data are not as useful for scale-up purposes when considering flow in round tubes as are the pressure-drop–flow-rate data obtained from capillary tube viscometers (pp. 41–48).

In all rotational instruments the problem of internal heat generation by the shearing action tends to be more serious than in capillary instruments, since the fluid is sheared for much longer periods of time. However, the resulting temperature change is small in well-designed instruments, and the reader is referred directly to the literature for discussion of this problem. (See Refs. 16, 48, 50, and 122, for example.)

Bob-and-Cup Instruments. For consistency, the convention of calculating shearing stress and rate at the bob, regardless of whether the bob or the cup is rotating, will be used. The shearing stress at the bob is given in Ref. 59:

$$\tau_i = \frac{2t}{\pi D_i^2 l} \tag{59}$$

---

* Both density and thermal conductivity were assumed to be constant when deriving the differential equations. While these may not be assumptions which are greatly restricting, the claim that variations in thermal diffusivity and density were accurately considered is invalid. It also appears that the variations of density with temperature were considered in the expansion term of the equation but neglected in the others. Since the results obtained were only compared with integrated flow-rate data, no critical check of the errors due to these assumptions is available.

The corresponding shearing rate is[43, 59, 77]

$(-du/dr)_i$

$$= \frac{4\pi N}{1 - 1/s^2}\left\{1 + k_1\left(\frac{1}{n''} - 1\right) + k_2\left[\left(\frac{1}{n''} - 1\right)^2 + \frac{d\left(\frac{1}{n''} - 1\right)}{d(\log t)}\right]\right\} \quad (60)$$

where

$$k_1 = \frac{s^2 - 1}{2s^2}\left(1 + \frac{2}{3}\ln s\right) \quad (61)$$

$$k_2 = \frac{s^2 - 1}{6s^2}\ln s \quad (62)$$

i.e., k_1 and k_2 are instrument constants.

Equation (60) is valid for cup-to-bob diameter ratios (s) of less than 1.2;* for greater ratios than this, additional terms are required in Eq. (60). As the cup-to-bob ratio approaches unity the shearing rate in all portions of the fluid approaches that at the bob and Eq. (60) reduces to

$$(-du/dr) = \frac{2\pi RN}{\Delta R} \quad (63)$$

where ΔR is the width of the space (i.e., the radial clearance) between the cup and bob. In many cases the derivative in Eq. (60) is nearly equal to zero and may be neglected; for power-law fluids this is rigorously the case.

For the case of "infinite" cup-to-bob diameter ratios, as for a cylindrical bob of a "Brookfield" viscometer, the shear rate at the bob is given in Refs. 2, 43, and 59

$$(-du/dr)_i = \frac{4\pi N}{n''} \quad (64)$$

The shear stress in this case is still given by Eq. (59).

In all cases the shear stress was based solely on the cylindrical area of the bob. In most cases the shearing forces on the end (or ends) of the bob are accounted for simply by calibrating the instrument with a standard Newtonian fluid, expressing the result in terms of an "equivalent" bob length which is somewhat greater than the true bob length. While the application of equivalent lengths as determined with a Newtonian fluid to non-Newtonian measurements definitely would appear to be questionable, excellent†

* The similar equations given by Ref. 48 contain a numerical error and reduce (incorrectly) to $4\pi RN/\Delta R$.

† As defined by noting the agreement between such data and measurements taken on another type of instrument.

results are usually obtained even for equivalent bob lengths which are as much as 20 per cent greater than the true length, for fluids with flow behavior indices as low as 0.20.[74] Mooney and Ewart[71] have described a bob-and-cup viscometer with conical lower ends on both the bob and cup; such an instrument has no end effect (other than due to frictional effects) and represents an excellent design if the clearance between bob and cup is kept very small.

Cone-and-Plate Instruments. Piper and Scott[84] and McKennell[49] showed that if a fluid is sheared in the space between a flat plate and a conical surface, the tip of which just touches the plate, the shear rate will be perfectly uniform. This occurs because the relative velocity and the thickness of the fluid layer being sheared both increase at the same rate as one proceeds radially from the point of the cone or center of the plate. In a commercially available instrument* the angle formed by the cone and plate is extremely small, so that temperature control should be excellent, and secondary flow due to the differing centrifugal forces at the cone and plate is apparently prevented.

The shearing stress given by

$$\tau = \frac{3t}{2\pi R^3} \tag{65}$$

$$(du/dr) = \frac{2\pi N}{\alpha} \tag{66}$$

where α denoted the angle between the cone and the plate, expressed in radians.

Capillary-Tube Viscometers. Measurement of the pressure-drop–flow-rate relationships at several pressure drops enables one to calculate the wall shear stress and the corresponding shear rate from equations presented earlier. They are

$$\tau_w = \frac{D\Delta p}{4L} \tag{39}$$

$$\left(\frac{-du}{dr}\right)_w = \frac{3n' + 1}{4n'} \frac{32q}{\pi D^3} \tag{32}$$

As discussed in earlier sections, for many purposes it is not necessary or even desirable to convert the flow rates to true shear rates. Instead, scale-up may be achieved directly from the $D\Delta p/4L$ vs. $32q/\pi D^3$ relationships.

End effects will always be present in capillary-tube units; the usual way of correcting for them in the case of polymer melts is to obtain pressure-

---

* Other recently built cone-and-plate viscometers, their construction and use, are outlined in some detail in Refs. 41 and 53.

drop–flow-rate data in tubes of various lengths. A plot of pressure drop vs. tube length (at each flow rate) enables determination of the end effect in terms of an "equivalent" tube length by extrapolation of the data to zero pressure drop.

Difficulties due to nonisothermal flow because of viscous heat generation within the fluid may also occur in capillary-tube viscometers, although the effect is not as important as in rotational instruments because the flow process itself may serve to carry the heat out rapidly. This problem has already been discussed on p. 60, but it should be noted that the magnitude of the error is much less in well-designed viscometers with tubes of small diameter than in the extrusion operations treated previously.

Miscellaneous Research Instruments. A "band" viscometer which consists of a band that is pulled between two fixed jaws and thereby drags the polymer into the spaces between the band and the jaws has been used;[3, 39, 116] parallel and opposite plates, one of which is rotated, have been suggested but apparently never used; a parallel-plate unit in which the plates are squeezed rather than rotated has been used on polymers in their Newtonian (low shear rate) range.[20, 21, 55] A "translated cylinder" unit in which one cylinder is pulled out of another (slightly larger) concentric one—shearing the fluid sample in the annulus between the two cylinders—has been used at low shear rates[5] as well as at intermediate rates.[109] All have some restricted utility but seem to have no advantages over the more conventional units which have been perfected mechanically to a greater degree.

Control Instruments. The state of the art in so far as development of rheologically useful instruments, which are suitable for routine production use, is concerned still appears to be as underdeveloped as when discussed in earlier reviews,[59, 108] to which the reader is accordingly referred.

Time-Dependent Effects

Elasticity While methods for obtaining elastic moduli in samples which have only small displacements imposed by the test method are well developed, no similarly extensive studies of elastic stresses, while the fluid sample is undergoing steady shear, appear to exist. However, recent studies of normal stresses in flowing polymer solutions (see, e.g., Refs. 14 and 80) offer an excellent introduction to the problem.

Thixotropy and Rheopexy. No new approaches to the measurement of these properties have been developed since an earlier review,[59] to which the reader is referred.

ACKNOWLEDGMENT

The aid of the many individuals who reviewed and constructively criticized this chapter was very greatly appreciated.

NOMENCLATURE

a	Constant in van der Waals' equation [Eq. (25)].
A	Surface area, sq ft or sq in.
A	Constant in Eq. (28) having units of viscosity.
A_{EP}, B	Constants in the Eyring-Powell equation relating shear stress to shear rate:

$$\tau = \mu \frac{du}{dr} + \frac{1}{B} \sinh^{-1} \left(\frac{du/dr}{A_{EP}} \right).$$

	A_{EP} has units of $\sec^{-1}$ and B has units of sq ft/lb$_F$.
b	Constant in van der Waals' equation [Eq. (25)].
B	One half the distance between parallel plates, ft or in.
d	Differential operator, dimensionless.
du/dr	Shear rate, $\sec^{-1}$ $(du/dr)_w$, $(du/dr)_i$, and $(du/dr)_o$ refer to the shear rates at a wall, at the inner cylinder (bob), and at the outer cylinder (cup) of a rotational viscometer, respectively.
D	Diameter, ft (or in.) D_i and D_o refer to the bob-and-cup diameters of a rotating cylinder-type viscometer, respectively.
$D\Delta p/4L$	Shear stress at the wall of a round pipe or tube, lb$_F$/sq ft or lb$_F$/sq in.
e	Basis of Napierian logarithms, dimensionless.
E	Energy of activation for viscous flow [Eq. (28)].
E	Modulus of elasticity (Young's modulus) lb$_F$/sq in. or lb$_F$/sq ft.
F	Force or shearing force, lb$_F$.
g_c	Dimensional conversion factor in Newton's second law:

$$g_c = ma/F, \text{ or } 32.2 \text{ lb}_M \text{ft}/(\sec^2)(\text{lb}_F).$$

G	Shearing modulus of elasticity, lb$_F$/sq ft or lb$_F$/sq in.
J	Mechanical equivalent of heat, 778 (ft)(lb$_F$)/Btu.
k_1 and k_2	Instrument constants in Krieger-Maron equations for calculation of shear rates from speed and dimensions of a rotational viscometer, dimensionless:

$$k_1 = \frac{s^2 - 1}{2s^2} \left(1 + \frac{2}{3} \ln s \right)$$

$$k_2 = \frac{s^2 - 1}{6s^2} \ln s.$$

K, K'	Fluid consistency indexes with units of (lb$_F$)($\sec^n$) per sq ft (or per sq in.) and (lb$_F$)($\sec^{n'}$) per sq ft (or per sq in.), respectively K is the consistency in the power-law relationship $\tau = K(du/dr)^n$. K' represents the analogous term in a relationship useful in the

consideration of laminar flow through round tubes:

$$\tau_w = D\Delta p/4L = K'(8V/D)^{n'}.$$

l Equivalent length of a rotational viscometer bob, ft.

L Length, ft.

L_o Initial length, ft.

n Flow-behavior index, i.e., exponent in the power-law relation $\tau = K(du/dr)$,^{n} over some well-defined range of shear stresses, dimensionless.

n' Integrated value of flow-behavior index as obtained from pressure-drop–flow-rate data in a round tube, dimensionless:

$$n' = \frac{d(\ln D\Delta p/4L)}{d(\ln 8V/D)}.$$

n'' Slope of a logarithmic plot of torque—rotational speed data obtained using a rotational viscometer, dimensionless:

$$n'' = \frac{d(\ln t)}{d(\ln N)}.$$

N'_{Re} Generalized Reynolds number, $D^{n'} V^{2-n} \rho/\gamma$, dimensionless.

p Pressure, lb_F/sq ft or lb_F/sq in. Pressure drop is denoted by Δp, pressure drop at a contraction by Δp_c, and pressure drop due to changes in fluid kinetic energy by Δp_{KE}.

q Flow rate per unit time:
         of heat, Btu/hr.
         of fluid, cu ft/hr, cu ft/sec, cu in./min, or cu in./sec.

r Lineal or radial distance, ft.

R Radius (internal) of a round tube, ft (or in.). R_i and R_o refer to the radii of the inner and outer surfaces of an annular space.

R Constant in the perfect gas law or in van der Waals' equation, molar basis (1.987 cal/gm mole).

R' R on a mass basis.

s D_o/D_i, dimensionless.

t Torque, ft lb_F or in. lb_F.

t Time, sec or hr.

T Absolute temperature, °K or °R.

u Local velocity, ft/sec or longitudinal component of local velocity, ft/sec (or in./sec).

V Volume, cu ft.

V Volumetric average velocity, ft/sec.

$8V/D$ Shear rate of a *Newtonian* fluid at the wall of a pipe or tube (laminar flow), sec^{-1}.

γ Denominator of the generalized Reynolds number:

$$\gamma = g_c K' \, 8^{n'-1}, \qquad \mathrm{lb}_M/(\mathrm{ft})(\mathrm{sec}^{2-n'}).$$

γ_s Shearing strain, dimensionless.

γ_T Fractional elongation or strain, dimensionless.

Δ Finite difference, dimensionless.

λ Radial position coordinate; max. velocity obtained in annular flow at a radius equal to λR_o.

μ Constant in the Eyring-Powell equation [Eq. (21)] $(\mathrm{lb}_F)(\mathrm{sec})/$ sq ft.

μ_M Newtonian viscosity, $\mathrm{lb}_M/(\mathrm{sec})(\mathrm{ft})$ or $\mathrm{lb}_M/(\mathrm{hr})(\mathrm{ft})$.

μ_F Newtonian viscosity $(\mathrm{lb}_F)(\mathrm{sec})/$sq in. or $(\mathrm{lb}_F)(\mathrm{sec})/$sq ft.

$$\left(\mu_F = \frac{\mu_M}{g_c} \right).$$

μ_a *Apparent* viscosity of a non-Newtonian evaluated at some particular shear stress.

$$\mu_a = \frac{\tau}{du/dr}.$$

μ_o and μ_∞ refer to the apparent viscosity at zero and infinite shear rates, respectively.

μ_d *Differential* viscosity of a non-Newtonian.

$$\mu_d = \frac{d(\tau)}{d(du/dr)},$$

i.e., it is the slope of a $\tau - du/dr$ plot at some particular shear stress.

π 3.1415 . . . .

π_i Internal pressure, or cohesive energy density, $\mathrm{lb}_F/$sq in. or $\mathrm{lb}_F/$sq ft.

ρ Density, $\mathrm{lb}_M/$cu ft.

τ Stress or shear stress $(=F/A)$, $\mathrm{lb}_F/$sq ft or $\mathrm{lb}_F/$sq in. τ_o or τ_w are used to denote shear stress at the wall of a round tube and τ_i the shear rate at a viscometer bob.

τ_T Tensile stress, $\mathrm{lb}_F/$sq in. of $\mathrm{lb}_F/$sq ft.

ω Volume term in simplified van der Waals' equation-of-state [Eq. (26)], cu ft. or cubic cm per unit mass.

REFERENCES

1. Alfrey, T., Jr., "Mechanical Behavior of High Polymers," New York, Interscience Publishers, Inc., 1948.
2. Alves, G. E., Boucher, D. F., and Pigford, R. L., *Chem. Eng. Progr.*, **48**, 385 (1952).

3. Asbeck, W. K., and Van Loo, M., *Ind. Eng. Chem.*, **46**, 1291 (1954).
4. Bagley, E. B., *J. Appl. Phys.*, **28**, 624 (1957).
5. Bergen, J. T., and Patterson, W., Jr., *J. Appl. Phys.*, **24**, 712 (1953).
6. Bestul, A. P., and Belcher, H. V., *J. Appl. Phys.*, **24**, 696 (1953).
7. Beyer, C. E., and Towsley, F. E., *J. Colloid Sci.*, **7**, 236 (1952).
8. Bird, R. B., *SPE Journal*, **11**, No. 7, 35 (1955).
9. Bondi, A., *J. Appl. Phys.*, **16**, 539 (1945).
10. Boyer, R. F., and Spencer, R. S., *J. Appl. Phys.*, **15**, 398 (1944).
11. Bridgman, P. W., "The Physics of High Pressure," London, George Bell & Sons, Ltd., 1949.
12. Bridgman, P. W., *J. Colloid Sci.*, **7**, 202 (1952).
13. Brinkman, H. C., *Appl. Sci. Research*, **A2**, 120 (1951).
14. Brodnyan, J. G., Gaskins, F. H., and Philippoff, W., *Trans. Soc. Rheol.* **1**, 109 (1957).
15. Christiansen, E. B., Ryan, N. W., and Stevens, W. E., *A.I.Ch.E. Journal*, **1**, 544 (1955).
16. Colwell, R. E., *SPE Journal*, **11**, No. 7, 24 (1955).
17. da C. Andrade, E. N., *Endeavour*, **13**, 117 (1954).
18. Davies, R. O., and Jones, G. O., *Proc. Roy. Soc. (London)*, **A217**, 26 (1953).
19. Dexter, F. D., *J. Appl. Phys.*, **25**, 1124 (1954).
20. Dienes, G. J., *J. Colloid Sci.*, **4**, 257 (1949).
21. Dienes, G. J., and Klemm, H. F., *J. Appl. Phys.*, **17**, 458 (1946).
22. Dodge, D. W., Ph.D. thesis in chemical engineering, University of Delaware, Newark, 1957.
23. Dodge, D. W., and Metzner, A. B., paper presented at the Chicago A.I.Ch.E. Meeting, December, 1957.
24. Eirich, F. R., "Rheology," Vol. I, Chap. 1, New York, Academic Press, Inc., 1956.
25. Ferrell, J. K., Richardson, F. M., and Beatty, K. C., Jr., *Ind. Eng. Chem.*, **47**, 29 (1955).
26. Fox, T. G., Jr., and Flory, P. J., *J. Appl. Phys.*, **21**, 581 (1950).
27. Fredrickson, A. G., and Bird, R. B., *Ind. Eng. Chem.*, **50**, 347 (1958).
28. Garner, F. H., and Nissan, A. H., *Nature*, **158**, 634 (1946).
29. Garner, F. H., Nissan, A. H., and Wood, G. F., *Phil. Trans. Roy. Soc. London*, **A243**, 37 (1950).
30. Gee, R. E., and Lyon, J. B., *Ind. Eng. Chem.*, **49**, 956 (1957).
31. Glasstone, S., "Textbook of Physical Chemistry," 2nd Ed., Princeton, N. J., D. Van Nostrand, Company, Inc., 1946.
32. Green, H., "Industrial Rheology and Rheological Structures," New York, John Wiley & Sons, Inc., 1949.
33. Greensmith, H. W., and Rivlin, R. S., *Phil. Trans. Roy. Soc. London*, **A245**, 399 (1953).
34. Grigull, V., *Chem. Ing. Tech.*, **27**, 480 (1955).
35. Grunberg, L., "Proceedings of the 2nd International Congress on Rheology," Harrison, V. G. W. (Ed.), p. 437, New York, Academic Press, Inc., and London, Butterworth & Co. Publishers, Ltd., 1954.
36. Hermans, J. J., "Flow Properties of Disperse Systems," Amsterdam, North-Holland Publishing Company, 1953. (U. S. distributor: Interscience Publishers, New York.)
37. Hersey, M. D., and Hopkins, R. F., "Viscometry of Lubricants Under Pressure," New York, Am. Soc. Mech. Engrs., 1954.

38. Hopkins, I. L., *J. Appl. Phys.* **24**, 1300 (1953).
39. Hull, H. H., *J. Colloid Sci.*, **7**, 316 (1952).
40. Keefe, R. L., Jr., M.Ch.E. thesis, University of Delaware, Newark, 1958.
41. Kepes, M., *J. Polymer Sci.*, **22**, 409 (1956).
42. Kovacs, A. J., Industrie des Plastiques Modernes (Paris) Vol., 7, (1955): Issue ⚹1, pp. 30–4; ⚹2, pp. 39, 41, 43, 45; ⚹3, pp. 36–40; ⚹6, pp. 41–45; ⚹7, pp. 44–48; ⚹8, pp. 41–45; ⚹9, pp. 37, 38; Vol. 8, (1956): Issue ⚹1, pp. 37–43; ⚹2, pp. 38, 41–46.
43. Krieger, I. M., and Maron, S. H., *J. Appl. Phys.*, **25**, 72 (1954).
44. Laird, W. M., *Ind. Eng. Chem.*, **49**, 138 (1957).
45. Lewis, W. K., Squires, L., and Broughton, G., "Industrial Chemistry of Colloidal and Amorphous Materials," New York, The MacMillan Company, 1942.
46. McAdams, W. H., "Heat Transmission, 3rd Ed., New York, McGraw-Hill Book Company, Inc., 1954.
47. Mack, C., *J. Polymer Sci.*, **13**, 279 (1954).
48. McKelvey, J. M., Gavis, J., and Smith, T. G., *SPE Journal*, **13**, No. 9, 29 (1957).
49. McKennell, R., "Proceedings of the 2nd International Congress on Rheology," Harrison, V. G. W. (Ed.), p. 350, 1954.
50. McKennell, R., *Kolloid-Z.* **145**, 114 (1956) and *Anal. Chem.*, **28**, 1710 (1956).
51. McMillen, E. L., *Chem. Eng. Progr.*, **44**, 537 (1948).
52. Markovitz, H., *Trans. Soc. Rheol.*, **1**, 37 (1957).
53. Markovitz, H., Elyash, L. J., Padden, F. J., Jr., and De Witt, T. W., *J. Colloid Sci.*, **10**, 165 (1955).
54. Markovitz, H., and Williamson, R. B., *Trans. Soc. Rheol.*, **1**, 25 (1957).
55. Marshall, O. I., *Ind. Eng. Chem.*, **45**, 2748 (1953).
56. Maxwell, B., and Jung, A., *Modern Plastics*, **35**, No. 3, 174 (1957).
57. Maxwell, B., and Matsuoka, S., *SPE Journal*, **13**, No. 2, 27 (1957).
58. Metzner, A. B., *Chem. Eng. Progr.*, **50**, 27 (1954).
59. Metzner, A. B., "Non-Newtonian Technology—Fluid Mechanics, Mixing and Heat Transfer," in "Advances in Chemical Engineering," Vol. I, Drew, T. B., and Hoopes, J. W., Jr. (Eds.), New York, Academic Press, Inc., 1956.
60. Metzner, A. B., *Ind. Eng. Chem.*, **49**, 1429 (1957).
61. Metzner, A. B., paper presented at the 1957 Annual Meeting of the Society of Rheology.
62. Metzner, A. B., and Otto, R. E., *A.I.Ch.E. Journal*, **3**, 3 (1957).
63. Metzner, A. B., and Reed, J. C., *A.I.Ch.E. Journal*, **1**, 434 (1955).
64. Metzner, A. B., and Whitlock, M., paper presented at the 1957 meeting of the Society of Rheology.
65. Mooney, M., *J. Rheol.*, **2**, 210 (1931).
66. Mooney, M., *J. Colloid Sci.*, **6**, 96 (1951).
67. Mooney, M., *J. Appl. Phys.*, **24**, 675 (1953).
68. Mooney, M., *Trans. Soc. Rheol.* **1**, 63 (1957).
69. Mooney, M., and Black, S. A., *J. Colloid Sci.*, **7**, 204 (1952).
70. Mooney, M., and Black, S. A., *Rubber Chem. and Technol.*, **26**, 311 (1953).
71. Mooney, M., and Ewart, R. H., *Physics (J. Appl. Phys.)*, **5**, 350 (1934).
72. Nason, H. K., *J. Appl. Phys.*, **16**, 338 (1945).
73. Noll, W., *J. Rational Mech. & Anal.*, **4**, 3 (1955).
74. Otto, R. E., Ph.D. thesis in chemical engineering, University of Delaware, Newark, 1957.
75. Padden, F. J., and DeWitt, T. W., *J. Appl. Phys.*, **25**, 1086 (1954).
76. Pao, Yoh-Han, *J. Appl. Phys.*, **28**, 591 (1957).

77. Pawlowski, J., *Kolloid-Z.* **130,** 129 (1953).
78. Philippoff, W., Report of Symposium VII, "Incendiary Gels and Their Instrumentation," 27 and 28 June, 1955, Chemical Corps Chemical and Radiological Laboratories, Army Chemical Center, Maryland (unclassified).
79. Philippoff, W., *J. Appl. Phys.*, **27,** 984 (1956).
80. Philippoff, W., *Trans. Soc. Rheol.* **1,** 95 (1957).
81. Philippoff, W., and Gaskins, F. H., *J. Polymer Sci.*, **21,** 205 (1956).
82. Pilpel, N., *Trans. Faraday Soc.*, **50,** 1369 (1954).
83. Pilpel, N., *Trans. Faraday Soc.*, **51,** 1307 (1955).
84. Piper, G. H., and Scott, J. R., *J. Sci. Instsr.*, **22,** 206 (1945).
85. Pollett, W. F. O., "Proceedings of the 2nd International Congress on Rheology," Harrison, V. G. W. (Ed.), p. 85, 1954.
86. Powell, R. E., and Eyring, H., *Nature*, **154,** 427 (1944).
87. Prager, W., "Finite Plastic Deformation," in "Rheology," Vol. I, Eirich, F. R. (Ed.), New York, Academic Press, Inc., 1956.
88. Rabinowitsch, B., *Z. physik. Chem.*, **A145,** 1 (1929).
89. Ree, T., and Eyring, H., *J. Appl. Phys.*, **26,** 793 and 801 (1955). See also Report of Symposium VII, "Incendiary Gels and Their Instrumentation," 27 and 28 June, 1955, Chemical Corps Chemical and Radiological Laboratories, Army Chemical Center, Maryland (unclassified).
90. Reiner, M., "Deformation and Flow," London, H. K. Lewis & Co., 1949.
91. Reiner, M., *Bull. Research Council Israel*, **2,** 65 (1952).
92. Reiner, M., "Phenomenological Macrorheology," in "Rheology," Vol. I, Eirich, F. R. (Ed.), New York, Academic Press, Inc., 1956.
93. Richardson, R. J., "The Flow of Wood Pulp Slurries," Sc.D. thesis in chemical engineering, M.I.T., Cambridge, Mass., 1954.
94. Riggs, L. C., B.Ch.E. thesis, University of Delaware, Newark, 1956.
95. Rivlin, R. S., *Proc. Roy. Soc. (London)*, **A193,** 260 (1948).
96. Rivlin, R. S., *Trans. Faraday Soc.*, **45,** 739 (1949).
97. Rivlin, R. S., and Ericksen, J. L., *J. Rational Mech. & Anal.*, **4,** 323 (1955).
98. Roberts, J. E., "Proceedings of the 2nd International Congress on Rheology," Harrison, V. G. W. (Ed.), p. 91, New York, Academic Press, Inc., and London, Butterworth & Co. Publishers, Ltd., 1954.
99. Schnell, E., *J. Appl. Phys.*, **27,** 1149 (1956).
100. Severs, E. T., Ph.D. thesis in chemical engineering, University of Delaware, Newark, 1950.
101. Smith, T. L., *J. Polymer Sci.*, **14,** 37 (1954).
102. Spencer, R. S., *J. Polymer Sci.*, **5,** 591 (1950).
103. Spencer, R. S., "Proceedings of the 2nd International Congress on Rheology," Harrison, V. G. W. (Ed.), p. 21, 1954.
104. Spencer, R. S., and Boyer, R. F., *J. Appl. Phys.*, **17,** 398 (1946).
105. Spencer, R. S., and Dillon, R. E., *J. Colloid Sci.*, **4,** 241 (1949).
106. Spencer, R. S., and Gilmore, G. D., *J. Appl. Phys.*, **20,** 502 (1949) and **21,** 523 (1950).
107. Stevens, W. E., abstract of Ph.D. thesis in chemical engineering, University of Utah, Salt Lake City, 1953.
108. Thomas, B. W., *Ind. Eng. Chem.*, **45,** No. 6, 87A (1953).
109. Tollenaar, D., and Bisschop, M. C., *J. Colloid Sci.*, **10,** 151 (1955).
110. Toor, H. L., *Ind. Eng. Chem.*, **48,** 922 (1956).
111. Toor, H. L., *Trans. Soc. Rheol.* **1,** 177 (1957).
112. Toor, H. L., and Eagleton, S. D., *J. Appl. Chem. (London)*, **3,** 351 (1953).

113. Tordella, J. P., *J. Appl. Phys.*, **27,** 454 (1956).
114. Tordella, J. P., *SPE Journal*, **13,** No. 8, 36 (1957).
115. Tordella, J. P., *Trans. Soc. Rheol.*, **1,** 203 (1957).
116. Wachholtz, F., and Asbeck, W. K., *Kolloid-Z.*, **93,** 280 (1940).
117. Weber, N., and Bauer, W. H., Report of Symposium VII, "Incendiary Gels and Their Instrumentation," 27 and 28 June, 1955, Chemical Corps Chemical and Radiological Laboratories, Army Chemical Center, Maryland (unclassified).
118. Weir, C. E., *J. Research Natl. Bur. Standards*, **53,** 245 (1954).
119. Weissenberg, K., conference British Rheologists' Club, London, 1946.
120. Weissenberg, K., *Nature*, **159,** 310 (1947).
121. Weissenberg, K., "Proceedings of the 1st (1948) International Rheological Congress," p. 29, Amsterdam, North-Holland Publishing Company, 1949.
122. Weltmann, R. N., and Kuhns, P. W., *J. Colloid Sci.*, **7,** 218 (1952).
123. Werner, A. C., *Modern Plastics*, **34,** No. 6, 137 (1957).
124. Westover, R. F., and Maxwell, B., *SPE Journal*, **13,** No. 8, 27 (1957).
125. Whitlock, M., "Flow Behavior of Concentrated Suspensions," M.Ch.E. thesis, University of Delaware, Newark, 1957.

2. HEAT TRANSFER AND THERMO-DYNAMICS

J. M. McKelvey, Ph. D.

Department of Chemical Engineering
Washington University

INTRODUCTION

All thermoplastics processes involve transportation and transformation of energy. Particular interest is centered in the transformation of electrical and mechanical energy into heat (thermal energy) and in the rate at which heat can be transferred.

The classical thermodynamic relationships are logically deduced from two general laws of nature, known as the first and second laws of thermodynamics. No assumptions are made regarding the structure of matter or the mechanism of the process, and the resulting thermodynamic relationships have a very general validity, although they are somewhat limited in scope. Using the thermodynamic relationships, the over-all energy (heat and work) requirements of processes can be calculated.

In engineering, however, the over-all energy requirements of a process are only part of the required information. It is equally important to know something about the *rate* at which the process occurs. In many processes the over-all rate is controlled by the rate at which heat can be transferred either to or from the system. This is the subject matter of the science of heat transfer.

The sciences of thermodynamics and heat transfer are therefore complementary. Thermodynamics enables the over-all energy requirements of processes to be calculated, and, in many cases, heat-transfer calculations enable the over-all rate of the process to be estimated.

In this chapter some of the principles of each science which are of particular interest in thermoplastics processing are discussed. However, the chapter is not intended to be a unified treatment of either science. For this, reference should be made to the standard engineering texts in each field.[4, 5, 11, 12, 13, 15]

In making numerical computations with the equations and formulas presented in this chapter, any consistent set of units can be used. In any particular problem the best system to use is probably that one which involves the least amount of work in converting units.

In all scientific work and in some engineering research, units based on the metric system are preferable. It is recognized, however, that many types of engineering computations do not lend themselves to the use of metric units. This is particularly true in the analysis of data obtained from plant operations and in certain types of machine- and plant-design work. Here the British system is firmly entrenched and will probably remain so for some time to come. On the other hand, certain kinds of thermophysical calculations and heat-conduction problems are greatly simplified by the use of metric units, because the sources of most of the physical properties and constants used in these calculations are the scientific journals and handbooks which use the metric system exclusively.

Many of the examples presented in this chapter are most conveniently handled with metric units and, in these cases, this is the system used. All symbols used in the chapter, along with their metric units, are given at the end of the chapter. It should be noted that these units do not constitute a consistent system. All mechanical quantities are given in the cgs system where the unit of energy is the erg, but, for quantities which are primarily thermal in nature, the calorie is used as the unit of energy. In equations in which both mechanical- and thermal-energy terms appear, it is necessary to convert from one to the other system. A few electrical quantities are used, and they are, for the most part, given in practical units. The conversion factors given at the end of the chapter will be useful in making numerical computations.

The method used to indicate temperatures and temperature differences should be noted. In the metric system unit *difference* in temperature is the centigrade degree, for which the symbol (degC) is used. For example, if a specific heat is given as 0.85 cal/g-degC, this means that 0.85 calorie of heat is required to raise the temperature of one gram of the material through one centigrade degree. On the other hand, *temperatures* are expressed either in degrees centigrade, for which the symbol (°C) is used, or on the absolute (Kelvin) scale, for which the symbol (°K) is used. Corresponding symbols used with British units are degF, °F, and °R.

THERMODYNAMICS AND THERMOPHYSICAL CALCULATIONS

Thermodynamic Functions

Thermodynamics deals with the interchange of energy, between a system and its surroundings, when the system passes from one equilibrium state to another. An equilibrium state is uniquely determined by the properties of the system. Therefore, the change in the value of a property between two equilibrium states is entirely independent of the path of the process. Other thermodynamic functions, notably heat and work, are not properties, and for a given process their value depends upon the path of the process. Consequently, these functions are often called path functions.

Thermodynamics is therefore concerned with changes in properties and path functions when a system undergoes a process from one equilibrium state to another. The concept of the reversible process, in which a system passes through an infinite number of equilibrium states, is of great utility in thermodynamics, as it enables limiting values of heat and work and changes in properties to be calculated for various processes.

The first law of thermodynamics is a statement of the principle of conservation of energy and is the basis of many thermophysical calculations. The first law is written

$$dE = dQ - dW \qquad (1)$$

where E, the internal energy, is a property. The quantity of heat transferred to or from the system Q is a path function, as is W, the amount of work done by or on the system. The usual convention is that heat added to the system from the surroundings and work done by the system on the surroundings are taken to be positive quantities.

In this chapter all extensive properties, such as internal energy, are taken as specific properties, i.e., on the basis of unit mass—e.g., internal energy will have units of calories per gram. Similarly, the path functions Q and W will be expressed on the basis of unit mass of the system under consideration.

One further comment should be made concerning Eq. (1). In many texts, equations containing mechanical- and thermal-energy terms will be written with the conversion factor J, which is the mechanical equivalent of heat. In this system Eq. (1) would be written

$$dE = dQ - \left(\frac{1}{J}\right) dW \qquad (2)$$

In this chapter, however, the thermodynamic equations will be written without the conversion factor, it being assumed that consistent units will always be used in making calculations.

A system does work whenever it acts against an external force. In the present discussion the only type of work that will be considered is mechanical work due to the expansion or compression of a substance. In this case, for a reversible process,

$$dW = P \, dv \qquad (3)$$

where P is the pressure and v is the specific volume of the substance. Pressure and specific volume are properties of a system.

Pressure, temperature, and volume are directly measurable. Other properties, such as internal energy, enthalpy, the specific heats, compressibility, and coefficient of volume expansion must be obtained, through the defining thermodynamic relationships, from P-V-T and calorimetric data.

Enthalpy is defined by the equation

$$H = E + Pv \tag{4}$$

which, in differential form, becomes

$$dH = dE + P\,dv + v\,dP \tag{5}$$

Combining Eqs. (1), (3), and (5),

$$dH = dQ + v\,dP \tag{6}$$

Specific heat at constant pressure is defined by the equation

$$c_P = \left(\frac{\partial H}{\partial T}\right)_P \tag{7}$$

and it follows from Eqs. (6) and (7) that

$$dQ = dH = c_P\,dT \tag{8}$$

for a constant-pressure process. Therefore, the heat added to or removed from a system at constant pressure is equal to the change in enthalpy of the system and can be calculated if c_P data are available.

Specific heat at constant volume is defined by the equation

$$c_v = \left(\frac{\partial E}{\partial T}\right)_v \tag{9}$$

and it follows from Eqs. (1), (3), and (9) that

$$dQ = dE = c_v\,dT \tag{10}$$

for a constant-volume process. Therefore, the heat added to or removed from a system at constant volume is equal to the change in internal energy of the system and can be calculated if c_v data are available.

The relationship between the specific heats is given by the equation

$$c_v = c_P - \left(\frac{T\kappa^2}{\rho\beta}\right) \tag{11}$$

where

β = compressibility

κ = coefficient of volume expansion

The compressibility is defined by the equation

$$\beta = -\frac{1}{v}\left(\frac{\partial v}{\partial P}\right)_T \tag{12}$$

Since specific volume is the reciprocal of density, Eq. (12) can be written

$$\beta = \frac{1}{\rho}\left(\frac{\partial \rho}{\partial P}\right)_T \tag{13}$$

The coefficient of volume expansion is defined by the equation

$$\kappa = \frac{1}{v}\left(\frac{\partial v}{\partial T}\right)_P = -\frac{1}{\rho}\left(\frac{\partial \rho}{\partial T}\right)_P \tag{14}$$

Equations (12) and (14) give the effect of temperature and pressure on the volume of a substance. A single equation relating the three variables of temperature, pressure, and volume is known as an equation-of-state. Many equations-of-state have been proposed for gases, but very few for liquids and solids. The simplified equation-of-state proposed by Spencer and Gilmore[17] for liquid and solid polymers was derived from van der Waals' equation and, because of its simplicity, is of considerable interest in plastics processing. It is written

$$(P + \pi_i)(v - \omega) = R'T \tag{15}$$

where π_i, ω, and R' can be considered as empirical constants.

Example 1: It has been reported[15] that, at atmospheric pressure and at temperatures above 120°C, the specific volume of polyethylene is given approximately by the equation

$$v = 0.900 + 0.00089T \tag{16}$$

where

$$v = \text{specific volume (cc/g)}$$

$$T = \text{temperature (°K)}$$

Calculate ρ and κ at atmospheric pressure and 200°C.
From Eq. (16)

$$\rho = \frac{1}{v} = \frac{1}{0.900 + (0.00089)(473)} = 0.757 \text{ g/cc}$$

By differentiation of Eq. (16),

$$\left(\frac{\partial v}{\partial T}\right)_P = 0.00089$$

and from Eq. (14)

$$\kappa = \left(\frac{1}{v}\right)\left(\frac{\partial v}{\partial T}\right)_P = (0.757)(0.00089) = 0.000675 \text{ degC}^{-1}$$

Example 2: Parks and Richards[14] reported the following compressibility data for liquid polyethylene:

$T(°C)$	$\beta \times 10^3$ (atm^{-1})
120	0.088
140	0.102
160	0.119

Assuming that, at any given temperature, β is constant over the range of pressures from 1 atm to 100 atm, calculate the increase in density of liquid polyethylene at 140°C when the pressure is increased from 1 to 100 atm.

The calculation is based on Eq. (13) which can be written, for a change occurring at constant temperature, as

$$\int_{P_1}^{P_2} \beta \, dP = \int_{\rho_1}^{\rho_2} \frac{d\rho}{\rho}$$

Assuming β constant and carrying out the integrations,

$$\frac{\rho_2}{\rho_1} = e^{\beta \Delta P}$$

where

$$\Delta P = (P_2 - P_1) = 100 - 1 = 99 \text{ atm}$$

and

$$\beta = 0.102 \times 10^{-3} \text{ atm}^{-1}$$

therefore

$$\frac{\rho_2}{\rho_1} = e^{0.0101} = 1.01$$

There is a 1 per cent increase in the density of the polyethylene.

Example 3: It has been reported[6] that c_P data for liquid polyethylene at 1 atm pressure fit the following equation:

$$c_P = a + bT \tag{17}$$

where

$$c_P = \text{specific heat (cal/g-degC)}$$

$$T = \text{absolute temperature (°K)}$$

$$a = 0.277$$

$$b = 0.000807$$

Calculate the increase in the enthalpy of liquid polyethylene when it is heated at 1 atm from 150°C to 250°C.

Equation (17) is introduced into Eq. (8)

$$\Delta H = \int_{T_1}^{T_2} c_P \, dT = \int_{T_1}^{T_2} (a + bT) \, dT$$

and, upon integration, the following result is obtained:

$$\Delta H = \Delta T \left[a + \left(\frac{b}{2}\right)(T_1 + T_2) \right] \tag{18}$$

where

$$\Delta T = (T_2 - T_1) = 100 \text{ degC}$$

and

$$(T_1 + T_2) = 423 + 523 = 946 \text{ degC}$$

The change in enthalpy calculated with Eq. (18) is

$$\Delta H = +65.9 \text{ cal/g}$$

Example 4: Spencer and Gilmore[17] reported that if the constants of Eq. (15) were assigned the following values, the equation would be applicable to polyethylene.

$$R' = 43.0 \text{ cc-psi/g-°K}$$

$$\omega = 0.875 \text{ cc/g}$$

$$\pi_i = 47,600 \text{ psi}$$

Calculate κ and β at 120°C and 1 atm pressure using these data and compare the results with the data given in Examples 1 and 2.

Rearranging Eq. (15) so that it is explicit in v gives

$$v = \omega + \frac{R'T}{(P + \pi_i)} \tag{19}$$

from which the following partial derivatives are obtained:

$$\left(\frac{\partial v}{\partial T}\right)_P = \frac{R'}{(P + \pi_i)} \tag{20}$$

$$\left(\frac{\partial v}{\partial P}\right)_T = -\frac{R'T}{(P + \pi_i)^2} \tag{21}$$

Introducing Eqs. (19) and (20) into Eq. (14) gives

$$\kappa = \frac{1}{v}\left(\frac{\partial v}{\partial T}\right)_P = \frac{1}{T + (\omega/R')(P + \pi_i)} \tag{22}$$

and introducing Eqs. (19) and (21) into Eq. (12) gives

$$\beta = -\frac{1}{v}\left(\frac{\partial v}{\partial P}\right)_T = \frac{1}{(P + \pi_i) + (\omega/R'T)(P + \pi_i)^2} \tag{23}$$

At 393°K (120°C) and 14.7 psi (1 atm) the value of κ, as computed with Eq. (22) is

$$\kappa = 0.735 \times 10^{-3} \text{ degC}^{-1}$$

which is approximately 9 per cent higher than the more accurate result obtained in Example 1.

Under the same conditions the value of β, as computed with Eq. (23), is

$$\beta = 0.00606 \times 10^{-3} \text{ psi}^{-1} = 0.089 \times 10^{-3} \text{ atm}^{-1}$$

which is about 1 per cent higher than the data given in Example 2.

Example 5: How much work is done when 1 kg of molten polyethylene at 140°C is compressed, by increasing the pressure from 1 atm to 1,000 atm, assuming that the compression is carried out isothermally and reversibly? If the compression is to be accomplished in a period of 2 sec, how much power will be required?

The work of a reversible process is obtained by integrating Eq. (3),

$$dW = P \, dv \tag{3}$$

It is, however, first necessary to determine the relationship between P and v. This is done by integrating Eq. (12) under the assumption of a constant β.

$$\int \frac{dv}{v} = -\beta \int dP + C \tag{24}$$

where C is the constant of integration. Carrying out the indicated integrations and evaluating the constant of integration at zero absolute pressure gives the following relationship between P and v,

$$v = v_o e^{-\beta P} \tag{25}$$

which, upon differentiation, gives dv in terms of P.

$$dv = -v_o \beta e^{-\beta P} \, dP \tag{26}$$

where v_o is the specific volume at zero pressure and 140°C. Substituting Eq. (26) into Eq. (3) gives

$$dW = -v_o \beta P e^{-\beta P} \, dP \tag{27}$$

Integration of Eq. (27) between the limits of 1 atm and 1,000 atm gives the work done on the polyethylene during the compression.

The calculations are somewhat simplified if, instead of using 1 atm as the lower limit, zero pressure is chosen. This will give a result only slightly in error. With this simplification, Eq. (27) becomes

$$W = v_o \left[\frac{1}{\beta} \left(e^{-\beta P_2} + 1 \right) + P_2 e^{-\beta P_2} \right] \tag{28}$$

The value of v_o is taken as 1.29 cc/g, while the value of β is taken as 10^{-4} atm^{-1}. The work of the compression, as calculated with Eq. (28) is

$$W = -57.1 \text{ cc-atm/g}$$

the negative sign indicating that work must be done on the system (the polyethylene) to accomplish the process. Since 1 kg (1,000 g) of material is to be compressed, the total work required is 57,100 cc-atm or 5,760 joules.

The power required depends upon the rate at which this work is done. If the time for the process is 2 sec and the work is done at a uniform rate, the power is 2,880 joules/sec or 2.88 kw.

Actual processes cannot, of course, be carried out in a perfectly reversible manner. The work calculated for a process assuming reversibility represents a theoretical minimum amount of work. Any departure from reversibility will make the actual amount of work, and power, larger.

The General Energy Balance for a Flow Process

Consider the steady flow of a fluid through a mechanism which can transfer heat and work either to or from the fluid. The resulting changes in

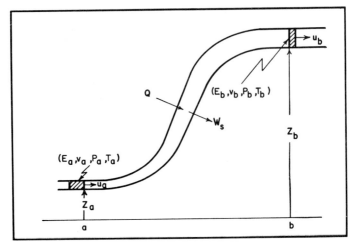

Fig. 2.1. Schematic diagram for a steady flow process.

fluid velocity, elevation, pressure, and temperature are related to the transferred heat and work by the general energy balance, which is derived below.

Referring to Fig. 2.1, the section of the flow system under consideration is located between positions a and b. Since steady-state operation is assumed, there is no accumulation of mass or energy within the section of the system under consideration. The fluid entering the system at a, at elevation Z_a, has velocity u_a, specific volume v_a, temperature T_a, and pressure P_a. The heat transferred *to* the fluid, per unit mass, is Q, while the total work done *by* the fluid, per unit mass, is $\sum W$. The fluid leaving the system at b, at elevation Z_b, has velocity u_b, specific volume v_b, temperature T_b, and pressure P_b.

The principle of conservation of energy requires that the energy of the entering fluid plus the heat added to the fluid equal the energy of the outgoing fluid plus the total work done by the fluid. It should be remembered that in a flow system the fluid has (in addition to its internal energy) potential energy due to its position and kinetic energy due to its motion. Consequently, the energy equation is written

$$E_a + (KE)_a + (PE)_a + Q = E_b + (KE)_b + (PE)_b + \sum W \quad (29)$$

where (KE) represents kinetic energy and (PE) potential energy. Equation (29) can be written in terms of energy changes, as shown by the equation

$$\Delta E + \Delta(PE) + \Delta(KE) = Q - \sum W \quad (30)$$

The change in potential energy, as the elevation of unit mass of the fluid is increased, is given by the equation

$$\Delta(PE) = g\Delta Z = g(Z_b - Z_a) \tag{31}$$

where g is the gravitational acceleration.

The change in kinetic energy as unit mass of the fluid is accelerated from u_a to u_b is given by the equation

$$\Delta(KE) = k\Delta u^2 = k(u_b^2 - u_a^2) \tag{32}$$

where k is a factor which depends upon the velocity profile of the fluid in the tube. For a flat profile (plug flow) $k = 0.5$, while for a parabolic profile (laminar Newtonian flow) $k = 1$. (See Fig. 1.14, p. 51)

The various ways in which the fluid can do work, or work can be done on the fluid, must now be considered. A pump can transfer mechanical energy to the fluid, while a turbine can extract mechanical energy from the fluid. In either case, work of this type is usually called shaft work and is designated by the symbol W_s.

The so-called flow work must also be considered, as it is necessary to do work on the fluid to force it into the system at a, while at b the fluid does work on the surroundings as it emerges from the system. It can be shown that the flow work done at a is simply $-(Pv)_a$, while the flow work done at b is $(Pv)_b$.

The general energy balance Eq. (30) can now be written

$$\Delta E + g\Delta Z + k\Delta u^2 + \Delta(Pv) = Q - W_s \tag{33}$$

An alternate form of Eq. (33) is obtained by introducing the relationship between internal energy and enthalpy Eq. (4).

$$\Delta H + k\Delta u^2 + g\Delta Z = Q - W_s \tag{34}$$

Each term in the general energy balance represents energy per unit mass. Since ΔH, ΔE, and Q will usually be expressed in thermal units (e.g., calories per gram, and the other terms in mechanical units as ergs per gram), care must be taken to convert all terms to one system or the other. The necessary conversions can be made using the factors at the end of the chapter. Examples 6 and 7 show the application of the general energy balance to two specific problems arising in plastics engineering.

Example 6: Molten polyethylene is flowing through a tube. At one point in the tube the pressure is 100 atm and the temperature 160°C, while a short distance downstream the pressure is 1 atm. Assuming that there is no heat transferred either to or from the polyethylene in this section of the tube, calculate the increase in the average temperature of the polyethylene.

Since there is no change in elevation, no acceleration of the fluid, no heat transfer, and no shaft work, Eq. (34) reduces to

$$\Delta H = 0 \tag{35}$$

where ΔH represents the change in enthalpy of the polyethylene.

Although, in the tube, changes in temperature and pressure occur simultaneously, it is more convenient to consider that these changes occur consecutively. This is permissible because changes in properties are independent of the path of the process. Therefore, the process is considered to occur in two stages, first isothermal expansion at 160°C and then isobaric heating at 1 atm. The total change in enthalpy is equal to the sum of the changes occurring for each of these processes.

$$\Delta H = (\Delta H)_T + (\Delta H)_P \tag{36}$$

where

$$(\Delta H)_T = \text{change in enthalpy for the isothermal step}$$

$$(\Delta H)_P = \text{change in enthalpy for the isobaric step}$$

The effect of temperature on enthalpy at constant pressure is given by Eq. (7), which is expressed in integral form below:

$$(\Delta H)_P = \int_{T_1}^{T} c_P \, dT \tag{37}$$

The effect of pressure on enthalpy at constant temperature is given by the well-known thermodynamic equation

$$\left(\frac{\partial H}{\partial P}\right)_T = v(1 - \kappa T) \tag{38}$$

which can be written in integral form as

$$(\Delta H)_T = -\int_{P_1}^{P_2} v(1 - \kappa T) \, dP \tag{39}$$

It should be remembered that the integral of Eq. (37) is to be evaluated at the constant pressure of 1 atm, while the integral of Eq. (39) is to be evaluated at the constant temperature of 160°C.

It is assumed that the specific heat of the polyethylene is constant over the small temperature change involved in this process. An expression for the temperature rise is obtained by integrating Eq. (37) and combining it with Eqs. (39), (36), and (35).

$$\Delta T = -\frac{1}{c_P} \int_{P_1}^{P_2} v(1 - \kappa T) \, dP \tag{40}$$

where ΔT represents the average temperature rise of the fluid.

The following relationship between v and P at constant temperature was derived in Example 5.

$$v = v_o e^{-\beta P} \tag{25}$$

where v_o now represents the specific volume of the polyethylene at 160°C and zero pressure. Combining Eqs. (25) and (40),

$$\Delta T = -\left(\frac{v_o}{c_P}\right) \int_{P_1}^{P_2} (1 - \kappa T) e^{-\beta P} \, dP \tag{41}$$

Upon integration, Eq. (41) becomes

$$\Delta T = \frac{\beta v_o (1 - \kappa T)}{c_P} (e^{-\beta P_2} - e^{-\beta P_1}) \tag{42}$$

where it is understood that β and κ represent average values between 1 and 100 atm at 160°C.

The following values of the physical properties of polyethylene are used in the calculation:

$$v_o = 1.285 \text{ cc/g}$$

$$\beta = 0.12 \times 10^{-3} \text{ atm}^{-1}$$

$$c_P = 0.623 \text{ cal/g-degC}$$

$$\kappa = 0.692 \times 10^{-3} \text{ degC}^{-1}$$

$$T = 433°\text{K } (160°\text{C})$$

$$P_1 = 100 \text{ atm}$$

$$P_2 = 1 \text{ atm}$$

The conversion factor 24.2 cal/liter-atm is also needed in the calculation. Substituting into Eq. (42) gives the following result:

$$\Delta T = 3.5 \text{ degC}$$

It should be noted that a thermodynamic calculation of this type cannot give detailed information concerning heat generation. The calculated temperature rise is simply the number of degrees that the *average* temperature of the fluid would be increased. In reality, heat generation occurs nonuniformly, and the temperature of certain regions of the fluid will rise much higher than the 3.5 degC. Other regions will, of course, not rise so much.

Example 7: The following data for a polyethylene extrusion operation are to be used to calculate the total heat losses of the process.

Power input to electric motor........................40.0 kw
Total power input to the electric heaters...........18.0 kw
Flow rate of cooling water..........................10.0 gpm
Inlet temperature of cooling water.................60°F
Outlet temperature of cooling water...............62°F
Efficiency of electric motor........................95%
Efficiency of gearbox...............................98%
Extrusion rate.....................................550 lb/hr
Melt temperature at die............................380°F
Temperature in feed hopper........................80°F
Linear speed of extrudate..........................100 ft/min

Assuming that the insulation of the machine could be improved to the extent that the heat losses could be reduced 50 per cent calculate the number of kwhr of electrical energy that would be saved in one year of continuous operation.

The solution to this problem is based on the general energy balance. Considering unit time, the *net* heat transferred to the system Q consists of three terms.

$$Q = Q_H + Q_W + Q_L \tag{43}$$

where

$$Q_H = \text{heat generated in electric heaters}$$

$$Q_W = \text{heat removed by cooling water}$$

$$Q_L = \text{heat losses}$$

Substituting Eq. (43) into Eq. (34) and rearranging,

$$Q_L = \Delta H + g\Delta Z + k\Delta u^2 - Q_H - Q_W + W_s \qquad (44)$$

To evaluate Q_L from Eq. (44), a system of units and a basis of calculation must be chosen. In this example each energy term will be expressed in calories per gram of polyethylene extruded.

$$\text{Mass flow rate} = \frac{(550 \text{ lb/hr})(454 \text{ g/lb})}{(3,600 \text{ sec/hr})} = 69.3 \text{ g/sec}$$

$$Q_H = \frac{(18 \text{ kw})(239 \text{ cal/kw-sec})}{(69.3 \text{ g/sec})} = +62.1 \text{ cal/g}$$

The flow rate of 10.0 gpm of cooling water expressed in mass units is 1.39 lb of water per second. Taking the specific heat of water as 1.0 Btu/lb-degF, the rate of heat removal by the cooling water is found to be 2.78 Btu/sec. Therefore,

$$Q_W = \frac{(2.78 \text{ Btu/sec})(252 \text{ cal/Btu})}{(69.3 \text{ g/sec})} = -10.1 \text{ cal/g}$$

The negative sign is introduced because heat is being removed from the system.

The shaft work obtained from the electric motor is calculated below, taking into account the inefficiencies of the motor and the gearbox.

$$W_s = \frac{(40 \text{ kw})(239 \text{ cal/kw-sec})(0.98)(0.95)}{(69.3 \text{ g/sec})} = -128.2 \text{ cal/g}$$

The thermal data of Dole, Hettinger, Larson, and Wethington[6] are used to calculate the change in enthalpy of the polyethylene. These data are the basis of the curve shown in Fig. 2.2, which is a plot of enthalpy versus temperature, with 0°C selected

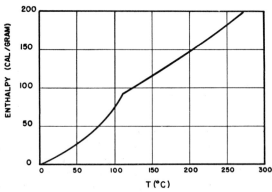

FIG. 2.2. Enthalpy of polyethylene.

as the reference temperature. From Fig. 2.2 the enthalpy of polyethylene at 193°C (380°F) is seen to be 144 cal/g, while at 26.7°C (80°) the enthalpy is 13 cal/g. Therefore,

$$\Delta H = 144 - 13 = +131 \text{ cal/g}$$

It is easily shown that the kinetic-energy term is very small and can be neglected. Furthermore, the change in elevation of the polyethylene is negligible. Therefore, Eq. (44) becomes

$$Q_L = -39.2 \text{ cal/g}$$

The negative sign indicates that heat is lost from the system. Expressing the loss in electrical terms,

$$Q_L = -\frac{(39.2 \text{ cal/g})(69.3 \text{ g/sec})}{(239 \text{ cal/kw-sec})} = -11.35 \text{ kw}$$

If this loss were reduced by 50 per cent, the electrical energy that would be saved in one year is 48,500 kwhr.

HEAT TRANSFER

It is customary to distinguish among three modes of heat transfer—conduction, convection, and radiation. In conduction (which occurs in solids, liquids, and gases) heat transfer is due to motion at the molecular, atomic, or electronic levels. In convection (which occurs only in fluids) heat transfer is due to the bulk motion of the fluid. In radiation (which involves no material medium) heat or radiant energy is transferred in the form of electromagnetic waves.

The basic equation of heat conduction is Fourier's law, which can be written

$$\left(\frac{dQ}{d\theta}\right) = q = -kA\left(\frac{dT}{dx}\right) \tag{45}$$

for conduction in the x-direction. Equations similar to Eq. (45) can be written for conduction in the y- and z-directions. The definitions of the symbols of Eq. (45) and their metric units are

q = rate of conduction (cal/sec)

A = area normal to heat flow (sq cm)

k = thermal conductivity (cal/cm-sec-degC)

T = temperature (°C)

Using Fourier's law, the rate of conduction at any point in a body can be calculated, provided the temperature gradient at that point is known. To determine the temperature gradient, the temperature distribution must be calculated, and in many problems this is the only information that is required. The following partial differential equation is used to calculate temperature distributions in isotropic substances in which the thermal conductivity, density, and specific heat can be considered constant. Its derivation is based on Fourier's law and is available in most of the standard texts.

$$\left(\frac{\partial T}{\partial \theta}\right) = \alpha \left[\left(\frac{\partial^2 T}{\partial x^2}\right) + \left(\frac{\partial^2 T}{\partial y^2}\right) + \left(\frac{\partial^2 T}{\partial z^2}\right)\right] + \left(\frac{G}{c_P \rho}\right) \tag{46}$$

x, y, and z are distances along the coordinate axes and

$$T = \text{temperature}$$

$$\theta = \text{time}$$

$$\alpha = \text{thermal diffusivity}$$

$$G = \text{rate of internal heat generation}$$

The last term on the right side is the generation term which takes into account the heat which is generated internally in the material. The thermal diffusivity is defined by the equation

$$\alpha = \left(\frac{k}{c_P \rho}\right) \tag{47}$$

Heat transfer by convection is an extremely complicated phenomenon, as the rate of convective heat transfer depends upon the bulk motion of the fluid and also upon conduction within the fluid. In the special case where convection occurs within a fluid which is flowing in steady laminar motion, the temperature distribution is described by a particular solution of the following differential equation.

$$\frac{\partial T}{\partial \theta} + u_x \frac{\partial T}{\partial x} + u_y \frac{\partial T}{\partial y} + u_z \frac{\partial T}{\partial z} = \alpha \nabla^2 T + (G/c_P \rho) \tag{48}$$

where

$$\nabla^2 T = \frac{\partial^2 T}{\partial x^2} + \frac{\partial^2 T}{\partial y^2} + \frac{\partial^2 T}{\partial z^2}$$

and the u's are the velocity components. It should be noted that Eq. (48) reduces to Eq. (46) when the velocity components are zero, as in this case the convection problem becomes one of conduction.

In principle, convection problems involving laminar flow can be analyzed by coupling the equations of motion of the fluid with Eq. (48) and obtaining particular solutions satisfying the boundary conditions of the problem. In practice, only a few special cases have been handled in this manner.

The problem of convective heat transfer from a solid surface to a fluid is usually handled by defining a coefficient of convective heat transfer and then investigating the variation of this coefficient with various operating conditions. The defining equation is usually written

$$q = hA(T_s - T_f) \tag{49}$$

where

q = rate of heat transfer

T_s = surface temperature of the solid

T_f = bulk temperature of the fluid

h = coefficient of convective heat transfer

In the metric system the units of h are cal/sq cm-sec-degC, while in the British system they are Btu/hr-sq cm-degF.

The basic equation for radiant heat transfer is obtained from the Stefan-Boltzman law and can be written

$$q = \sigma A T^4 \tag{50}$$

where

q = rate of emission of radiant energy

A = surface area of emitter

T = absolute temperature of emitter

σ = the Stefan-Boltzman constant

Equation (50) applies only to the emission of radiant energy from a black body. Methods of handling problems involving radiation from actual materials will be discussed later. Inspection of Eq. (50) shows that the units of the Stefan-Boltzman constant must be expressed as energy per unit time per unit area per fourth power of the absolute temperature. Using metric units, σ has the value of 1.36×10^{-12} cal/sq cm-sec-$(°K)^4$.

Conduction

In heat conduction the basic problem is to find a function of time and position which will satisfy the heat equation [Eq. (46)] and a given set of boundary conditions. This solution of the heat equation enables heat flow rates at any point in the object to be calculated by the direct application of Fourier's law [Eq. (45)].

The following example illustrates the procedure for an extremely simple case, that of one-dimensional steady heat flow.

Example 8: Calculate the rate at which heat flows through a slab of solid plastic which is 3.0 cm thick, when one face is maintained at 100°C and the other face at 40°C. The other dimensions are very large compared to the thickness, so that the heat flow is essentially unidirectional. The thermal conductivity of the material is 0.80×10^{-3} cal/cm-sec-degC. Temperatures at all points within the slab are constant, so that the heat flow does not change with time.

Under these circumstances the heat equation reduces to

$$\left(\frac{d^2T}{dx^2}\right) = 0 \tag{51}$$

The problem is to find a function which is a solution of Eq. (51) and which will meet the boundary conditions of the problem.

$$T(0) = 100°C$$

$$T(3) = 40°C$$

The function

$$T = 100 - 20x \tag{52}$$

meets these conditions.

The temperature gradient is obtained by differentiating Eq. (52)

$$\left(\frac{dT}{dx}\right) = -20$$

The rate of heat flow is now calculated directly from Fourier's law [Eq. (45)].

$$\left(\frac{q}{A}\right) = -(0.80 \times 10^{-3})(-20) = +16.0 \times 10^{-3} \text{ cal/sq cm-sec}$$

The positive sign indicates that the heat flow is in the $+x$ direction; that is, in the direction of decreasing temperature.

Unsteady-state (heating and cooling) problems cannot be handled in such a simple manner. As an example, unsteady-state conduction in a slab is considered in some detail. The heat equation reduces to

$$\left(\frac{\partial T}{\partial \theta}\right) = \alpha\left(\frac{\partial^2 T}{\partial x^2}\right) \tag{53}$$

We consider the case where heat transfer at the surfaces occurs by convection to a fluid at temperature T_f. It is assumed that the convective heat-transfer coefficient h is constant. Initially, the slab is at the uniform temperature T_i. The origin of the coordinate system is located in the midplane of the slab, so that the temperature distribution is symmetrical about the origin. Under these circumstances the boundary conditions for the problem are written

$$T(x, 0) \quad = T_i$$

$$T'(a, \theta) \quad = -(h/k)[T(a, \theta) - T_f]$$

$$T'(-a, \theta) = (h/k)[T(-a, \theta) - T_f]$$

where T' represents the first partial derivative of T with respect to x, and $2a$ is the thickness of the slab.

It can be shown that the following function is a solution of Eq. (53) and meets the above boundary conditions.

$$Y = \sum_{n=1,2}^{\infty} f(M_n)e^{-M_n^2\phi} \cos (M_n x/a) \qquad (54)$$

The quantities Y and ϕ are, respectively, dimensionless temperature and time, as defined by the equations

$$Y = \left(\frac{T - T_f}{T_i - T_f}\right) \qquad (55)$$

$$\phi = \left(\frac{\alpha\theta}{a^2}\right) \qquad (56)$$

The M_n are the positive roots of the equation

$$M \tan (M) = N$$
$$N = (ah/k) \qquad (57)$$

and the function $f(M_n)$ is defined as

$$f(M_n) = \left[\frac{4 \sin (M_n)}{2M_n + \sin (2M_n)}\right] \qquad (58)$$

The first six roots of Eq. (57) for a wide range of N are tabulated by Carslaw and Jaeger.[4]

Computations involving Eq. (54) are often laborious and time-consuming. In practice, charts are usually used. Groeber,[8] Gurnie and Lurie,[9] Heisler,[10] and Carslaw and Jaeger,[4] among others, have presented graphical solutions of Eq. (54). Usually, the dependent variable Y is plotted against one of the three independent variables (ϕ, N, x) and the other two are treated as parameters. Figures 2.3 and 2.4 are similar to the Carslaw and Jaeger charts, in which a separate chart is made for each position and N is the parameter. Figure 2.3 applies to the surface and Fig. 2.4 to the mid-plane.

Example 9: A slab having a thickness of 2 cm and an initial uniform temperature of 100°C is immersed in a fluid having a temperature of 20°C. If the parameter N has the value 5 and the thermal diffusivity of the slab is 10^{-3} sq cm/sec, calculate the temperature of the mid-plane and the surfaces of the slab after 100 sec of cooling.

The dimensionless time variable ϕ, calculated from Eq. (56) is

$$\phi = \left(\frac{\alpha\theta}{a^2}\right) = \frac{(0.001)(100)}{(1.0)^2} = 0.10$$

The dimensionless temperature Y at the surface of the slab is found from Fig. 2.3 to be 0.31, while from Fig. 2.4 the value of Y at the mid-plane is found to be 0.97.

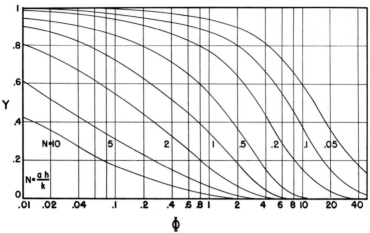

Fɪɢ. 2.3. Cooling curves for surface of slab.

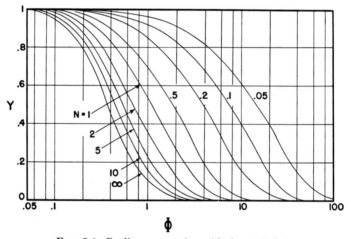

Fɪɢ. 2.4. Cooling curves for mid-plane of slab.

The actual temperatures calculated from Eq. (55) are

$$\text{At the surface:} \quad T = 44.8°C$$

$$\text{At the center:} \quad T = 97.6°C$$

If the cooling were carried out under conditions such that the convective heat-transfer coefficient were reduced by a factor of 5, the parameter N would be reduced to 1, but the thermal diffusivity would remain the same. Under these conditions the following temperatures would be obtained after 100 sec of cooling.

$$\text{At the surface:} \quad T = 78°C$$

$$\text{At the center:} \quad T = 99°C$$

Under certain conditions the graphical procedures can be replaced with a simple analytical method.* Plots of ln (Y) vs. ϕ with N and x constant become straight lines for certain ranges of the variables. This means that the first term only of the series Eq. (54) is important. For this special case Eq. (54) can be written

$$Y = f(M_1)e^{-M_1{}^2\phi}\cos{(M_1x/a)} \tag{59}$$

where M_1 is the first positive root of Eq. (57).

Equation (59) can be written in the form

$$\ln{(Y)} = K + \ln{[\cos{(M_1x/a)}]} - M_1^2\phi \tag{60}$$

where K is defined by the equation

$$K = \ln{\left[\frac{4\sin{(M_1)}}{2M_1 + \sin{(2M_1)}}\right]} \tag{61}$$

Since K and M_1 are functions *only* of the parameter N, they can be represented by the single lines shown in Fig. 2.5.

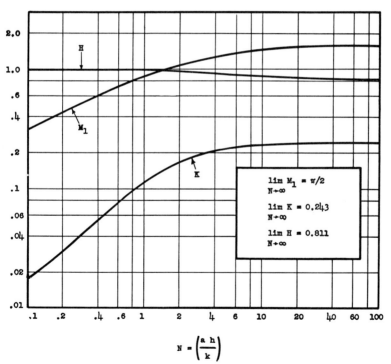

$$N = \left(\frac{a\,h}{k}\right)$$

FIG. 2.5. Values of coefficients for Eqs. (2–60) and (2–65).

* Suggested by Mr. Robert Colwell of the Monsanto Chemical Company.

The conditions under which it is permissible to use Eq. (60) depend upon the relative values of the three independent variables. It is not possible to give a concise and general statement of these conditions. The following are a set of sufficient conditions:

$$x = 0 \qquad x = a$$
$$N > 2 \qquad N > 1$$
$$\phi > 10^{-2} \qquad \phi > 1$$

Reference is often made to the mean temperature of a slab during heating or cooling. This temperature is defined by the equation

$$\bar{T} = \frac{1}{2a} \int_{-a}^{+a} T \, dx \tag{62}$$

Introducing the dimensionless temperature Y, Eq. (62) becomes

$$\bar{Y} = \frac{1}{2a} \int_{-a}^{+a} Y \, dx \tag{63}$$

where Y is defined as

$$\bar{Y} = \left(\frac{\bar{T} - T_f}{T_i - T_f} \right) \tag{64}$$

Substituting Eq. (59) into Eq. (63) and integrating yields

$$\ln (\bar{Y}) = \ln (H) - M_1^2 \phi \tag{65}$$

where H is defined by the equation

$$H = \left[\frac{4 \sin^2 M_1}{2M_1^2 + M_1 \sin (2M_1)} \right] \tag{66}$$

H is a function of the parameter N only. Values of H are given in Fig. 2.5.

A special case of particular interest occurs when there is negligible resistance ($h = N = \infty$) to the transfer of heat between the fluid and the surface. Under these circumstances the surface instantaneously assumes the temperature of the fluid. The boundary conditions for the problem become

$$T(\pm a, \theta) = T_f$$

and Eq. (57) becomes

$$M \tan (M) = \infty$$

Solutions using the charts (Figs. 2.3 and 2.4) are obtained as before, using the curves for $N = \infty$. If the solution is to be obtained with Eq. (59), the limiting values of M_1, K, and H shown in Fig. 2.5 should be used.

In this section we have considered only the heating and cooling of the slab. Cylinders, spheres, cubes, and other simple geometrical shapes lead to analogous problems. Reference should be made to the standard texts for details.

Example 10: Two flat sheets of a solid material are being bonded together with a thin layer of a thermoplastic adhesive. The platens of the press are maintained at a constant temperature of 200°C. If the thermoplastic adhesive fuses and forms a good bond when it reaches a temperature of 150°C, what should be the length of the heating cycle, if the sheets and the adhesive are initially at 30°C?

The data for the problem are as follows:

$$k = 2.0 \times 10^{-3} \text{ cal/cm-sec-degC}$$

$$c_p = 0.20 \text{ cal/g-degC}$$

$$\rho = 2.5 \text{ g/cc}$$

$$a = 1.0 \text{ cm}$$

$$\alpha = 4 \times 10^{-3} \text{ sq cm/sec}$$

This is a unidirectional, unsteady-state heat-conduction problem of the type discussed above. If we assume that the press platens make good contact with the surfaces of the sheets, then these surfaces will assume the platen temperature almost instantaneously, and we have isothermal boundary conditions. This is equivalent to stating that the resistance to heat transfer between the platen and sheet surfaces is negligible.

The temperature at the interface between the sheets must reach 150°C at the end of the cycle, and the value of Y at the end of the cycle is given by the following calculation:

$$Y = \left(\frac{150 - 200}{30 - 200}\right) = 0.294$$

The problem is solved using the analytical method rather than the charts. The use of the analytical method is justified, upon completion of the problem, by showing that the values of N and ϕ fall within the range of sufficient conditions stated above.

Since there is negligible resistance to heat transfer at the surface, N is infinite and the values of K and M_1 are

$$K = (\pi/2)$$

$$M_1 = 0.243$$

Substituting into Eq. (60) gives

$$\ln (0.294) = 0.243 + \ln [\cos (0)] - \pi^2\phi/4$$

Solving for ϕ,

$$\phi = 0.593$$

The time required for the heating cycle is then calculated from Eq. (56).

$$\theta = \frac{a^2\phi}{\alpha} = \frac{(0.593)}{4 \times 10^{-3}} = 148 \text{ sec}$$

Convection

Exact mathematical analyses of convective heat-transfer processes become very complicated. They have been made only in a few special cases. One of the special cases that has been treated analytically with some success is that of steady-state forced convection within a fluid in laminar flow in a circular tube. The usual treatment neglects conduction in the axial direction of the tube, heat generation due to fluid friction, and assumes that the physical properties of the fluid are independent of the fluid temperature. Under these conditions Eq. (48), in cylindrical coordinates, becomes

$$u_x \left(\frac{\partial T}{\partial x} \right) = \alpha \left[\frac{\partial^2 T}{\partial r^2} + \left(\frac{1}{r} \right) \frac{\partial T}{\partial r} \right] \tag{67}$$

For laminar isothermal Newtonian flow in a circular tube, u_x is expressed in terms of the mean velocity by the equation

$$\frac{u_x}{u_m} = \left[1 - \left(\frac{r}{R} \right)^2 \right] \tag{68}$$

where

$$u_m = \text{mean velocity}$$

$$R = \text{radius of tube}$$

Equations (67) and (68) can be combined to form a partial differential equation with T as the dependent variable and x and r as the independent variables. The boundary conditions of the problem are

$$T(x, R) = T_R$$

$$T(0, r) = T_i$$

$$\left(\frac{\partial T}{\partial r} \right)_{r=0} = 0$$

where T_R is the temperature of the tube wall and T_i is the uniform temperature of the fluid before it enters the tube. Jakob[11] describes in some detail methods of obtaining solutions of this problem. He gives the following result

$$\left(\frac{T - T_R}{T_i - T_R} \right) = \sum_{n=1}^{\infty} C_n N_n e^{B_n X} \tag{69}$$

where the dimensionless position variable X is defined by the equation

$$X = \frac{\alpha x}{R^2 u_m} \tag{70}$$

The mean temperature of the fluid at any distance down the tube is given by the equation

$$\left(\frac{T_m - T_R}{T_i - T_R}\right) = \sum_{n=1}^{\infty} D_n e^{B_n X} \tag{71}$$

The first three terms of the series [Eqs. (69) and (71)] are usually sufficient, since the series converge rapidly. They can be calculated with the constants listed below, which are based on the work of Jakob.[11]

$$B_1 = -3.7 \qquad C_1 = 1.5 \qquad D_1 = 0.82$$

$$B_2 = -22 \qquad C_2 = -0.8 \qquad D_2 = 0.10$$

$$B_3 = -53 \qquad C_3 = 0.4 \qquad D_3 = 0.014$$

The N_n's are functions of the radial distance r. Figure 2.6 gives the values of the first three N's as a function of (r/R).

Equations (69) and (71) are, of course, only as good as the assumptions under which they were derived. The most questionable assumption is that the velocity profile is parabolic. Nonisothermal conditions due to heat conduction within the fluid, the non-Newtonian nature of most thermo-

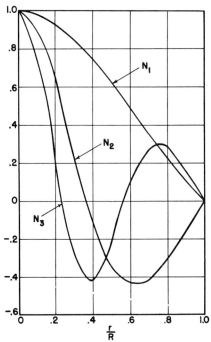

FIG. 2.6. Values of coefficients for Eq. (2–69). Reprinted with permission from "Heat Transfer," Vol. I, by Max Jakob, 1949, John Wiley & Sons, Inc.

plastic melts, heat generation due to viscous friction, and thermodynamic cooling due to the expansion of the fluid all cause the velocity profile to become distorted.

Toor[18] has discussed the cooling effect due to the expansion of the fluid and shows that under certain circumstances it can be significant.

A more rigorous formulation of this problem has been made by Gee and Lyon.[7] They determined particular solutions of their differential equations by numerical integration using high-speed digital computing equipment. Reference should be made to their paper for details of the procedure.

Example 11: Molten polyethylene which is initially at a temperature of 200°C is being extruded through a circular tube which is 10 cm long and 0.40 cm in diameter. The walls of the tube are maintained at the constant temperature of 250°C. The mass flow rate is 10 g/min. Calculate the mean temperature of the polyethylene leaving the end of the tube and make a plot showing the temperature profile at the end of the tube.

The following physical properties of polyethylene are used in the calculation:

$$\rho = 0.757 \text{ g/cc}$$

$$c_p = 0.659 \text{ cal/g-degC}$$

$$k = 8 \times 10^{-4} \text{ cal/cm-sec-degC}$$

$$\alpha = 1.6 \times 10^{-3} \text{ sq cm/sec}$$

The mean velocity u_m of the polyethylene, calculated from the mass flow rate, is 1.75 cm/sec. The dimensionless position variable X, as defined by Eq. (70), is obtained from the calculation

$$X = \frac{\alpha x}{R^2 u_m} = \frac{(1.6 \times 10^{-3})(10)}{(0.04)(1.75)} = 0.229$$

In this problem the series equation [Eq. (71)] can be approximated reasonably well with the first term only.

$$\frac{T_m - T_R}{T_i - T_R} = (0.82)e^{-(3.7)(0.229)} = 0.36$$

from which the value of T_m is found to be 232°C.

The temperature profile at the end of the tube is calculated with Eq. (72). As an illustration of the method, the calculation of the temperature at the center of the tube is shown below.

At $r = 0$ all the N's are unity, and Eq. (71) becomes

$$\frac{T_o - T_R}{T_i - T_R} = 1.5e^{-(3.7)(0.229)} = 0.64$$

from which the value of T_o is found to be 218°C.

Temperatures at other positions at the end of the tube are calculated in a similar manner. Figure 2.7 shows the complete temperature profile across the end of the tube. The broken line represents the mean temperature at that point.

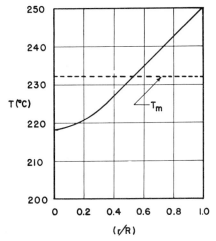

FIG. 2.7. Temperature profile of liquid polyethylene flowing through a heated tube.

Some special cases of convective heat transfer between a solid surface and a fluid are now considered. One of the most useful techniques for handling problems of this type is dimensional analysis, as it enables a large number of variables to be reduced to a few dimensionless groups. The dimensionless groups used in this discussion are the Nusselt number, the Prandtl number, the Grashof number, and the Reynolds number. They are defined by the following equations.

$$\text{Nusselt number:} \qquad N_{\text{Nu}} = \left(\frac{hD}{k}\right) \tag{72}$$

$$\text{Prandtl number:} \qquad N_{\text{Pr}} = \left(\frac{c_p\mu}{k}\right) \tag{73}$$

$$\text{Grashof number:} \qquad N_{\text{Gr}} = \left(\frac{g\kappa\rho^2 D^3 \Delta T}{\mu^2}\right) \tag{74}$$

$$\text{Reynolds number:} \qquad N_{\text{Re}} = \left(\frac{v_o x \rho}{\mu}\right) \tag{75}$$

It has been established by many experiments that the transfer of heat from a horizontal cylinder to a fluid can be represented by an equation of the form[11]

$$N_{\text{Nu}} = f(N_{\text{Gr}}, N_{\text{Pr}}) \tag{76}$$

For the special case where the product of the Grashof and Prandtl numbers is greater than about 10,000, the functional relationship of Eq.

(76) can be written

$$N_{\text{Nu}} = 0.52(N_{\text{Gr}} \cdot N_{\text{Pr}})^{1/4} \qquad (N_{\text{Gr}} \cdot N_{\text{Pr}} > 10^4) \qquad (77)$$

Example 12: Compare the film coefficient for heat transfer by natural convection from a horizontal cylinder to water to the coefficient obtained when the fluid is air. The diameter of the cylinder is 4 cm, its surface temperature is 50°C, and the fluid temperature is 20°C.

The physical properties of the fluids needed for the calculations are given in the table below. Most authors recommend that the fluid properties be evaluated at the mean temperature between the surface and the bulk of the fluid. In this problem the physical properties are therefore evaluated at 35°C.

Property	Water	Air	Units
c_p	1.0	0.24	cal/g-degC
μ	0.0072	1.9×10^{-4}	poise (dyne-sec/sq cm)
k	1.5×10^{-3}	6.2×10^{-5}	cal/cm-sec-degC
κ	3.5×10^{-4}	3.3×10^{-3}	degC^{-1}
ρ	1.0	12×10^{-4}	g/cc

The Prandtl number for each fluid is calculated with Eq. (73).

$$\text{Water:} \qquad N_{\text{Pr}} = 4.7$$

$$\text{Air:} \qquad N_{\text{Pr}} = 0.73$$

The Grashof number for each fluid is calculated with Eq. (74).

$$\text{Water:} \qquad N_{\text{Gr}} = 12.5 \times 10^6$$

$$\text{Air:} \qquad N_{\text{Gr}} = 22.7 \times 10^4$$

The products of the Prandtl and Grashof numbers

$$\text{Water:} \qquad N_{\text{Pr}}N_{\text{Gr}} = 59 \times 10^6$$

$$\text{Air:} \qquad N_{\text{Pr}}N_{\text{Gr}} = 17 \times 10^4$$

are greater than 10^4 for both fluids. The Nusselt numbers calculated from Eq. (77) are given below.

$$\text{Water:} \qquad N_{\text{Nu}} = 45.6$$

$$\text{Air:} \qquad N_{\text{Nu}} = 10.5$$

The film coefficients for each fluid are calculated using the defining equation [Eq. (72)].

$$\text{Water:} \qquad h = 17.3 \times 10^{-3} \text{ cal/sq cm-sec-degC}$$

$$\text{Air:} \qquad h = 16.3 \times 10^{-4} \text{ cal/sq cm-sec-degC}$$

Expressed in the more conventional British units, the film coefficients are as follows:

$$\text{Water:} \qquad h = 128 \text{ Btu/hr-sq ft-degF}$$

$$\text{Air:} \qquad h = 1.2 \text{ Btu/hr-sq ft-degF}$$

Another case of interest is that of forced convection between a solid plane surface and a fluid in laminar motion parallel to the surface. The equation

$$N_{Nu} = (0.664)(N_{Re})^{1/2}(N_{Pr})^{1/3} \tag{78}$$

can be used when the Reynolds number is less than about 300,000.

Example 13: Consider the cooling of a film of molten polyethylene in the air gap between the die of an extruder and the nip rolls, where it is combined with a substrate.

If the linear speed of the extrusion is 50 cm/sec (about 100 ft/min), the polyethylene film 0.00254 cm thick (1 mil), the air gap 10 cm long, the initial uniform temperature of the polyethylene 600°F, and the surrounding air about 80°F, calculate the *surface* temperature of the polyethylene at the nip.

The Reynolds number is calculated with Eq. (75) with the physical properties of air evaluated at the mean temperature of 340°F. We have,

$$v_o = 50 \text{ cm/sec}$$

$$\rho = 7.8 \times 10^{-4} \text{ g/cc}$$

$$x = 10 \text{ cm}$$

$$\mu = 2.5 \times 10^{-4} \text{ poise}$$

and

$$N_{Re} = 1590$$

Applying Eq. (78) and taking the Prandtl number for air as 0.715,

$$N_{Nu} = (0.664)(1590)^{1/2}(0.715)^{1/3} = 23.6$$

The film coefficient is calculated from the defining equation [Eq. (72)].

$$h = \frac{kN_{Nu}}{D} = \frac{(8.6 \times 10^{-5})(23.6)}{(10)}$$

$$= 20.2 \times 10^{-5} \text{ cal/sq cm-sec-degC}$$

$$= 1.48 \text{ Btu/hr-sq ft-degF}$$

The exposure time of the film in the air gap is given by the following calculation:

$$\theta = \frac{L}{v_o} = \frac{10}{50} = 0.20 \text{ sec}$$

The parameters N and ϕ are given by the calculations

$$N = \frac{ah}{k} = \frac{(0.00127)(20.2 \times 10^{-5})}{(8 \times 10^{-4})}$$

$$= 3.2 \times 10^{-4}$$

$$\phi = \frac{\alpha\theta}{a^2} = \frac{(1.6 \times 10^{-3})(0.20)}{(0.00127)^2}$$

$$= 198$$

The surface temperature is calculated with Eq. (60).

$$\ln (Y) = K + \ln (\cos M_1) - M_1{}^2\phi$$

The following approximations are valid for small values of N:

$$N = M_1{}^2$$

$$K = 0$$

$$\cos(M_1) = 1$$

The above equation reduces to

$$Y = e^{-M_1{}^2\phi} = e^{-N\phi} = e^{-0.0634}$$

$$Y = 0.94$$

$$Y = \left(\frac{T_s - T_f}{T_i - T_f}\right)$$

$$T_s = 80 + 0.94\ (520)$$

$$T_s = 570°F$$

There is a drop of 30°F in the surface temperature of the film as it passes through the air gap.

Radiation

All bodies emit energy in the form of electromagnetic waves. When these waves strike an object which is not transparent to them, they are absorbed, and the energy is converted to heat. The rate at which a body emits radiant energy depends primarily upon its temperature. At low temperatures (less than 100°C) the rate of energy emission is very low, but as the temperature increases the rate increases very rapidly, in proportion to the fourth power of the absolute temperature. Above 300°C a very substantial portion of the radiant energy emitted by a body has a wave length in the infrared region of the spectrum. Consequently, heat transfer by radiation is often spoken of as infrared heating.

When radiation strikes an object, it may be either absorbed, reflected, or transmitted. The fraction absorbed is known as the absorptivity of the substance, the fraction reflected as the reflectivity, and the fraction transmitted as the transmittancy. Since these fractions must total unity, they are related by the equation

$$1 = \alpha + \rho + \tau \tag{79}$$

where

$$\alpha = \text{absorptivity}$$

$$\rho = \text{reflectivity}$$

$$\tau = \text{transmittancy}$$

A perfect black body absorbs all incident radiation and consequently has an absorptivity of unity. The rate of emission of radiant energy is given by the Stefan-Boltzman law [Eq. (50)]. Actual bodies do not emit as much radiant energy as black bodies and are sometimes called gray bodies, provided the spectral distribution of the energy emitted is the same as a black body. The ratio of the rate of energy emission of a gray body to that of a black body at the same temperature is called the emissivity. For gray bodies, then, the Stefan-Boltzman equation becomes

$$q = \epsilon \sigma A T^4 \tag{80}$$

where

$$\epsilon = \text{emissivity}$$

Kirchhoff's law states that the emissivity of a body is equal to its absorptivity. Values of emissivities of various substances are tabulated in the handbooks. Two extremes are lampblack, with an emissivity of about 0.95, and highly polished aluminum, with an emissivity of about 0.04.

In principle, the rate of radiant heat interchange between two surfaces can be calculated if the emissivities and the geometrical configurations of the surfaces are known. In practice, the calculations become very complicated for all cases other than those of very simple geometry.

One very simple case, that of radiant heat transfer between infinite parallel plates, is considered here. Referring to Fig. 2.8, Plate 1 has an absolute temperature T_1, an absorptivity α_1, and an emissivity ϵ_1. The rate at which radiant energy is emitted from Plate 1 is given by

$$q_1 = \sigma \epsilon_1 A T_1^4 \tag{81}$$

The radiation emitted from Plate 1 strikes Plate 2, where the fraction α_2 is absorbed and the fraction $(1 - \alpha_2)$ is reflected back to Plate 1. At Plate 1 the fraction α_1 of this reflected energy is absorbed, and the fraction $(1 - \alpha_1)$ is reflected back to Plate 2. The first few steps of the process, which continues indefinitely, are shown in Fig. 2.8. The process can be expressed mathematically by the infinite geometric series

$$q_{1 \to 2} = q_1[1 - (1 - \alpha_2) + (1 - \alpha_2)(1 - \alpha_1) - \cdots]$$

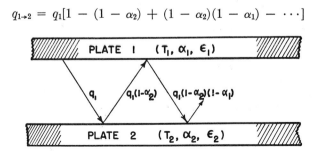

FIG. 2.8. Radiant heat exchange between infinite parallel plates.

which has as its sum

$$q_{1 \to 2} = q_1 \frac{\alpha_2}{\alpha_1 + \alpha_2 - \alpha_1 \alpha_2} \tag{82}$$

where the symbol $q_{1 \to 2}$ represents the rate of transfer of radiant energy from Plate 1 to Plate 2.

The same process must be considered for the radiant energy leaving Plate 2. In this case the infinite geometric series has as its sum

$$q_{2 \to 1} = q_2 \frac{\alpha_1}{\alpha_1 + \alpha_2 - \alpha_1 \alpha_2} \tag{83}$$

where

$$q_2 = \sigma \epsilon_2 A T_2^{\,4}$$

The net rate of heat exchange between the two plates is found by subtracting Eq. (83) from Eq. (82).

$$q_{net} = q_{1 \to 2} - q_{2 \to 1} = \frac{\alpha_2 q_1 - \alpha_1 q_2}{\alpha_1 + \alpha_2 - \alpha_1 \alpha_2} \tag{84}$$

Since the absorptivities and emissivities of each plate are equal, Eq. (84) can be written in the following form:

$$q_{net} = \sigma \left(\frac{\epsilon_2 \epsilon_1}{\epsilon_1 + \epsilon_2 - \epsilon_1 \epsilon_2} \right) A (T_1^{\,4} - T_2^{\,4}) \tag{85}$$

Equation (85) is usually written as

$$q_{net} = \sigma F_\epsilon A (T_1^{\,4} - T_2^{\,4}) \tag{86}$$

where the factor F_ϵ is called the emissivity factor and is defined by the equation

$$F_\epsilon = \frac{\epsilon_2 \epsilon_1}{\epsilon_1 + \epsilon_2 - \epsilon_1 \epsilon_2} \tag{87}$$

Example 14: A strip of plastic is heated from both sides in a continuous operation by being drawn between a pair of high-temperature tubular heating elements arranged in reflectors. The heating operation requires that the enthalpy of the plastic be increased by 30 Btu/lb. The plastic strip is 2 ft wide, 0.01 in. thick, has a density of 90 lbs/cu ft, and moves at a speed of 20 ft/min.

Neglecting losses, calculate the theoretical power requirements for the heaters. Assuming that the heat transfer is entirely by radiation, that the emissivity of the heater surfaces is 0.90, that each of the heaters has an area of 0.10 sq ft, and that the reflectivity of the reflectors is unity, calculate the temperature of the elements.

The mass flow rate of the plastic through the oven is given by the following calculation:

$$\dot{m} = VW2a\rho = (20)(2)(0.01/12)(90) = 3.0 \text{ lb/min}$$

The power requirements are

$$q = \dot{m}\Delta H = (3.0)(30) = 90 \text{ Btu/min}$$

which, when converted to electrical units, gives a power requirement of 1.58 kw.

Since the surface area of the heating elements is negligibly small compared to the surface area of the plastic sheet, the absorption of radiant energy by the element can be neglected. Furthermore, since the reflectivity of the reflectors is unity, all radiation striking the reflectors is reflected back to the plastic sheet. Therefore, all heat radiated from the surface of the heating elements is transferred to the plastic, and the applicable rate equation is Eq. (81).

$$q = \sigma \epsilon A T^4$$

where

$$q = (90)(60) = 5{,}400 \text{ Btu/hr}$$

$$A = (2)(0.10) = 0.20 \text{ sq ft}$$

$$\sigma = 0.172 \times 10^{-8} \text{ Btu/hr-sq ft-degR}^4$$

$$\epsilon = 0.90$$

Solving for temperature gives the result

$$T = 2050°\text{R}$$

It should be noted that a calculation of this type gives no information concerning the temperature distribution within the strip of plastic. This depends upon conduction within the strip. Materials of high thermal diffusivity would have a fairly uniform distribution of temperature, while materials having a low thermal diffusivity would have a high surface temperature and a low temperature at the center.

The temperature distribution in a flat sheet heated from both sides by infrared radiation is now considered. This is a problem of conduction within the sheet. Three assumptions are made. First, it is assumed that the sheet is opaque to infrared radiation. In this case the radiant energy is converted to heat at the surface and *conducted* into the sheet. Second, heat transfer by convection at the surface is neglected. Third, it is assumed that the rate of heat transfer to the sheet is independent of the surface temperature, so that the heat flux across the surface is a constant.

The temperature distribution in the sheet is given by a solution of the heat equation [Eq. (53)] which will satisfy the following boundary conditions:

$$T(x, 0) = T_i$$

$$T'(0, \theta) = 0$$

$$T'(a, \theta) = (q_s/k)$$

where

$$T_i = \text{initial uniform temperature of the sheet}$$

$$q_s = \text{heat flux across surface, a constant}$$

$$a = \text{half thickness of sheet}$$

$$k = \text{thermal conductivity of the sheet}$$

and T' represents the first partial derivative of T with respect to x.

The following function[4] will satisfy Eq. (53) and the above boundary conditions:

$$(T - T_i) = \left(\frac{q_s a}{k}\right)\left[\left(\frac{\alpha\theta}{a^2}\right) + \left(\frac{3x^2 - a^2}{6a^2}\right)\right.$$
$$\left. - \frac{2}{\pi^2}\sum_{n=1}^{\infty}\frac{(-1)^n}{n^2}\, e^{-n^2\pi^2\alpha\theta/a^2}\,\cos\,(n\pi x/a)\right] \tag{88}$$

Equation (88) can be specialized to give the center ($x = 0$) temperature and the surface ($x = a$) temperature. For the center temperature,

$$(T_c - T_i) = \left(\frac{q_s a}{k}\right)\left[\left(\frac{\alpha\theta}{a^2}\right) - \left(\frac{1}{6}\right) - \frac{2}{\pi^2}\sum_{n=1}^{\infty}\frac{(-1)^n}{n^2}\, e^{-n^2\pi^2\alpha\theta/a^2}\right] \tag{89}$$

and for the surface temperature:

$$(T_s - T_i) = \left(\frac{q_s a}{k}\right)\left[\left(\frac{\alpha\theta}{a^2}\right) + \left(\frac{1}{3}\right) - \frac{2}{\pi^2}\sum_{n=1}^{\infty}\frac{1}{n^2}\, e^{-n^2\pi^2\alpha\theta/a^2}\right] \tag{90}$$

In many heating applications a relatively uniform temperature distribution is required. The temperature distribution can be obtained directly from Eq. (88), but this involves a great many calculations. The dimensionless ratio

$$I = \left(\frac{T_s - T_i}{T_c - T_i}\right) \tag{91}$$

can be considered as a uniformity index for heating problems of this type. Dividing Eq. (90) by Eq. (89),

$$I = \frac{\left(\dfrac{\alpha\theta}{a^2}\right) + \left(\dfrac{1}{3}\right) - \left(\dfrac{2}{\pi^2}\right)\sum\dfrac{1}{n^2}\, e^{-n^2\pi^2\alpha\theta/a^2}}{\left(\dfrac{\alpha\theta}{a^2}\right) - \left(\dfrac{1}{6}\right) - \dfrac{2}{\pi^2}\sum\dfrac{(-1)^n}{n^2}\, e^{-n^2\pi^2\alpha\theta/a}} \tag{92}$$

Note that I is a function only of the dimensionless group $(\alpha\theta/a^2)$. Equation

(92) can be written

$$I = f\left(\frac{\alpha\theta}{a^2}\right) \tag{93}$$

The functional relationship shown by Eq. (93) is plotted in Fig. 2.9.

Example 15: Consider the temperature distribution in a flat sheet of plastic 0.10 in. thick and moving through the infrared heating oven described in Example 14 at a speed of 20 ft/min. If the oven is 2 ft long and the thermal diffusivity of the plastic is 2×10^{-3} sq cm/sec, what is the value of the index I? What would have to be done to reduce I to a value of 1.20 and still meet the requirement that the enthalpy of the plastic be increased by 30 Btu/lb?

The exposure time to the infrared radiation is 0.10 min, or 6 sec, and the dimensionless group $(\alpha\theta/a^2)$ is given by the calculation

$$\frac{\alpha\theta}{a^2} = \frac{(2 \times 10^{-3})(6)}{(0.127)^2} = 0.74$$

The value of the index I is found from Fig. 2.9.

$$I = 1.86$$

If I is to be reduced to a value of 1.20, Fig. 2.9 shows that the value of the group $(\alpha\theta/a^2)$ will have to be increased to 2.67. Since the thickness and the thermal diffusivity of the sheet cannot be changed, the time of exposure will have to be changed. The new exposure time will be 21.5 sec, accomplished by slowing the speed to 5.6 ft/min.

Since the increase in enthalpy of the sheet is to remain the same, the intensity of the radiation will have to be reduced to compensate for the increased exposure time. Since the exposure time is increased by a factor of 3.6, the flux must be decreased by

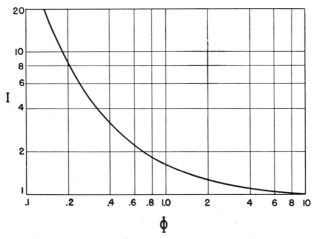

Fig. 2.9. Graph of Eq. (93).

a factor of (1/3.6). The flux is proportional to the fourth power of the absolute temperature, so that the element temperature would have to be reduced by a factor of $(1/3.6)^{1/4}$ or 0.727.

HEAT GENERATION

In thermoplastics processing the most convenient source of energy is electric energy, and the conversion of electric energy to heat is an important aspect of plastics engineering. It should be pointed out that in some large-scale heating applications it is more economical to generate heat directly from the combustion of hydrocarbon fuels, in which case the heat is usually carried to the point of application through the medium of steam or circulating oil. However, the design of combustion units and steam plants is outside the scope of plastics engineering, and the discussion in this section is limited to three methods of converting electric energy into heat: resistance heating, dielectric heating, and induction heating. One additional topic of particular importance in some thermoplastics processes, that of heat generation in viscous liquids from fluid friction, is also included in this section.

Electric-Resistance Heating

An alternating or direct current passing through a conductor dissipates energy (or generates heat) at the rate p, as given by the equation

$$p = I^2R \tag{94}$$

where

$$I = \text{current (amps)}$$

$$R = \text{resistance (ohms)}$$

and the rate of energy dissipation, or power loss, is expressed in watts.

Most electric heating is done with resistance elements where heat generation is due to the I^2R losses. Resistance heating elements, used in conjunction with a transformer to control the voltage, offer a convenient means of controlling temperatures in thermoplastics processing equipment.

Dielectric Heating

Dielectric heating refers to heat generation in materials of low electrical conductivity when they are placed in an electric field that alternates at a high frequency. In dielectric heating, heat is generated throughout the entire mass of the object. Consequently, the maximum temperature usually appears at the center of the object. This is to be contrasted to ordinary heating, where all heat reaching the center must be *conducted* through the object, and the center is usually at the minimum temperature.

The discussion in this section is concerned primarily with transient temperature distributions in objects being heated dielectrically. Reference should be made to other texts, for example, Cable[3] and Brown, Holyer, and Bierwirth,[2] for details concerning the theory and application of dielectric heating.

In its simplest form the arrangement of the electrodes and the work in dielectric heating can be compared to a parallel-plate capacitor, where the electrodes of the heating unit correspond to the plates of the capacitor and the work corresponds to the dielectric of the capacitor. At low frequencies most good dielectrics are nearly perfect insulators. In the radio-frequency range, however, the dielectric loss in many insulators becomes large enough for heat effects to be observed. These heat effects are assumed to be due to the frictional heat generated by the polarized molecules of the dielectric, alternately arranging themselves first in one direction and then in another to correspond to the change in direction of the alternating electric field.

In dielectric heating, the rate of energy dissipation in the work can be calculated with the formula

$$p = 2\pi f C V^2 \cot \phi \tag{95}$$

where

p = rate of energy dissipation (watts)

f = frequency (sec^{-1})

C = capacitance of the work (farads)

V = applied potential (volts)

ϕ = phase angle

The capacitance of a parallel-plate capacitor is given by the formula

$$C = 8.85 \times 10^{-14} \left(\frac{KA}{b} \right) \tag{96}$$

where

K = dielectric constant (dimensionless)

C = capacitance (farads)

A = plate area (sq cm)

b = plate separation (cm)

The heat-generation rate, expressed in thermal units and on a unit volume basis, is obtained by combining Eqs. (95) and (96), dividing by the volume of the work, and introducing the proper conversion factor.

$$G = 13.3 \times 10^{-14} \left(\frac{fV^2}{b^2}\right) (K \cot \phi) \tag{97}$$

The units of the heat-generation rate G are cal/cc-sec. Equation (97) shows that the heat-generation rate depends upon two operating variables, voltage and frequency, upon the thickness of the work, and upon the factor $(K \cot \phi)$ which is termed the "loss factor."

Other terms in common use in dielectric heating are power factor, dissipation factor, and loss angle. The ASTM definitions[1] of these terms are as follows:

$$\text{Phase angle} = \phi$$

$$\text{Loss angle} = (90 - \phi)$$

$$\text{Power factor} = \cos \phi = \sin \delta$$

$$\text{Dissipation factor} = \cot \phi = \tan \delta$$

$$\text{Loss factor} = K \cot \phi = K \tan \delta$$

Since the loss angle δ is usually very small, the power factor and the dissipation factor are very nearly equal and are used interchangeably in many calculations.

Since the heat-generation rate is proportional to frequency and to the second power of the voltage, rapid heating and high temperatures are obtained by using high frequencies and high voltages. However, the dielectric strength of the material limits the voltages that can be used, and it is necessary in many cases to operate at extremely high frequencies (say, 100 megacycles) to obtain the desired rate of heating.

Table 2.1 gives representative values of the dielectric properties of some of the common thermoplastics. In making calculations it should be remembered that both dielectric constant and power factor are functions of frequency and temperature. The values given in Table 2.1 apply at 1 megacycle and room temperature.

TABLE 2.1

Dielectric Properties of Some Thermoplastics

Material	Dielectric constant at 1 megacycle	Power factor at 1 megacycle	Dielectric strength (volts/mil)
Polyethylene	2.2	0.0005	500
Polystyrene	2.4	0.0001	500
"Nylon"	3.5	0.03	400
"Saran"	3.0	0.05	350
"Teflon"	2.0	0.003	500

The following is an analysis of heating during dielectric heat sealing. In order to simplify the analysis, it is assumed that the temperature of the electrodes remains constant and that the thermal and dielectric properties of the work do not change with temperature. The problem is to calculate the time required for the temperature of the plastic at the interface between the two films to rise to the point where the plastic will soften and fuse. This is a problem of unidirectional unsteady-state heat conduction with generation. The applicable differential equation is Eq. (46) which reduces to

$$\left(\frac{\partial T}{\partial \theta}\right) = \alpha \left(\frac{\partial^2 T}{\partial x^2}\right) + \frac{G}{c_p \rho} \tag{98}$$

Taking the origin of the coordinate system at the interface, the boundary conditions can be written

$$T(x, 0) = T(\pm a, \theta) = T_i$$

where a is the thickness of one of the films being sealed.

A solution of Eq. (98) which meets the above boundary conditions is given by Carslaw and Jaeger.[4]

$$(T - T_i) = \left(\frac{Ga^2}{2k}\right)\left\{1 - \left(\frac{x}{a}\right) - \frac{32}{\pi^3} \sum_{0,1,2}^{\infty} \frac{1}{(2n+1)^3} e^{-(2n+1)^2 \pi^2 \phi/4} \right.$$
$$\left. \cdot \sin\left[\frac{\pi(2n+1)(x+a)}{2a}\right]\right\} \tag{99}$$

where ϕ is a dimensionless time variable defined as $(\alpha\theta/a^2)$.

Equation (99) can be specialized to give the temperature at the interface by setting x equal to zero.

$$\Delta T = \left(\frac{a^2 G}{2k}\right)\left\{1 - \frac{32}{\pi^3} \sum \frac{(-1)^n}{(2n+1)^3} e^{-(2n+1)^2 \pi^2 \phi/4}\right\} \tag{100}$$

where ΔT represents $(T_o - T_i)$. Note that Eq. (100) can be written in the form

$$\left(\frac{k\Delta T}{a^2 G}\right) = f(\phi) = f(\alpha\theta/a^2) \tag{101}$$

Computations using Eq. (100) are greatly simplified by using the graph of Fig. 2.10, where the dimensionless group $(k\Delta T/a^2 G)$ is plotted against ϕ.

Example 16: A plastic film is being heat sealed in an apparatus that operates at 45 megacycles and 500 volts. Each film is 2 mils thick, giving a total separation between the electrodes of 0.01 cm (4 mils). The electrodes are 10 cm long and 0.5 cm wide. The electrodes are maintained at room temperature during the operation, and the film is initially at room temperature. Assuming that it is necessary to increase the tempera-

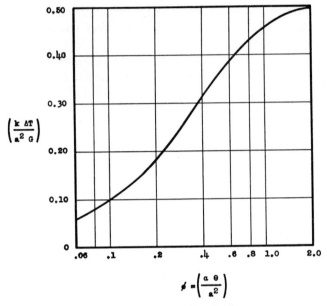

$$\left(\frac{k\,\Delta T}{a^2\,G}\right)$$

$$\phi = \left(\frac{\alpha\,\theta}{a^2}\right)$$

FIG. 2.10. Graph of Eq. (101).

ture at the interface by 150 degC to obtain a good seal, calculate the cycle time and the power requirements. The physical properties of the plastic are given below.

$$K = 3.5$$

$$\cos\phi = 0.05$$

$$\alpha = 4 \times 10^{-4}\text{ sq cm/sec}$$

$$k = 2 \times 10^{-4}\text{ cal/cm-sec-degC}$$

The heat-generation rate is calculated directly from Eq. (97).

$$G = 2,620\text{ cal/cc-sec}$$

The left side of Eq. (101) is given by the following calculation:

$$\frac{k\Delta T}{a^2G} = \frac{(2 \times 10^{-4})(150)}{(0.005)^2(2,620)} = 0.458$$

The value of ϕ (obtained from Fig. 2.10) is 1.0. The cycle time is given by the calculation

$$\theta = \frac{a^2\phi}{\alpha} = \frac{(0.005)^2(1.0)}{(4 \times 10^{-4})} = 0.063\text{ sec}$$

The power required per unit volume of the work is 2,620 cal/cc-sec. Since the total volume of the work is 0.05 cc, the total power required is 131 cal/sec, which, expressed in electrical units, is 548 watts.

Induction Heating

Induction heating finds many applications in the metallurgical and metalworking industries but few in thermoplastics processing. However, because of its unique characteristics, it is a tool of potential interest to the plastics processor, and its general characteristics are described here. Brown, Holyer, and Bierwirth[2] give a detailed description of its theory and Cable[3] describes many applications.

In induction heating an alternating electric current is passed through a primary coil which surrounds the work to be heated. The action of the electric current in the primary coil sets up a magnetic field which changes its direction with the same frequency as the alternating current. The alternating magnetic field then induces an electromotive force in the work. This action is similar to that occurring in the transformer, where the alternating current in the primary sets up an alternating magnetic field which induces an emf in the secondary. In the transformer, power is fed into the primary and withdrawn at a different voltage from the secondary. In induction heating, however, the secondary may be considered to be short-circuited, so that the induced emf simply causes a current to circulate in the work. The I^2R losses of this circulating current are responsible for the heating effect.

In a conductor carrying a *direct* current, the current density over the cross section of the conductor is constant. With an alternating current the current density will be higher at the surface than at the center of the conductor. At very high frequencies almost all of the current is carried by a thin layer near the surface. This is the so-called skin effect. Cable[3] gives the following rule for computing the skin thickness:

$$s = \frac{2}{\sqrt{f}} \tag{102}$$

where

$$s = \text{skin thickness (in.)}$$

$$f = \text{frequency (sec}^{-1})$$

Using high frequencies, the current induced in the work will be restricted to a relatively thin surface layer. For example, using a frequency of 10 kc, the heating effect will be restricted to a surface layer 0.02 in. thick. This is one of the outstanding characteristics of induction heating and is responsible for many of its applications, such as casehardening.

Another characteristic is that heat is generated only within the region of the magnetic field. Since the field is restricted to the immediate vicinity of the coil, heat is generated only in that part of the work directly within the coil.

To summarize, induction heating finds many applications with good electrical conductors (metals) in which it is desired to localize heat generation and to obtain high temperatures rapidly. It is, of course, not suitable for the direct heating of thermoplastics (poor conductors) but may find applications in special heat-control problems in processing equipment.

Heat from Fluid Friction

Referring to Fig. 2.11, consider the small element of fluid which initially is a cube having sides of length dx, dy, and dz. Assuming that flow occurs only in the x-direction and that there is a velocity gradient only in the y-direction, the fluid element will, in a short period of time, be strained or distorted to the shape shown in the figure.

If the velocity of the top surface of the cube relative to the bottom surface is du, then the shear rate (du/dy) is a measure of the rate of strain of the fluid. To maintain a velocity differential between the upper and lower surfaces of the fluid element, it is necessary to apply a steady force to the upper surface. The force applied per unit area is the shear stress. For a Newtonian fluid the shear stress is directly proportional to the shear rate.

$$\tau = \mu \left(\frac{du}{dy} \right) \tag{103}$$

where

$$\tau = \text{shear stress}$$

and μ, the proportionality constant, is known as the viscosity of the fluid.

The work done by the action of the shear force in straining the fluid appears as heat. It is referred to here as the heat generated by fluid friction.

Energy is dissipated at a rate p equal to the product of the force and the velocity. On a basis of unit volume

$$p = \frac{(\tau \, dx \, dz)(du)}{dx \, dy \, dz} = \tau \left(\frac{du}{dy} \right) \tag{104}$$

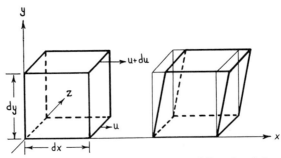

FIG. 2.11. Strain of fluid element in unidirectional flow.

Combining Eqs. (103) and (104),

$$p = \mu \left(\frac{du}{dy}\right)^2 = \frac{\tau^2}{\mu} \tag{105}$$

where

$p =$ rate of energy dissipation (ergs/cc-sec)

$\mu =$ viscosity (poise)

$\tau -$ shear stress (dynes/sq cm)

$(du/dy) =$ shear rate (sec^{-1})

The energy-dissipation rate is expressed in thermal units by multiplying Eq. (105) by the conversion factor J.

$$G = J\mu \left(\frac{du}{dy}\right)^2 = J\frac{\tau^2}{\mu} \tag{106}$$

where

$G =$ heat-generation rate (cal/cc-sec)

$J =$ conversion factor (2.39×10^{-8} cal/erg)

Example 17: A molten plastic is being sheared in an apparatus whose geometry can be considered to approximate infinite parallel plates. The lower plate is stationary, and the upper plate moves at a constant velocity of 10.0 cm/sec.

The two plates are maintained at a constant temperature of 100°C, and the process has continued for a long enough period of time for steady state to have been reached. Calculate the temperature at the mid-point between the two plates using the following data for the molten plastic.

$$\mu = 10^3 \text{ poise}$$

$$k = 10^{-4} \text{ cal/cm-sec-degC}$$

This is a problem of steady-state one-dimensional heat conduction in a moving fluid with generation. The applicable differential equation is Eq. (48) which, for this special case, reduces to

$$\alpha \left(\frac{d^2T}{dy^2}\right) = -\frac{G}{c_p\rho}$$

The problem is simplified by neglecting the effect of temperature on viscosity. In this case the shear rate (du/dy) is constant and can be written (V/b) where V is the velocity of the plate and b is the plate separation. Introducing Eq. (106) into the above equation and rearranging gives

$$\frac{d^2T}{dy^2} = -\left(\frac{JV^2\mu}{kb^2}\right)$$

The boundary conditions to be satisfied are

$$T(0) = T_p \qquad T(b) = T_p$$

where T_p is the plate temperature (100°C). The solution can be written

$$T = T_p + \left(\frac{JV^2\mu}{2b^2k}\right)(by - y^2)$$

The temperature at the mid-plane T_m is obtained from the above equation by setting y equal to $b/2$.

$$T_m = T_p + \left(\frac{JV^2\mu}{8k}\right)$$

The value of T_m, found by introducing numerical values into the above equation is 103°C.

NOMENCLATURE

Symbol	Quantity	Units
α	Thermal diffusivity	sq cm/sec
α	Absorptivity	dimensionless
β	Compressibility	$(\text{dynes/sq cm})^{-1}$
δ	Loss angle	dimensionless
ϵ	Emissivity	dimensionless
θ	Time	sec
κ	Coefficient of volume expansion	degC^{-1}
μ	Viscosity	poise
π_i	Constant in (2-15)	dynes/sq cm
ρ	Density	grams/cc
ρ	Reflectivity	dimensionless
σ	Stefan-Boltzman constant	cal/sq cm-sec-$(°K)^4$
τ	Shear stress	dynes/sq cm
τ	Transmittancy	dimensionless
ϕ	Phase angle	dimensionless
ϕ	Dimensionless time defined by Eq. (56)	dimensionless
ω	Constant in Eq. (15)	cc/g
a	Linear dimension	cm
c_p	Specific heat at constant pressure	cal/g-degC
c_v	Specific heat at constant volume	cal/g-degC
f	Frequency	sec^{-1}
g	Acceleration of gravity	cm/sec^2
h	Convective heat-transfer coefficient	cal/sq cm-sec-degC
k	Thermal conductivity	cal/cm-sec-degC
p	Power	watts
q	Rate of heat transfer	cal/sec
r	Radial distance	cm
u	Velocity	cm/sec
v	Specific volume	cc/g

Symbol	Quantity	Units
A	Area	sq cm
B	Temperature coefficient of viscosity	poise/degC
C	Capacitance	farads
E	Internal energy	cal/g
F	Emissivity factor	dimensionless
G	Heat-generation rate	cal/cc-sec
H	Enthalpy	cal/g
H	Constant defined by Eq. (66)	dimensionless
I	Index defined by Eq. (91)	dimensionless
I	Current	amp
K	Constant defined by Eq. (61)	dimensionless
K	Dielectric constant	dimensionless
L	Constants in Eq. (69)	dimensionless
M_n	The nth root of Eq. (57)	dimensionless
P	Pressure	dynes/sq cm
Q	Quantity of heat	cal/g
R	Radius	cm
R	Electrical resistance	ohms
R	Constant in Eq. (15)	dyne-cm/g-°K
T	Temperature	°C
V	Electrical potential	volts
W	Work	ergs/g
X	Position variable defined by Eq. (70)	dimensionless
Y	Temperature variable defined by Eq. (55)	dimensionless
Z	Elevation	cm

CONVERSION FACTORS

Multiply	By	To convert to
atm	1.01×10^6	dynes/sq cm
cal	4.18×10^{-7}	ergs
cc-atm	2.42×10^{-2}	cal
Btu	252	cal
hp	745	watts
joules	107	ergs
watts	1	joules/sec
cal/sq cm-sec-degC	7,380	Btu/hr-sq ft-degF
poise	1.45×10^{-5}	$lb_{(F)}$ sec/in.^{2}
hp	550	ft $lb_{(F)}$/sec
gallon (U. S.)	231	in.^{3}

REFERENCES

1. *ASTM Standards*, D 150–54T, Part 6, p. 500, 1955.
2. Brown, G. H., Holyer, C. N., and Bierwirth, R. A., "Radio-Frequency Heating," Princeton, N. J., D. Van Nostrand Company, Inc., 1947.
3. Cable, J. W., "Induction and Dielectric Heating," New York, Reinhold Publishing Corp., 1954.
4. Carslaw, H. S., and Jaeger, J. C., "Conduction of Heat in Solids," New York, Oxford University Press, 1947.
5. Dodge, B. F., "Thermodynamics," New York, McGraw-Hill Book Company, Inc., 1944.
6. Dole, M., Hettinger, W. P., Larson, N. R., and Wethington, J. A., *J. Chem. Phys.*, **20**, 781 (1952).
7. Gee, R. E., and Lyon, J. B., *Ind. Eng. Chem.*, **49**, 956 (1957).
8. Groeber, H., *Z. Ver. deut. Ing.*, **69**, 705 (1925).
9. Gurnie, H. P., and Lurie, J., *Ind. Eng. Chem.*, **15**, 1170 (1923).
10. Heisler, M. P., *Trans. ASME*, **69**, 227 (1947).
11. Jakob, Max, "Heat Transfer," Vol. 1, New York, John Wiley & Sons, Inc., 1949.
12. Lee, J. F., and Sears, F. W., "Thermodynamics," Reading, Mass., Addison-Wesley Publishing Company, 1955.
13. McAdams, W. H., "Heat Transmission," New York, McGraw-Hill Book Company, Inc., 1947.
14. Parks, W., and Richards, R. B., *Trans. Faraday Soc.*, **45**, 203 (1949).
15. Raff, R. A. V., and Allison, J. B., "Polyethylene," New York, Interscience Publishers, Inc., 1956.
16. Schneider, P. J., "Conduction Heat Transfer," Reading, Mass., Addison-Wesley Publishing Company, 1955.
17. Spencer, R. S., and Gilmore, G. D., *J. Appl. Phys.*, **21**, 523 (1950).
18. Toor, H. L., *Ind. Eng. Chem.*, **48**, 922 (1956).

3. MIXING AND DISPERSING

W. D. Mohr, Sc.D.[*]

Department of Chemical Engineering
Massachusetts Institute of Technology

INTRODUCTION

In the production, compounding, and use of thermoplastic resins, mixing and dispersing are becoming exceedingly important operations. At the same time, these operations are least well understood from fundamental engineering bases, and it is but slowly that a coherent picture is emerging in these areas.

Throughout this section, the term "mixing" will be used for the process in which two or more starting components are interspersed in space with one another. A mixture results from a mixing process. Mixing involves only the alteration of the initial distribution in space of the components. The term "dispersing" will be used to describe the multitude of processes in which some intrinsic change takes place in the physical character of one or more of the components. The change taking place may be the incorporation of solid pigment powder into a resin matrix, the dissolution of a dye from dye particles into the resin, or the reduction in particle size of pigment within a resin matrix. Mixing and dispersing operations are often carried out concurrently, but it is exceedingly useful in the analysis and improvement of the operations if each objective is viewed separately.

The study of mixtures and mixing processes has been greatly advanced in the past 10 years. Several fundamental articles have appeared in the literature which have placed the conceptualization of mixing processes on a firm foundation.[7, 12, 15, 17]

By contrast, the technology of dispersing still lacks fundamental bases. Some initial work has been reported,[3] but, in general, the operations are considered an "art" and best handled from experience in any one local field. The discussion in this section will attempt to provide a view of this operation.

[*] Present address: Polychemicals Department, E. I. du Pont de Nemours & Co., Inc.

MIXING

The manufacture of resins tailored for specific uses by the incorporation of additives such as stabilizers, fillers, and colorants has become increasingly important for resin producers. Many different colored articles are produced by fabricators. The knowledge of the fundamentals underlying mixing processes are thus essential to the efficient manufacture of resins and the fabrication of thermoplastic articles.

Mixing has been generally considered more of an art than a science. The multitude of devices to effect similar mixing operations testifies to the lack of fundamental understanding of the process. This lack of understanding is not surprising, however, when the difficulty of describing both a mixing process and the resulting mixture is considered. Consider the situation in which two components are to be mixed. The initial placement of the two components relative to one another could take an infinite variety of forms. From each one of these forms an infinite variety of flow paths within the system could produce acceptable results which would appear equivalent. This multitude of possibilities has made difficult the fundamental analysis of mixing processes. The mixture from a process is "good" or "bad," and quantitative descriptions of these sometimes subjective terms have been lacking.

Recently, advances have been made in the analysis of mixing processes starting from fundamental bases. These advances now provide ways of looking at mixing processes which permit the rational design of mixing processes and an efficient approach to the improvement of existing processes.

Ideally, a theory of mixing should permit prediction of the quality of a mixture obtained in any operation from fundamental considerations such as the geometry of the system and the physical characteristics of the components being mixed. The theory should be useful in the mixing of particulate solids as well as of fluids. The role of such a theory would be to permit rational design of systems to achieve a desired end with minimum of cost.

The sections to follow describe an engineering approach to the problem of mixing. The mixture itself is examined, and certain quantitative ways of describing mixtures are presented. A mixture need not be random to be acceptable, and this fact is emphasized. It is shown that the initial orientation of the components to be mixed relative to the flow streamlines in the equipment is a prime consideration in the analysis of the mixing process. The roles of diffusion and of shear and tensile deformation in the system being mixed are analyzed in a quantitative manner, and the application of these concepts to batch and continuous mixing operations is illustrated. The power requirement of mixing processes is considered.

Description of Mixtures

The quantitative description of a given mixture has proved to be exceedingly difficult, and this difficulty has markedly slowed progress in the analysis of mixing processes. Hypothetical ordered arrangements of the ultimate particles of a mixture can be described accurately. Such hypothetical arrangements, however, can be achieved only if some type of force can act specifically on the different species present. In general, statistical randomness of the ultimate particles is the most complete mixture that can be attained. As a result, mixtures are often described by their deviation from a completely random mixture in terms of conventional statistical parameters.

Mixtures are best described in terms of two components. If more than two components are being mixed, analysis is made easier by considering the operation as concurrent mixing of each component with the rest of the system. Any mixing process can thus be considered as a two-component operation.

The description of a mixture is made easier if it is possible to nondimensionalize the two starting components with respect to the property being mixed. It is desirable to arrange the property so that in the minor component the property has the value 1.0, while it is 0 in the other component. For example, if black and white cubes are being mixed, the property to be evaluated could be the fraction by number of the black cubes in the sample. This number is 1.0 in the starting black material and 0 in the starting white material. The appropriate transformation (number fraction, weight fraction, volume fraction, concentration ratio, etc.) depends upon the property which can be analyzed in any mixture and upon the characteristics of each starting material.

The analysis of mixtures of particles of finite size requires the use of statistical techniques of description. The analysis which is presented here can be directly applied only to mixtures of particles of the same size, modifications being required when a spectrum of particle sizes is present.[4] The following analysis assumes that all particles are of the same size.

The general approach to the description of a mixture involves first the determination of whether the mixture can be considered random. Measurements are made on samples taken from points systematically distributed throughout the mixture, and the results are compared statistically with the hypothesis that the mixture being sampled was actually random. Several tests of this hypothesis are presented below. If the tests indicate that the mixture cannot be taken as random, measures of the scale and intensity of segregation must be computed to characterize the mixture.

Consider first the system in the unmixed state; call one component black, the other white. Let the fraction by number of the black particles be θ; the fraction white particles is $(1 - \theta)$. Before mixing, the samples taken would contain either all black or all white (the small probability of taking samples containing the interface being ignored). Noting that the fraction by number of black cubes in the black is 1.0 and in the white region is 0, the expectation (average) of the number fraction black (c) in each sample would be

$$E(c) = 1.0\theta + 0 (1 - \theta) = \theta \qquad (1)$$

The expectation (average) of the variance would be

$$\sigma^2 = E((c - \theta)^2) = (1 - \theta)^2\theta + (-\theta)^2(1 - \theta) = \theta(1 - \theta) \qquad (2)$$

The coefficient of variation for this unmixed system would be

$$C = \frac{\sqrt{\sigma^2}}{\theta} = \frac{\sqrt{\theta(1 - \theta)}}{\theta} = \sqrt{\frac{1 - \theta}{\theta}} \qquad (3)$$

These values would be independent of sample size.

Consider now the randomly mixed system in which the fraction black is θ, fraction white is $(1 - \theta)$. Assume that each sample contains n particles, and that the amount of sample is insignificant compared with that of the system being investigated. In such a random system the probability that any particle is black is θ, and this probability is independent of position in the system. The probability that a sample of n particles contains exactly x black particles is given by the binomial distribution.[11]

$$p_n(x) = \binom{n}{x} \theta^x (1 - \theta)^{n-x} \quad (x = 0, 1, \cdots n) \quad (4)$$

where $p_n(x)$ denotes the probability that x particles are black in a sample of number n,

$$\binom{n}{x} = \frac{n!}{x! (n - x)!}$$

is the binomial coefficient.

The probability distribution of the number fraction black is

$$p_n(c) = p_n(x/n) = \binom{n}{x} \theta^x (1 - \theta)^{n-x} \quad \begin{matrix} (x = 0, 1, \cdots n) \\ (c = 0, 1/n, 2/n, \cdots 1) \end{matrix} \quad (5)$$

The expectation of this probability distribution can be shown to be

$$E(c) = \theta \qquad (6)$$

The variance of this probability distribution is

$$\sigma^2 = E[(c - \theta)^2] = \frac{\theta(1 - \theta)}{n} \qquad (7)$$

The coefficient of variation for this distribution is

$$C = \frac{\sqrt{\sigma^2}}{\theta} = \sqrt{\frac{1 - \theta}{n\theta}} \tag{8}$$

The binomial distribution may be approximated by the normal distribution of the same mean and variance for the cases in which $n\theta(1 - \theta) > 9$.[11] If possible, a sample size n large enough to meet this requirement should be selected.

The mixture under examination is first postulated to be a random mixture. N samples containing n particles each are taken from all parts of the mixture so as to characterize the system. The results of analysis of the N samples are evaluated statistically with the hypothesis that the mixture is actually random.

The mean of the samples is calculated from the N samples.

$$\bar{c} = \frac{1}{N} \sum_{i=1}^{N} c_i \tag{9}$$

As a first test, the difference between the mean of the samples $\bar{c}$ and the population mean θ is compared with the standard deviation to be expected for the mean of the samples $\sqrt{(1 - \theta)\theta/nN}$.

$$\left| \frac{\bar{c} - \theta}{\sqrt{\dfrac{\theta(1 - \theta)}{nN}}} \right| > \frac{u_{0.9995} - u_{0.0005}}{2} = 3.3 \tag{10}$$

where u_P equals the number of standard deviations from the mean below which lies the fraction P of the normal distribution. If the absolute value of the parameter calculated is greater than 3.3, the probability that the samples came from a random mixture is less than 0.001, and the hypothesis that the mixture is random may be rejected. Other confidence limits may be used, the proper numerical value on the right-hand side of the inequality being taken from tables of the cumulative normal distribution function. If the true population mean θ is not known from information of the relative amounts of the starting components, this test cannot be applied.

A second and more powerful statistical test is based on the comparison of the estimate of the variance calculated from the samples with the variance of a random system with the corresponding θ or $\bar{c}$. The estimate of variance may be calculated by

$$s^2 = \frac{1}{N - 1} \sum_{i=1}^{N} (c_i - \bar{c})^2 = \frac{1}{N - 1} \sum_{i=1}^{N} c_i^2 - \frac{N}{N - 1} \bar{c}^2 \tag{11}$$

or

$$\hat{s}^2 = \frac{1}{N} \sum_{i=1}^{N} (c_i - \theta)^2 \tag{12}$$

The samples should not be grouped in any way prior to calculation of the estimate of variance.

The population variance of a random system may be computed from the known population mean, or from the mean of the samples with small error.

$$\sigma^2 = \frac{\theta(1 - \theta)}{n} \cong \frac{\bar{c}(1 - \bar{c})}{n} \tag{13}$$

The ratio s^2/σ^2 is computed and compared with tabulated values of χ^2/f. (f is the number of degrees of freedom in the system and is equal to N if θ is known. If $\bar{c}$ is used to calculate s^2, $f = N - 1$.)

$$\left. \frac{s^2}{\sigma^2} \right|_{\text{exptl}} = \frac{\chi^2}{f} \tag{14}$$

$$P\left\{ \left. \frac{s^2}{\sigma^2} \right|_{\text{random}} < \left. \frac{s^2}{\sigma^2} \right|_{\text{exptl}} \right\} = P\left\{ \left. \frac{s^2}{\sigma^2} \right|_{\text{random}} < \frac{\chi_p^2}{f} \right\} = P \tag{15}$$

The probability that the ratio s^2/σ^2 from a truly random sample is less than χ_p^2/f is equal to P. An abridged χ_p^2/f table is presented in Table 3.1 for $P = 0.95$ and $P = 0.999$.

Consider a numerical example in which $N = 11$, $s^2 = 0.0080$, and $\sigma^2 = 0.0025$. $(s^2/\sigma^2)_{\text{exptl}} = 3.2$; for this case $\chi^2_{0.999}/f = 2.96$, and the probability of having s^2/σ^2 from a random mixture as large as 2.96 is 0.999. Therefore, there exists less than 1 chance in 1,000 that the samples came from a truly random mixture, and the hypothesis that the system is a random mixture may be rejected.

For any mixture, the coefficient of variation $(C = \sqrt{\sigma^2/\theta})$ is the important parameter to characterize the intensity of segregation. This coefficient is a measure, expressed as a fraction, of the spread of the individual sample

TABLE 3.1. FRACTILES OF THE χ^2/f DISTRIBUTION*

f	P Probability	
	0.95	0.999
1	3.84	10.83
2	3.00	6.91
3	2.60	5.42
4	2.37	4.62
6	2.10	3.74
8	1.94	3.27
10	1.83	2.96
15	1.67	2.51
20	1.57	2.27
50	1.35	1.73
100	1.24	1.49

* This table has been abridged by permission from Table VI of A. Hald, "Statistical Tables and Formulas," John Wiley & Sons, Inc., New York, 1952.

values about the mean. The coefficient of variation for individual samples of size n from a random mixture in which the probability of minor component (black) is θ may be shown to be

$$C = \frac{\sqrt{\sigma^2}}{\theta} = \frac{\sqrt{\dfrac{\theta(1 - \theta)}{n}}}{\theta} = \sqrt{\frac{1 - \theta}{n\theta}} \tag{16}$$

For any system in which the fraction of black particles must be within 1 per cent of the population mean 99.9 per cent of the time, the coefficient of variation must be

$$C = \frac{0.01}{\left(\dfrac{u_{0.9995} - u_{0.0005}}{2}\right)} = \frac{0.01}{3.3} = 0.003$$

The number of particles which must thus be taken in a sample from a random system (with $\theta = 0.1$) is

$$n = \frac{1 - \theta}{\theta C^2} = \frac{1 - 0.1}{0.1(0.003)^2} = 10^6 = 1{,}000{,}000$$

In the sampling of liquids and melts, no sample is taken which does not have many times the above number of particles, and one may speak of the concentration at a point. In sampling mixes of particulate solids, however, note must be taken of the possible fluctuation of the fractions of the components caused by chance alone.

The size of sample taken to evaluate whether a mixture is random at the size level of the ultimate particle should be such that $n > (9/\theta(1 - \theta))$, where θ is the fraction in the system of the most minor component. This sample size permits the binomial distribution to be approximated by the normal distribution for purposes of subsequent statistical tests. The sample should be large enough that the variances of analytical and measuring errors are sufficiently small. The number of samples taken should be sufficiently large to characterize all portions of the mixture. For statistical purposes, more than 10 samples is desirable, while the improvement in certainty is slow with increasing number of samples over 50.

If the mixture has been shown to be random at the size level of the sample, the mixture will be random for any larger sample sizes, and the preceding calculation of the coefficient of variation may be applied. If the mixture is not random at the size level of the sample, the mixture may still exhibit a tolerably small coefficient of variation at the size level important to the use of the mixture. The mixture may not be random at the level of the ultimate particle, but if the coefficient of variation $\sqrt{\sigma^2}/\theta$ were suitably small at the size level of use, the mixture would still be acceptable. Randomness at the level of ultimate particle is not essential for acceptability in some applications. These considerations are discussed further in the next section.

The foregoing discussion has presented tests to indicate whether a mixture was or was not random. If the mixture is random, the system is defined in a statistical sense. If the mixture is not random, it has been shown that two parameters are sufficient to characterize the mixture.[6] These two parameters are (1) the scale of segregation and (2) the intensity of segregation. The scale of segregation is a measure of the average distance between clumps of the same component in the mixture and may be reduced in the mixing process by shear and tensile deformation of the system. The intensity of segregation is a measure of the average deviation of the concentration at a point from the mean concentration. The intensity of segregation may be reduced only by some random process at the level of the ultimate particle, and this requires the action of a process akin to diffusion (diffusion of molecules due to their random velocities, Brownian motion of larger particles in liquid or gases, or random motion of individual solid particles when the solids mass is undergoing shear). The diffusion-type process tends to average out the concentration of the components in the volumes adjacent to the interfacial surface of the components.

The most useful measure of the scale of segregation is the average striation thickness, which is defined as the average distance between like interfaces in the system. It has been shown that the average striation thickness (r) may be computed from the ratio of the interfacial surface area between the components and the total volume of the system[17] (see Fig. 3.1).

$$r = \frac{2}{S/V} \tag{17}$$

This expression for the average striation thickness results from picturing the material as being deformed by the mixing process into roughly plane, parallel sheets. The volume of the mixture is therefore one half the product of the interfacial surface area and the average striation thickness. (Two

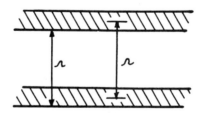

FIG. 3.1. Definition of striation thickness.

elements of interfacial surface area are "cut" by an average striation distance.)

$$V = \frac{Sr}{2}; \qquad r = \frac{2}{S/V}$$

The average striation thickness in a mixture may be measured by taking many small samples in the mixture and determining the average of the shortest distance from a point of maximum concentration of one component to the nearest maxima of concentration of that same component.

Several other expressions for the scale of segregation in a nonuniform mixture have been devised;[6] these expressions do not have the ease of physical visualization, nor are they useful in determining how the scale of segregation would be affected in time in a given mixing process.

The intensity of segregation is best defined as the coefficient of variation of concentration in the system, defined as the quotient of the standard deviation of the concentration of one component divided by the average concentration of that component.

$$I = C = \frac{\sqrt{\sigma^2}}{\theta} \tag{18}$$

$$\sigma^2 = \lim_{N \to \infty} \frac{1}{N} \sum_{i=1}^{N} (c_i - \theta)^2 \tag{19}$$

In practice, only a sufficient number of samples need be taken from all parts of the mixture to bring s^2 sufficiently close to the limiting value σ^2. If the variance of the analytical method is known, the actual variance of the mixture is

$$\sigma^2 = \sigma^2_{meas} - \sigma^2_{anal}$$

The intensity of segregation is dependent upon the volume of the sample. If the volume of the sample is much smaller than r^3, the value of c_i in any sample results from the probability of the component at the sampling point, and the standard deviation thus calculated would depend on the number of particles in the sample and the probability of the minor component, as indicated previously, as well as on the spatial distribution of the probability throughout the volume. If the volume of the sample is of order of magnitude of r^3 or greater, the standard deviation of concentration depends only on the number of striations enclosed by the sample volume, decreasing as the number of enclosed striations increases. This effect is due to the averaging process resulting when a number of striations are included in a sample. The quantitative effect is shown in App. 2.

It is to be expected that the intensity of segregation will decrease as the quality of the mixture improves. However, the lowest possible value is not zero but depends on the number of particles in the sample and on the fraction of the minor component.

$$I_{\text{random}} = C_{\text{random}} = \frac{\sqrt{\sigma^2}}{\theta} = \sqrt{\frac{1 - \theta}{n\theta}} \tag{20}$$

The asymptotic value of the intensity of segregation on prolonged mixing is thus I_{random}, and the experimental values obtained would be expected to fluctuate at random about this asymptote with a χ^2 distribution.

Several other measures of the intensity of segregation have been proposed.[6, 12, 14, 18] The expression of the intensity of segregation as the coefficient of variation provides the description of the spread of data about the mean value (expressed as per cent) which has physical significance in all applications. In addition, negative values are not possible.

Description of Ideal Mixing Process

Since mixing processes may involve so many kinds of materials in many different types of mixing apparatus, it has been difficult to arrive at the fundamental factors involved by generalization from one or even several specific mixing processes. Recent investigations, however, have laid emphasis on the fundamentals involved so that a generalized ideal mixing theory has evolved. Full visualization and appreciation of this ideal mixing theory permits the engineer to go from the general to any specific problem by placing the unique factors of the specific problem in their proper perspective. Certain elements of the general theory are well in hand; other facets of the problem require further study.

The objective of a mixing process is to alter the original distribution in space of the probability of finding a particle of any one component at any particular point, such that an acceptable spatial probability distribution is achieved.

In an ideal mixing problem, the system is examined from the point of view of how a continuum would be distorted from the initial orientation by the flow pattern in the system. Diffusion is first assumed to be nonexistent. The following sections show that the initial orientation of the interfacial surface of the components being mixed relative to the flow streamlines in the system is of paramount importance. The deformation of the continuum by shear and tensile action must be such as to increase the interfacial area between the components. This increase in interfacial area leads to a decrease in the scale of segregation, i.e., in the average striation thickness in the system. The deformation in the system is continued until the thickness of the striations is sufficiently small with respect to the volume scale on which the mixture is to be evaluated. The mixing is then considered adequate. If diffusional information is not at hand and the system must be randomly mixed, the striation thickness must be reduced to the order of the ultimate particle size. If the diffusion coefficients in the system are known, the necessary striation thickness such that diffusion can randomize the mixture in a fixed time may be calculated.

The concepts stated above apply to all mixing systems—solid, liquid, or gas. In the melt of thermoplastic resins, diffusion rates of dyes and the Brownian movement of pigments and fillers may be small in absolute magnitude, but the striation thicknesses may be made sufficiently small so that the rate of diffusion is significant. In the mixing of particulate solids, the individual solid particles undergo random movements relative to one another when the mass of particles is sheared or deformed; these random movements indicate that a process akin to diffusion occurs when solids are being mixed and that the general mixing theory applies to such systems.

Consider the simple mixing example shown in Fig. 3.2. The initial orientation shown in Fig. 3.2a could be mixed at the grid size shown in Fig. 3.2b if the interfacial area were deformed as shown. The striking fact to be considered is that the interfacial area must be increased so that the area passes through each of the volume elements of the system. Secondly, the amount of material of the two kinds in each volume element must be in the same ratio as that for the whole system. Three factors are thus of importance in mixing problems: (1) the interfacial area between the components must be greatly increased in the mixing process; (2) elements of the interfacial area must be distributed throughout the system being mixed; and (3) the material must be distributed so that in any volume element the ratio of the components is the same as in the whole system. The first factor is attacked in a quantitative way in the sections to follow. The second factor is approached by consideration of the initial orientation of the interfacial surface relative to the flow streamlines in the system. The third factor has been

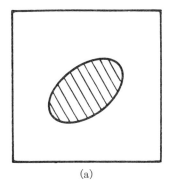
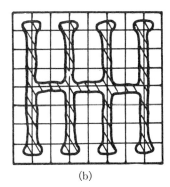

(a)   (b)

FIG. 3.2. Simple illustration of mixing.

approached in the least satisfying way by assuming that, if there are a large number of interfacial elements within the volume element being considered, the chance that the volume ratios are markedly different from that of the whole mixture is negligible. The example shown in Fig. 3.2 is for illustrative purposes only, since there exist no ways of "reaching into" the system to deform it in exactly the manner required.

The importance of increase in interfacial area was shown in the preceding paragraph. The quantitative calculations of the increase in interfacial area upon deformation of the system being mixed by means of shear deformation and by tensile deformation are derived in App. 1.

The increase in interfacial area under the influence of shear may be expressed[17] as

$$S = S_o\sqrt{1 - 2M\cos\alpha_x\cos\alpha_y + M^2\cos^2\alpha_x} \tag{21}$$

where

$S =$ interfacial area after shear deformation

$S_o =$ initial interfacial area

$M =$ net amount of shear $= \dfrac{du_x{}^*}{dy}$

$\cos\alpha_x$, $\cos\alpha_y =$ direction cosines on the initial interfacial surface relative to the coordinate system determined by the direction of shear

The increase in interfacial area under the influence of tensile deformation may be expressed as

$$S = S_o\sqrt{\frac{\cos^2\alpha_x}{X^2} + \frac{\cos^2\alpha_y}{Y^2} + \frac{\cos^2\alpha_z}{Z^2}} \tag{22}$$

where

$X, Y, Z =$ ratio of distance between the same particles in the x, y, and z directions, respectively, after: before deformation.

$$\left\{ \frac{\partial u_x{}^*}{\partial x}, \frac{\partial u_y{}^*}{\partial y}, \frac{\partial u_z{}^*}{\partial z} \right\}$$

Since the derivations result from consideration of plane surfaces, an original interfacial surface of complex shape should be divided into smaller surfaces which may be considered planar, the above computations applied to each, and the final interfacial surface computed as the sum. If the flow through the system is complex, the process may be separated into a series of steps, each of which may be considered as either shear or tensile deformation, the starting orientation for one step being the result of the step preceding.

If an element of the system undergoes a shear rate du/dr while traversing a certain length in the system L with a velocity u, the amount of shear received by the element is

$$M = \int_0^L \frac{du/dr}{u} \, dl \qquad (23)$$

Computation of the amount of shear thus involves knowledge of the velocity profile at all points in the system.

It was shown on p. 124 that the average striation thickness r is a measure of the scale of segregation in a nonrandom mixture. The average striation thickness was related to the interfacial surface to total volume ratio by

$$r = \frac{2}{S/V} = \frac{2}{(S/S_o)(S_o/V)} \qquad (24)$$

Since the initial surface to volume ratio (S_o/V) may be computed from the initial orientation (which must be specified), and since the ratio of final to initial interfacial surface (S/S_o) may be computed as shown above from the flow profile in the system, the average striation thickness may be computed. For a given system, the striation thickness thus computed may be compared with criteria established for the end use of the product. Conversely, knowing the required striation thickness and the initial orientation of the components, the amount of shear necessary may be computed and equipment may be designed to achieve this amount of shear.

It has been shown that diffusion is the only process capable of leading to true randomization in the system being mixed. In certain types of mixing apparatus with particular orientations, diffusion is the only mechanism by which mixing can occur. Lacey[12] has shown such a dependence in the case of a cylinder rotating about a horizontal axis in which the two components are initially placed at opposing ends of the cylinder. If the diffusion coefficient is known, computation of the rate of reduction of the intensity of segregation may be performed from the original system geometry and the defining equation of the diffusion coefficient. Analogies with calculations for transient heat conduction in solids permit use of published charts (Gurney-Lurie, Hottel) for simple geometries.[13] Since diffusion over the lengths required in commercial mixing equipment is usually slow, reliance on diffusion alone should be avoided.

In the cases in which diffusion and the increase of interfacial area by shear and tensile deformation are occurring simultaneously, a general quantitative approach has proved too difficult. One approach which gives semiquantitative results to this problem is based on the assumption that the average striation thickness is inversely proportional to time. The derivation of the required time to mix to achieve a desired intensity of segregation I_D is presented in App. 2. The resulting expression for the time to mix in a system with a given shear rate $[(du/dr)_{avg}]$ is

$$t_M = \sqrt[3]{\frac{3V^2 \ln\left(\frac{\sqrt{2}\sin\theta\pi}{I_D\theta\pi}\right)}{\pi^2 D_V S_o^2 \left[\left(\frac{du}{dr}\right)_{avg} \cos\alpha_x\right]^2}} \tag{25}$$

In all cases, most efficient use of a mixer is obtained when the initial interfacial surface is optimally oriented with respect to the flow streamlines in the system. This usually requires $\cos\alpha_x = 1$.[17] The designer of mixing apparatus generally does not know, however, how the user is going to orient the components in the mixer at the start of the process. The designer must therefore design the equipment to give flow patterns which achieve the same time of mixing when the minor component is a very small fraction of the batch, no matter where that minor fraction is placed in the equipment. This result is not necessarily the most efficient use of mixing power for the orientation used in practice, and it should be appreciated that efficiencies can be improved when the initial orientation of components can be specified before the mixing equipment is designed.

Mixing of systems is accomplished by causing relative movement to occur within the system in the form of shear and tensile deformation, as discussed above. The only way in which this can occur in the system is through relative motion of the boundaries of the system, sometimes with the aid of gravity. It is thus apparent that the motion at any point in the system depends on the movement of the boundaries of the system *and* on the shear-stress–shear-rate characteristics at all points within the system. For example, cubes of very high-viscosity resin suspended in a matrix of much lower viscosity will not be deformed, even though the bulk of the resin itself is deformed. Unless the cubes of high viscosity can be deformed, no increase in interfacial area is possible, and no change in the quality of the mixture can occur. The designer of mixing equipment must know the physical characteristics of the components being mixed at all possible combinations of the components in order to develop a workable process. In the case of the example above, the flow patterns in the equipment must be such that all of the material passes through sufficiently small clearances at some time during the mixing process.

One particular initial orientation which is of interest in plastics fabrication is that of a random mixture of resin cubes.[15] This mixture is produced by tumbling cubes of the two components; the resulting random mixture is plasticated and deformed in a second mixing device, e.g., an extruder or roll mill. The calculation of the average striation thickness from such a starting mixture is outlined in App. 3. The resulting expression for the average striation thickness (r) is

$$r = \frac{L_1}{M\theta} \tag{26}$$

This expression presents quantitatively the relationships experienced in practice.

(1) The larger the initial scale of segregation (L_1), the more mixing need be done (larger M required).

(2) The smaller the necessary final average striation thickness (r), the more mixing need be done.

(3) The smaller the volume fraction of the minor component (θ), the more mixing need be done. It is more difficult to mix a small amount into a large amount than to achieve an acceptable 50-50 mixture.

Since the starting mixture is considered to be random, the average striation thickness must be made less than the striation thickness over which the average concentration is desired, in order to minimize the probability that any one striation will be greater than the value desired. This result is achieved by applying a safety factor to the calculation of the amount of shear required.

The principal deviations from the assumptions on which this general mixing theory is based occur in the mixing of particulate solids. If the solids are of different size, shape, density, or surface characteristics, or are acted upon by electrostatic forces, the necessary conditions implied in the usual use of a diffusion coefficient do not apply. In these cases the mixing theory must be modified by experiment to achieve best the end desired in the particular case.

Application to Batch Mixing Processes

The objective of batch mixing processes is to distribute all components of the initial system throughout the volume of the system such that the fraction of each component within any element of given size taken from the system deviates only by a tolerably small percentage from the over-all fraction of that component. The process is accomplished by relative movement of the boundaries of the system for a period of time sufficient to make a "good" mixture. This period of time is called the "time to mix."

The initial orientation of the interface between the components being mixed relative to the flow streamlines in the equipment is of paramount importance. With some pieces of equipment the time to mix can be cut drastically by proper initial placement of the components. The initial placement should be such as to provide the maximum rate of increase of the interfacial surface by the flow streamlines. In such a way the striation thickness is reduced as rapidly as possible, thus shortening the path for diffusion and increasing the number of striations taken in any sample.

In the design of equipment, the flow patterns in the equipment must be

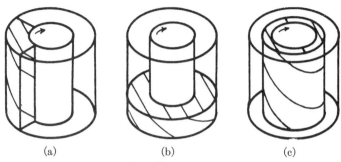

(a)   (b)   (c)

Fɪɢ. 3.3. Importance of initial orientation.

produced in such a manner that the time to mix from *any* initial placement is the same.[9] The flow patterns should be such that the time to mix for a very small minor fraction, say 0.01, is the same, regardless of its initial position in the system. Such an arrangement will guarantee the same time to mix independent of initial orientation. If the initial orientation can be specified by the equipment designer, the flow pattern to achieve the minimum mixing time should, of course, be sought.

Certain pieces of equipment, such as roll mills and revolving drum mixers, have closed-flow streamlines. The initial orientation in such equipment must be such that the average concentration taken along every streamline is the average concentration for the system. If this requirement is not met, diffusion over long distances is required, with its attendant slowness. A practical way around this problem is to reorient the material in the mixer periodically during the operation.

As an example of a simple batch mixer, consider the rotational viscometer shown in Fig. 3.3. If the material is initially placed as in Fig. 3.3a, the shear resulting when the inner cylinder rotates increases rapidly the interfacial area. Orienting the coordinate system as shown, $\cos \alpha_x$ is unity, thereby producing rapid increase in interfacial area with shear. Figs. 3.3b and 3.3c show initial orientations in which $\cos \alpha_x$ is zero and in which subsequent shear produces no increase in interfacial area whatsoever. Such orientations would rely solely on diffusion which would be relatively slow. Note also that any small-volume element remains at the same height from the bottom and at the same distance from the cylinders while the shearing operation proceeds. Each element moves around the cylinder in a closed streamline. The same average concentration around each closed streamline was achieved in Fig. 3.3a by using sector-shaped elements of each component as the starting orientation.

Continuous Mixing Processes

Continuous mixing processes are processes in which the material to be mixed is fed into the volume of the system at one point and the product is removed from another point while a mixing operation is carried out on the material in the system. The addition and removal may be done continually or intermittently. In no case is the volume of the system completely emptied, as in batch operation.

There are two objectives of a continuous mixing process, and it is important to decide which objective is sought from any given system. (1) The components may be individually fed to the equipment at the desired rate, and it is desired that the composition within a certain sample volume size at any point over the outlet area be tolerably close to the average composition. (2) The components are fed to the system with a ratio which varies with time, and it is the object of the process to reduce the time fluctuations of the concentration averaged over the outlet area. These two objectives are quite distinct, and, since different principles of design and analysis are required in the two cases, the objective for any given application must be determined. In some instances, both objectives may be required.

In the first case the components are individually fed to the apparatus at the desired rate. Across the inlet cross section the concentration within the necessary sample volume size varies excessively from point to point. The purpose of the mixing device is to produce, at the necessary sample volume size, negligible variance of concentration from point to point across the outlet cross section. This purpose is accomplished by causing the bulk of the material to be deformed by the relative motion of the boundaries of the system as the material passes from inlet to outlet. The initial interfacial surface of the components being mixed must be so oriented relative to the flow streamlines passing through the apparatus that the interfacial surface of every volume element is increased sufficiently during its transit through the equipment. The initial interfacial surface must intersect each streamline that passes through the equipment. The optimum flow pattern in the equipment is achieved when each volume element entering receives the same amount of shear, when this shear is optimally applied to the initial orientation, and when all shear applied to each volume element is in one direction.

In laminar flow systems the path of each volume element in the system is known from the system flow pattern and the starting point of the element. Laminar flow systems arise in the mixing of very viscous fluids, and many processes involving mixing of particulate solids can be viewed as laminar flow systems. The mixing process is best analyzed by determining the amount of shear deformation received by elements entering at all points over the inlet cross section. The amount of shear is calculated from the velocity profile which must be known at all points in the system. From the initial interfacial surface orientation, the effect of the amount of shear and the tensile deformation at the inlet and outlet permit calculation of the striation thickness at all points over the cross section of the outlet material. This striation thickness can be evaluated with respect to the time in the equipment and the diffusion coefficient to see if randomization had occurred. The relative magnitude of the striation thickness at all points of the outlet material permits the mixture to be evaluated against criteria for the end use of the product. The constancy of the striation thickness at all points of the outlet material gives an indication of the efficiency with which the equipment is deforming the material passing through it.

A simple example of this calculation is presented in App. 4 for the case in which alternate disks of material are forced through a tube in laminar flow. The calculations show that the striation thickness is appreciably reduced only at the surface of the output, and it depends on the type of material and on the end use whether this would be acceptable. The extent of the calculations required for this simple system indicates the difficulty of analysis for more complex flow patterns.

The second objective of mixers is the case in which the mixer or blender is desired to even off fluctuations in the concentration of one of the entering components; this situation has been expertly analyzed by Danckwerts.[7] The input concentration of one component is assumed to be a random function of time, and the ratio of the statistical variances of the output concentration:input concentration may be calculated as a function of the normalized autocorrelation function of the input concentration and the distribution of residence times in the mixer.

$$\frac{\sigma_o^2}{\sigma_i^2} = \frac{\overline{\delta_o^2(t)}}{\overline{\delta_i^2(t)}} = 2 \int_{\tau=0}^{\infty} \int_{t=0}^{\infty} \phi_{ii}(\tau) E(t) E(t + \tau) \, dt \, d\tau \qquad (27)$$

where

$E(t) =$ distribution of holdup times in the equipment

$\phi_{ii}(\tau) = \dfrac{\overline{\delta_i(t)\delta_i(t + \tau)}}{\overline{\delta_i^2(t)}} =$ normalized autocorrelation of the input fluctuations

$\delta_i, \delta_0 =$ deviations from the mean concentration at inlet and outlet, respectively

The normalized autocorrelation of the input fluctuations provides information as to the time scale over which deviations from the mean concentration persist. An estimate of this function is necessary before equipment can be designed to effect a desired reduction in the variance ratio. The distribution of holdup times depends on the flow pattern and volume of the equipment. This distribution can be obtained by tracer experiments on the existing equipment or models, or by computation if the flow profiles in the system are known. The manner in which these computations are handled for a practical case is reported by Danckwerts and Sellers.[5] The computations for a simple case of interest are presented in App. 5.

A closely allied problem occurs in the estimation of the time required to purge a continuous mixing device, i.e., the period of time during which the concentration of old material is greater than tolerable following a change in feed. The distribution of holdup times mentioned above provides information as to the concentration at times following a change. The decision as to what level is tolerable depends on the characteristics of both the old and new material and must be determined from the requirements of use for the material in any particular case. ("Black is more difficult to purge than a pastel color.") In addition, the question as to where in the product the old material lies is sometimes as important as the question of concentration for particular end uses.

Power Requirements in Mixing

Application of the general mixing theory presented in the sections preceding permits an estimate of the power required in any mixing process. From the desired striation thickness to be attained, and from information on the initial orientation of the components, the necessary amount of shear may be computed by use of the preceding relationships. If the time to mix is specified, and the shear-stress–shear-rate relationships for the components being mixed are known, the power requirement may be calculated. The basic relationship is

$$\frac{dP}{dV} = (\text{shear stress})(\text{shear rate}) = \tau \left(\frac{du}{dr}\right) \tag{28}$$

The power per unit volume is equal to the product of the shear stress and shear rate. Most processing equipment is built to produce a certain shear rate. Since the shear stress may vary with time (batch operations) or with position in the equipment (continuous operations), an integration must be performed over the volume of the system to estimate the total instantaneous power required in the operation.

Consider a batch mixing operation in which the time to mix is t_M, and the amount of shear which must be attained in the operation is M. Assume that the shear rate is constant at all parts of the system; the average shear rate is therefore

$$\frac{du}{dr} = \frac{M}{t_M} \tag{29}$$

If the shear-stress–shear-rate relationship of the material in the system may be expressed as

$$\tau = K \left(\frac{du}{dr}\right)^n \tag{30}$$

the power requirement of the mixing process is

$$P = K \left(\frac{du}{dr}\right)^{n+1} V = KV \left(\frac{M}{t_M}\right)^{n+1} \tag{31}$$

where K must be evaluated for the conditions in the system. With particulate solids, K is not effected by the processing, and the power consumption does not change with time. With viscous liquids, however, the work put into the system causes the temperature to rise, thereby decreasing K and the power required with time. Since the power requirement must be satisfied at all times, the requirement should be estimated on conditions at the start of the process.

Consider a continuous mixing operation in which the volume of the system is V, the volumetric throughput rate is q, and the necessary amount of shear to be attained is M. If all elements of the material had the same residence time in the system and if the shear rate were the same at all parts of the equipment, the necessary shear rate would be

$$\frac{du}{dr} = \frac{Mq}{V} \tag{32}$$

If the shear-stress–shear-rate relation were that presented in Eq. (30), and if the value of K were constant throughout the equipment (particulate solids or isothermal mixing of viscous liquids), the power requirement would be

$$P = \frac{KM^{n+1}\, q^{n+1}}{V^n} \tag{33}$$

If the processing of a viscous liquid were performed other than isothermally, the temperature profile in the system must be known to permit integration over the system volume.

The total power requirement of a mixing process is least if the system is operated adiabatically. If heat is removed from the system, additional shaft power must be employed to deform the material at the higher viscosity. On the other hand, if heat is added to the system, the shaft power requirement is reduced, but the total power requirement is increased and would be exhibited by the fact that the outlet temperature of the mixture would be higher.

The calculations of the power requirement of mixers presented above are the minimum to attain the desired end result. The actual power requirement would be greater owing to deviation from one or more of the above assumptions. (1) The shear rate is constant at all parts of the system. (2) All shear acts in one direction. (3) All material remains in a continuous mixer for the same length of time. Proper design of mixing equipment tends to make the above assumptions more valid, and the power efficiency of any mixing device

$$\eta_P = \frac{\text{theoretical power}}{\text{actual power}} \tag{34}$$

is a good measure of the efficiency with which the operation is performed.

Information Required for Evaluation of Mixing Processes

To summarize the concepts presented in this section, the four major categories of information essential to the evaluation of mixing processes are presented below. Within each category are presented the kinds of questions which must be asked about every mixing process.

(1) The physical characteristics of the components to be mixed must be fully known. What is the ultimate particle in each component? Are the particle sizes, shapes, and densities comparable enough so that segregation will be minor? If liquids, are the components physically compatible over the range of concentrations required? Are the viscosities of the two components sufficiently close over the possible range of temperature of operation? Are the shear-stress–shear-rate characteristics available at all possible concentrations? Is the diffusion coefficient in the system known?

(2) The flow pattern within the volume of the system must be known. Is the flow laminar or turbulent? Are there sections of completely "dead water"? Is it possible to describe the velocity at all points by a set of equations? Do any closed-flow streamlines exist in the system? Is the shear in the system additive, or are back-and-forth motions encountered? If a continuous mixer, is the distribution of residence times known?

(3) The possible initial orientations of the components must be known. Is it possible to select the initial orientation of the components, or is this condition dependent upon preceding equipment? Do the two components intersect all closed-flow streamlines? Is the interfacial surface oriented so as to be most rapidly increased by the shear in the system?

(4) The requirement for acceptance of the final mixture must be accurately stated. What is the size of sample volume at which the composition is to be evaluated? What tolerance limits are permissible in the composition at this sample size? What is the variance of the analytical error?

DISPERSING

Dispersing is the term used to describe processes in which one or more of the components of a mixture undergo some fundamental change in physical characteristics. As an example, consider the attainment of a pigmented resin. The pigment initially exists as solid particles surrounded by a fluid (air or some other carrier), and a dispersing operation must be performed to obtain an intimate suspension of pigment in resin.

Dispersing operations are generally divided into two phases. The first phase may be termed the incorporation of solids into the resin matrix; the second phase is the deagglomeration or dissolution of the solids to yield the desired product.

The incorporation of solids into resin requires that the resin be plasticized by heat so that a folding-over process may trap clumps of solid particles within the volume of the resin system. If the fluid surrounding the solids is air, this must be eliminated from the trapped clumps by manipulation or by diffusion into the resin; this elimination is speeded by the application of shear, heat, and pressure. The smaller the clumps of solid before entrapment, the less extraneous fluid captured. The clumps of solid should be as small and as widely distributed in space as possible prior to the start of the incorporation process. If the resin "wets" the solids, the rate of diffusion of the extraneous fluid is increased owing to the increase in surface area. Surface-active agents may thus be helpful. The incorporation of dyes into resins is simpler than pigments, since diffusion can speed the process. The particles should be as small as possible to permit them to dissolve entirely during the time of the processing operation.

The deagglomeration or dissolution of the solids in the resin matrix is greatly speeded by the application of a shear stress to the resin matrix. The clumps of ultimate particles of solid are held together by surface and/or electrostatic forces which must be exceeded by the stress applied to the resin in order to break up the clumps. The shear stress in the resin is increased by employing higher rates of shear on resin that is as cold as possible while still being deformable. Since in most processing equipment the shear stress varies with position in the equipment, it is essential that flow patterns exist which cause all the material being processed to pass through the region of maximum stress at some time during the operation.

Deagglomeration of solids is performed most efficiently by first producing a heavily loaded concentrate, with the solids 30 to 70 per cent by volume. The power input is more efficiently utilized, since large volumes of resin are not being sheared. In addition, the local stress field on a clump of solids may be very much higher than the over-all average owing to collision of clumps moving along adjacent streamlines. The concentrate thus produced may then be extended to the proper level by mixing with sufficient natural resin. This technique is called "master-batching."

Dissolution of solids (dyes) is speeded by subjecting the matrix to a shear rate owing to the fact that the distance for diffusion about any clump of solid is continually being reduced. Since dyes are normally used at levels far below their equilibrium solubility, manufacture of concentrates may be beneficial in this case.

APPENDIX 1
Increase in Interfacial Area by Shear and Tensile Deformation

SHEAR DEFORMATION

Assume that an element of plane surface passes through the origin of a rectangular coordinate system. The orientation of this plane surface may be specified by two of the three direction cosines of the normal to the surface. Consider a unit of surface and that the length of the normal vector represents the area of the surface. (See Fig. 3.A1.)

$$\mathbf{N} = \cos \alpha_x \mathbf{i} + \cos \alpha_y \mathbf{j} + \cos \alpha_z \mathbf{k}$$

$\mathbf{N}$ = unit normal vector to plane
$\cos \alpha_x$, $\cos \alpha_y$, $\cos \alpha_z$ = direction cosines to the normal
$\mathbf{i}, \mathbf{j}, \mathbf{k}$ = unit vectors in direction x, y, and z, respectively

$$\cos^2 \alpha_x + \cos^2 \alpha_y + \cos^2 \alpha_z = 1$$

Consider, now, two vectors in the plane of the surface, one of which is also in plane $x - z$ (**a**), the other being in plane $x - y$ (**b**). The equations of these vectors are:

$$\mathbf{a} = A_1 \mathbf{i} + 0\mathbf{j} + A_3 \mathbf{k} \tag{A1}$$

$$\mathbf{b} = B_1 \mathbf{i} + B_2 \mathbf{j} + 0\mathbf{k} \tag{A2}$$

where A_1, A_3, B_1, and B_2 are constants to be determined which satisfy the relations

$$\mathbf{N} \cdot \mathbf{a} = 0$$
$$\mathbf{N} \cdot \mathbf{b} = 0$$
$$\mathbf{a} \times \mathbf{b} = \mathbf{N}$$

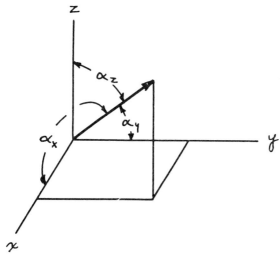

FIG. 3.A1. Coordinate system of vectors.

Two vectors which satisfy the above relationships are

$$\mathbf{a} = \frac{\cos \alpha_z}{\sqrt{\cos \alpha_x}}\mathbf{i} + 0\mathbf{j} - \sqrt{\cos \alpha_x}\,\mathbf{k} \tag{A3}$$

$$\mathbf{b} = -\frac{\cos \alpha_y}{\sqrt{\cos \alpha_x}}\mathbf{i} + \sqrt{\cos \alpha_x}\,\mathbf{j} + 0\mathbf{k} \tag{A4}$$

When the system containing the plane surface is deformed, let the vector $\mathbf{u}^*$ represent the displacement from an initial point (x, y, z) to the same point after deformation (x', y', z'). In simple viscous shear deformation, let $M = \partial u^*_x/\partial y =$ the amount of shear.

If $\mathbf{u}^* = 0$ at the origin, $\mathbf{u}^*_x = M \cdot y\mathbf{i}$, and this vector is added to $\mathbf{a}$ and $\mathbf{b}$ to obtain the vectors in the plane of the surface after deformation, $\mathbf{a}'$, $\mathbf{b}'$. $\mathbf{a}$ is unchanged since the $x - z$ plane is undistorted by shear.

$$\mathbf{b}' = \mathbf{b} + \mathbf{u}_x^* = \mathbf{b} + My\mathbf{i} = \left(M\sqrt{\cos \alpha_x} - \frac{\cos \alpha_y}{\sqrt{\cos \alpha_x}}\right)\mathbf{i} + \sqrt{\cos \alpha_x}\,\mathbf{j} + 0\mathbf{k}$$

The ratio of surface area after deformation to that before is

$$\frac{S}{S_o} = \frac{|\mathbf{a}' \times \mathbf{b}'|}{|\mathbf{a} \times \mathbf{b}|} = \frac{|\cos \alpha_x\mathbf{i} + (\cos \alpha_y - M\cos \alpha_x)\mathbf{j} + \cos \alpha_z\mathbf{k}|}{1} \tag{A5}$$

$$= \sqrt{1 - 2M \cos \alpha_x \cos \alpha_y + M^2 \cos^2 \alpha_x}$$

TENSILE DEFORMATION

Assume an initial surface to be that described above with two vectors $\mathbf{a}$, $\mathbf{b}$ in the plane of the surface. Assume that the system is deformed by tensile deformation. (See Fig. 3.A2.)

Define the ratios

$$X = \frac{x_2}{x_1}; \qquad Y = \frac{y_2}{y_1}; \qquad Z = \frac{z_2}{z_1}$$

as the tensile multipliers in the x, y, and z directions, respectively. If the

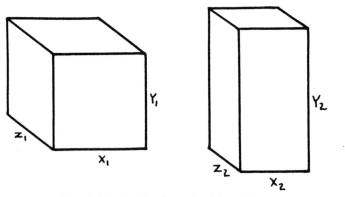

FIG. 3.A2. Result of tensile deformation.

volume is constant,

$$XYZ = \frac{x_2 y_2 z_2}{x_1 y_1 z_1} = 1$$

The deformed vectors $\mathbf{a}''$, $\mathbf{b}''$ result from the multiplication of each of their coefficients by the appropriate tensile multiplier.

$$\mathbf{a}'' = X \frac{\cos \alpha_z}{\sqrt{\cos \alpha_x}} \mathbf{i} + Y \cdot 0 \mathbf{j} - Z \sqrt{\cos \alpha_x} \, \mathbf{k}$$

$$\mathbf{b}'' = -X \frac{\cos \alpha_y}{\sqrt{\cos \alpha_x}} \mathbf{i} + Y \sqrt{\cos \alpha_x} \, \mathbf{j} + Z \cdot 0 \mathbf{k}$$

The ratio of final to initial surface area is

$$\frac{s}{s_0} = \frac{|\mathbf{a}'' \times \mathbf{b}''|}{|\mathbf{a} \times \mathbf{b}|} = \frac{|YZ \cos \alpha_x \mathbf{i} + XZ \cos \alpha_y \mathbf{j} + XY \cos \alpha_z \mathbf{k}|}{1}$$

$$= \sqrt{\frac{\cos^2 \alpha_x}{X^2} + \frac{\cos^2 \alpha_y}{Y^2} + \frac{\cos^2 \alpha_z}{Z^2}}$$

(A6)

COMBINED SHEAR AND TENSILE DEFORMATION

In the case of stepwise shear, tensile, shear, tensile, ...deformation, the amount of shear and the tensile multipliers may be represented in the following order.

	Shear	Tensile	Shear	Tensile	Shear	Tensile
Amount of shear	M_0		M_1		M_n	
Tensile deformation		X_0, Y_0, Z_0		X_1, Y_1, Z_1		X_n, Y_n, Z_n

The ratio of final to initial interfacial surface area is

$$\frac{s}{s_0} = \sqrt{\left(\frac{\cos \alpha_x}{X_0 X_1 \cdots X_n}\right)^2 + \left[\frac{\cos \alpha_y}{Y_0 Y_1 \cdots Y_n} - \frac{\cos \alpha_x}{X_0 X_1 \cdots X_n} \cdot \left(M_0 \frac{X_0 X_1 \cdots X_n}{Y_0 Y_1 \cdots Y_n} + M_1 \frac{X_1 \cdots X_n}{Y_1 \cdots Y_n} + \cdots + M_n \frac{X_n}{Y_n}\right)\right]^2 + \left(\frac{\cos \alpha_z}{Z_0 Z_1 \cdots Z_n}\right)^2}$$

(A7)

where $\cos \alpha_x$, $\cos \alpha_y$, and $\cos \alpha_z$ are the direction cosines of the normal to the original surface oriented to the direction of shear.

APPENDIX 2

Simultaneous Shear Deformation and Diffusion

Consider a rectangular parallelapiped of volume V with initial length L_0 and surface area A_0 perpendicular to this length. If the surface area is

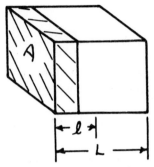

FIG. 3.A3. System for simultaneous shear and diffusion.

increased linearly with time,

$$A = A_o(1 + kt) \qquad k = \text{a constant (time}^{-1}) \qquad \text{(See Fig. 3.A3)}$$

$$t = \text{time}$$

If the volume remains constant,

$$L = \frac{V}{A} = \frac{L_o A_o}{A_o(1 + kt)} = \frac{L_o}{(1 + kt)}$$

Assume that the two components are oriented as shown in the figure. Defining the fractional distance from the left face to a point in the volume as

$$x = \frac{l}{L}$$

the diffusion equation becomes

$$\frac{\partial c}{\partial t} = D_V \frac{\partial^2 c}{\partial l^2} = \frac{D_V}{L^2} \frac{\partial^2 c}{\partial x^2} \qquad \text{(A8)}$$

where

$c = $ concentration at a point

$t = $ time

$l = $ distance from left face

$L = $ length of the volume

$x = $ fractional distance from left face

$D_V = $ diffusion coefficient

This relation is subject to the following conditions

Initial $\qquad\qquad\qquad\qquad\qquad c = 1; \qquad 0 \leq x < \theta$

$\qquad\qquad\qquad\qquad\qquad\qquad c = 0; \qquad \theta < x \leq 1$

Boundary: $\dfrac{\partial c}{\partial x} = 0; x = 0$ and $x = 1$

and

$$L = \frac{L_o}{(1 + kt)}$$

The solution of this problem is

$$(c - \theta) = \frac{2}{\pi} \sum_{q=1}^{\infty} \exp \left\{ \frac{-\pi^2 q^2 D_V ((1 + kt)^3 - 1)}{3L_o^2 k} \right\} \frac{\sin q\pi\theta}{q} \cos q\pi x \quad (A9)$$

The average square of the deviation from the average composition θ is

$$\sigma^2 = \frac{\displaystyle\int_0^1 (c - \theta)^2 \, dx}{\displaystyle\int_0^1 dx} = \int_0^1 \left[\frac{2}{\pi} \sum_{q=1}^{\infty} \exp \left\{ \frac{-\pi^2 q^2 D_V ((1 + kt)^3 - 1)}{3L_o^2 k} \right\} \right. \tag{A10}$$

$$\left. \frac{\sin q\pi\theta}{q} \cos q\pi x \right]^2 dx = \frac{2}{\pi^2} \sum_{q=1}^{\infty} \exp \left\{ \frac{-2\pi^2 q^2 D_V ((1 + kt)^3 - 1)}{3L_o^2 k} \right\} \frac{\sin^2 q\pi\theta}{q^2}$$

If kt is large compared with 1 (the usual case), and if

$$\frac{\pi^2 D_V k^2 t^3}{3L_o^2} > 1.0$$

all terms of the infinite series become negligible except the first. Taking the square root of the expression and dividing by the average composition, the intensity of segregation is obtained.

$$I = \frac{\sqrt{\sigma^2}}{\theta} = \sqrt{2} \exp \left\{ \frac{-\pi^2 D_V k^2 t^3}{3L_o^2} \right\} \frac{\sin \pi\theta}{\pi\theta} \tag{A11}$$

The time to mix to a desired intensity of segregation I_D is

$$t_M = \sqrt[3]{\frac{3L_o^2 \ln \left(\dfrac{\sqrt{2} \sin \pi\theta}{I_D \pi\theta} \right)}{\pi^2 D_V k^2}} \tag{A12}$$

The above calculation may be applied to systems previously considered by noting that $L_o = \frac{1}{2} r_o$, where r_o is the initial striation thickness. (See Fig. 3.A4.)

The previous relation for the increase of interfacial surface area with shear is

$$S = S_o \sqrt{1 - 2M \cos \alpha_x \cos \alpha_y + M^2 \cos^2 \alpha_x} \tag{A5}$$

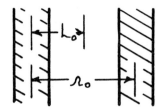

FIG. 3.A4. Relation of system dimension and striation thickness.

If M increases at a linear rate,

$$M = \left(\frac{du}{dr}\right)_{\text{avg}} t;$$

$$S = S_o \sqrt{1 - 2\left(\frac{du}{dr}\right) t \cos \alpha_x \cos \alpha_y + \left(\frac{du}{dr}\right)^2 t^2 \cos^2 \alpha_x}$$

For large values of $(du/dr)t$, the approximations may be made,

$$S \cong S_o\left(\frac{du}{dr} t \cos \alpha_x\right) \cong S_o\left(1 + \frac{du}{dr} t \cos \alpha_x\right) \cong A_o(1 + kt)$$

Therefore

$$k = \frac{du}{dr} \cos \alpha_x$$

The solution obtained is thus directly applicable to the case in which an average shear rate acts on a system for a period of time. The solution gives an indication of how the intensity of segregation will decrease with time as a function of initial striation thickness, shear rate, and diffusion coefficient. Presented in terms of the system geometry, the time to mix is

$$t_M = \sqrt[3]{\frac{3V^2\ln\left(\frac{\sqrt{2}\sin \theta\pi}{I_D\theta\pi}\right)}{\pi S_o^2 D_V \left(\frac{du}{dr} \cos \alpha_x\right)^2}} \tag{A13}$$

The above calculation assumed that the dimension of the sample taken was small with respect to the striation thickness at all times. If the sample dimension is of order of magnitude with the striation thickness, it may be shown that the intensity of segregation measured would be smaller as indicated by the expression

$$I_y = \frac{|\sin \pi y|}{\pi y} I \tag{A14}$$

where y is the number of striations contained in the sample and I is the intensity of segregation given in Eq. (A.11).

APPENDIX 3

Striation Thickness Resulting from Randomly Distributed Cubes

Assume that the initial mixture is formed of randomly distributed cubes with side L_1 in which the fraction of the minor component is θ. Assume that the mass of cubes is plasticated by heat, and focus attention on the effect of viscous shear on a single cube. (See Fig. 3.A5.)

$$s_{1_o} = s_{2_o} = s_{3_o} = s_2 = s_3 \;; \qquad \frac{s_1}{s_{1_o}} = \frac{L_1\sqrt{L_1^2 + (ML_1)^2}}{L_1^2} = \sqrt{1 + M^2} \cong M$$

The ratio of interfacial surface area to initial surface area is

$$\frac{S}{S_o} = \frac{2(s_1 + s_2 + s_3)}{6s_{1_o}} = \frac{1}{3}\left(\frac{s_1}{s_{1_o}} + \frac{s_2}{s_{2_o}} + \frac{s_3}{s_{3_o}}\right) \tag{A15}$$

$$\cong \tfrac{1}{3}(M + 1 + 1) \cong \tfrac{1}{3}M$$

The ratio of original surface area to volume of the system is

$$S_o/V = \frac{6L_1^2}{L_1^3/\theta} = \frac{6\theta}{L_1} \tag{A16}$$

Incorporating these relations with the expression for the average striation thickness,

$$r = \frac{2}{S/V} = \frac{2}{(S/S_o)(S_o/V)} \cong \frac{2}{\frac{1}{3}M\dfrac{6\theta}{L_1}} = \frac{L_1}{M\theta} \tag{A17}$$

The derivation assumes that no cubes of the minor component are touching, and therefore is limited to the case in which $\theta < 0.1$. The particular initial orientation of the cube should not affect the results for cases in which all three dimensions of the particles are of the same order of magnitude.

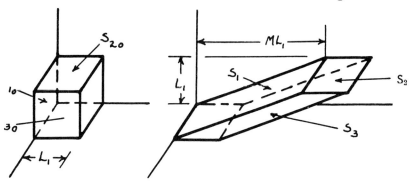

FIG. 3.A5. Cube of material under shear.

APPENDIX 4

Calculation of Mixing in Laminar Continuous-Flow System

As an example of the considerations and calculations which must be applied to a continuous mixer, consider laminar flow through a tube. Assume that a tube is 1 in. in diameter and 3 in. long, and that the feed consists of disks of alternate kinds of material 1 in. in diameter and 0.1 in. thick. The material fed is assumed to be solid to the point of entrance to the tube, becomes a Newtonian fluid in the tube, and leaves the tube as a solid rod 1 in. in diameter. The system is shown in Fig. 3.A6.

Owing to change in velocity profile on entrance and exit, the elements of material undergo tensile deformation on entrance and on exit. Owing to the viscous effect in the tube, the elements undergo shear deformation in the tube. Assume that for every element the mixing process may be divided into three steps—tensile, shear, tensile deformation.

The velocity at the inlet is

$$u_o = \frac{q}{\pi R_o^2}$$

q = volumetric throughput rate

The velocity as a function of radius in the tube is

$$u_1 = \frac{2q}{\pi R_1^2}\left(1 - \left(\frac{r_1}{R_1}\right)^2\right) = \frac{2q}{\pi R_1^2}(1 - \rho_1^2)$$

where $\rho_1 = r_1/R_1$ = reduced radius.

Define the coordinate system at a point in the tube as the axial direction $-x$; radial direction $-y$; circumferential direction $-z$. Noting that the flow is laminar, all material entering from the axis to r_o passes through the tube from the axis to r_1. These positions are related by

$$\frac{q\pi r_o^2}{\pi R_o^2} = \int_o^{r_1} u_1 2\pi r_1 \, dr_1 = \int_o^{r_1} 2\pi r_1 \left[\frac{2q}{\pi R_1^2}\left(1 - \left(\frac{r_1}{R_1}\right)^2\right)\right] dr,$$

$$\rho_o^2 = \rho_1^2(2 - \rho_1^2)$$

This relationship is presented graphically in Fig. 3.A7.

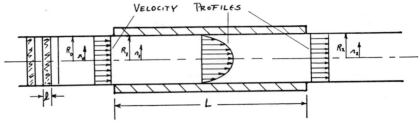

VELOCITY PROFILES

Fig. 3.A6. System in simple tube mixer.

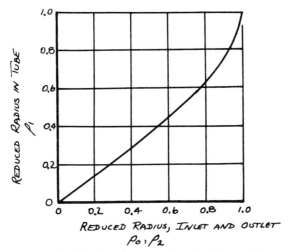

FIG. 3.A7. Reduced radius in tube *vs.* reduced radius on inlet and outlet.

The position of an element in Section 2 is the same as in Section 0.

$$\rho_0 = \rho_2$$

The tensile deformation in the x-direction on inlet is

$$X_o = \frac{u_1}{u_o} = \frac{\dfrac{2q}{\pi R_1^2}(1 - \rho_1^2)}{\dfrac{q}{\pi R_o^2}} = 2\left(\frac{R_o}{R_1}\right)^2 (1 - \rho_1^2)$$

The tensile deformation in the y-axis on inlet can be computed from the fact that the flow between laminae is the same.

$$\frac{q}{\pi R_o^2} \cdot 2\pi r_o \, dr_o = u_1 2\pi r_1 \, dr_1 = \frac{2q}{\pi R_1^2}(1 - \rho_1^2)2\pi r_1 \, dr_1$$

$$Y_o = \frac{dr_1}{dr_o} = \frac{\rho_0 R_1}{2R_o \rho_1(1 - \rho_1^2)}$$

The tensile deformation in the z-direction is

$$Z_o = \frac{2\pi r_1}{2\pi r_o} = \left(\frac{R_1}{R_o}\right)\frac{\rho_1}{\rho_o}$$

The shear rate at a point in the tube is

$$\frac{du_1}{dr_1} = -\frac{2q}{\pi R_1^2}\left(2\frac{\rho_1}{R_1}\right)$$

The amount of shear received by an element in the tube is

$$M_1 = \frac{\left(\dfrac{du_1}{dr_1}\right)L}{u_1} = \frac{-\dfrac{2q}{\pi R_1^2}\left(2\dfrac{\rho_1}{R_1}\right)L}{\dfrac{2q}{\pi R_1^2}(1 - \rho_1^2)} = \frac{-2L\rho_1}{R_1(1 - \rho_1^2)}$$

The tensile deformations at the outlet of the tube are calculated in a similar manner.

$$X_1 = \frac{(R_1/R_2)^2}{2(1 - \rho_1^2)}; \qquad Y_1 = \frac{2\rho_1 R_2(1 - \rho_1^2)}{\rho_2 R_1}; \qquad Z_1 = \frac{\rho_2}{\rho_1}\left(\frac{R_2}{R_1}\right)$$

From the initial orientation of the interfacial surface with respect to the direction of shear,

$$\cos \alpha_x = 1, \qquad \cos \alpha_y = 0, \qquad \cos \alpha_z = 0$$

From Eq. A7,

$$\begin{aligned}
\frac{S}{S_o} &= \sqrt{\left(\frac{\cos \alpha_x}{X_o X_1}\right)^2 + \left(\frac{\cos \alpha_y}{Y_o Y_1} - \frac{\cos \alpha_x}{X_o X_1}\left[M_1\frac{X_1}{Y_1}\right]\right)^2 + \left(\frac{\cos \alpha_z}{Z_o Z_1}\right)^2} \\
&= \sqrt{\left(\frac{R_2}{R_o}\right)^4 + \frac{L^2 R_1^4 \rho_2^2}{4R_o^4 R_2^2(1 - \rho_1^2)^6}}
\end{aligned}$$

For the problem given,

$$R_o = R_1 = R_2; \qquad L = 6R_1$$

$$\frac{S}{S_o} = \sqrt{1 + 9\frac{\rho_2^2}{(1 - \rho_1^2)^6}}; \qquad \rho_2^2 = \rho_1^2(2 - \rho_1^2)$$

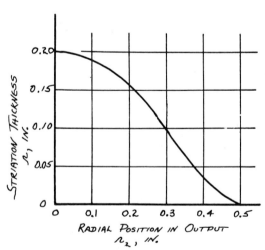

Fig. 3.A8. Resulting striation thickness *vs.* radial position in output.

The initial interfacial surface to volume ratio is

$$\frac{S_o}{V} = \frac{2\pi R_o^2}{2\pi R_o^2 l} = \frac{1}{l} \qquad l = \text{disk thickness}$$

Therefore,

$$r = \frac{2}{S/V} = \frac{2}{(S/S_o)(S_o/V)} = \frac{2}{\sqrt{1 + 9\dfrac{\rho_2^2}{(1 - \rho_1^2)^6}}\dfrac{1}{l}} = \frac{2l}{\sqrt{1 - 9\dfrac{\rho_2^2}{(1 - \rho_1^2)}}}$$

A plot of the striation thickness as a function of radius at the outlet is presented in Fig. 3.A8. The striation thickness at the center is unchanged from the starting material, while at the outer edge the striation thickness goes to zero. For transparent materials or if the product were to be sectioned, the mixing would appear unsatisfactory to the eye. With sufficiently opaque materials for use of the product as a rod, the mixing attained could be quite satisfactory.

APPENDIX 5

Calculation of Effectiveness of Continuous-Flow Blender

Consider the case in which the inlet concentration to a perfect mixer fluctuates sinusoidally with amplitude δ_{i_M} about the mean value with a period of T_P minutes.

$$\delta_i(t) = \delta_{iM} \cos \frac{2\pi t}{T_P}$$

The variance of the inlet concentration is

$$\sigma_i^2 = \overline{\delta_i^2} = \frac{1}{T_P} \int_o^{T_P} \left[\delta_{iM} \cos \frac{2\pi t}{T_P} \right]^2 dt = \frac{\delta_{iM}^2}{2}$$

The normalized autocorrelation of the input is

$$\phi_{ii}(\tau) = \frac{\overline{\delta_i(t)\delta_i(t + \tau)}}{\sigma_i^2} = \frac{\dfrac{1}{T_P} \displaystyle\int_o^{T_P} \delta_{iM} \cos \dfrac{2\pi t}{T_P} \, \delta_{iM} \cos \dfrac{2\pi(t + \tau)}{T_P} \, dt}{\delta_{iM}^2/2}$$

$$= \cos \frac{2\pi\tau}{T_P}$$

If the mixer is a perfect mixer, following a step change in the input

$$\frac{\delta_o}{\delta_i} = [1 - e^{-(qt/V)}] = F(t)$$

The distribution of residence times is

$$E(t) = \frac{dF(t)}{dt} = \frac{q}{V} e^{-(qt/V)}$$

Applying these results to Eq. 27,

$$\frac{\sigma_o{}^2}{\sigma_i{}^2} = 2 \int_{t=0}^{\infty} \int_{\tau=0}^{\infty} \cos \frac{2\pi\tau}{T_P} \left(\frac{q}{V} e^{-(qt/V)} \right) \left(\frac{q}{V} e^{-(q(t+\tau)/V)} \right) dt \, d\tau$$

$$= \frac{1}{1 + \left(\dfrac{2\pi V}{qT_P} \right)^2}$$

The ratio of the outlet to the inlet variance for a sinusoidally varying inlet concentration to a perfect mixer depends upon the flow rate, the holdup volume of the vessel, and the period of the fluctuation.

If the desired ratio of variances $(\sigma_o{}^2/\sigma_i{}^2)_D$ is known, the necessary volume of mixer required to achieve this is

$$V = \sqrt[2]{\frac{1}{(\sigma_o{}^2/\sigma_i{}^2)_D} - 1} \frac{qT_P}{2\pi}$$

NOMENCLATURE

A Surface area.

c Concentration, mass or moles per unit volume, or number fraction.

$\bar{c}$ Estimate of population concentration.

C Statistical coefficient of variation.

d Differential operator.

du/dr Shear rate.

D Diameter.

D_V Molecular or particle diffusivity.

f Number of statistical degrees of freedom.

F Force or shearing force.

I Intensity of segregation.

K Fluid consistency index $[\tau = K(du/dr)^n]$.

l Distance in length direction.

L Length of a pipe or tube.

M Amount of shear deformation.

n Flow behavior index (exponent in the power-law relation of viscosity).

       Number of particles in a sample.

N Number of samples taken.

P Power.

       Probability.

q	Flow rate (of fluid, volumetric).
Q	Integral or finite quantity of heat or fluid.
r	Lineal or radial distance.
	Scale of segregation expressed as average striation thickness.
R	Radius of round tube.
$s^2, \hat{s}^2$	Estimate of the statistical variance.
S	Cross-sectional area for flow.
	Interfacial surface area.
t	Time.
T	Temperature.
u	Local velocity.
u^*	Displacement distance.
u_P	Number of standard deviations from the mean, below which lies the fraction P of the normal distribution.
V	Volume.
x	Distance along path.
	Number of minor fraction particles in sample.
X	Multiplier for tensile deformation in x-direction.
y	Distance normal to path.
	Number of striations intersected by sample.
Y	Multiplier for tensile deformation in y-direction.
z	Distance normal to x-y plane.
Z	Multiplier for tensile deformation in z-direction.
α	Direction angle.
∂	Partial differential operator.
δ	Deviation from mean concentration.
η	Efficiency.
θ	Fraction or probability of minor component.
ρ	Density.
σ^2	Statistical variance.
τ	Shear stress.
χ^2	Statistical parameter.

REFERENCES

1. Adams, J. F. E., and Baker, A. G., *Trans. Instn. Chem. Engrs.* (*London*), **34**, 91 (1956).
2. Blumberg, R., and Maritz, J. S., *Chem. Eng. Sci.*, **2**, 240 (1953).
3. Bolen, W. R., and Colwell, R. E., paper given at meeting of Soc. Plastics Engrs., January, 1958.
4. Buslik, D., *ASTM Bull.*, **165**, 66 (1950).
5. Danckwerts, P. V., and Sellers, E. S., *Ind. Chemist*, **27**, 395 (1951).
6. Danckwerts, P. V., *Appl. Sci. Research*, **A3**, 279 (1952).
7. Danckwerts, P. V., *Chem. Eng. Sci.*, **2**, 1 (1953).
8. Gray, J. B., *Chem. Eng. Progr.*, **53**, 25J (1957).

9. Greathead, J. A. A., and Simmonds, W. H. C., *Chem. Eng. Progr.*, **53,** 194 (1957).
10. Hald, A., "Statistical Tables and Formulas," New York, John Wiley & Sons, Inc., 1952.
11. Hald, A., "Statistical Theory with Engineering Applications," New York, John Wiley & Sons, Inc., 1952.
12. Lacey, P. M. C., *J. Appl. Chem. (London)*, **4,** 257 (1954).
13. McAdams, W. H., "Heat Transmission," New York, McGraw-Hill Book Company, Inc., 1954.
14. Michaels, A. S., and Puzinauskas, V., *Chem. Eng. Progr.*, **50,** 604 (1954).
15. Mohr, W. D., Saxton, R. L., and Jepson, C. H., *Ind. Eng. Chem.*, **49,** 1855 (1957).
16. Quillen, C. S., *Chem. Eng.*, **61,** 177 (1954).
17. Spencer, R. S., and Wiley, R. M., *J. Colloid Sci.*, **6,** 133 (1951).
18. Weidenbaum, S. S., and Bonilla, C. F., *Chem. Eng. Progr.*, **51,** 27 (1955).

Section II

Applications

4. EXTRUSION

J. B. Paton, B. S.   CHAPTER COORDINATOR; INTRODUCTION

P. H. Squires, Ph. D.   EXTRUSION THEORY;
DESIGN OF MELT AND
PLASTICATING EXTRUDERS

W. H. Darnell, Ph. D.   THEORY OF SOLIDS CONVEYING;
DESIGN OF PLASTICATING EXTRUDERS

F. M. Cash, B. S.   TAKE-OFF EQUIPMENT

Polychemicals Department, E. I. du Pont de Nemours & Co., Inc.

The Section on Die Design was prepared by:

J. F. Carley, Ph. D.

Modern Plastics Magazine, Breskin Publications, Inc.

INTRODUCTION TO EXTRUSION

Description of the Extrusion Process

Extrusion may be defined as the act of shaping a material by forcing it through a die. This definition, as applied to the extrusion of thermoplastic materials, covers two general processes—screw extrusion and ram extrusion.

Extrusion of the first themoplastic material dates to 1870 when cellulose nitrate was extruded as a rod by means of a hydraulic ram. Screw extruders were first used for thermoplastics extrusion in the early 1930's. The first machines were adaptations of rubber extruders.

Thermoplastics are extruded predominantly through screw extruders; more specifically, through single-screw extruders (Fig. 4.1). The major portion of this chapter concerns the analysis of plastic flow through single-

(*Courtesy National Rubber Machinery Co.*)
FIG. 4.1. Six in. diameter, electrically heated, single-screw extruder with cable-covering crosshead.

screw extruders and the application of this information to screw and die design.

The ram extrusion process is not used extensively for plastics extrusion and is therefore described only briefly. In this process the plastic is extruded through a die by the direct force of a ram on a reservoir of material. It is used for the extrusion of some types of fluorocarbons and for thermally sensitive materials such as cellulose nitrate.

Extrusion is employed in the production of plastic films, pipes, sheet, profiles, and coatings on wire, paper, and other substrates. Extruders are also used for compounding, mixing, and conveying in resin manufacturing operations.

Modern screw extruders are expected to be truly pulse-free pumps which deliver a thermally homogeneous melt at a uniform and high rate. To achieve this control of the extrusion process requires a sound understanding of the functions and operation of these machines. This chapter describes some of the basic studies and technical developments which have been carried out to obtain this fundamental understanding of extruder design and operation.

Elements of an Extruder

Single-Screw Extruders. The elements of a typical single-screw extruder are shown in Fig. 4.2. The plastic material is fed from a hopper through the feed throat into the channel of the screw. The screw rotates in a barrel which has a hardened liner. The screw is driven by a motor through

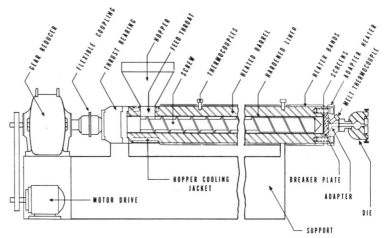

Fig. 4.2. Elements of an extruder.

a gear reducer, and the rearward thrust of the screw is absorbed by a thrust bearing. Heat is applied to the barrel from external heaters, and the temperature is measured by thermocouples. As the plastic granules are conveyed along the screw channel, they are melted. The melt is forced through a breaker plate which, in some cases, supports a screenpack. The melt then flows through the adapter and through the die.

The size of single-screw extruders is described by the inside diameter of the barrel. Common extruder sizes are 1, $1\frac{1}{4}$, $1\frac{1}{2}$, 2, $2\frac{1}{2}$, $3\frac{1}{4}$, $3\frac{1}{2}$, $4\frac{1}{2}$, 6, and 8 in. Larger machines are made on a custom basis. Their capacities range from about 5 lb/hr for the 1-in.-diameter unit to approximately 1,000 lb/hr for 8-in.-diameter machines.

A list of commercial machine manufacturers is given in the *Modern Plastics Encyclopedia.*[49]

A more detailed review of the functions of various extruder elements will be helpful in understanding their design.

The Feed Throat. Extruder feed throats may be of rectangular or circular cross section and may have vertical or sloped sides. The feed throat may meet the screw tangentially or, in some instances, may be undercut. Several types are shown in Fig. 4.3. For rubber and rubberlike materials which are fed to the extruders as strips, an undercut feed throat is commonly employed. This type of throat is not suited for use with a pelletized molding powder, because pellets tend to wedge between the screw lands and the barrel wall.

The feed-throat opening generally is made at least one screw diameter in length.

The Screw. The heart of the extruder is the screw. Its function is to con-

VERTICAL FEED THROAT   SLOPED FEED THROAT   UNDERCUT FEED THROAT

FIG. 4.3. Extruder feed throats.

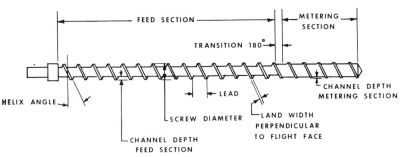

FIG. 4.4. Metering screw.

vey unplasticated resin from the hopper and deliver it to the die at a uniform rate, and as a homogeneous melt.

The functional sections of a widely used screw are shown in Fig. 4.4. This is a rapid-transition, metering-type screw. The channel depth is greatest in the feed section. In the transition the channel depth changes through an involute spiral to the depth of the metering section.

The cross-sectional area of the screw channel decreases toward the die to compensate for the change in bulk density and differences in the conveying efficiency for solid and molten plastics. This change in cross-sectional area is accomplished by reducing the channel depth, the pitch, or both.

Other common extruder screw designs are shown in Fig. 4.5.

The Barrel. The barrel provides one of the surfaces for imparting shear to the plastic and the surface through which external heat is applied to the polymer. Long barrels for plastic extruders are desirable. They provide a greater heat-transfer area and additional opportunity for mixing, resulting in greater melt uniformity.

The length-to-diameter ratio of extruders is an important design specification. This ratio is the effective length of the machine (from the rear of the

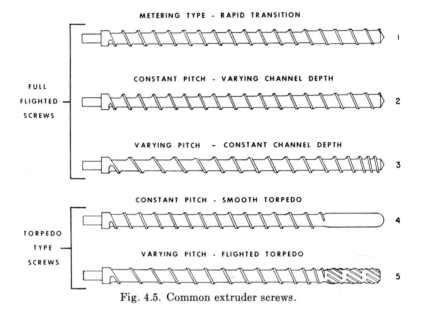

METERING TYPE - RAPID TRANSITION

CONSTANT PITCH - VARYING CHANNEL DEPTH

FULL FLIGHTED SCREWS

VARYING PITCH - CONSTANT CHANNEL DEPTH

CONSTANT PITCH - SMOOTH TORPEDO

TORPEDO TYPE SCREWS

VARYING PITCH - FLIGHTED TORPEDO

Fig. 4.5. Common extruder screws.

feed hopper to the breaker plate) divided by the nominal diameter (inside diameter of the barrel). Length-to-diameter $\left(\dfrac{L}{D}\right)$ ratios for thermoplastics extruders normally are between 16:1 and 24:1.

Extruder barrels may be heated electrically, either by resistance or induction heaters, or by means of jackets through which oil or other heat-transfer media are circulated.

Electric heating of the barrel offers the advantages of rapid response, zone control, and operating temperatures beyond the range of oil heat. Electric resistance heaters can be made in a wide range of sizes, shapes, and watt densities. Electrically heated barrels may be cooled by the use of blowers, cooling water, mist, or a vapor-condensing system.[74]

Heating of jacketed barrels by means of heat-transfer fluids permits heat transfer to the plastic material being processed as well as efficient heat removal from the resin. Heat removal becomes important if the resin tends to overheat owing to excessive mechanical working in the screw channel.

The control of barrel temperatures is described in a later portion of this chapter.

Multiple-Screw Extruders. Some commercial extruders are manufactured with multiple screws. Usually these are twin-screw extruders, but some are made with three or more screws. The multiple-screw extruder may be of an intermeshing or a nonintermeshing type. Screws which rotate in the same direction must be of the same hand (direction of flight). Conversely, screws which rotate in opposite directions must be of opposing hand.

Extruders with intermeshing screws tend to operate as positive-displacement pumps, and their output is relatively independent of back pressure. However, they consume less energy than single-screw machines, and their plasticating capacity is more dependent upon heat transfer from external heaters. Nonintermeshing screws are usually made to rotate in opposing directions. Twin-screw extruders of this design are frequently equipped with vent zones and find application in resin compounding and devolatilization.

Multiple-screw extruders are described further by Baigent[5] and by Fischer.[29]

Summary of Simplified Extruder Operation

The following discussion is designed to give to the casual reader a brief summation of the most important flow patterns which influence extruder performance. The theoretical analysis which forms the basis for these conclusions, and a more thorough and quantitative treatment follow in later sections of this chapter.

In the conventional single-screw plasticating extruder, the plastic is conveyed in three states: first, as a particulate solid, then as a mixture of melt and solid, and finally, as a melt.

In a metering-type screw the metering section in which the polymer is pumped as a melt is the simplest to analyze, because in this zone the laws of viscous flow apply.[8] The metering section is important to the extruder, because it usually determines the output characteristics of the machine.

In the metering section, three major flow components exist: *Drag flow* is the forward conveying action produced by the relative motion between the screw and the cylinder. *Pressure flow* may be thought of as a backflow down the screw channel caused by pressure in the head of the extruder.

The third flow component is *leakage flow*. The back pressure at the die and the resultant difference in pressure between successive turns of the thread cause a backward leakage between the land and the barrel. Usually this leakage flow is only a small fraction of the other flows and may be neglected.

The output of the metering section is the drag flow minus the pressure flow and the leakage flow.

Drag Flow. Drag flow is the forward conveying action produced by the relative motion between the screw and the cylinder. This can be illustrated very simply by considering an extruder which contains no restriction following the metering section. There are no screen packs or die, and the stock is allowed to drop out of the screw at the extruder head. Then the "die pressure" is zero, and there is no pressure flow. The material will be conveyed by the action of the flight upon the material being sheared between the stationary surface of the barrel and the moving surface at the root of the screw channel. Drag flow is merely a volumetric forward displacement of the material in the screw channel. The major factors which influence this drag-flow capacity are channel depth, channel width, screw speed, and screw diameter.

Pressure Flow. Pressure flow is caused by pressure in the head of the extruder and has been referred to as a backflow down the extruder channel. To illustrate this type of flow, assume that the screw is stationary, but that there is a melt under pressure at the die. Under these hypothetical conditions the screw channel will act like a very long rectangular orifice, and the melt will travel backward down the helical channel, forced by the pressure at the die. In actual operation, however, pressure flow is only a reaction to drag flow, caused by a die restriction and pressure in the die head. There is never any net flow rearward along the screw axis. It becomes apparent that pressure flow is influenced by these principal factors: channel depth, channel width, extruder diameter, metering-section length, melt viscosity, and back pressure.

Extruder Performance Characteristics. The principal flow patterns which contribute to the output of the extruder screw have now been illustrated. An understanding of these flow patterns within the extruder makes it possible to predict the general performance characteristics of different screw designs under varying conditions.

For example, Fig. 4.6 shows output vs. head-pressure characteristics of three screws with different metering sections operating under identical conditions (same screw speed and resin viscosity, and assuming Newtonian

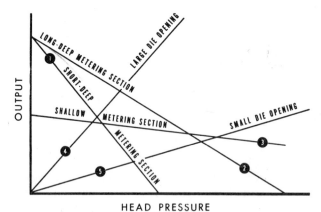

FIG. 4.6. Screw and die characteristics.

behavior and isothermal conditions). Discharge characteristics of a large-orifice and a small-orifice die are shown on the same graph.

A screw with a deep metering section would have an output vs. head-pressure characteristic like the one shown in Line 1. The output of such a screw at "open discharge" (zero head pressure) would be high, because the deep channel causes a very high drag-flow capacity. At the same time, the output of this screw is very sensitive to head pressure, since the deep channel constitutes a very large orifice through which pressure flow can take place. This accounts for the rapid decrease in delivery as back pressure increases.

Line 2 shows the discharge characteristic of the same deep-channel screw as in Line 1, but with a longer metering section. The drag flow at zero pressure or "open discharge" is unchanged, but the effect of back pressure is reduced through the additional channel length in the metering section.

If the screw had a shallow metering section (Line 3), the output at zero back pressure ("open discharge") would be reduced, because the drag-flow capacity of a screw is in proportion to its channel depth. At the same time the output of the screw would be much less sensitive to changes in back pressure, because the shallow channel provides a very much greater restriction to pressure flow.

When a Newtonian fluid is extruded, changes in screw speed would result in parallel displacement of these lines. Changes in resin viscosity would produce changes in the slopes.

Lines 4 and 5 merely indicate the discharge characteristics of a large and a small die opening, plotted on the same coordinates. At zero head pressure, there is no flow through either orifice. As the head pressure generated by the screw is built up, the flow (output) of the die orifices increases. The flow through the larger orifice increases faster than the flow through the small one.

The intercept of the appropriate die and screw characteristics constitutes the operating point of a given extruder screw-die combination.

Power Consumption and Mechanically Generated Heat in the Extrudate. In the preceding analysis, only volumetric displacement of the material being extruded has been covered. The power requirements and temperature changes during the extrusion process have not been considered.

In any melt-extrusion operation, the relative motion between the screw and the barrel wall causes shearing of the material in the screw channel. The power consumed in shearing the polymer is converted into heat and contributes to the temperature rise of the resin. The amount of heat thus generated in the resin increases as the screw channel is made shallower or longer, and as the screw speed is increased.

The flow properties of the polymer constitute another factor which exerts an important influence on the amount of heat generated owing to mechanical working of the resin. High melt viscosities and a low dependence of viscosity on temperature contribute to increased power consumption and raise the amount of heat generated within the plastic during the extrusion process.

The amount of heat generated in the resin through mechanical working can also be increased by reducing the die opening. A more severe die restriction raises the head pressure, reduces the output per turn of the screw, and consequently exposes the resin to a greater amount of shear.

This explains how restrictions to flow in the discharge of the extruder, such as screenpacks and valves, can be used to increase the temperature of the extrudate and the amount of mixing to which the polymer is exposed in the screw channel. It will be apparent that these devices will find application primarily with deep-flighted screws which may do an inadequate mixing job unless the additional restriction is used, and in which a given increase in head pressure will produce a relatively large reduction in output.

In the preceding paragraphs, some of the most important interrelationships of extrusion variables have been outlined in qualitative terms. To analyze the performance of extrusion equipment, however, a quantitative evaluation of these variables is indispensable.

To cite only one example: It may occur that at relatively high screw speeds the metering section of a screw runs starved, because the capacity of the feed and transition zones to deliver melted polymer may be less than the pumping capacity of the metering section. The melting capacity, in certain instances, may depend largely upon the heat-transfer capacity of the barrel wall. Higher speeds in these cases will not increase the melting capacity of the feed and transition section very much, while the pumping capacity of the metering section goes up directly with screw speed. As a consequence, the capacity of the feed and transition section may limit the output of the machine. Under such conditions, surging and uneven extrusion may result.

An accurate calculation of the actual capacity of the metering zone under the given operating conditions would tell whether or not this section of the screw was indeed being starved, and whether the above hypothesis was correct. The example illustrates the fact that problems encountered in the operation and the design of extruders require a precise and quantitative understanding of the performance of the various functional sections of the screw. A subsequent portion of this chapter will provide the tools required to solve practical extruder design and operating problems on such a quantitative basis.

Extruders for Special Purposes

Devolatilizing Extruders. In many extrusion operations it is necessary to process polymers which contain volatiles in the form of moisture, solvents, or adsorbed gases. Unless these volatiles are removed before the resin leaves the die opening, bubbles in the extrudate will result.

Two approaches have been used to remove volatiles from the resin being processed. In the more conventional method, a vent port is provided in the barrel wall (Fig. 4.7).

In the other method described by Bernhardt,[10] the volatiles are extracted through a hole drilled into the bottom of the screw channel to the hollow core of the screw. The gases are then withdrawn through a rotary union at the rear of the screw.

In both methods the extraction of volatiles takes place in a zone of the screw in which the channel is only partially filled.

Figure 4.8 shows a sketch of the vented screw, in which the volatiles are removed through the core of the screw. The screw has essentially four functional zones, as follows.

Feed Zone. The feed zone has a deep channel of high conveying capacity. In this zone the granular polymer is heated and melted. Slots, approximately $\frac{1}{2}$ in. wide and approximately 180 deg apart, may be cut into the last flights of this section, as shown in Figs. 4.7 and 4.8, to prevent the build-up of excessive pressure in the feed zone. This feature helps to pre-

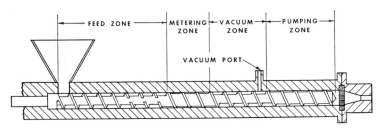

Fig. 4.7. Vented barrel extruder.

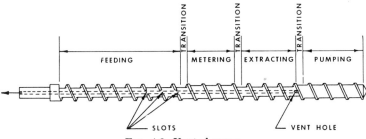

FIG. 4.8. Vented screw.

vent forward surges past the metering section into the following zones of the screw.

Metering Zone. The metering zone governs the flow from the feed zone and determines the output rate of the extruder. It has the shallowest channel.

Extraction Zone. The extraction zone is usually about four times as deep as the metering section, and, since it is being fed from a screw section of smaller conveying capacity, it will run starved. As a result, only a portion of the channel in front of the leading flight face will be filled, and volatiles can separate behind the trailing flight face. The performance of partially filled screw channels is considered later (pp. 186–189). The extraction port is drilled behind the trailing flight face in the last flight of the extraction zone. A small stack, approximately one half as high as the channel depth, may be placed over the hole to prevent seepage of resin into the vent.

Pumping Zone. The pumping zone must generate sufficient pressure to force the extrudate through the die. It must also have a pumping capacity greater than that of the metering zone, so that the extraction zone will not become flooded. The optimum channel depth of this section is 50 per cent deeper than that of the metering section.

In vented barrel extruders (Fig. 4.7), screw designs similar to the vented screw, except for omission of the vent hole, are commonly used. The barrel vent is usually placed near the forward end of the extraction zone and must be carefully contoured to avoid holdup of resin. In some screw designs for vented barrels, the metering section is replaced with throttling devices to regulate the flow into the extraction zone.

Mixing Extruders. Extruders are frequently used as compounding and mixing devices for thermoplastics. Many special mixing heads have been designed as extensions of ordinary screws to improve the homogenizing action of the extruder. Two of these are shown in Fig. 4.5, Screws 4 and 5. Other devices employing rotating disks and gears have been used. Mixing in single-screw extruders is covered in detail in Chap. 7 of this text.

Extruders for Intermittent Discharge. It has long been recognized that extruders are able to plasticate more material and achieve more uniform melt temperatures than can injection-molding cylinders of the same size. Consequently, many attempts have been made to convert extruders into intermittent-discharge devices so that they may be applied in molding operations.

A number of machines have been designed in which ordinary extruders are operated intermittently to pump plastic melt either directly into one or more molds or into a secondary injection cylinder.[1, 2]

Extruders have also been equipped with manifolds leading to two or more valves. The valves are operated on automatic cycles, so that at least one valve is always open. This technique finds application in the manufacture of plastic bottles. It is described in Chap. 9.

Intermittent discharge can be achieved using extruder screws which may rotate continuously and which reciprocate in a stationary barrel. When the discharge is stopped, the rotating screw gradually retracts and accumulates melt in the front of the barrel. This material is pushed through the die opening on the next portion of the cycle when the screw is returned to its forward position by hydraulic pressure.[7, 73]

In another method for achieving intermittent discharge, a standard extruder with a continuously rotating screw is used. An automatically actuated shutoff valve at the extruder head opens and closes on a controlled cycle, and shots of controlled weight and temperature are ejected. Special screw designs must be used which prevent the build-up of excessive heat and pressure while the valve is closed.[11]

DEVELOPMENT OF SCREW-EXTRUDER FLOW EQUATIONS

Introduction

Screw extruders are normally, but not necessarily, used for the extrusion of materials having relatively high viscosities. Indeed, the screw melt pump can generate pressure only because of the existence of a finite viscosity in the fluid being pumped. The principle of operation is thus distinctly different from that encountered in centrifugal, reciprocating, or gear pumps. For this reason, some early workers have referred to screw pumps as "screw viscosity pumps."[61]

Because of the high fluid viscosity, the flow in a screw pump is invariably laminar rather than turbulent. The well-known equations for conservation of mass, energy, and momentum in a laminar system,[54] along with equations describing the physical state of the material being pumped, can thus be used to describe the operation of a screw pump. As is inevitably the situation in a complex flow system, the attainment of the idealized general solution to these equations is exceedingly difficult. Continuing advances in the technology of high-speed computing and in the understanding of the flow behavior of fluids bring such a general solution closer to the realm of reality. For the time being, however, we must be content with solutions of restricted applicability as defined by necessary simplifying assumptions. Fortunately, these assumptions have been found not to restrict severely the utility of the results in many instances, and useful working extrusion equations have been developed.

Schematic Representation of a Single-Screw Extruder

The unique and somewhat complex geometric system that is encountered in the analysis of the hydraulics of a screw extruder makes it imperative that a clear picture be obtained of the system model and reference axes. A schematic diagram of a screw pump is shown in Fig. 4.9. For the sake of generality, a screw having two channels is illustrated. Although single-flighted screws are most commonly used, the working extrusion equations will be developed in a form applicable to a screw having any number n of channels. In most instances, multiple channels can be viewed simply as individual single channels operating in parallel.

It is not difficult to demonstrate, and indeed it is perhaps intuitively obvious, that it makes no difference whether the screw is assumed to rotate within a stationary barrel or the barrel is assumed to rotate about a stationary screw. An extruder will actually perform in an identical fashion, in all respects, in either mode of operation. Because of mechanical considerations, screw extruders are commonly made with a rotating screw. The visualization of screw performance is simplified, however, if the barrel is assumed to rotate about a stationary screw. If this viewpoint is taken, it becomes much easier to see that it is the material which tends to "rotate" with the barrel, rather than that which tends to adhere to the screw, that is being conveyed in the direction of the screw axis. For this reason, the convention of a rotating barrel will be adopted where convenient.

In Fig. 4.9, the x, y, z, and auxiliary l reference axes are stationary and are superimposed on the screw with positive directions as noted. The z-axis is directed along the screw helix and the l-axis along the screw length. The helix angle, i.e., the angle between the flight face and a plane normal to the screw axis, increases from a minimum at the screw crest to a maximum at the screw root. The helix angle is given by $\phi = \arctan \dfrac{t}{\pi D}$ where the diameter D could be measured at any depth within the channel. Although argu-

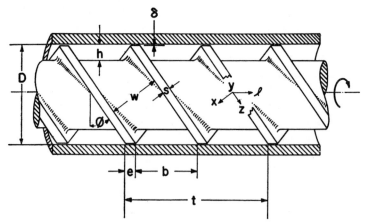

FIG. 4.9. Single-screw extruder (Double flighted).

ments can be raised for using helix angles as measured at different depths depending on the particular proposed use, the crest or minimum helix angle will be used throughout this discussion. The difference between the crest and root helix angle is small for shallow-channel screws.

Considerable simplification will result if the curvature of the channel around the screw axis is ignored. If this is done, the screw channel can figuratively be unrolled and laid out flat, as illustrated in Fig. 4.10. The barrel is now visualized as an infinitely wide flat plate which slides across the unrolled channels in the direction perpendicular to the screw axis. This simplification of the model does result in some error and ambiguity as to the proper diameter to be used in certain of the calculations. This is of little consequence for shallow-channel screws but can become appreciable for deeper-channel screws. An approximate method for accounting for this channel curvature effect will be presented.

The circumferential velocity of the barrel U_c can be resolved into the two perpendicular components U_z and U_x, which are directed respectively along and across the screw channel. In a similar fashion the fluid velocity at any point within the channel is described by the perpendicular components v_z and v_x. In order to maintain the mass continuity required to sustain the transverse flow v_x it is obvious that a fluid velocity in the y direction, v_y, must exist, particularly near the front and rear flight faces where the circulating fluid is "turned under or over," as the case may be. Inasmuch as this serves to distort only the transverse velocity component v_x, the effect will be ignored, and v_y will be assumed to be zero at all times. As will be

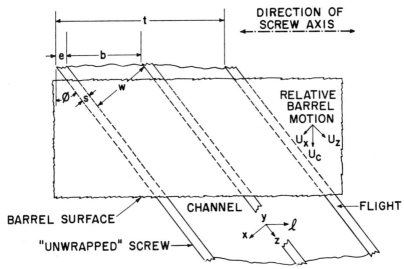

FIG. 4.10. Flat-plate model of a double-flighted single-screw extruder.

seen, the transverse fluid velocity does not contribute directly to the screw pumping capacity. The error introduced in flow calculations by neglecting v_y will thus be small.

Since the consequences of the existence of a down-channel velocity v_z and transverse-channel velocity v_x are quite dissimilar, it is convenient to treat these flow components separately. Simplification of the mathematics also results.

Because of their basic significance, the equations which describe the flow patterns in a screw channel will be developed in some detail. By so doing, the implications of some underlying assumptions are made more obvious.

Velocity Distribution in Channel

Distribution Along Screw Helix (z-Axis). The general expression for conservation of momentum,[54] or the "equation of motion" as it is commonly called, can be used as a starting point for establishing the flow patterns and volumetric flow rates in an extruder screw channel. If laminar steady-state flow of an incompressible isotropic fluid is considered, the equation of motion for flow in the z direction reduces to

$$\frac{\partial p}{\partial z} = \mu\left(\frac{\partial^2 v_z}{\partial x^2} + \frac{\partial^2 v_z}{\partial y^2}\right) + \left(\frac{\partial v_z}{\partial x}\right)\left(\frac{\partial \mu}{\partial x}\right) + \left(\frac{\partial v_z}{\partial y}\right)\left(\frac{\partial \mu}{\partial y}\right) \qquad (1)$$

In this expression the viscosity may be a function of the position within the channel by virtue of the particular temperature or shear rate which exists at that position. In other words, Eq. (1) is not restricted to the flow of Newtonian fluids, nor is it restricted to isothermal flow.

Normally, there is very little variation in viscosity in the cross-channel or x direction, since both the fluid temperature level and the shear rate do not vary appreciably from one side of the channel to the other. The partial derivative $\left(\frac{\partial \mu}{\partial x}\right)$ can thus safely be assumed equal to zero in Eq. (1), which can now be written as

$$\frac{\partial p}{\partial z} = \mu\left(\frac{\partial^2 v_z}{\partial x^2} + \frac{\partial^2 v_z}{\partial y^2}\right) + \left(\frac{\partial v_z}{\partial y}\right)\left(\frac{\partial \mu}{\partial y}\right) \qquad (2)$$

Equation (2), for all practical purposes, is valid for describing the flow of a non-Newtonian fluid in a screw channel under nonisothermal conditions. A general analytic solution of Eq. (2) would be extremely complex and to date has not been obtained. Useful solutions to Eq. (2) have been obtained, however, for certain special cases of screw-channel geometry, fluid-viscosity behavior, and method of extruder operation, viz., isothermal and adiabatic operation. These are of sufficient scope so that, in most instances, they will be found to bracket closely the particular situation of interest and will provide a firm basis for predicting and analyzing screw pump performance.

If, for the time being, the fluid viscosity is assumed to be uniform across the depth of the screw channel, the last term in Eq. (2) vanishes, since $\left(\dfrac{\partial \mu}{\partial y}\right)$ equals zero. This situation implies that the screw is neutral, i.e., is neither heated nor cooled to such an extent that the viscosity of the nearby fluid is affected. Also, the rate of heat transfer from the barrel wall is implied to be sufficiently low so that the fluid viscosity near the barrel wall may be assumed to equal that near the screw root. (Removal of these restrictions will be discussed later.) Note that no restrictions have been placed on the variation of fluid viscosity along the length of the screw channel, i.e., in the z direction.

With the above restriction, Eq. (2) now becomes

$$\frac{\partial p}{\partial z} = \mu \left(\frac{\partial^2 v_z}{\partial x^2} + \frac{\partial^2 v_z}{\partial y^2} \right) \tag{3}$$

The solution to this equation satisfying the boundary conditions found in screw pumps has been presented variously by Boussinesq,[16] Maillefer,[46] Rowell and Finlayson,[61] Strub,[68] Pigott,[58] and Carley and Strub.[22] The form in which the solution is presented is quite different in the case of each of the groups of authors. In 1955 Meskat[48] critically reviewed the results of these workers and demonstrated that their solutions are equivalent. In the following discussion the solution will be presented in a form believed to be more convenient than those used by the preceding authors.

Drag Flow. If the flow caused by the viscous drag of the barrel on the fluid, i.e., the drag flow, is considered for the present, the boundary conditions $v_z = 0$ at $x = 0$, $x = w$, $y = 0$ and $v_z = U_z$ at $y = h$ must be satisfied. Reference should be made to Fig. 4.11 for an expanded diagram of a channel cross section in which these boundary conditions are shown more clearly. When flow occurs by viscous drag only, $\partial p / \partial z$ is zero, and the desired result is the homogeneous solution to Eq. (3). The solution which satisfies the imposed boundary conditions is

$$v_{zd} = \frac{4U_z}{\pi} \sum_{g=1,3,5,\ldots}^{\infty} \frac{1}{g} \frac{\sinh g\pi(y/w)}{\sinh g\pi(h/w)} \sin g\pi(x/w) \tag{4}$$

The volumetric drag-flow rate in the z direction is obtained by integrating Eq. (4) over the cross section of the channel. Thus,

$$q_d = n \int_0^w \int_0^h v_z \, dx \, dy \tag{5}$$

where n is the number of parallel screw channels. The result has been ex-

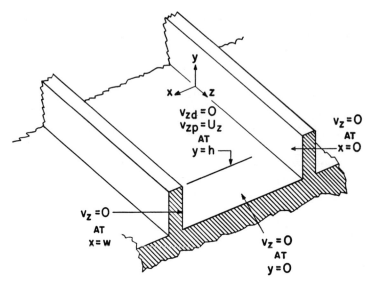

FIG. 4.11. Channel cross-section; Boundary conditions for drag and pressure flow.

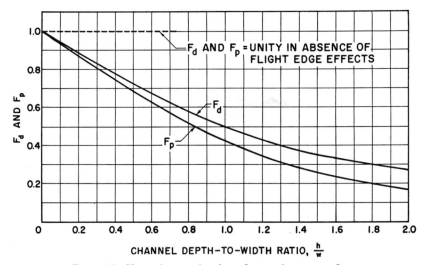

FIG. 4.12. Shape factors for drag flow and pressure flow.

pressed in a different form by each of the previously mentioned workers. The most convenient form is believed to be that proposed by Squires.[66] Thus

$$q_d = \frac{nU_zwh}{2} F_d \qquad (6)$$

where F_d is a "shape factor for drag flow" which is defined by

$$F_d = \frac{16}{\pi^3(h/w)} \sum_{g=1,3,5,\dots}^{\infty} \frac{1}{g^3} \tanh \left[\frac{g\pi(h/w)}{2} \right] \qquad (7)$$

Note in particular that F_d depends only on the geometry of the screw channel as given by the depth-to-width ratio h/w. Values of F_d from Eq. (7) for ratios of h/w up to 2.0 are given graphically in Fig. 4.12.

An experimental verification of this drag-flow shape factor has been reported by Squires.[66] Measurements of the drag-flow pumping capacity of 2-in. diameter screws encompassing a wide range of channel geometries were obtained. Polyisobutylene and molten polyethylene were the materials extruded in obtaining these data. Some of the screws that were employed when extruding polyisobutylene are shown in Fig. 4.13. The experimentally determined drag-flow shape factors are shown in Fig. 4.14.

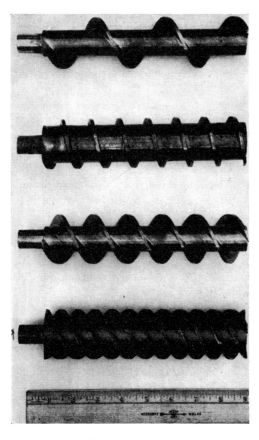

Fig. 4.13. Experimental screws.

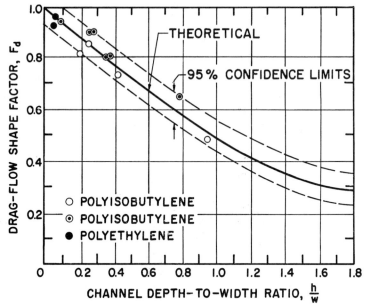

FIG. 4.14. Experimental verification of drag-flow shape factor, F_d .

The agreement between theory and experiment provides a verification of the theoretical drag-flow shape factor.

Pressure Flow. In general, a pressure gradient $\partial p/\partial z$ will exist in the screw channel, because most screw extruders either generate a discharge pressure or act as metering devices for flow from a high-pressure region, i.e., as a "dynamic choke." The flow created by this pressure gradient can be expressed by the particular solution to Eq. (3) where the boundary conditions $v_z = 0$ at $x = 0$, $x = w$, $y = 0$, and $y = h$ are satisfied. The solution for the pressure-flow velocity distribution which satisfies these boundary conditions can be written as

$$
v_{zp} = \frac{1}{\mu}\left(\frac{\partial p}{dz}\right)\left\{\frac{y^2}{2} - \frac{hy}{2}\right.
$$

$$
\left. + \frac{4h^2}{\pi^3}\sum_{g=1,3,5,\cdots}^{\infty}\frac{1}{g^3}\frac{\cosh\left[\dfrac{g\pi(2x - w)}{2h}\right]}{\cosh\left[\dfrac{g\pi}{2(h/w)}\right]}\sin\, g\pi(y/h)\right\}
$$

(8)

This form for the velocity distribution is that proposed by Gore and Mc-Kelvey.[34]

Integration of Eq. (8) over the cross section of the screw, as noted by Eq. (5), results in an expression for the volumetric flow rate arising from the pressure gradient in the channel. This can be written as

$$q_p = - \frac{nwh^3}{12\mu} \left(\frac{\partial p}{\partial z} \right) F_p \tag{9}$$

where F_p is a "pressure-flow shape factor"[66] defined by

$$F_\nu = 1 - \frac{192(h/w)}{\pi^5} \sum_{g=1,3,5\cdots}^{\infty} \frac{1}{g^5} \tanh \left[\frac{g\pi}{2(h/w)} \right] \tag{10}$$

As was the case with the drag-flow shape factor, the pressure-flow shape factor depends only on the channel depth-to-width ratio h/w. F_p, as given by Eq. (10), is shown graphically in Fig. 4.12 for values of h/w up to 2.0.

Combined Drag and Pressure Flow; One-Dimensional Theory. The net volumetric flow rate and local fluid velocity in the screw channel can be obtained by adding the drag and pressure-flow contributions. (The "leakage flow" over the flight lands will be ignored for the present time.) Thus, by combining Eqs. (6) and (9), the net volumetric flow rate q is found to be

$$q = q_d + q_p$$
$$q = \frac{nU_z wh}{2} F_d - \frac{nwh^3}{12\mu} \left(\frac{\partial p}{\partial z} \right) F_p \tag{11}$$

By making use of the substitutions

$$U_z = U_c \cos \phi \tag{12}$$
$$= \pi DN \cos \phi \tag{13}$$
$$w = b \cos \phi \tag{14}$$
$$= \left(\frac{t}{n} - e \right) \cos \phi \tag{15}$$
$$= \frac{\pi D \left(1 - \frac{ne}{t} \right) \sin \phi}{n} \tag{16}$$
$$t = \pi D \tan \phi \tag{17}$$
$$z = l/\sin \phi \tag{18}$$

where

N = screw rotational speed in revolutions per unit time
n = number of parallel screw channels (or flights)

and the other terms are as shown in Fig. 4.11, Eq. (11) can be rewritten in terms of more convenient screw dimensions. Thus alternate forms of Eq. (11) are

$$q = \frac{F_d n \pi D N h w \cos \phi}{2} - \frac{F_p n h^3 w \sin \phi}{12\mu}\left(\frac{\partial p}{\partial l}\right) \tag{19}$$

$$q = \frac{F_d n \pi D N h \left(\frac{t}{n} - e\right)\cos^2 \phi}{2} - \frac{F_p n h^3 \left(\frac{t}{n} - e\right)\sin \phi \cos \phi}{12\mu}\left(\frac{\partial p}{\partial l}\right) \tag{20}$$

$$q = \frac{F_d \pi^2 D^2 N h \left(1 - \frac{ne}{t}\right)\sin \phi \cos \phi}{2} - \frac{F_p \pi D h^3 \left(1 - \frac{ne}{t}\right)\sin^2 \phi}{12\mu}\left(\frac{\partial p}{\partial l}\right) \tag{21}$$

Any one of the above equivalent equations may be written as

$$q = F_d \alpha N - F_p \frac{\beta}{\mu}\left(\frac{\partial p}{\partial l}\right) \tag{22}$$

where α, β, F_d, and F_p depend only on the screw geometry. The alternate definitions of α and β can be inferred by examination of Eqs. (19) through (21). Thus, if the form used in Eq. (21) is chosen,

$$\alpha = \frac{\pi^2 D^2 h \left(1 - \frac{ne}{t}\right)\sin \phi \cos \phi}{2} \tag{23}$$

and

$$\beta = \frac{\pi D h^3 \left(1 - \frac{ne}{t}\right)\sin^2 \phi}{12} \tag{24}$$

Several important operating characteristics of screw pumps are disclosed by the preceding extrusion equations. In the first place, the screw drag flow is seen to be independent of the fluid viscosity as long as the initial assumption of a uniform viscosity across the channel depth is satisfied. (The effects of a viscosity variation across the depth of the channel will be considered later.) Within the limitations of this usually minor restriction, the drag-flow term in Eq. (22) applies equally well to either Newtonian or non-Newtonian fluids. Secondly, if the second-order variations in F_d and $\left(1 - \frac{ne}{t}\right)$ are neglected, the drag flow increases in proportion to the square of the screw diameter for a constant helix angle and to the first power of the channel depth. Finally, the screw drag flow is directly proportional to the screw rotational speed.

In contrast to drag flow, the pressure flow does depend on the fluid viscosity. Departure from Newtonian viscosity and variations in viscosity along the axial screw direction must therefore be considered when calculating the pressure flow. (Methods for taking these effects into account are discussed on pp. 183–186.) Furthermore, the pressure flow is strongly dependent on the channel depth—it being proportional to the cube of the depth as contrasted to the first-power dependency of the drag flow. Finally, the pressure flow varies directly with the diameter and is independent of screw speed except in so far as screw speed might affect the fluid viscosity through temperature effects or non-Newtonian fluid behavior.

The definitions of F_d and F_p were chosen to have a useful physical significance. These factors express the ratio of the actual drag or pressure flow, as the case may be, to that which would exist if the flight edge effects were absent. It is sometimes convenient to consider these factors as efficiency factors. The flight faces cause a distortion of the flow in the nearby region. This distortion reduces both the drag and pressure flow per unit of channel width over the values they would have if the channel could be considered infinitely wide in the x direction. The values of F_d and F_p approach unity as the depth-to-width ratio of the screw channel becomes small.

If F_d and F_p are assumed equal to unity, Eq. (11) reduces to

$$q = \frac{nU_zwh}{2} - \frac{nwh^3}{12\mu}\left(\frac{\partial p}{\partial z}\right) \tag{25}$$

or its equivalent

$$q = \alpha N = \frac{\beta}{\mu}\left(\frac{\partial p}{\partial l}\right) \tag{26}$$

where α and β were defined previously by Eqs. (23) and (24), respectively. Since the velocity is assumed to vary only in the y direction in Eq. (25), this expression has been referred to as the "one-dimensional" or "simplified" extrusion equation.[21]

Equation (25) can be derived directly from the initial differential equation, Eq. (3), if $\left(\dfrac{\partial^2 v_z}{\partial x^2}\right)$ is assumed zero, as is the case for a channel of small depth-to-width ratio. Thus,

$$\frac{\partial p}{\partial z} = \mu\left(\frac{\partial^2 v_z}{\partial y^2}\right) \tag{27}$$

which, upon integration with the appropriate boundary conditions, $v_z = 0$ at $y = 0$ and $v_z = U_z$ at $y = h$, results in the velocity distribution

$$v_z = \frac{U_z y}{h} + \frac{(y^2 - hy)}{2\mu}\left(\frac{\partial p}{\partial z}\right) \tag{28}$$

The two terms on the right-hand side of this equation are the limiting forms of the drag and pressure-induced velocities given by the two-dimensional Eqs. (4) and (8), respectively, as h/w becomes small. Integration of Eq. (28) across n parallel screw channels results in

$$q = \frac{nU_z wh}{2} - \frac{nwh^3}{12\mu}\left(\frac{\partial p}{\partial z}\right) \tag{29}$$

for the volumetric flow rate in a relatively shallow channel. This expression is seen to be identical to Eq. (25), the limiting form of the two-dimension extrusion equation for shallow screw channels.

As was pointed out by Mohr, Saxton, and Jepson,[51] Eqs. (28) and (26), respectively, can be written in the alternate forms

$$v_z = U_z[(1 - 3a)\,(y/h) + 3a(y/h)^2] \tag{30}$$

and

$$q = \frac{nU_z hw}{2}\,(1 - a) \tag{31}$$

where a is the ratio of pressure flow to drag flow,

$$a = -q_p/q_d \tag{32}$$

$$= \frac{h^2}{6U_z\mu}\left(\frac{\partial p}{\partial z}\right) \tag{33}$$

The minus sign is introduced to make a positive, since q_p is normally a negative quantity in the present coordinate system. By making use of Eqs. (12) and (18), the alternate form

$$a = \frac{h^2 \tan \phi}{6\pi DN\mu}\left(\frac{\partial p}{\partial l}\right) \tag{34}$$

is obtained. In general, a can assume any positive or negative value if externally induced pressures are imposed on the ends of the screw. In the absence of any such effects, a varies from zero, for a screw extruder with an unrestricted discharge, to unity for an extruder with a completely closed discharge and no leakage flow. (As will be seen later, the existence of a finite leakage flow causes a to be always somewhat less than unity.)

In all of the foregoing discussions, the flow of fluid through the clearance between the flight land and barrel wall has been ignored. A method for taking into account this so-called "leakage" flow will be discussed on pp. 192–195.

Transverse-Channel Flow. Since the barrel motion is directed at an angle to the down-channel z direction, the fluid in the channel does have a velocity component in the direction perpendicular to the channel walls, as shown in Fig. 4.10. Previously, only that component parallel to the channel walls has been considered, since it is only this velocity component which contributes to the net output of the extruder. The transverse flow, however, does contribute to the screw power dissipation and affects the extruder heat-transfer characteristics and the mixing capabilities of the screw. It is significant that the first detailed study published on transverse flow was in connection with a recent discussion of mixing in single-screw extruders by Mohr, Saxton, and Jepson.[51]

Expressions analogous to Eqs. (30) and (31) can be written to describe the transverse-channel flow. Thus

$$v_x = U_x[(1 - 3c) (y/h) + 3c(y/h)^2] \tag{35}$$

where

$$U_x = \pi DN \sin \phi \tag{36}$$

and

$$\frac{q_x}{(L/\sin \phi)} = \frac{U_x h}{2} (1 - c) \tag{37}$$

where $\left(\dfrac{q_x}{L/\sin \phi}\right)$ is the net flow rate in the transverse plane per unit of channel length. The ratio of pressure flow to drag flow in the transverse plane, c, is given by

$$c = \frac{h^2}{6U_x\mu} \left(\frac{\partial p}{\partial x}\right) \tag{38}$$

Channel edge effects, leakage flow over the flight lands, and variation in viscosity over the channel depth are implicity assumed negligible in writing Eqs. (35) through (38).

Leakage flow over the flight lands is usually small, and if it is neglected the net flow in the transverse plane obviously must equal zero, since the flow passage is closed at each end by the screw flights. Therefore, q_x is zero and c equals unity. Under this circumstance Eq. (35) becomes

$$v_x = U_x[3(y/h)^2 - 2(y/h)] \tag{39}$$

Velocity Profiles. The equations developed in the previous discussion define completely the flow patterns which exist within an extruder screw channel except, of course, for the turning under or over of the fluid at the ends of the flow path in the transverse plane. This turning under or over implies the existence of a velocity v_y perpendicular to the channel root near the flight faces, which here is ignored. A closer look at these flow patterns provides an interesting insight into the operation of a screw extruder.

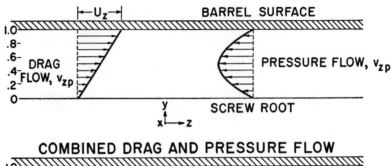

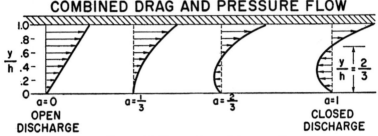

FIG. 4.15. Down-channel flow profiles.

Down-Channel Flow (Along the Screw Helix). If attention is confined to a channel with a relatively small depth-to-width ratio, the down-channel velocity profile is given by Eq. (30). In Fig. 4.15 are shown typical velocity profiles calculated by means of this expression.

The drag-flow and pressure-flow profiles, when considered separately, take the form of a linear and parabolic cross section, respectively, as shown in the top sketch. Actual net profiles, as established by the combination of drag and pressure flow, are shown in the lower sketch for various ratios of drag flow to pressure flow a.

The profile for $a = \frac{1}{3}$ has special significance for, as will be shown later, this represents the optimum profile for conveying at the maximum rate against any given back pressure.

A word of caution: One might be tempted to infer from examination of only these velocity profiles in a plane parallel to the channel helix (z-axis) that, because of pressure flow, there exists a movement of fluid backward along the screw axis toward the inlet of the extruder in a region near the screw root. Actually, except for the usually negligible leakage flow over the lands, there is never any flow backward along the screw axis under any circumstances, as long as the net flow is directed forward. This fact will shortly be clearly established when the influence of the transverse flow on the velocity profile in the channel is considered. Repeated references in the literature to a backflow along the screw channel[8, 33, 43, 45, 58, 62] have fostered the misconception that an actual backward motion of fluid in the channel occurs. This so-called "backflow" should be appreciated for what it is, viz., the projection on the z-axis of the true flow at any point within the channel. This projected flow component, real only in the observer's mind, is sometimes negatively directed, even though the true flow at the same point is directed toward the discharge end of the extruder.

The idea of a negatively directed pressure flow, or backflow, is nevertheless a useful aid in visualizing the gross dependency of extruder performance on discharge pressure and screw geometry. Care should be taken, however, not to draw erroneous conclusions about the actual fluid flow patterns within the screw channel on the basis of only the one frequently pictured down-channel component of the true flow. The orthogonal flow component in the transverse or x direction must be considered in order to obtain a true picture of actual fluid motion.

Transverse-Channel Flow. The velocity profile of flow in the transverse plane, i.e., in the x direction across the channel, is a closed-circuit flow given approximately by Eq. (39). In Fig. 4.16 is shown a diagram of this profile. The transverse-velocity distribution is unaffected by the extruder discharge pressure and depends only on the channel geometry and screw speed.

Resultant Velocity Distribution. The local velocities in the transverse and down-channel planes can be combined vectorially to give a composite three-dimensional view of the flow in an extruder channel. This composite flow picture is shown in Fig. 4.17. In this figure the flow components at various depths within the channel are sketched as they would be seen by an observer looking into the channel along the y-axis. A perspective view of the same flow patterns is shown in Fig. 4.18. A 17.7-deg helix angle corresponding to the common "square pitch" is depicted here; the conclusions that will be drawn are valid for any helix angle, however.

The velocity components in the down-channel z and transverse direction x were calculated as before for various values of y/h at open discharge

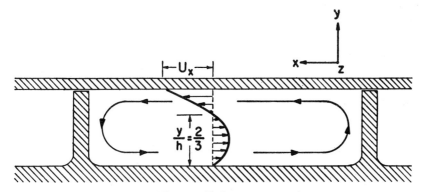

Fig. 4.16. Flow profile in transverse plane.

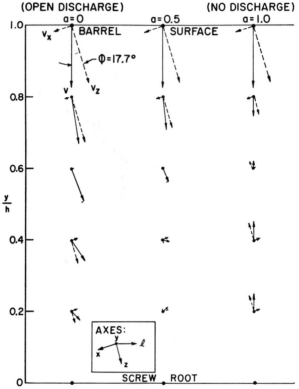

FIG. 4.17. Flow distribution in channel (as viewed by an observer looking into the channel along the y-axis).

$(a = 0)$, at closed discharge $(a = 1.0)$, and at an intermediate discharge rate $(a = 0.5)$. These components are sketched as dotted vectors. Note that, as previously mentioned, the transverse-velocity components remain unchanged as the degree of backflow a is changed.

The two orthogonal-component vectors have been added vectorially to give the true net local flow velocities in the channel. These are shown by solid-line vectors. Note in particular the following points:

(1) Under no circumstances does there exist a local velocity directed backward along the screw axis, i.e., in the negative l direction.

(2) No plane of stagnation, i.e., of zero velocity, exists except in the usually trivial situation of closed discharge. Under this circumstance both the down-channel and transverse velocities pass simultaneously through zero at a plane two thirds of the distance up from the channel root.

(3) The result of changing the relative amount of pressure flow is best described as a rather subtle altering of the local angles of direction of flow.

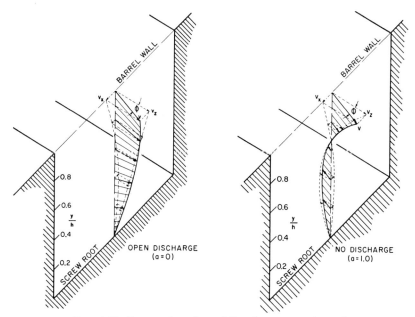

FIG. 4.18. Perspective view of flow in a screw channel.

(4) At closed discharge the fluid motion becomes a closed-circuit flow in a plane perpendicular to the screw axis.

(5) Under all circumstances the fluid velocity obviously remains fixed at $v = 0$ at the screw root and $v = U_c$ at the barrel wall as long as no slippage occurs.

Eccher and Valentinotti recently have published direct experimental measurements of local fluid velocities in a transparent screw pump.[26] Their work represents the first published information on local fluid behavior inside an extruder; previously published experimental information was confined to measurement of gross integrated flow rates. For this reason, the work of Eccher and Valentinotti is believed to provide the most critical test of extrusion theory yet available. It is extremely encouraging to find that their experimental results are in remarkably good agreement with theory. In particular, the theoretical velocity distributions shown in Figs. 4.17 or 4.18 are well confirmed by their studies.

Two-Dimensional Flow. Since equations based on the one-dimensional extrusion theory were used in calculating the down-channel flow profiles in Fig. 4.15, no indication of the influence of the flight faces on the flow pattern was given. A more nearly true picture of the actual flow pattern is obtained if the results of the two-dimensional theory are utilized. Flight-edge effects will be made clearly evident.

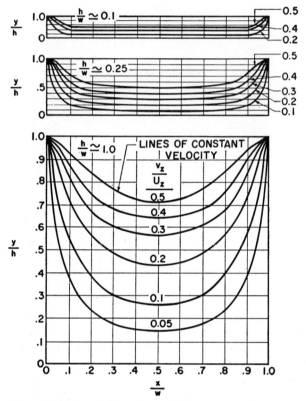

FIG. 4.19. Map of down-channel flow at open discharge.

Open Discharge. When there is no restriction at the end of the extruder, no back pressure is generated, and only drag flow exists. Equation (4) can be used to calculate the profile for down-channel flow under these conditions. The results are shown in Fig. 4.19 for channels of three depth-to-width ratios.* The channel geometry in the relatively shallow metering section of most metering-type screws for plastics is approximated by the top sketch. Channel geometries corresponding to the second sketch in Fig. 4.19 are found, for example, in diminishing-pitch screws and in feed or transition sections of metering screws. A screw channel as deep as depicted in the bottom sketch would be unusual for a plastics extruder but not uncommon for a rubber extruder.

The distortion of the otherwise linear profile by the flight faces is plainly evident. This distortion becomes relatively more severe as the channel be-

* Fig. 4.19, a map of the down-channel flow at open discharge, is derived from a similar figure previously developed by Gore and McKelvey[34] in a work not yet published at the time of the present writing.

comes relatively deeper. The use of the drag-flow shape factor F_d, as given in Fig. 4.12, permits the influence of this velocity distortion on the net flow rate to be taken into account.

The fluid near the channel root corners is seen to be very nearly stagnant. If this fluid were a heat-sensitive polymer, the use of generous root fillets would be advisable in order to eliminate this semistagnant region and reduce polymer degradation.

Closed Discharge. If the discharge end of the extruder is completely closed, the net flow rate is zero, and the maximum discharge pressure is developed. Under these circumstances the drag flow is entirely offset by the pressure flow, or

$$q_d + q_p = 0 \tag{40}$$

If this expression is combined with Eq. (11), there results

$$\frac{1}{\mu}\left(\frac{\partial p}{\partial z}\right) = \frac{6U_z}{h^2}\left(\frac{F_d}{F_p}\right) \tag{41}$$

By combining Eqs. (41) and (8), an expression for the local velocity due to pressure at closed discharge is obtained. The net local velocity is then given by the sum of this pressure-induced velocity and the drag-flow velocity from Eq. (4). There results

$$\frac{v_z}{U_z} = \frac{4}{\pi}\sum_{g=1,3,5,\ldots}^{\infty}\frac{1}{g}\frac{\sinh g\pi(y/w)}{\sinh g\pi(h/w)}\sin g\pi(x/w) \tag{42}$$

$$+ \left(\frac{F_d}{F_p}\right)\left\{\frac{3y}{h^2}(y-h) + \frac{24}{\pi^3}\sum_{g=1,3,5,\ldots}^{\infty}\frac{1}{g^3}\frac{\cosh\left[\dfrac{g\pi(2x-w)}{2h}\right]}{\cosh\left[\dfrac{g\pi}{2(h/w)}\right]}\sin g\pi(h/w)\right\}$$

A typical closed-discharge velocity pattern in a plane perpendicular to the z-axis given by this equation is shown in Fig. 4.20. Again the reader should be cautioned about drawing erroneous inferences as to the existence of a flow backward along the screw axis from this illustration in which only the flow component in the down-channel direction is depicted.

In the previously cited work, Eccher and Valentinotti[26] obtained an excellent experimental confirmation of the existence of a flow pattern of the type shown in Fig. 4.20 in a screw channel at closed discharge.

Flow with Nonuniform Viscosity Across Channel Depth. In all of the previous discussions, it has been assumed that a constant viscosity prevailed over the cross section of the screw channel. Because screw extruders are often provided with external means for heating or cooling the screw or barrel, it is of interest to know the influence of a temperature gradient across the layer of fluid in the channel. This problem was treated by

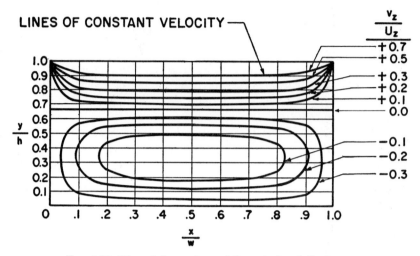

FIG. 4.20. Map of down-channel flow at closed discharge.

Strub,[68] who obtained solutions for an assumed linear and exponential viscosity distribution across the depth of the channel.

Unfortunately, a misapplication of a form of the Navier-Stokes equation of motion in which viscosity was assumed constant to the present problem, in which the viscosity is position-dependent, invalidated a portion of Strub's results. In effect, Strub ignored the term $\left(\dfrac{\partial v_z}{\partial y}\right)\left(\dfrac{\partial \mu}{\partial y}\right)$ which appears in the more generalized equation of motion, Eq. (2). The problem has been re-examined[67] and a presumably correct solution for an assumed linear viscosity variation across the channel depth is presented below.

If flight edge effects are neglected, i.e., if the flow profile down the channel is assumed one-dimensional, Eq. (2) reduces to

$$\frac{\partial p}{\partial z} = \mu \left(\frac{\partial^2 v_z}{\partial y^2}\right) + \left(\frac{\partial v_z}{\partial y}\right)\left(\frac{\partial \mu}{\partial y}\right) \tag{43}$$

where μ is now allowed to vary over the depth of the channel, i.e., along the y-axis. If a linear variation in viscosity over the channel depth is assumed, integration of Eq. (43) results in a channel velocity distribution given by

$$v_z = \frac{U_z}{\ln \gamma} \ln \left[1 - \frac{y}{h}(1 - \gamma)\right] - \frac{yh}{\mu_s - \mu_b}\left(\frac{\partial p}{\partial z}\right)$$
$$+ \frac{h^2}{(\mu_s - \mu_b)\ln \gamma}\left(\frac{\partial p}{\partial z}\right) \ln \left[1 - \frac{y}{h}(1 - \gamma)\right] \tag{44}$$

where

$$\mu_b = \text{fluid viscosity at the barrel wall}$$

$$\mu_s = \text{fluid viscosity at the screw root}$$

$$\gamma = \frac{\mu_b}{\mu_s}$$

Integration of Eq. (44) over the channel cross section results in an expression for the volumetric flow rate that can be written as

$$q = F_{\mu d}\alpha N - F_{\mu p}\left(\frac{\beta}{\mu_m}\right)\left(\frac{\partial p}{\partial l}\right) \tag{45}$$

where μ_m is the mean viscosity in the channel as given by

$$\mu_m = \frac{(\mu_b + \mu_s)}{2} \tag{46}$$

The terms $F_{\mu d}$ and $F_{\mu p}$ are viscosity factors for the drag and pressure flow, respectively. These factors are functions only of γ and are given by

$$F_{\mu d} = 2\left[\frac{\gamma}{\gamma - 1} - \frac{1}{\ln \gamma}\right] \tag{47}$$

and

$$F_{\mu p} = \frac{3(1 + \gamma)}{1 - \gamma}\left[1 - 2\left(\frac{\gamma}{\gamma - 1} - \frac{1}{\ln \gamma}\right)\right]$$

$$= \frac{3(1 + \gamma)}{1 - \gamma}\left[1 - F_{\mu d}\right] \tag{48}$$

The drag and pressure-flow viscosity factors are shown graphically in Fig. 4.21.

When $\mu_b = \mu_s$, both $F_{\mu d}$ and $F_{\mu p}$ equal unity, and Eq. (45) reduces to that previously found for flow with a constant viscosity over the channel depth. If the screw is cooled, thereby increasing the viscosity in the channel root over that near the barrel surface so that μ_b/μ_s is less than unity, drag flow decreases, as noted by the decrease in $F_{\mu d}$ in Fig. 4.21. Conversely, as the screw is heated, the drag-flow output increases until, at the limit, it reaches twice that obtained when μ_b/μ_s equals unity. In the absence of opposing pressure flow, this latter situation corresponds, in effect, to complete slippage of the fluid over the screw surface.

The opposing pressure flow is seen to increase as μ_b/μ_s deviates either above or below unity. Cooling the screw will thus always result in decreasing the pumping rate at a given screw speed as long as the average viscosity

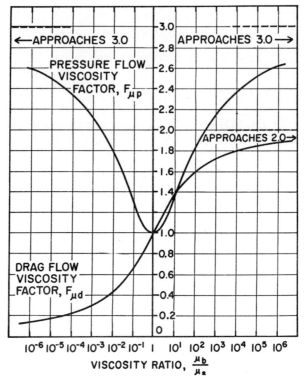

FIG. 4.21. Extruder channel viscosity factors.

of the fluid μ_m is not permitted to increase excessively. Heating the screw can either increase or decrease the net output, depending on the relative magnitude of the drag and pressure flows. Since drag flow frequently predominates, and the increase in drag flow exceeds the offsetting increase in pressure flow for values of μ_b/μ_s up to about 100, heating the screw can often be expected to produce some increase in pumping rate at a fixed screw speed.

Mori, Ototake, and Igarashi[52, 53] have considered the variation of viscosity across the channel depth because of the non-Newtonian behavior of the fluid. A Bingham-model fluid was assumed.

Partially Empty Screw Channels. Recent interest in extractor screws in which a portion of the channel is only partially filled with fluid has prompted an investigation into the pumping capacity of such partially filled channels. A sketch of a typical extractor screw is shown in Fig. 4.22, along with a cross section of the channel. The differential equation, Eq. (3), with $\partial p/\partial z$ set equal to zero, suffices to describe the flow in this situation, since there can be no axial pressure build-up in a partially empty channel and, hence, no pressure flow. The boundary conditions used in

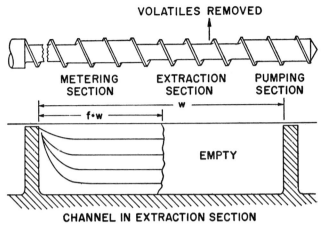

CHANNEL IN EXTRACTION SECTION

FIG. 4.22. Extractor screw with partially empty channels.

arriving at a solution are different from those used for a full channel, however. The fluid surface at $x = fw$ is now a free interface where $\dfrac{\partial v_z}{\partial x} = 0$ rather than being constrained by contact with the trailing flight face.

Squires[66] has shown that the volumetric pumping rate of such a partially empty channel, corrected for flight edge effects, can be written simply as the one-dimensional drag flow as calculated for a full channel multiplied by a shape factor for drag flow in a partially empty channel. Thus

$$q_d = F_d \alpha N \tag{49}$$

where α depends only on the channel geometry and remains as previously defined for a full channel by Eq. (23), i.e.,

$$\alpha = \frac{\pi^2 D^2 h \left(1 - \dfrac{ne}{t}\right) \sin \phi \cos \phi}{2} \tag{23}$$

The term F_d is now a drag-flow shape factor which accounts both for distortion of the flow due to flight edge effects and for the reduction in pumping capacity due to the decreased contained fluid volume. This shape factor depends only on the channel geometry and degree to which the channel is filled, f, and is given by

$$F_d = \frac{32 f^2}{\pi^3 (h/w)} \sum_{g=1,3,5,\cdots}^{\infty} \frac{1}{g^3} \tanh\left[\frac{g\pi(h/w)}{4f}\right] \tag{50}$$

This drag-flow shape factor for partially empty screw channels is shown graphically in Fig. 4.23 as a family of curves with f as a parameter for values

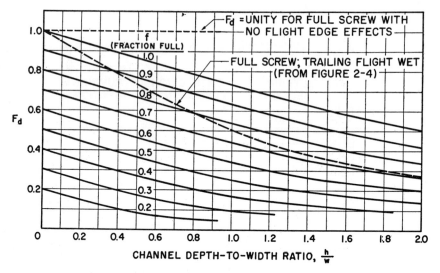

FIG. 4.23. Shape factor for partially empty screws.

of h/w up to 2.0. This shape factor has a convenient physical significance in that it can be interpreted as the pumping efficiency of the screw relative to the same screw running completely full and without flight edge effects. The curve for F_d at $f = 1.0$ is that for a full screw channel in which the fluid is slipping on, rather than adhering to, the trailing flight surface.

The drag-flow shape factor F_d from Fig. 4.12 for a full channel in which all surfaces are wet by the fluid, is superimposed on Fig. 4.23 in order to illustrate a point of interest. As the filled fraction f of the channel is increased, the pumping capacity increases, but when the channel becomes completely full and the fluid contacts and wets the trailing flight face, the pumping capacity abruptly drops to that value shown by this superimposed curve of F_d for a full channel. In other words, when operating with a partially empty screw channel in the region above this latter curve, the screw will actually convey at a *greater* rate than the same screw completely full of fluid. This rather surprising situation can occur because the retarding edge effect of the trailing flight face is absent when the screw is only partially filled.

This situation could represent one cause for instability in the operation of a metering section which performs on the verge of being starved. A "stick-slip" could conceivably occur along the trailing flight face that would cause the pumping rate to oscillate between the value indicated by the top curve in Fig. 4.23, in the case of slip, to the superimposed curve from Fig. 4.12, in the case of stick on the trailing flight face.

It can also be seen from Fig. 4.21 that the pumping capacity of a screw increases more than proportionately as the channel becomes fuller. Thus, for example, with a channel depth-to-width ratio of 1.0, the pumping rate of an 80 per cent full channel is about three times that of a 40 per cent full channel, rather than twice as much as might be superficially inferred.

Correction for Channel Curvature. In developing the previous extrusion equations, it has been assumed that a flat-plate model provided a satisfactory representation of the actual screw geometry. For the case of relatively shallow screw channels, this appears to be a reasonable assumption. In deeper-flighted screws, however, the channel geometry departs radically from that assumed in the flat-plate model. Immediate questions arise concerning the magnitude of the errors which are incurred by the use of the flat-plate model in this situation. Equations (19) through (21), for example, based on the flat-plate model, each involve as included terms a diameter and a helix angle. Obviously, the flat-plate model can afford no basis for logical choice of the "correct" diameter or helix angle to be used in these expressions. (Note that the helix angle varies with the diameter corresponding to the depth at which the angle is measured. The dependency on the diameter is given by $\phi = \arctan t/\pi D$.) Crest, arithmetic mean, and, to a lesser extent, the screw root diameter have been variously employed in the literature.

The use of the crest, i.e., outside, screw diameter (assumed equal to the barrel bore diameter for the time being) and the corresponding crest helix angle in this present text is not arbitrary but is based on the results of a recent effort by Squires[66] to develop a method for accounting for the curvature of the screw channel. As will be seen, a curvature factor has been developed which has a value close to unity if the equations are based on the crest screw diameter. An approximation is still involved, however, since only the existence of a curved channel, per se, has been considered, and not that of a radially varying helix angle. The crest helix angle is employed primarily to retain convenience.

If the flight helix angle is assumed to be small, the motion of a fluid contained between two concentric cylinders rotating with respect to each other approximates that of drag flow along a screw channel. This geometry is illustrated in Fig. 4.24. Here again, the barrel is assumed to be the rotating member. Identical results are obtained if the screw is assumed to rotate; in this case, however, one must take care to remember that it is the fluid which is retarded by the barrel, and not that which rotates with the screw that is being pumped in drag flow.

The velocity distribution for the model system shown in Fig. 4.24 is well known and can be found in most fluid dynamics reference texts,[54] for this model is basically equivalent to a rotating concentric-cylinder viscome-

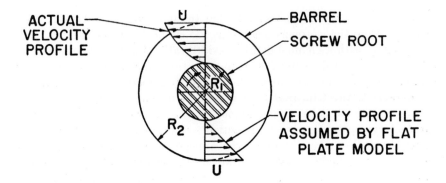

(Velocities Relative to Stationary Screw)

FIG. 4.24. Concentric cylinder extruder model.

ter. For a Newtonian fluid the velocity of the fluid relative to the channel wall at the same depth is given by

$$v_z = 2\pi N r \left[\frac{1 - \left(\dfrac{R_1}{r}\right)^2}{1 - \left(\dfrac{R_1}{R_2}\right)^2} \right] \cos \phi \qquad (51)$$

If this velocity distribution is now assumed to exist within the screw channel, and if flight edge effects are neglected, integration across the channel area leads to an expression for the drag-flow rate in this curved-channel model. This expression can be written in a form analogous to that for drag flow in a flat-plate model system if a "channel curvature factor" is included. Thus, it is found that the drag flow in a curved channel is given by

$$q_d = F_{cd} \alpha \, N \qquad (52)$$

The drag flow constant α is defined as before by

$$\alpha = \frac{\pi^2 D^2 h \left(1 - \dfrac{ne}{t}\right) \sin \phi \cos \phi}{2} \qquad (23)$$

except that the diameter is expressly taken as the barrel bore diameter or, if land clearance is neglected, the outside screw diameter, instead of some other arbitrary mean diameter. The channel curvature factor F_{cd} after some manipulation, is found to be given by

$$F_{cd} = \frac{1}{2\left(\dfrac{h}{D}\right)} - \frac{\ln\left[\dfrac{1}{1 - 2(h/D)}\right]}{\left(\dfrac{h}{D}\right)\left[\left(\dfrac{1}{1 - 2(h/D)}\right)^2 - 1\right]} \qquad (53)$$

where D again refers specifically to the outer diameter.

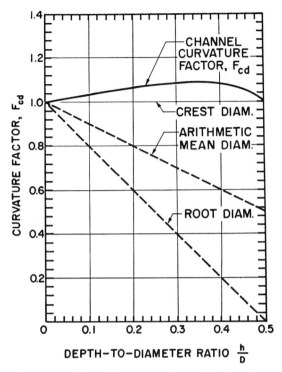

FIG. 4.25. Channel curvature factor for drag flow.

This curvature factor depends only on the depth-to-diameter ratio of the screw and is shown graphically as the solid curve in Fig. 4.25. This factor is exact only for the limiting case of a zero helix angle. However, it is probable that this factor can be applied with little error to screws having a small helix angle, i.e., less than 20 deg, where the flow is essentially circumferential. In view of the proximity of the curvature factor to unity, there is justification on practical grounds for assuming it equal to unity until a more exact analysis for finite helix angles is available.

The data on screw drag-flow pumping capacity obtained by Squires[66] which were used in calculating the experimental drag-flow shape factor presented in Fig. 4.14 provide an indirect verification of the curvature factor for screws having a helix angle of less than about 20 deg. These data also substantiate the choice of the outside screw diameter or barrel bore diameter for use in the flow equations based on the flat-plate model, as opposed to some other mean diameter.

Of significance is the fact that the curvature factor is greater than unity. In effect, this implies that the correct mean diameter to use in the flat-plate model would be *greater* than the crest diameter if this approach to the calculations were employed. Intuition has previously led most workers to use a diameter less than the crest diameter—usually an arithmetic-mean diameter for lack of something better.

In Fig. 4.25 are also shown the curvature factors that, in effect, are implicitly (and erroneously) assumed if either the screw root, arithmetic mean, or crest diameters are used, uncorrected for channel curvature effects, in estimating the drag-flow term in Eq. (22). The error incurred in each instance is given by the difference between the appropriate dotted curve and the solid line representing the more nearly true situation. At an h/D ratio of 0.1, for example, the actual pumping capacity is about 17 per cent greater than that indicated by use of the arithmetic-mean diameter.

At the present time, no analogous curvature factor for pressure flow is available.

Leakage Flow

In addition to flow in the screw channel proper, there exists a usually very small flow of fluid through the clearance between the screw flight lands and the barrel wall. This flow is termed leakage flow. In a recent paper, Mohr and Mallouk[50] developed extrusion-flow equations by considering flow across a plane perpendicular to the screw axis, plane AA' in Fig. 4.26, rather than perpendicular to the helical axis of the channel, as has been done in all earlier works. Their analysis demonstrates the role played by

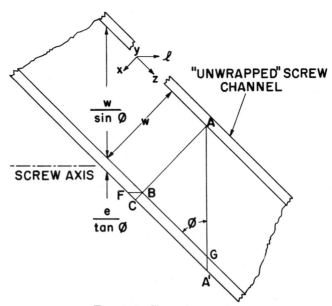

FIG. 4.26. Channel geometry.

leakage flow in a much clearer manner than has been done by previous workers.

The flow across the plane AA' is divided into that occurring in the channel AG and that over the intersected flight GA'. The flow across AG is found by integrating the axial components of the down-channel and transverse velocities over the circumferential channel area. Thus

$$q_{AG} = \int (v_z \sin \phi - v_x \cos \phi) \, dA \tag{54}$$

where

$$dA = \frac{w}{\sin \phi} \, dy \tag{55}$$

If flight edge effects are neglected, the down-channel velocity v_z is given by the previously presented Eq. (30)

$$v_z = U_z[(1 - 3a)(y/h) + 3a(y/h)^2] \tag{30}$$

and the transverse velocity v_x by Eq. (35)

$$v_x = U_x[(1 - 3c)(y/h) + 3c(y/h)^2] \tag{35}$$

where a and c have previously been defined by Eqs. (33) and (38), respectively. The term c represents the ratio of drag flow to pressure flow in the transverse plane. If a clearance exists between the flight land and barrel surface, not all of the fluid moved across the channel in the $+x$ direction by transverse drag flow is "turned under" and returned by transverse pressure flow; some escapes over the flight in the $+x$ direction. Therefore c is less than unity when a clearance exists between the flight land and barrel surface.

Mohr and Mallouk showed that c is given by

$$c = \frac{(1 - J) - \dfrac{[J^3(\mu/\mu_L)\pi Da]}{ne \tan \phi}}{1 + \dfrac{[J^3(\mu/\mu_L)w]}{e \cos \phi}} \tag{56}$$

where J is defined by

$$J = \delta/h \tag{57}$$

The dimension h is specifically defined by Mohr and Mallouk as the barrel radius minus the screw root radius rather than the screw channel depth. Since J is usually small compared to unity, Eq. (56) can satisfactorily be approximated by

$$c = 1 - J \tag{58}$$

If Eqs. (55), (30), and (35) are substituted into Eq. (54), and the indicated integration is performed, there results

$$q_{AG} = \frac{nU_z wh}{2} (1 - a) - \frac{nU_z wh}{2 \tan \phi} (1 - c) \tag{59}$$

As would be expected, the first term in this expression is identical to the earlier Eq. (31) and represents the combined drag and pressure flow down the channel. The last term in Eq. (59) accounts for the influence of leakage flow on the net channel flow. This term equals zero if c is unity, i.e., if the clearance δ and therefore the leakage flow are equal to zero.

By making use of the substitutions,

$$U_x = \pi DN \sin \phi \tag{36}$$

$$U_z = \pi DN \cos \phi \tag{13}$$

and

$$w = \frac{\pi D \left(1 - \dfrac{ne}{t}\right) \sin \phi}{n} \tag{16}$$

Equation (59) can be transformed into

$$q_{AG} = \frac{\pi^2 D^2 Nh \left(1 - \dfrac{ne}{t}\right) \sin \phi \cos \phi}{2} (c - a) \tag{60}$$

or

$$q_{AG} = \frac{\pi^2 D^2 Nh \left(1 - \dfrac{ne}{t}\right) \sin \phi \cos \phi}{2} (1 - a - J) \tag{61}$$

Flow over the plane GA' will now be considered. The axial leakage flow over this plane can be pictured as flow through the clearance slit of height δ and width $\dfrac{ne}{\tan \phi}$ induced by an axial pressure gradient. Under these circumstances the flow is given by

$$q_{GA'} = \frac{(ne/\tan \phi)\delta^3}{12\mu_L} \left(\frac{\partial p}{\partial l}\right)_{BF} \tag{62}$$

Mohr and Mallouk have shown, and the present writer has independently verified, that

$$\left(\frac{\partial p}{\partial l}\right)_{BF} = \frac{-6\mu\pi DN \cos \phi}{h^2} \left[a \left(\frac{\pi D \cos \phi}{ne} + \sin \phi \right) + \frac{bc \sin \phi}{e} \right] \tag{63}$$

Equation (62) for axial flow in the flight clearance thus becomes

$$q_{GA'} = \frac{-n\delta^3\pi DN \cos^2\phi}{2h^2}\left(\frac{\mu}{\mu_L}\right)\left[bc + a\left(\frac{\pi D}{n\tan\phi} + e\right)\right] \quad (64)$$

It is interesting to note that, because of the pressure gradient across the channel in the transverse plane, Eq. (64) predicts the existence of a finite leakage flow even in the absence of an axial pressure gradient in the channel.

The net extruder discharge rate is given by the sum of Eqs. (61) and (64). Thus

$$q = \frac{\pi^2 D^2 Nh\left(1 - \frac{ne}{t}\right)\sin\phi\cos\phi}{2}(1 - a - J)$$
$$- \frac{n\delta^3\pi DN \cos^2\phi}{2h^2}\left(\frac{\mu}{\mu_L}\right)\left[bc + a\left(\frac{\pi D}{n\tan\phi} + e\right)\right] \quad (65)$$

For the great majority of cases, the second term in Eq. (65) is considerably smaller than the first and can be ignored. Under these circumstances the extruder output is given by the first term alone in Eq. (65), or, its equivalent, Eq. (61). The major effect of clearance over the flights is thus seen to be the decreasing of the axial flow in the channel, as indicated by the fact that $J > 0$ in the first term of Eq. (65).

Examination of Eq. (61) will show that if a is zero, i.e., if there is no pressure flow, the net discharge rate is given by the drag-flow term of Eqs. (19) through (21) in which h is replaced by $h - \delta$, the screw crest-to-root distance.

Note should be made of the fact that a does not equal unity when the die is completely blocked in an extruder having a finite leakage flow. In this case the pressure flow does not equal the drag flow but rather is equal to the drag flow less the leakage flow. The ratio of pressure flow to drag flow a is therefore slightly less than unity.

Summary of Screw-Extrusion Equations

In the previous sections, solutions of the differential equation of motion for flow in a screw-extruder channel have been presented for several possible conditions of boundary values, cross-channel fluid viscosity, and assumed model geometry. In every instance the solution has been presented in such a form that the "complicating element" is conveniently accounted for by the use of a multiplying factor which is applied to either the drag or pressure-flow terms as calculated on the basis of the simple one-dimensional flat-plate model.

It is recognized that these various multiplying factors cannot rigorously be linearly combined and applied at the same time to the one-dimensional model, since the resulting equation cannot simultaneously satisfy all of the conditions imposed during the development of these various factors. In spite of this known lack of rigor, there is some value in presenting the results of the previous sections in the summary form

$$q = q_d + q_p$$

$$= F_d'\alpha N - F_p'\left(\frac{\beta}{\mu}\right)\left(\frac{\partial p}{\partial l}\right) \tag{66}$$

where the various F factors have been linearly combined into F_d' and F_p' by

$$F_d' = F_d F_{\mu d} F_{cd} \tag{67}$$

$$F_p' = F_p F_{\mu p} \tag{68}$$

It is hoped that a pressure-flow curvature factor F_{cp} analogous to F_{cd} will be developed in the near future to incorporate into Eq. (68).

In the absence of an exact approach, there is believed to be justification in combining the various F factors in a linear fashion, as has been done in the above equations. In most practical instances the error incurred by this assumed linear combination of these factors will be small.

In Eqs. (66) through (68),

(1) α and β are, respectively, drag- and pressure-flow geometric screw constants defined in alternate forms by Eqs. (23) and (24) or Eqs. (19) through (21).

(2) N is the screw rotational speed.

(3) μ is the viscosity over the channel cross section.

(4) $\partial p/\partial l$ is the axial pressure gradient along the screw.

(5) F_d and F_p are drag- and pressure-flow shape factors, respectively, as presented graphically in Fig. 4.12 for a full channel or Fig. 4.23 for a partially empty channel. These factors correct for flight edge effects and the fraction to which the channel is filled.

(6) $F_{\mu d}$ and $F_{\mu p}$ account for a varying viscosity across the depth of the channel on drag and pressure flow, respectively. They are shown graphically in Fig. 4.21.

(7) F_{cd} and F_{cp} account, in part, for the effects of channel curvature. F_{cd} is presented in Fig. 4.25. No solution for F_{cp} is yet available.

Power Dissipated by the Screw

The earliest published reference to a method for estimating the power requirements of a screw pump appears to be that by Rowell and Finlayson in 1928.[61] Rogowsky[60] later presented a dimensional analysis approach to the subject. A more detailed and satisfying analysis of screw power requirements was presented in 1953 by Mallouk and McKelvey.[47] Mohr and Mallouk[50] and Gore and McKelvey,[34] in subsequent papers, recognized the importance of the previously ignored transverse flow on the power dissipation and developed expressions which incorporated this factor into the derived power equations.

The power dissipated in the screw channel can be calculated by two rather dissimilar approaches:

(1) From a knowledge of the fluid viscisoty and properly directed shear rates $(dv/dy)_b$ in the fluid at the barrel surface (obtained by differentiation of the appropriate velocity-distribution functions, Eqs. (4), (8), and (39), or (30) and (39)), the shear stress τ_b on the barrel acting in the direction of rotation may be caclulated by $\tau_b = \mu(dv/dy)_b$. The screw power requirements may then be calculated as the product of wall shear stress, area, and rotation speed.

(2) The screw power may also be obtained as the sum of the power dissipated as viscous heat and the power expended as flow energy in raising the pressure of the fluid.

In both of the above approaches, the power dissipated in the space between the flight land(s) and the barrel surface must also be considered.

The first method of calculating power, which is essentially an external force balance on the screw or barrel, is readily available in the cited references. The second method, involving viscous heat generation, is developed in detail here, since it is a somewhat more basic approach. Mohr and Mallouk[50] alluded to this method of calculating the screw power, and Booy[15] independently developed power equations by this technique.

The total power required by a differential volume of the screw is given by

$$dZ = dZ_s + dZ_p + dZ_L$$
$$= \psi_s \, dV_s + dZ_p + \psi_L \, dV_L \tag{69}$$

where

$\psi_s \, dV_s =$ the power dissipated as viscous shear energy (heat) in the screw channel

$dZ_p =$ the power required to raise the pressure of the fluid

$\psi_L \, dV_L =$ the power dissipated as viscous shear energy in the clearance between the flight land(s) and barrel surface

$\psi =$ the dissipation function for viscous shear energy

and dV_s and dV_L represent a differential section of channel and clearance volume, respectively. Each of the contributing terms will be considered separately.

Power Dissipated as Shear Energy in the Screw Channel. The rate of heat generation per unit volume of fluid caused by viscous shear is given by the dissipation function ψ found in the general equation for conservation of energy when written in differential form.[54] If the fluid is assumed to be incompressible and flight edge effects are neglected, the dissipation function for the fluid in the channel ψ_s reduces to

$$\psi_s = \mu \left[\left(\frac{\partial v_x}{\partial y} \right)^2 + \left(\frac{\partial v_z}{\partial y} \right)^2 \right] \tag{70}$$

In arriving at this equation, it also has been assumed that the channel geometry remains uniform along the screw length being considered. Acceleration terms such as $\left(\frac{\partial v_z}{\partial z} \right)^2$ that would otherwise exist can then be ignored. Even if present, these acceleration terms are usually negligibly small.

The differential volume dV_s may be taken as

$$dV_s = nw \, dy \, dz \tag{71}$$

The power dissipated as shear energy in the screw channel thus becomes

$$dZ_s = \mu \left[\left(\frac{\partial v_x}{\partial y} \right)^2 + \left(\frac{\partial v_z}{\partial y} \right)^2 \right] nw \, dy \, dz \tag{72}$$

By differentiation of Eqs. (39) and (30), respectively, it can be determined that

$$\frac{\partial v_x}{\partial y} = \frac{2U_x}{h} \left[3 \left(\frac{y}{h} \right) - 1 \right]$$

and

$$\frac{\partial v_z}{\partial y} = \frac{U_z}{h} \left[1 - 3a \left(1 + 2 \frac{y}{h} \right) \right]$$

If these expressions are substituted into Eq. (72), it is found that

$$dZ_s = \mu \left\{ \left(\frac{2U_x}{h} \right)^2 \left(\frac{3y}{h} - 1 \right)^2 \right. $$
$$\left. + \left(\frac{U_z}{h} \right)^2 [1 - 3a(1 + 2y/h)]^2 \right\} nw \, dy \, dz \tag{73}$$

Upon making the substitutions,

$$U_x = \pi DN \sin \phi \tag{36}$$

$$U_z = \pi DN \cos \phi \tag{13}$$

$$w = \frac{\pi D \left(1 - \frac{ne}{t} \right) \sin \phi}{n} \tag{16}$$

$$dz = \frac{dl}{\sin \phi} \tag{18}$$

and integrating Eq. (73) with respect to y between the limits of 0 and h, there results

$$dZ_s = \frac{\pi^3 D^3 N^2 \mu \left(1 - \frac{ne}{t}\right)}{h} [(1 + 3a^2) \cos^2 \phi + 4 \sin^2 \phi] \, dl \quad (74)$$

This expression gives the power dissipated by viscous shear as heat in the screw channel. The $4 \sin^2 \phi$ term is attributable to transverse flow. This term would be absent were transverse flow ignored, and appreciable error would be introduced.

Power to Raise the Fluid Pressure. The power required to cause an increase in the fluid pressure is given simply by

$$dZ_p = q \, dp \quad (75)$$

Power Dissipated as Shear Energy in the Clearance over the Flight(s). The power dissipated as viscous shear energy in the clearance between the flight land(s) and barrel wall can be expressed in a form analogous to that for power dissipation by shear in the channel.

Thus, as previously noted in Eq. (69),

$$dZ_L = \psi_L \, dV_L \quad (76)$$

where, if only the circumferential velocity due to shear between the barrel and flight land(s) in the clearance is considered, ψ_L is given by

$$\psi_L = \mu_L \left(\frac{\partial v_c}{\partial y}\right)^2 \quad (77)$$

The differential volume may be taken as

$$dV_L = n\delta e \, dz \cos \phi \quad (78)$$

where δ is the radial clearance and e is the axial land width. The circumferential velocity distribution arising from circumferential viscous drag by the barrel is given by

$$v_c = U_c(y/\delta) \quad (79)$$

from which it is seen that

$$\frac{\partial v_c}{\partial y} = \frac{U_c}{\delta} \quad (80)$$

Substitution of Eqs. (77), (78), and (80) into (76) results in

$$dZ_L = \frac{n U_c^2 \mu_L e \cos \phi}{\delta} \, dz \quad (81)$$

Since

$$U_c = \pi DN \tag{82}$$

and

$$dz = dl/\sin \phi \tag{18}$$

Eq. (81) may be written as

$$dZ_L = \frac{n\pi^2 D^2 N^2 \mu_L e}{\delta \tan \phi} \, dl \tag{83}$$

It is advisable to distinguish between the viscosity in the land clearance μ_L and that in the screw channel proper, μ. Localized heating, caused either by heat conducted in from the barrel or generated by viscous shear [Eq. (83)], can cause the viscosity of the fluid in the land clearance to be considerably lower than that in the channel proper.

Total Screw Power. The total power dissipated by the screw, as seen from Eq. (69), is the sum of that given by Eqs. (74), (75), and (83). Thus

$$dZ = \frac{\pi^3 D^3 N^2 \mu \left(1 - \dfrac{ne}{t}\right)}{h} [(1 + 3a^2) \cos^2 \phi + 4 \sin^2 \phi] \, dl \\ + q dp + \frac{h\pi^2 D^2 N^2 \mu_L e}{\delta \tan \phi} \, dl \tag{84}$$

where the first and last terms represent power which appears as heat in the fluid being pumped.

By making use of the substitution

$$dp = \frac{6\pi DN \mu a}{h^2 \tan \phi} \, dl \tag{85}$$

which is obtained from Eq. (34), along with

$$q = q_d(1 - a) \tag{86}$$

and the expression for q_d from the first term in Eq. (21) (with $F_d = 1.0$), it is possible to transform the power expression given by Eq. (84) into the alternate form,

$$dZ = \frac{\pi^3 D^3 N^2 \mu \left(1 - \dfrac{ne}{t}\right)}{h} [(1 + 3a) \cos^2 \phi + 4 \sin^2 \phi] \, dl \\ + \left(\frac{n\pi^2 D^2 N^2 \mu_L e}{\delta \tan \phi}\right) dl \tag{87}$$

The channel shear energy and pressure-rise energy contributions have now been combined in the first term of Eq. (87). It is rather surprising that this expression differs from the previous Eq. (84) only in the exponent on a and the absence of qdp.

Another alternate form of Eq. (84) is

$$dZ = \frac{\pi^3 D^3 N^2 \mu \left(1 - \frac{ne}{t}\right)}{h} [1 + 3 \sin^2 \phi] \, dl + q_d \, dp$$
$$+ \frac{n\pi^2 D^2 N^2 \mu_L e}{\delta \tan \phi} \, dl \tag{88}$$

Mohr and Mallouk[50] extended the above analysis to include the situation where c in Eq. (35) cannot be assumed equal to unity, i.e., where leakage flow over the flight lands cannot be neglected. Their expression for the power dissipated by the screw accounts both for the influence of leakage flow on the transverse channel flow and for the existence of a pressure-induced leakage-flow component. It can be expressed as

$$dZ = \frac{\pi^3 D^3 N^2 \mu \left(1 - \frac{ne}{t}\right)}{h} [(1 + 3a) \cos^2 \phi + (4 - 3J) \sin^2 \phi] \, dl$$
$$+ \frac{n\pi^2 D^2 N^2 \mu_L e}{\delta \tan \phi} \left\{ 1 + 3J^2(\mu/\mu_L) \left(\frac{a \cos^2 \phi - \pi Da \sin \phi \cos \phi}{ne} \right) \right. \tag{89}$$
$$\left. - \left[\frac{\pi Dc \left(1 - \frac{ne}{t}\right) \sin^2 \phi \tan \phi}{ne} \right] \right\} \, dl$$

where c is as previously defined and

$$J = \delta/h \tag{57}$$

When the clearance is small, as is usually the situation, J can be assumed zero, and Eq. (89) becomes identical to the previous Eq. (87) in which leakage flow was ignored.

The equations presented thus far for calculating the screw power have been based on the assumption that flight edge effects were negligible, i.e., that the screw channel was shallow relative to its depth. Gore and McKelvey[34] have developed a modified form of Eq. (88) in which the effect of the flight faces on the power dissipated in the channel is accounted for.

Their results may be expressed as

$$dZ = \frac{\pi^3 D^3 N^2 \mu \left(1 - \frac{ne}{t}\right)}{h} (F_z \cos^2 \phi + 4 \sin^2 \phi) \, dl + q_d \, dp$$
$$+ \frac{n\pi^2 D^2 N^2 \mu_L e}{\delta \sin \phi} \, dl \tag{90}$$

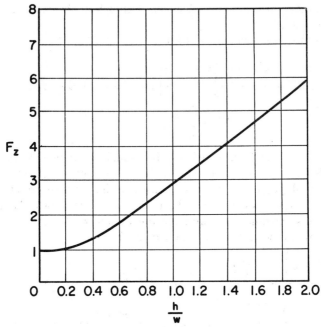

Fig. 4.27. Power shape factor.

where F_z depends only on the depth-to-width ratio of the channel and is shown graphically in Fig. 4.27. For shallow channels F_z approaches unity, and Eq. (90) becomes equivalent to the previous Eq. (88) in which flight edge effects were ignored.

OPERATING EQUATIONS FOR MELT EXTRUDERS

Introduction

The various equations for screw-extruder flow rate and power presented thus far have all been in a differential form with respect to the screw length. In other words, each equation describes the performance at a particular axial position along the screw. To obtain useful working equations describing the over-all extruder performance, it is necessary to integrate these expressions over the effective screw length. When so doing, the axial variations in polymer viscosity and channel geometry must be considered. Analytic solutions of the integrated flow equations have been obtained for certain idealized conditions of operation and screw geometry. Isothermal operation in which the viscosity of the fluid is assumed constant over the length of the screw is one mode of operation considered. Analytic solutions have also been obtained for pumping capacity during operation under adiabatic conditions. Many melt-extrusion operations can be approximated to a satisfactory degree by one or the other of these idealized cases.

The operating equations which will be presented are strictly applicable only to those sections of an extruder which contain a homogeneous melt. The theory and particular problems associated with conveying solids or semiplastic masses will be considered later.

General Case

Extruder Discharge Characteristics. For the general case where the fluid viscosity, density, and/or channel dimensions vary in the axial direction, the relationship between the extruder output and discharge pressure is given by the integrated form of Eq. (66) if leakage flow is neglected. Thus

$$\Delta p = \int_0^L \frac{\rho F_d' \alpha N - q_w}{\rho (F_p' \beta / \mu)} \, dl \qquad (91)$$

where Δp is the pressure difference over the axial length of the screw L.

In arriving at this expression, Eq. (66) was converted into mass units by multiplying by the fluid density ρ; q_w is the mass rate of flow.

The terms F_d', F_p', α, and β are functions only of the cross-sectional screw geometry, provided that the cross-channel viscosity profile is assumed to remain unchanged along the screw axis. Since, in the general case, the screw geometry varies with the axial distance l, these various factors become functions of l. Once determined, however, the functional relationships remain the same for any given screw and are not dependent upon operating conditions.

The viscosity can vary in a complex manner in the axial direction. This variation depends on the cross-sectional mean temperature of the fluid, as established by rates of viscous heat generation and screw and barrel heating or cooling, and on the viscosity–shear-rate relationship for the particular substance being pumped. In the absence of the solution to the complex energy balance required for establishing the local fluid temperatures, the axial viscosity distribution can only be estimated. If the intent is the analysis of performance of an existing extruder rather than the design of a new machine, measurement of fluid temperatures at axial locations should permit close estimation of the axial viscosity distribution. Estimation of the axial variation in fluid density is also aided by such measurements.

With the above information in hand, the graphical integration of Eq. (91) is straightforward. A series of such integrations for various values of N and q_w will yield the screw performance characteristics, i.e., the discharge rate as a function of discharge pressure for various screw speeds.

The use of this general method has been discussed by Strub.[68] Maillefer[46] has obtained an experimental verification of Eq. (91) in the extrusion of an oil and a thermoplastic (polyethylene). This general technique has also been applied by Yoshida *et al.*[76] in analyzing the flow of molten polyethylene in a screw extruder.

Screw Power. The total screw power in the general case may be obtained in a manner similar to that employed for determining the screw output-pressure relationship. Thus, for example, the total screw power is given by integration of Eq. (90) over the length of the screw,

$$
Z = \int_0^L \left\{ \frac{\pi^3 D^3 N^2 \mu \left(1 - \dfrac{ne}{t} \right)}{h} [F_z \cos^2 \phi + 4 \sin^2 \phi] \right.
$$
$$
\left. + \frac{n\pi^2 D^2 N^2 \mu_L e}{\delta \tan \phi} \right\} dl + \int_{P_0}^{P_L} q_d \, dp \tag{92}
$$

If the channel is shallow relative to its width, the integrated form of Eqs. (84), (87), or (88) may be used instead of Eq. (90). If the clearance between the flight land and barrel wall is large, then the integrated form of Eq. (89) should be used.

Isothermal Operation

If the fluid temperature can be assumed constant over the axial length of the screw, the fluid viscosity and density remain constant, and a particularly simple set of extruder operating equations can be developed. In order to maintain such isothermal conditions, it is necessary to remove continuously the heat generated within the fluid by viscous shear. It is often found that relatively shallow metering sections in metering-type screws approximate isothermal operation, particularly in small extruders where the surface-to-volume ratio is favorable to heat transfer.

In any event, the approximation to true isothermal operation frequently need not be too close in order to justify the use of isothermal extrusion equations. Deviations from nonisothermal operation (in the axial direction) affect only the pressure flow, which often is small compared to the drag flow.

Uniform Channel Dimensions. *Screw and Die Characteristics.* For the case of isothermal flow in a channel of constant dimensions,

$$
\left(\frac{\partial p}{\partial l} \right) = \frac{\Delta p}{L} \tag{93}
$$

where Δp is the pressure difference (discharge minus inlet) over the screw section of axial length L. If leakage flow is neglected, the screw discharge rate is given by Eq. (66) with $(\partial p/\partial l)$ replaced by $\Delta p/L$. Thus

$$
q = F_d' \alpha N - \left(\frac{F_p' \beta}{\mu} \right) \frac{\Delta p}{L} \tag{94}
$$

or, if the appropriate substitutions are made for α and β,

$$q = \frac{F_d' \pi^2 D^2 N h \left(1 - \dfrac{ne}{t}\right) \sin \phi \cos \phi}{2} - \frac{F_p' \pi D h^3 \left(1 - \dfrac{ne}{t}\right) \sin^2 \phi}{12\mu L} \Delta p \qquad (95)$$

The above screw characteristic for an isothermal extruder with uniform channel dimensions indicates that, if the volumetric discharge rate at any fixed screw speed is plotted against the pressure difference, a line with an intercept $F_d' \alpha N$ at $\Delta p = 0$ and a slope of $\dfrac{-F_p' \beta}{\mu L}$ is obtained. When operating with no pressure difference across the screw, the discharge rate is independent of the fluid viscosity and directly proprotional to the screw speed.

Equation (94) is shown graphically in Fig. 4.28 for screws of two different channel depths at two rotational speeds. The shallower screw has the flatter characteristic, i.e., is less sensitive to back pressure. For either screw, the slope of the characteristic becomes steeper as the screw speed is increased, since the resulting higher shear rates in the channel decrease the fluid viscosity because of non-Newtonian behavior of the fluid.

In near-isothermal operation, it is found experimentally that the screw characteristic remains essentially a straight line even for non-Newtonian fluids such as polyethylene melts. This straight-line relationship has been observed and reported by Gaspar,[31] Sackett,[62] Carley,[17] Maddock,[45] and Grant and Walker.[35] This is not surprising when one remembers that the effective average shear rate on the fluid is comprised of the shear due to

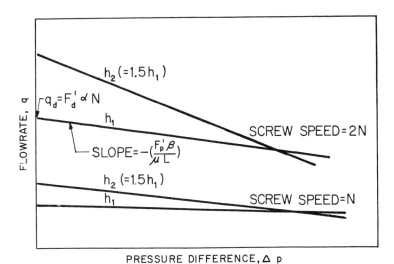

FIG. 4.28. Screw characteristics under isothermal conditions.

transverse flow, which is entirely independent of the die pressure, and the shear due to down-channel flow, in which the average absolute value is only moderately dependent upon the die pressure.

When the die is completely closed so that there is no discharge from the extruder, the maximum discharge pressure is developed. Examination of Eqs. (94) and (95) with q set equal to zero shows that the maximum discharge pressure from an isothermal screw section of uniform dimensions is given by

$$\Delta p_{\max} = \frac{F_d{}' \alpha N}{\left(\dfrac{F_p{}' \beta}{\mu L}\right)} \tag{96}$$

$$= \frac{6 F_d{}' \pi D N \mu L}{F_p{}' h^2 \tan \phi} \tag{97}$$

This maximum pressure is always decreased to some extent in actual practice because of leakage flow and unavoidable heating of the fluid from mechanical work supplied by the screw.

The over-all performance of the extruder is established by the interaction of the performance of both the screw and die. In general, the flow through any die can be expressed as

$$q = k \frac{\Delta p_D}{\mu_D} \tag{98}$$

where k is a constant established by the geometry of the die, Δp_D is the pressure drop through the die, and μ_D is the viscosity of the fluid in the die which, in general, is dependent upon the shear rate and, hence, the flow rate q. Even during isothermal operation this viscosity need not equal that in the screw channel because of the different shear rates which exist at these different locations. The shear rate in the die is frequently higher than that in the screw channel for the more common screw and die geometries. This causes the viscosity in the die to be lower than that in the screw channel for all non-Newtonian fluids except those exhibiting dilatant behavior. The latter are seldom encountered in screw extruders.

For a cylindrical die the die constant k is given by

$$k = \frac{\pi R_D{}^4}{8 L_D} \tag{99}$$

and for a slit die by

$$k = \frac{w_D h_D}{12 L_D} \tag{100}$$

where
R_D = radius of a cylindrical die

h_D = gap opening of a slit die (minor dimension)

w_D = slit width measured perpendicular to the direction of flow

L_D = die land length measured parallel to the direction of flow

These dimensions are shown on a cylindrical and slit die sketched in Fig. 4.29.

Equation (100) can also be used as a good approximation for the die constant of a tubular die if h_D is taken as the annular thickness and w_D as the mean circumference.

If the pressure at the inlet to the screw section and the discharge side of the die are equal, the pressure difference across the screw, Δp, equals that across the die, Δp_D, and Eqs. (94) and (98) may be combined to give

$$q = \frac{F_d' \alpha N}{1 + \left(\dfrac{\mu_D}{\mu}\right)\left(\dfrac{F_p'\beta}{kL}\right)} \tag{101}$$

and

$$\Delta p = \frac{F_d' \alpha N}{\left(\dfrac{k}{\mu_D}\right) + \left(\dfrac{F_p'\beta}{\mu L}\right)} \tag{102}$$

These expressions describe the performance of an extruder as determined by the interaction of the screw and die characteristics.

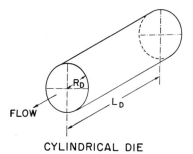

FLOW L_D

CYLINDRICAL DIE

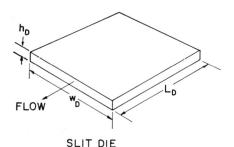

h_D

FLOW w_D L_D

SLIT DIE

Fig. 4.29. Basic extrusion die shapes.

If the fluid being pumped were a Newtonian fluid so that $\mu = \mu_D$ for the isothermal case, Eqs. (101) and (102) become, respectively,

$$q = \frac{F_d'\alpha N}{1 + \left(\dfrac{F_p'\beta}{kL}\right)} \tag{103}$$

and

$$\Delta p = \frac{F_d'\alpha N \mu}{k + F_p'\beta/L} \tag{104}$$

Examination of these last two equations shows that the output of an isothermal extruder, when pumping a Newtonian fluid, is *independent* of the viscosity (or temperature) of the system. The pressure developed at the die, however, is directly proportional to the fluid viscosity.

The previous Eqs. (103) and (104) shed some light on the extrusion of non-Newtonian materials and also on extrusion where both the screw and die are isothermal, but at different temperature levels. Equation (103) indicates that even for non-Newtonian fluids the discharge rate is independent of temperature, since the channel and die viscosities, although different because of the different existing shear rates, both vary in approximately the same manner with temperature. The ratio $\left(\dfrac{\mu_D}{\mu}\right)$ thus remains nearly constant.

One familar with extruder operation has probably observed that the output rate can be influenced to some degree by changing only the die temperature. The reason for this occurrence is made evident by Eq. (103). If the die temperature is raised, the mean viscosity of the material in the die μ_D will be decreased and the ratio (μ_D/μ) decreased, thus increasing the discharge rate. The die pressure will be lower, as shown by Eq. (104). The size of these changes depends on the relative magnitudes of the die constant k and screw pressure-flow constant, $F_p'\beta/L$. For example, if $F_p'\beta/L$ is small compared to k, as would occur with a relatively shallow screw and a large die opening, the "screw is controlling," so to speak, and changes in die viscosity have little influence on the discharge rate, although the die pressure is strongly affected. The discharge rate from a shallow screw is therefore less sensitive than that from a deeper screw to variations in die temperature caused, for example, by the cyclic "on-off" action of commonly employed electric-heater controllers.

The preceding screw and die characteristics can both be presented on the same graph of q vs. Δp, in which case the "operating point" of the extruder occurs at the intersection of these two lines. This method of representation provides a convenient map on which the complete spectrum of extruder

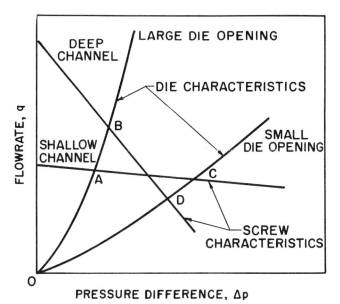

FIG. 4.30. Screw and die characteristics.

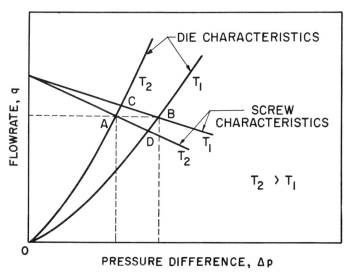

FIG. 4.31. Effect of screw and die temperature on extruder performance.

operation can be presented. In Figs. 4.30 and 4.31 the utility of such a map of operation is demonstrated.

Screw characteristics for a deep and a shallow screw of otherwise identical geometry are shown in Fig. 4.30, along with characteristics for a die with a small opening and a large opening. When using the large die, the shallow screw will operate at point A and the deeper screw at point B; in this case the deeper screw has the greater pumping capacitiy. When using the smaller die, the shallow screw operates at point C, and the deeper screw at point D. Use of the shallower screw in this case will result in higher die pressure and output rate. An optimum channel geometry obviously must exist for attainment of maximum rate through any given die. (This optimum channel geometry will be discussed further.)

The effect of the fluid temperature in the screw and die on output rate and die pressure is illustrated in Fig. 4.31. Screw and die characteristics are shown for temperatures of T_2 and T_1, where T_2 is greater than T_1. When both the screw and die fluid are at T_2, the operation is described by point A. If the over-all temperature is lowered to T_1, the pressure increases to that given by B, but the discharge rate remains essentially unchanged. If, however, the fluid in the screw is kept at T_2 while the die temperature is lowered to T_1, the discharge rate will now drop to that given by point D. Conversely, if the screw temperature is at T_1 and the die at the higher temperature T_2, point C corresponding to a higher discharge rate will describe the operation.

In general, it can be seen from such diagrams that the discharge rate from a long, shallow screw is less sensitive to variations in temperature than that from a deeper, shorter screw.

In order to utilize the extrusion-rate equations that have been presented, it is necessary that there be available characteristic values for the fluid viscosity in the screw channels and extrusion die. In the case of a non-Newtonian fluid, these viscosities must be evaluated at the shear rate existing in the channel or die, as the case may be.

The effective viscosity in the screw channel can be estimated if experimental data, consisting of a minimum of one experimental point of through-put rate and corresponding pressure drop over the screw section, are obtained at each screw speed and temperature of interest. With this information Eq. (95) can be solved for the viscosity if the channel geometry is known. McKelvey[40, 41] and Sackett[62] have used this technique to estimate effective extrusion viscosities. Recently, Maddock[45] reported success in predicting extrusion viscosities of polyethylene directly from viscosity–shear-rate data obtained in an orifice rheometer. In this case the peripheral velocity divided by the channel depth, or $\pi DN/h$, was taken as an approximation of the effective mean shear rate in the screw channel.

The flow characteristics of non-Newtonian fluids in dies of simple geometry can be calculated quite rigorously by the methods presented by Metzner in Chapter 1 of the present text. Often a satisfactory value for the viscosity in a die can be obtained from orifice rheometer, viscosity–shear-rate data if $4q/\pi R^3$ and $6q/wh^2$ are used as the shear rate in circular cross-sectional and slit dies, respectively. In the latter case, h is the gap opening (minor dimension) and w is the slit width measured perpendicular to the flow direction.

In addition to the confirmation of the isothermal theory implied in the previous papers, further experimental verification has been supplied by the studies of Rowell and Finlayson[61] on extrusion of viscous oils and soaps, and Pigott[58] on the extrusion of rubber stocks and oil.

Relatively shallow screws were employed in all of the previous studies, so that the drag- and pressure-flow shape factors were near unity. As a result, no critical check on the theoretical drag- and pressure-flow shape factors was afforded. The previously cited work by Squires[66] in deeper-flighted screws has provided a good experimental verification of the theoretical drag-flow shape factor in specific, and the isothermal extrusion theory in general.

"Optimum" Design for Maximum Pumping Rate. In a previous discussion it was pointed out that for any given die there existed an optimum channel geometry in so far as attainment of the maximum pumping rate at a fixed screw speed was concerned. The optimum channel depth can be obtained by equating the derivative with respect to h of Eq. (101) to zero. If this is done, there results

$$h = \left[\frac{6kL}{F_p' \left(\dfrac{\mu_D}{\mu} \right) \pi D \left(1 - \dfrac{ne}{t} \right) \sin^2 \phi} \right]^{1/3} \tag{105}$$

A screw having this channel depth will develop the maximum die pressure at any given screw-rotation speed.

If this expression for the channel depth is substituted into the expression for β in Eq. (101), it is found that

$$q = \frac{2}{3} q_d \tag{106}$$

which leads to

$$a = \frac{1}{3} \tag{107}$$

since $a = (q - q_d)/q_d$.

As pointed out earlier when discussing Fig. 4.15, this value of a corresponds to the down-channel flow profile in which the velocity gradient in the z direction is zero at the screw root.

Thus, for a given die, the screw that will deliver the most material at any rotational speed has the channel depth given by Eq. (105) and operates at two thirds of its maximum rate, i.e., two thirds of its potential rate at no back pressure. It also follows that the die pressure during this operation will be one third of the maximum pressure which the screw could develop at closed discharge, or

$$\Delta p = \frac{1}{3} \left(\frac{6\pi D N \mu L}{h^2 \tan \phi} \right) \left(\frac{F_d'}{F_p'} \right)$$

$$= \frac{2\pi D N \mu L}{h^2 \tan \phi} \left(\frac{F_d'}{F_p'} \right) \tag{108}$$

The optimum helix angle for any given channel depth and die is given by setting the derivative with respect to ϕ of Eq. (101) equal to zero. If this is done, there results after some manipulation

$$\sin^2 \phi = \cfrac{1}{\left[\cfrac{F_p' \left(\cfrac{\mu_D}{\mu} \right) \pi D h^3 \left(1 - \cfrac{ne}{t} \right)}{12kL} \right] + 2} \tag{109}$$

This equation shows that, for a screw with a given channel depth, the optimum helix angle ranges from between 45 deg for open discharge ($k = \infty$) to 0 deg for discharge through a die of infinitely high resistance ($k = 0$).

If both the channel depth and helix angle are to be optimized at the same time, Eqs. (105) and (109) must be simultaneously satisfied. If the various F factors are assumed equal to unity, the solution to this simultaneous set of equations is

$$\phi = 30 \text{ deg} \tag{110}$$

and

$$h = \left[\frac{24kL}{\pi D \left(\frac{\mu_D}{\mu} \right) \left(1 - \frac{ne}{t} \right)} \right]^{1/3} \tag{111}$$

A screw in which the helix angle and channel depth satisfy the above requirements will develop the maximum pressure at any given screw speed.

Although sometimes important, the attainment of this exact optimum screw geometry is seldom an overriding design consideration except, perhaps, in the case of melt-fed screw pumps. For plasticating extruders which are required to convey and melt solid feed particles, Darnell[24] has shown that the helix angle in the feed section of the screw should usually be about 17 to 20 deg for the more common granular plastics (see pp. 230–231). Since 17.7 deg is the convenient helix angle derived from a "square pitch," i.e., where the lead equals the diameter, this helix angle is in common usage and usually results in satisfactory performance, since the optimum in the helix angle in both the solids- and melt-conveying sections is fairly broad.

Considerations of screw strength frequently limit the channel depth to a value less than that given by the optimum from Eq. (105) or (111). The power dissipated in the channel and, hence, the fluid temperature rise also are strongly affected by the channel depth. These factors must therefore be considered when arriving at any so-called "optimum" design.

Power Dissipation. The power dissipated by the screw in an isothermal extruder section can be calculated by the use of any of the previously developed Eqs. (84), (87), (88), (89), or (90) if dp is replaced by Δp and dl by L.

The viscosity in the screw channel should be evaluated at an appropriate mean shear rate existing within the channel. In the absence of a rigorous values, the mean shear rate may be taken as $(\pi DN/h)$. Similarly, the shear rate in the clearance may be approximated by $(\pi DN/\delta)$.

The actual power dissipated as true pumping energy represented by $q\Delta p$ is usually a negligibly small portion of the total energy input when pumping very viscous fluids such as polymer melts. The thermodynamic pumping efficiency of a screw pump when defined in the usual manner as the ratio of the pump energy $q\Delta p$ to the total input is therefore very low. In the case of a screw extruder, however, the viscous heat dissipated by the screw often represents useful work in that it contributes to melting polymer feed cubes or raising the temperature of the melt to the desired extrusion level. This fact was recognized by Gaspar,[31] who reported over-all extruder efficiencies approaching 80 per cent. The major portion of the 20 per cent losses was attributable to external barrel-heater losses and waste heat in the screw cooling water.

Variable Channel Dimensions. If a screw does not have a uniform channel geometry over the length being considered, the integration indicated by Eq. (91) must be performed in order to establish the screw characteristic. Carley, Mallouk, and McKelvey[21] and Gore and McKelvey[34] have discussed the general case for the integration of this expression over an isothermal extruder having nonuniform dimensions in the axial direction.

For a screw consisting of a section of length L_1 in which the channel depth decreases continuously from h_1 to h_2, followed by a metering section of length L_2 and constant depth h_2, Gore and McKelvey[34] have combined Eq. (91) with the die flow equation $q = k\Delta p/\mu$ and performed the indicated integration to give

$$q = \frac{(6\pi DN \cos \phi/h^2)(L_2/h_2 + L_1/h_1)}{\dfrac{1}{k} + \dfrac{12}{\pi Dh_2{}^2 \sin \phi}\left[\dfrac{L_2}{h_2} + \dfrac{L_1}{h_1}\left(\dfrac{h_1 + h_2}{2h_1}\right)\right]} \tag{112}$$

Typical Calculations of Isothermal Melt-Extruder Performance.
The use of the foregoing isothermal melt-extrusion theory will be demonstrated by means of some typical calculations.

Consider an extruder barrel and screw, as shown in Fig. 4.9, having the following dimensions:

$$
\begin{aligned}
D &= 2.50 \text{ in.} \\
L &= 10.0 \text{ in.} \\
h &= 0.100 \text{ in.} \\
e &= 0.250 \text{ in.} \\
t &= 2.50 \text{ in.} \\
n &= 1 \\
\delta &= 0.007 \text{ in.}
\end{aligned}
$$

This extruder could represent a melt pump, per se, or the metering section of a plasticating extruder.

Equation (17) can be rewritten in the form

$$
\phi = \arctan \frac{t}{\pi D} \tag{17}
$$

and since the screw has a "square pitch," i.e., $t = D$, it follows that

$$
\phi = \arctan \frac{1}{\pi}
$$

$$
= 17.7 \text{ deg}
$$

The channel width w is given by Eq. (15). Thus

$$
w = \left(\frac{t}{n} - e \right) \cos \phi \tag{15}
$$

$$
= \left(\frac{2.50}{1} - 0.250 \right) \cos 17.7 \text{ deg}
$$

$$
= 2.14 \text{ in.}
$$

The channel depth-to-width ratio h/w is found to be 0.0467. If this value of h/w is used in conjunction with Fig. 4.12, it is seen that

$$
F_d = 0.97
$$

and

$$
F_p = 0.97
$$

Since these shape factors are nearly unity, it follows that flight edge effects are of minor importance in this screw. (Had the extruder been so designed or operated that the screw channels were only partially filled with fluid, Fig. 4.23 would be used to estimate a drag-flow shape factor.) The drag-flow curvature factor will be assumed equal to unity. Most conventional metering sections are shallow enough that negligible error is introduced if the shape and curvature factors are assumed to be unity.

It will be assumed that there is no viscosity gradient across the depth of the channel. Therefore $F_{\mu d}$ and $F_{\mu p}$, as shown in Fig. 4.21, are unity.

If the effects of leakage flow are neglected for the present time, the screw discharge characteristic may be obtained from Eq. (95)

$$q = \frac{F_d' \pi^2 D^2 N h \left(1 - \frac{ne}{t}\right) \sin \phi \cos \phi}{2}$$

$$- \frac{F_p' \pi D h^3 \left(1 - \frac{ne}{t}\right) \sin^2 \phi}{12 \mu L} \Delta p \tag{95}$$

Upon making the appropriate substitutions, it is found that

$$q = q_d + q_p$$

$$= 0.775N - 3.13 \times 10^{-4} \frac{\Delta p}{\mu} \tag{113}$$

where the units of q are cu in./min if N is in rpm, Δp in psi, and μ in lb$_F$ sec/sq in.

Discharge Rate. Let us now determine the discharge rate of this screw at 50 rpm when pumping "Alathon" 10 polyethylene resin at 374°F against an over-all pressure increase, Δp, of 1,000 psi. The mean shear rate in the channel is given as a first approximation by

$$\gamma = \frac{\pi D N}{h} \tag{114}$$

Substitution into this expression yields a value of $6.55 \times 10^1 \text{sec}^{-1}$ for the shear rate in the screw channel. From the graph of viscosity versus shear rate for "Alathon" 10 polyethylene resin (Section III), it is found that

$$\mu = 0.20 \text{ lb}_F \text{ sec/sq in.}$$

at the above shear rate at 374°F.

If the substitutions

$$N = 50 \text{ rpm}$$
$$\Delta p = 1,000 \text{ psi}$$
$$\mu = 0.20 \text{ lb}_F \text{ sec/sq in.}$$

are now made in Eq. (113), the flow rate is found to be

$$q = q_d + q_p$$
$$= 38.7 - 1.56$$
$$= 37.1 \text{ cu in./min}$$

Extrapolation of the graph of resin density vs. temperature (Section III) yields a density of 47.4 lb/cu ft at 374°F and 500 psi, an assumed mean pressure in the screw channel. The mass flow rate thus becomes

$$q_w = 61.0 \text{ lb/hr}$$

Had there been no pressure rise over the screw length, and consequently no pressure flow ($q_p = 0$), the discharge rate would have been 63.6 lb/hr. The 1,000 psi discharge pressure thus caused a 4.1 per cent decrease in pumping capacity.

Maximum Discharge Pressure. When the die is completely closed so that no net flow occurs, the maximum discharge pressure is developed. This maximum pressure is given by

$$\Delta p_{\max} = \frac{6F_d' \pi D N \mu L}{F_p' h^2 \tan \phi} \qquad (97)$$

Upon substitution, it is found that

$$\Delta p_{\max} = 2.48 \times 10^3 \, N\mu$$

which, for $N = 50$ rpm and $\mu = 0.20 \text{ lb}_F \text{ sec/sq in.}$, yields

$$\Delta p_{\max} = 24,800 \text{ psi}$$

Influence of Leakage Flow. The leakage flow through the clearance between the flight lands and barrel wall will reduce both the discharge rate and the maximum discharge pressure.

If the last term in Eq. (65) is neglected because of its small magnitude relative to the first, this expression for the flow rate in which leakage flow is considered becomes

$$q = \frac{F_d' \pi^2 D^2 N h \left(1 - \dfrac{ne}{t}\right) \sin \phi \cos \phi}{2} (1 - a - J) \qquad (115)$$

The factor Fd' has now been included in order to be consistent with Eq. (95). The term a is the negative of the ratio of pressure flow to drag flow. Reference to Eq. (113) shows that a is therefore given by

$$a = \frac{-(-3.13 \times 10^{-4} \Delta p / \mu)}{0.775 N} \qquad (116)$$

which, upon substitution for Δp, μ, and N, yields

$$a = 0.0403$$

Also,

$$J = \delta/h$$
$$= 0.007/0.100$$
$$= 0.070$$

Substitution into Eq. (115) yields

$$q = 38.7 \ (1 - 0.0403 - 0.070)$$
$$= 34.4 \text{ cu in./min}$$
$$= 56.5 \text{ lb/hr}$$

as compared to 61.0 lb/hr if leakage flow were absent.

If q is set equal to zero in Eq. (115), and a is replaced by Eq. (116), it if found that

$$\Delta p_{max} = 2.48 \times 10^3 \ N\mu \ (1 - J) \tag{117}$$

Upon making the appropriate substitutions for N, μ, and J, it follows that

$$\Delta p_{max} = 23,000 \text{ psi}$$

as compared to 24,800 if leakage were absent.

In practice, even the lower of the previous estimates of the maximum pressure would probably not be attained, since the heating of the melt by mechanical working would lower the fluid viscosity and, proportionately, the pressure. If the melt temperature increased by 25°F, for example, the maximum pressure would drop to about 15,000 psi.

If this screw section were the metering section of a plasticating extruder, pressure would be developed at the entry to the metering section by the preceding feed and transition zones. This pressure would have to be added to the calculated discharge pressure.

Increased Channel Depth. If the channel depth of the screw is increased to 0.200 in., the screw characteristic now becomes

$$q = 1.55 \ N - 2.50 \times 10^{-3} \ \Delta p/\mu \tag{118}$$

The shear rate in the channel, as given by Eq. (114), is reduced to $3.28 \times 10^1 \text{ sec}^{-1}$, and the resultant melt viscosity is found to be 0.27 lb_F sec/sq in.

The screw characteristics of this and the shallow screw described previously are shown graphically in Fig. 4.32. It can be seen that the shallower screw has the greater discharge rate above approximately 5,000 psi discharge pressure, while the deeper screw has greater capacity at lower pressures.

Combined Screw and Die Performance. The situation more usually encountered is that of pumping through a fixed opening such as a die, rather than pumping against a fixed discharge pressure. The extruder performance is thus established by the screw and die interaction.

Consider the case in which a die with a $\frac{3}{16}$-in.-diameter cylindrical hole having an L/D ratio of 3.6 is placed on the end of the extruder.

The shear stress at the die wall τ is related to the pressure by

$$\tau = \frac{\Delta p R_D}{2L} \tag{119}$$

which, in the present situation, becomes

$$\tau = \Delta p/14.4 \; \text{lb}_\text{F}/\text{sq in.} \tag{120}$$

if Δp is in pounds per square inch.

Furthermore, the apparent wall shear rate γ_A is related to the volumetric flow rate by

$$\gamma_A = \frac{4q}{\pi R_D{}^3} \tag{121}$$

which leads to

$$q = 6.39 \times 10^{-2} \, \gamma_A \; \text{lb/hr} \tag{122}$$

if γ_A is expressed in $\sec^{-1}$.

The use of Eqs. (120) and (122) in conjunction with the shear-stress-shear-rate data for "Alathon" 10 polyethylene resin (Section III) suffices to define the pressure-discharge-rate characteristic of the die. This characteristic has been calculated at 374 and 464°F and is shown graphically on Fig. 4.33. Also shown are the calculated characteristics for the two previous screws at these same temperatures. The operating point of the extruder is found at the intersection of the appropriate screw and die characteristics. For example, if the melt in both the screw and die is at 374°F, point A will describe the extruder operation in the case of the screw where $h = 0.200$ in., and point B where $h = 0.100$ in. At 464°F the respective operating points become C and D.

It can be seen that the discharge rate is quite insensitive to simultaneous changes in temperature of the melt in the screw and die, particularly in the case of the shallower screw. The discharge pressure, however, decreases by about 35 per cent for both screws if the over-all temperature is increased from 374 to 464°F.

The operating points obtained when only the die melt temperature is changed are also given in Fig. 4.33. If, for example, the temperature of the melt in the die were increased to 464°F while the screw melt temperature

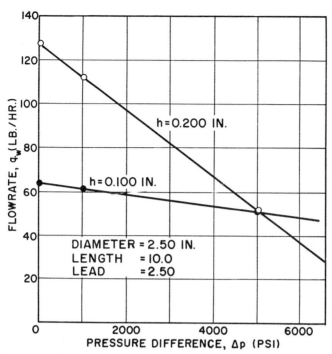

Fig. 4.32. Calculated characteristics for a 2.50-in. diameter screw.

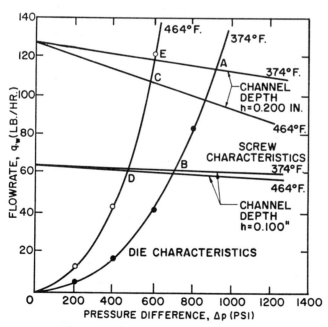

Fig. 4.33. Screw and die characteristics.

219

in the deeper screw were held constant at 374°F, the operating point would shift from A to E. (This could represent an extreme case of temperature cycling in the die owing to poor control of electrical heat input.) The discharge rate from the deep screw *increases* by about 4 per cent, while the die pressure *decreases* by 33 per cent.

The same temperature change in the case of the shallower screw causes only about a 1.5 per cent increase in discharge rate. Hence, in this particular instance, the deeper screw produces the greatest output rate but is more sensitive in performance to temperature disturbances in the extruder or die.

Optimum Channel Depth. If the sole intent is that of maximizing the discharge rate irrespective of the sensitiveness of the rate to temperature variations, examination of Fig. 4.33 indicates that a deeper screw would be required. An estimate of the optimum channel depth while retaining the existing helix angle can be obtained by the application of Eq. (105)

$$h = \left[\frac{6kL}{F_p' \left(\dfrac{\mu_D}{\mu} \right) \pi D \left(1 - \dfrac{ne}{t} \right) \sin^2 \phi} \right]^{1/3} \tag{105}$$

The die constant k is obtained from

$$k = \frac{\pi R_D{}^4}{8L_D} \tag{99}$$

which yields

$$k = 4.50 \times 10^{-5} \text{ cu in.}$$

for the present cylindrical die.

The viscosities μ_D and μ are indeterminate until the flow rate and channel depth are established. As a first approximation, μ_D will be taken as 0.02 and μ as 0.3 lb_F sec/sq in. Upon making the appropriate substitutions into Eq. (105), it is found that

$$h_{\text{opt}} = 0.40 \text{ in.}$$

If desired, an improved approximation for h_{opt} could now be obtained by re-estimating μ_D and μ based on the die and channel shear rates obtained if the channel depth were 0.40 in. Insertion of these revised viscosity values into Eq. (105) would yield an improved approximation for the optimum channel depth.

A screw having this optimum channel depth would be extremely sensitive in discharge rate to variations in operating temperature. Furthermore, this screw would be of little use for high-resistance dies, since the maximum pressure that it is capable of generating at 374°F is only about 1,500 psi. This screw would not be capable of supplying much mechanical work to the melt, because of the relatively low shear rates that would exist in such a deep channel. Difficulty would be exprerienced in maintaining the desired extrudate temperature at higher rates, since most of the energy would have to be supplied to the melt as conducted heat from the barrel wall. In general, the rate at which heat can be conducted into the melt will not keep pace with the throughput rate as screw speed is increased, and the extrudate temperature would drop.

In addition, if this screw section were acting as the metering section on the end of a plasticating extruder, the discharge rate would be extremely sensitive to the always present variations which exist in the feed pickup and conveying rate in the screw feed zone. A deep metering section is ineffective as a choke or dampener on the feed section, and nonuniformities in pressure or flow will persist through the metering section.

It is obvious that the use of screws possessing the optimum channel depth from the pumping capacity viewpoint must be tempered by consideration of these latter factors which, from a practical viewpoint, are of overriding importance.

Adiabatic Operation

The previous discussion has been concerned with the limiting case in which the rate of heat generation in the fluid was sufficiently low or the external heat transfer sufficiently high that isothermal conditions prevailed. An entirely different situation exists when the heat generated within the melt is not removed but, rather, accumulates within the fluid and causes a rise in fluid temperature in the axial direction. This limiting condition of complete heat retention is termed adiabatic extrusion.

The theory of adiabatic extrusion has assumed special significance within the last few years because of the trend in the plastics processing industry toward larger extruders and extruders with rapidly turning screws. Plasticating extruders in which essentially all of the heat is generated internally by viscous shear are not uncommon. Since the operation of such machines is not truly adiabatic—there being heat losses from the barrel or in the feed-hopper cooling water—it is referred to by some writers as "autogenous" extrusion, meaning self-generating.[36]

The theory of the adiabatic screw extrusion of Newtonian fluids was developed and reported by McKelvey.[42] As with isothermal extrusion, this mode of operation represents an idealized situation. Actual operation of melt screw pumps generally lies between these two idealized situations.

In the case of adiabatic extrusion there is needed, in addition to the differential flow relationship given by Eq. (66), an energy balance to permit calculation of the temperature rise of the fluid in the axial direction. In order to complete this energy balance, it is necessary that the fluid specific heat and viscosity be known. It is usually satisfactory to assume a constant mean specific heat, but the variation of viscosity with temperature must be considered. McKelvey used the relationship

$$\mu = ae^{-bT} \tag{123}$$

which leads to

$$\mu = \mu_i e^{-b(T-T_i)} \tag{124}$$

where T is the absolute temperature and the subscript i refers to inlet conditions. The more conventional form

$$\mu = Ae^{E/RT} \tag{125}$$

results in a solution in the form of a slowly converging series and was therefore not used.

The temperature rise of the fluid in the channel can be obtained by equating the increase in heat energy of the fluid as it passes through a section of the screw to the rate of dissipation of viscous shear energy in that section. The latter is given by the sum of Eqs. (74) and (83). Thus

$$q\rho C_p \, dt = \frac{\pi^3 D^3 N^2 \mu \left(1 - \dfrac{ne}{t}\right)}{h} [(1 + 3a^2) \cos^2 \phi + 4 \sin^2 \phi] \, dl$$
$$+ \frac{n\pi^2 D^2 N^2 \mu_L e}{\delta \tan \phi} \, dl \tag{126}$$

The bracketed term in this equation can be approximated with sufficient accuracy $(1 + 3 \sin^2 \phi)$ If $\left(1 - \dfrac{ne}{t}\right)$ is then replaced by the equivalent $(t - ne)/(\pi D \tan \phi)$, Eq. (126) becomes

$$q\rho C_p \, dt = \epsilon N^2 \mu \, dl \tag{127}$$

where

$$\epsilon = \frac{\pi^2 D^2}{\tan \phi} \left[\frac{(t - ne)(1 + 3 \sin^2 \phi)}{h} + \frac{ne}{\delta} \right] \tag{128}$$

With the use of, first, the energy balance given by Eq. (127), second, the flow equation given by Eq. (66), third, the viscosity-temperature relationship of Eq. (124), and fourth, the die flow characteristic given by Eq. (98), it is possible to develop complete working equations for adiabatic extrusion of a Newtonian fluid. In contrast to isothermal extrusion, these operating equations now define the temperature of the extrudate as well as the pressure and discharge rate.

The work of McKelvey[42] should be consulted for a detailed development of the final operating equations which are summarized below.

Discharge Rate. The discharge rate is given by

$$q = \frac{MN^2L}{R-1} \tag{129}$$

Pressure. The pressure drop across the screw (assumed equal to that across the die) may be found from

$$\Delta p = \frac{q\mu_i}{kR} \tag{130}$$

$$= \frac{\mu_i MN^2L}{kR(R-1)} \tag{131}$$

Temperature. The temperature increase of the extrudate over that of the entering fluid is given by

$$\Delta T = \frac{1}{b} \ln R \tag{132}$$

Power. The screw power may be calculated from

$$Z = \rho C_p q \Delta T + q \Delta p \tag{133}$$

In the preceding equations, M is a constant which depends only on the physical properties of the fluid and the screw geometry as given by

$$M = \frac{\mu_i b \epsilon}{\rho C_p} \tag{134}$$

The viscosity ratio R is defined by

$$R = \mu_i/\mu_D \tag{135}$$

and can be calculated from

$$\left(\frac{\beta}{kL}\right) = \left(\frac{\alpha}{MNL}\right) R \ln R - \frac{R \ln R}{R-1} \tag{136}$$

where leakage flow has been neglected. The form of Eq. (136) makes the direct calculation of R rather difficult. Values for R can be estimated quite readily, however, by use of the graph shown in Fig. 4.34, where various values of R have been plotted against the two dimensionless parameters (β/kL) and (α/MNL).

The calculation of the performance of an adiabatic extruder by the above

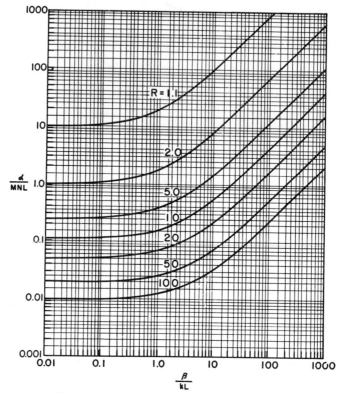

FIG. 4.34. Adiabatic extrusion design chart.

procedure is straightforward. Typical calculations were presented by Mc-Kelvey for a screw having the following dimensions (in inches):

$$D = 2.00 \qquad h = 0.200$$

$$L = 15.0 \qquad e = 0.200$$

$$t = 3.50 \qquad \delta = 0.005$$

The fluid being extruded was assumed to have the physical properties of molten polyethylene, viz.,

$\mu_i = 0.02$ lb-sec/sq in.

$b = 0.025°K^{-1}$ (obtained from the slope of a log μ vs. T plot)

$C_p = 300$ in.-lb/cu in. °K

At 120 rpm the discharge rate was found to be 1.89 cu in./sec at a pressure

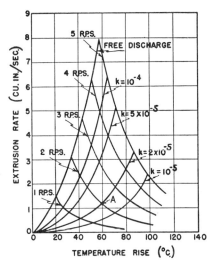

FIG. 4.35. Adiabatic performance diagram.

of 2,200 psi when pumping through a die with $k = 5 \times 10^{-5}$ cu in. The temperature rise of the melt was 49°C.

This operating point represents but one location on the complete map of the adiabatic performance of this screw shown in Fig. 4.35. It can be seen that for a given die, i.e., a given k, the temperature of the extrudate and the discharge rate increase as the screw speed increases. Although not explicitly

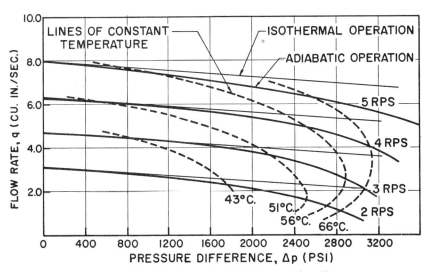

FIG. 4.36. Alternate form of adiabatic operating diagram.

shown in Fig. 4.35, the discharge pressure also increases according to the relationship of Eq. (130).

It is sometimes more convenient to present adiabatic screw characteristics in a manner analogous to that used for isothermal operation, i.e., as the discharge rate plotted against pressure rather than the temperature rise. This method of presentation has been used by Colwell.[23] In Fig. 4.36 is shown the operating map in this latter form for the present example of adiabatic extrusion. Isothermal screw characteristics are also shown for comparison.

An experimental study of the adiabatic extrusion of polyethylene was reported by Bernhardt and McKelvey.[12] In view of the sensitiveness of the extrusion operation to the variation in physical properties of the melt, the agreement between theoretically predicted operation and that observed experimentally was quite good.

DEVELOPMENT OF EQUATIONS FOR SOLIDS CONVEYING

Introduction

Up to this point, only the flow of completely molten resins in the screw channel has been considered. In extruders fed with solid thermoplastic granules, we must also be concerned with the conveying of unmelted particles in the feed section of the screw. As will be seen, a reasonably sound theoretical basis for analyzing the conveying of granular material in the feed section of a screw has been developed.

Theory of Solids Conveying

In the feed section of an extruder the pellets of thermoplastic resin are unmelted, and the plastic does not wet the metal wall. The feed material fills and moves forward in the helical channel of the screw. Because of the reduced volume in the forward sections of the screw, the plastic particles being conveyed forward encounter resistance to flow, and pressure builds up within the confined solids.

In the case of the feeding and conveying of powders or fine granules (like table salt), there is internal shear within the gross body of the particulate material, and the flow equations for fluids apply with sufficient accuracy (± 10 per cent) for engineering estimates.

The case more usually encountered, however, is the conveying of cubical, spherical, or cylindrical pellets of thermoplastic resin which are of the order of 0.10 to 0.20 in. major dimension. With feed materials of this size, little or no internal shear takes place in the solids-conveying section of the screw. Instead, the material behaves like a solid—but elastic—plug. This plug contacts all sides of the screw channel and can have internal pressure.

For the case where the extruder screw and barrel are both machined to the same degree of smoothness, the coefficient of friction will be the same between the plastic and the surface of the screw and between the plastic and the surface of the barrel, if the screw and barrel are at the same temperature. For this case the following equation for the conveying rate of solids in the feed section of an extruder screw has been derived:[24]

$$\frac{q_s}{N} = \pi^2 Dh(D - h)\left[\frac{\tan\theta \tan\phi_b}{\tan\theta + \tan\phi_b}\right] \tag{137}$$

where

θ = the angle of movement of the outer surface of the solid plug

ϕ_b = the helix angle of the screw at the outside diameter of the screw

h = the depth of the screw channel

D = the inside diameter of the barrel or, neglecting clearance, the outside diameter of the screw

N = the rotational speed of the screw (revolutions/unit time)

q_s = the volumetric delivery rate of the solids

In order to estimate the delivery rate by means of this equation [Eq. (137)], it is necessary to know the value of θ, the angle of the direction of movement of the elastic solid plug relative to a plane perpendicular to the axis to the screw.

The angle θ may be evaluated from the equation

$$\cos\theta = k\sin\theta + C(K\sin\phi_s + C\cos\phi_s) + \frac{2h}{t}(KC\tan\phi_s + E^2) \tag{138}$$

$$+ \frac{hE}{Lf_b}\sin\phi_a(E\cos\phi_a + K\sin\phi_a)\ln\frac{p_2}{p_1}$$

where

$$K = \frac{E(\tan\phi_a + f_s)}{1 - f_s\tan\phi_a} \tag{139}$$

$$C = \frac{D - 2h}{D} \tag{140}$$

ϕ_s = helix angle at the screw root

ϕ_a = helix angle of the screw at the average depth of the screw channel

t = lead of the screw thread

$E = \dfrac{D - h}{D}$

L = axial length of the solids-conveying section of the screw

f_b = coefficient of friction between the plastic solids and the surface of the extruder barrel

f_s = coefficient of friction between the plastic solids and the surface of the extruder screw

p_2, p_1 = pressure at the discharge and inlet end of the conveying section, respectively.

For the special theoretical case where the coefficient of friction between the plastic and the screw is negligible and where there also is no pressure build-up, Eq. (137) reduces to the simplified equation

$$\frac{q_s}{N} = \pi^2 D^2 h \sin \phi_b \cos \phi_b \qquad (141)$$

which gives a volumetric output exactly twice that which would be obtained if the material were fluid and could be sheared.

Another simplified equation that finds use in practical design is the following shortened version of Eq. (137), which is obtained when it is assumed that the resin is not in intimate contact with the trailing surface of the screw flight. This situation implies no pressure build-up in the particles being conveyed and is the state that normally prevails in the first several turns (up to six to eight turns in screws with a 20:1 L/D ratio) of the feed section.

$$\cos \theta = K \sin \theta + C(K \sin \phi_s + C \cos \phi_s) \qquad (142)$$

DESIGN OF PLASTICATING EXTRUDERS

Introduction

The extrusion theories which have been developed in the earlier sections of this chapter consider only the conveying of a viscous fluid or a granular solid material in the screw channel. In addition to these two conveying processes, in the design of an extruder used for processing thermoplastic materials, the complex operations of plasticating, compacting, and conveying which occur in the transition section of the screw must also be considered. In view of the obvious extreme complexity of the various processes simultaneously occurring in the transition region, it is not surprising that no general analytical techniques are yet available for use in examining the performance of this screw section. It is primarily because of the existence of this latter situation that the plasticating extrusion of thermoplastic resins still retains certain shadings of an art rather than being, in its entirety, a well-defined processing unit operation.

The text by Simonds, Weith, and Schack[63] provides a descriptive coverage of the technology of plasticating extrusion as of 1952. A more recent coverage of the subject by Fisher, entitled "Extrusion of Plastics," has just been made available.[29] In a text edited by Renfrew and Morgan, Kennaway and Weeks[38] apply the previously developed extrusion theory to the design of polyethylene plasticating extruders. They make a careful distinction between an "unrestricted" screw, in which the output is dictated by the feed section, and a "restricted" screw, in which the discharge end of the screw limits the rate to a value below the natural deliver rate of the feed section.

Additional papers describing the design of polyethylene extruders are that by McKelvey[40] and the more recent paper by Maddock,[45] who has also presented a review of the fundamentals of extrusion theory.[43] Gaspar[31] has presented extensive data on the operation of polyethylene extruders, with particular emphasis placed upon over-all thermal efficiencies.

Beck[6] has authored several papers describing the use of a high-speed extruder in which all of the energy for plastication is derived from viscous shear. Further descriptions of Euorpean plasticating extruder design and operation are available in articles by Whitcut,[72] Atkinson and Owen,[3] Fisher,[27, 28] and Baigent.[5] Multiple- as well as single-screw extruders are discussed in the last two articles.

A serious void in extrusion technology has been at least partially filled by a recent paper by Maddock[44] on factors influencing the quality of extrudates from single-screw plasticating extruders. He concluded that the amount of shear, as defined by the product of shear rate and residence time, was of fundamental importance in determining the uniformity of the extrudate. As will be seen in a later discussion of mixing in screw extruders, this same principle has been expounded by Mohr, Saxton, and Jepson,[51] who made use of the theory of laminar fluid flow in an extruder and die to describe quantitatively the degree of mixing in terms of the amount of shear imposed on the melt.

Theory and Design

When discussing the operation of a plasticating extruder, it is convenient to consider separately the performance of the individual functional sections of the screw that have been alluded to in the preceding paragraphs, i.e., the feed, transition, and melt sections. The screw feed section must be capable of removing the feed particles from the hopper of the extruder and conveying them forward along the screw at the desired rate. In the functional transition section the feed particles are plasticated and compacted into a void-free fluid mass. Plastication usually occurs through the action of both viscous shear energy and heat transferred in through the barrel. The melt section must be capable of further homogenizing the melt and delivering it at the desired pressure to the die.

These functional sections may or may not correspond to actual physically defined sections of the screw. The boundary between the functional feed and transitional sections, in particular, is often quite ill-defined and, moreover, the location of this boundary can be strongly influenced by operating variables such as barrel temperature, screw speed, and throughput rate. Exact correspondence between this functional boundary and any actual physical boundary on the screw is therefore usually only coincidental.

The boundary between the functional transition and melt regions is also usually poorly defined. However, it is becoming increasingly more common to incorporate a distinct screw section, viz., a metering section, on the end of the screw within the melt region. When a metering screw is designed and operated properly, the boundary between the functional transition and melt regions normally occurs at or upstream from the start of the metering section. This metering section is usually four to six diameters long and is relatively shallow in comparison with the preceding screw sections. In a properly designed metering screw, the metering section is the rate-controlling portion of the screw.

The use of a metering section provides both operational and design advantages. Since the output rate of a shallow metering section is relatively insensitive to variations in pressure at either end, the metering section has a stabilizing influence on the extruder discharge rate. The higher level of shear imposed on the melt in a metering section is also frequently desirable in that it contributes to achieving a more homogeneous extrudate both thermally and mechanically. From a design viewpoint, the use of a metering section is most advantageous, since the established melt-extrusion theories can be applied with reasonable confidence to the design of this screw section which, as previously mentioned, should be the rate-controlling section of the screw.

Feed Section. The solids-feed section of an extruder screw is usually so designed that there is no possibility that during operation the forward sections of the screw will ever be starved for material. This means that the feed section is purposely overdesigned to convey more than the average requirement of resin. For this reason, except for experimental studies, Eq. (137) in its complete form is seldom used. Instead, the simplified equations give approximations sufficiently accurate for use in screw design.

Practical design is also arrived at via useful empirical approximations which, experience has taught, afford a sufficient degree of accuracy for designing this section of the screw. The value of having the complete equation lies not so much in being able to make an absolute design calculation as in being able to examine the contribution of each of the several factors in the equation and obtain thereby a basis for judgment of their relative importance and contribution.

By examining the relationship of q_s/N, the solids-conveying rate, to the other variables in Eq. (137) (as was done in detail in Ref. 24), it can be deduced that solids conveying will be favored by (1) a deep screw channel, (2) low friction of the plastic on the screw, (3) high friction of the plastic on the barrel, and (4) a helix angle that gives the greatest conveying output obtainable for the particular coefficient of friction of the specific plastic on the screw.

The correctness of these facts has been borne out extensively by experience. Screw channels are normally made deep in the feed section. The primary practical limit in this case is that of having adequate strength remaining in the shaft. To favor low friction on the screw, the channel surfaces are machined to a fine finish and are then polished or chrome-plated. An important corollary here is that the periodic cleaning and polishing of screw surfaces will improve the conveying action of the feed section. Conversely, it is not necessary or even desirable to machine extruder barrels to a finish finer than that necessary for satisfactory cleaning.

Some indication of the relative effectiveness of a screw in conveying solids is given by the bracketed tangent function in Eq. (137). The value of this term depends on the screw helix angle ϕ and the angle of direction of the solids motion θ. This latter angle is a function of the coefficient of friction between the solids and the screw and barrel surfaces.

This tangent function has been calculated for a 2.0-in.-diameter screw with a 0.40-in.-deep channel for the case where there is no pressure generation. The results are shown in Fig. 4.37. The coefficients of friction for most plastics fall in the 0.25 to 0.50 range, with the majority being 0.4 to 0.5. Thus, a helix angle of 17 to 20 deg is the most efficient for most plastics. A helix angle of 17.7 deg, or pitch equal to the diameter, is considered a good choice not only for efficiency of feeding but also for simplicity in machining the screw.

For proper operation of a metering screw, it is important that the feed section of the screw have sufficient conveying capacity to keep the metering section fully supplied with polymer. To accomplish this in a screw with a constant pitch, it is necessary to make the channel depth of the feed section approximately three times as deep as the channel depth of the metering section. If the channel depth ratio is too small, the delivery end may occasionally receive less material than is required by the metering section. Erratic, or in extreme cases, interrupted extrusion ensues. Conversely, if the channel volume ratio is too high, the capacity of the rear portion of the screw may be too great. Forcing or overriding of the delivery zone of the screw may occur. Surging and nonuniform output result.

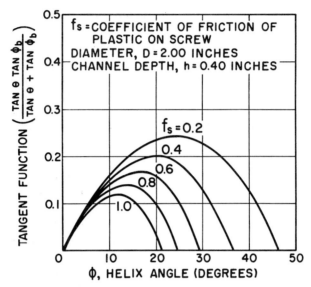

Fig. 4.37. Tangent function *vs.* helix angle for a typical feed screw.

The term "compression ratio," which is frequently used in the industry to describe the channel depth or channel volume ratio, can be misleading. The only pressure rise which normally takes place in the so-called "compression zone" is the usually small increment that arises from the normal melt pumping action of the screw. An expression analogous to Eq. (112) can be used to estimate this pressure increase. If unmelted, solid feed particles are forced into a diminishing volume section of the screw, a wedging action occurs that will indeed tend to compress these solid particles to some extent. It is only in this sense that the use of the term "compression" is at all valid. Even here it should be realized that this compression due to wedging does not result in any appreciable increase in hydrostatic pressure. Pressure will increase, but the increase results primarily from the usual solids- or melt-conveying action of a screw section having a partially restricted discharge.

For the sake of clarity, we therefore will use the term "channel volume ratio" or, in a constant-pitch screw, "channel depth ratio" rather than compression ratio.

The validity of choosing a channel volume ratio of about 3:1 to 4:1 may be deduced from some facts which have been learned by practical experience. The line of reasoning goes as follows:

(1) In the channel of a rotating screw the maximum theoretical volumetric displacement of a nonsheared solid equals twice the volumetric

displacement of a sheared fluid. (Refer to Eq. (141). This corresponds to plug-type flow.*)

(2) The bulk density of a cube or cylinder-cut plastic feed material is about one half that of the fluid plastic melt.

(3) Because of slippage and tumbling, the efficiency of solids conveying is 30 to 50 per cent, averaging about 40 per cent. This conveying efficiency is often influenced by screw speed.

(4) The normal variation in solids feeding resulting from tumbling, slippage, temporary blockage, etc., is ±10 per cent, but to avoid starved feeding there must be no negative variation, so the variation must be made +20 per cent, −0 per cent.

By combining these factors mathematically, we can estimate that the minimum ratio of volumetric displacement in the feed section to that in the metering section, i.e., the channel depth ratio, needed is

$$\text{C.D.R.} = \frac{1}{2} \times \frac{2}{1} \times \frac{1}{0.40} \times \frac{1}{1 - 0.20} = 3.1$$

As an example of the use of the simplified equation, Eq. (142), the conveying rate of a typical feed-screw section for an acrylic resin is computed as follows:

Dimensions of feed section of screw:

> Lead, $t = 2.29$ in.
>
> Diameter, $D = 2.00$ in.
>
> Channel depth, $h = 0.48$ in.
>
> $\cos \phi_s = 0.809$
>
> $\sin \phi_s = 0.588$

Resin properties:

> Coefficient of friction of resin $= 0.50$
>
> Bulk density of resin $= 0.613$ g/cc

$$E = \frac{D - h}{D}$$

$$= 0.755$$

---

* This plug flow should not be considered analogous to "nut and bolt" conveying. To illustrate this point, in a screw with an infinitely long lead, a "nut" would be conveyed at an infinite rate, whereas the "plug" referred to here would have no forward motion.

$$C = \frac{D - 2h}{D}$$

$$= 0.51$$

$$\tan \phi_b = \frac{t}{\pi D}$$

$$= 0.372$$

$$\phi_b = 20.4 \text{ deg}$$

$$\tan \phi_a = \frac{t}{\pi(D - h)}$$

$$= 0.492$$

$$\phi_a = 26.3 \text{ deg}$$

$$\tan \phi_s = \frac{t}{\pi(D - 2h)}$$

$$= 0.728$$

$$\phi_s = 36.0 \text{ deg}$$

$$K = \frac{E(\tan \phi_a + f_s)}{1 - f_s \tan \phi_a} = 0.997$$

Neglecting the width of the flight, the effects of contact with the trailing edge of the flight, and pressure, Eq. (142) is used to find θ.

$$\cos \theta = K \sin \theta + C \ (K \sin \phi_s + C \cos \phi_s) \tag{142}$$

$$\cos \theta = 0.997 \sin \theta + 0.508$$

This equation may be solved by trial and error or by the use of the design chart in Fig. 4.38. Here, M is defined by

$$M = C(K \sin \phi_s + C \cos \phi_s) + \frac{2h}{t} (KC \tan \phi_s + E^2)$$

$$\tag{143}$$

$$+ \frac{hE}{Lf_b} \sin \phi_a(E \cos \phi_a + K \sin \phi_a) \ln \frac{p_2}{p_1}$$

For this particular problem the last two terms in Eq. (143) are zero, and M therefore equals 0.508.

The angle of motion θ is found to be 24 deg, from which

$$\tan \theta = 0.445$$

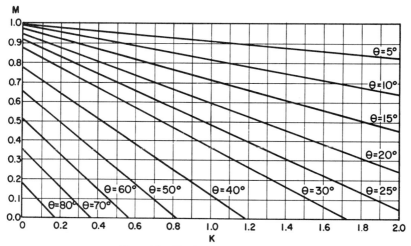

Fig. 4.38. Design chart; M vs. K.

Substituting into Eq. (137),

$$\frac{q_s}{N} = \pi^2 \frac{Dh(D - h) \tan \theta \tan \phi_b}{\tan \theta + \tan \phi_b} = 2.78 \text{ cu in./rev}$$

After being multiplied by the bulk density factor, the output is estimated to be 27.9 g/rev.

When a screw with these dimensions was tested in feeding and conveying "Lucite" 140 acrylic resin, the average measured conveying rate was 28.9 g/rev. This experiment was conducted with both the screw and the barrel having an average roughness estimated as 32 μ in. In this case the friction of the plastic on the barrel was probably about the same as that on the screw, i.e., $f_b = f_s$, which is the assumption that was made in the derivation of the equation used.

When the extruder barrel had an estimated average roughness of 128 μ in. and the friction on the barrel was undoubtedly greater than that on the screw, the average measured conveying rate was 32.9 g/rev. When the barrel was highly polished to an average roughness of 8 μ in., the measured rate fell to 24.3 g/rev.

Transition Section. Of the three zones of an extruder screw, only the melting or transition zone has not yet been analyzed mathematically. How much the lack of rigorous equations for this section has hampered the design of extruder screws is difficult to judge.

Experience has shown that, for hard thermoplastics with a sharp melting point such as 66 nylon, the transition from the deep feed section to the shallow metering section should be rapid, occurring in a turn of the screw or less. In the case of a soft thermoplastic, such as branched polyethylene, it does not matter whether the volumetric transition occurs in one, two, or even five turns.

Two connotations have been attached to the term "transition section" as used in this text: (1) the screw section in which the *channel dimensions* change from those of the feed section to the metering section; (2) the portion of the screw length in which the *polymer changes in phase* from a solid to a melt.

Where ambiguity might arise, we will refer to the latter as the *phase-transition zone*. In a well-designed metering screw, the phase transition should be completed before the material enters the metering section.

In the phase-transition zone, pellets are heated primarily by conduction, radiation, and internal shearing. At the same time the mode of mass transport changes in a complex manner, from tumbling and sliding, through alternating slipping and sticking, to laminar shear flow as the plastic becomes heated. The phase-transition section may comprise the major portion of the screw length. In relatively longer screws the phase transition may take place over a length of 12 to 16 screw diameters, which is frequently about two thirds of the total screw length.

The achievement of a rigorous, mathematical design basis for the longest section, the phase-transition zone of the extruder screw, remains a real challenge to plastics engineers. In practice the problem has been circumvented by purposely overdesigning the feed section and then regulating the output by means of a rigorously designed metering pump section just before the molten plastic reaches the die.

Metering Section. The design of a metering section for a plasticating extruder can be based upon the extrusion theory for screw melt pumps that previously has been developed. Sample calculations of the performance of a screw melt pump were presented earlier. These calculations are analogous to those encountered in the design of a plasticating extruder metering section.

Ideally, the performance of the metering section should establish the over-all pumping characteristics of the extruder. In practice this is found to be very nearly the case for a properly designed metering screw. However, the metering section cannot be considered completely isolated from the rest of the screw when its performance is being analyzed. The metering section restricts the discharge of the feed and transition sections, and thereby causes pressure to be built up at the forward end of the feed section. This pressure contributes to the over-all pressure difference across the metering section and therefore influences the pressure flow through the metering section. The pressure generated at this intermediate screw location is dependent on the combined pumping characteristics of both the feed and transition sections as well as on the degree of restriction which the metering section imposes on the flow. Several workers[10, 11, 34, 38] have recognized the existence of this intermediate pressure, but as yet no sound procedure has been developed for predicting its magnitude. Progress along this line must be preceded by a better understanding of the complex processes occurring in the polymer phase-transition region. Until this is available, these intermediate pressures can only be estimated on the basis of past measurements.

The influence of this intermediate pressure on the net discharge rate of the extruder depends primarily on the pumping characteristic of the metering section. If this characteristic is flat, as would be the case for a shallow metering section, the discharge rate is relatively insensitive to this upstream intermediate pressure. This is usually a desirable situation, since this pressure depends on the somewhat random processes occurring in the feed and transition regions and is therefore likely to be variable.

Pressure distributions within a 2½-in. plasticating extruder employing a conventional metering screw have been measured by the writer during the extrusion of polyethylene. Typical results are shown in Fig. 4.39. Curve *A* represents the situation found when employing a low-resistance die. The pressure generated by the feed and transition sections causes an overriding of the metering section. Pressure flow is directed toward the die, and the net output exceeds the drag-flow capacity of the screw. In effect, the metering section is functioning as a dynamic choke.

In curve *B* the situation is such that the inlet and outlet pressures of the

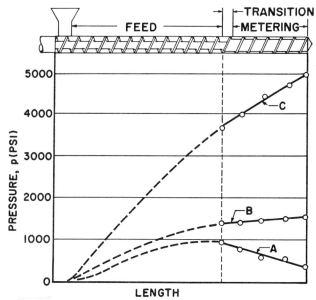

Fig. 4.39. Pressure distribution in a plasticating extruder.

metering zone are very nearly equal. The discharge rate now approximates that given by just the drag-flow term of Eq. (66).

Curve C illustrates the more commonly pictured situation in which the pressure increases along the length of the metering zone toward the die.

Extruder Length-to-Diameter Ratio.

The demand for extrusion free of pulses and temperature inhomogeneities has produced a trend toward machines with longer barrels. Whereas 10 years ago extruders commonly had barrel-length to barrel-diameter ratios of 12:1, few machines are built today for work on plastic materials with ratios of less than 18:1. Ratios of 20:1 and 24:1 have become common. Barrels up to 30 diameters in length have been built, but these are used primarily in machines for extraction processes. The longer machines increase the amount of mixing action to which the material may be exposed within the extruder. An increase in barrel length enables the processor to improve the uniformity of the extrudate at a given throughput rate, or the throughput rate may be increased without a reduction in the quality of the extrudate, provided that adequate power is available in the drive.

If the desired extrusion rate in a new installation is on the border between the anticipated maximum of one extruder and the nominal rate of the next larger extruder, the choice must be made between installing an extra long machine of the smaller diameter, or a standard-length machine of the greater diameter.

If the screw in either case were properly designed to supply the desired amount of energy through mechanical work to the resin, the drive power required to extrude at the desired rate would be the same, regardless of the machine used. Since the size of the required drive would therefore be essentially the same in either case, it usually develops that no *major* economies can be made by using the smaller-diameter extruder of greater barrel length. In addition, the larger-diameter extruder will usually provide somewhat greater flexibility in the range of different resins that can be extruded and in the range of extrusion conditions that can be attained.

Plasticating Extruder Power Consumption

The problems of predicting the power consumption of plasticating extruders logically fall into two categories. First, it is necessary to estimate the total power that *must* actually be supplied to the resin by the extruder in order to melt and pump the resin at the desired rate. Secondly, it is necessary to establish whether or not this necessary power *will* be provided to the resin by the extruder, and, if so, how the power will be proportioned between that received from the screw as mechanical work and that from the barrel heaters as transmitted heat energy. Also, it is desirable to have before-the-fact knowledge if barrel cooling will be necessary in order to remove excess mechanical energy dissipated by the screw.

These problems will be discussed separately.

Minimum Power Required for Extrusion. In a plasticating extruder a certain minimum amount of energy is required in order to melt the feed granules, raise the melt to the desired extrusion temperature, and force the melt through the die against the back pressure developed at the die. The calculation of this energy is a simple problem in thermodynamics and is not dependent in any way on the extruder design.

If the polymer is assumed to be incompressible and the small inertial effects are neglected, an energy balance around the extruder barrel results in

$$\frac{Z}{q_w} = \int_{t_1}^{t_2} \rho C_p \, dt + V \Delta p + \lambda \tag{144}$$

where

Z = net power to polymer

  = $Z_{\text{screw}} + Z_{\text{heaters}} - Z_{\text{cooling}}$

q_w = mass flow rate of polymer

t_1 , t_2 = inlet and discharge polymer temperature, respectively

C_p = heat capacity of the polymer

V = specific volume of the polymer

  = $1/\rho$

Δp = screw discharge pressure minus inlet pressure

λ = heat of fusion of polymer

The pressure-rise term $V \Delta p$ can usually be neglected. For even a relatively high discharge pressure of 10,000 psi, this term contributes only about 10 per cent to the total power for most polymers.

The energy required in the polymer thus becomes

$$\frac{Z}{q_w} = \int_{t_1}^{t_2} \rho C_p \, dt + \lambda \tag{145}$$

The energy per pound Z/q_w is thus easily determined if the heat capacity and latent heat of fusion are known. These data are tabulated in Section III for representative commercial polymers.

The energy content has been calculated from Eq. (145) for polyethylene over the normal range of extrusion discharge temperatures and for an as-

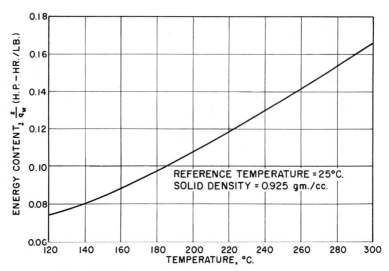

Fig. 4.40. Energy content of branched polyethylene.

sumed inlet temperature of 25°C. The results are shown in Fig. 4.40. From this graph it can be seen, for example, that the energy content of polyethylene at 200°C is 0.11 hp-hr/lb. Thus to extrude at a rate of 100 lb/hr would require that 11 hp be supplied to the melt.

The heat content of most commercial thermoplastic resins at extrusion temperatures is in the range of 0.08 to 0.15 hp-hr/lb. If the heat supplied from the barrel heaters is neglected, it follows as a rule of thumb that from 6 to 12 lb/hr can be extruded for each horsepower supplied to the screw.

Power Actually Delivered by the Screw. In the previous paragraphs it was shown as a typical example that 11 hp must be supplied to the polymer if polyethylene at 200°C is to be extruded at a rate of 100 lb/hr. Unfortunately, there is no guarantee that the screw actually will deliver exactly 11 hp to the polymer by mechanical working of the cubes and melt. The power that will be delivered by the screw and dissipated in the polymer depends, in a complex manner, on both the solid-state and melt properties of the polymer as well as on the bulk behavior of the polymer feed particles

In the above example, if the screw were to deliver only 10 hp, the melt temperature would drop by 15C° to 185°C unless heat were added through the barrel to make up for the difference. This is actually a desirable method of operation, since in this way some external control can be maintained over the extrusion temperature.

If the feed material were changed to a resin of higher viscosity, this same extruder might deliver 12 hp at 100 lb/hr. Heat would now have to be removed from the polymer if the desired 200°C discharge temperature were to be maintained.

Because of the complexity of the plasticating extrusion process, it is extremely difficult to calculate accurately the power consumption of such a process. Experience remains the best guide in this situation, and power-consumption estimates usually rely to a large extent on data obtained during the past operation of equipment of similar design.

For portions of the screw where laminar flow conditions can be assumed to prevail, the previously developed equations for power dissipation in a screw melt pump can be used. These equations will also predict power-consumption trends with screw speeds, viscosity, and screw geometry.

Scale-up of Melt and Plasticating Extruders

Scale-up in the operation of geometrically similar melt extruders for isothermal operation has been discussed by Strub[68] and later by Carley and McKelvey.[20] Gore and McKelvey[34] have considered scale-up of both isothermal and adiabatic melt extruders. By geometrically similar extruders is meant a pair of extruders in which the ratio of all linear dimensions is a constant value x.

If heat transfer, both external and internal, is assumed negligible, it is not difficult to demonstrate that if either an isothermal or an adiabatic extruder is scaled up to a geometrically larger machine, the developed pressures will be equal, while the discharge rates and power consumption will be proportional to the cube of the geometric scale-up factor for operation at any given screw speed. In the case of adiabatic extrusion, the temperature rise of the melt will be identical for geometrically similar extruders.

While the preceding cubical scale-up in rates may be realized in certain specific instances, the general attainment of this goal will not be possible—particularly in operations where heat transfer plays an important part. Some transfer of heat by conduction is always present in an extruder. This is true even for so-called "adiabatic" operation. In this case, by definition, there exists no external heat transfer. Internal conduction of heat within the melt in the channel and axially along the barrel walls and screw shaft does exist, however. In practice, complete adiabatic operation is seldom desirable; some external heat transfer is advantageous in order to increase the flexibility of operation by permitting some degree of independent control over the extrusion temperature.

The rate at which heat can be transferred by conduction varies approximately as the square of the geometric scale-up ratio, i.e., as the barrel area. In the extreme and unattainable case, if all of the heat in the extrudate were derived from conduction through the barrel wall or back along the screw shaft and none from mechanical work of the screw, the extruder melting capacity could be scaled up only in proportion to the square of the geometric scale-up ratio, rather than the cube. This implies that, for geometrically similar screws, the larger screw would have to rotate slower so as to maintain a constant peripheral velocity. The pumping rate would then be greater than that in the smaller machine by a factor x^2 rather than x^3, and the heat-transfer rate would be sufficient to maintain the same melt temperature in the large machine as in the small unit.

A second important factor that must be considered in addition to the melting rate is the effect of scale-up on the thermal homogeneity of the extrudate. Even if all of the heat in the fluid were derived from mechanical working by the screw and none from conduction through the barrel, temperature gradients would still exist within the fluid because of the nonuniform distribution of mechanical shear energy within the fluid. A high shear rate exists in the fluid between the flights and barrel wall, which causes this to be a region of high heat generation. Furthermore, the shear rate in the screw channel iteslf varies widely over the channel cross section, as can be seen by reference to Figs. 4.15 through 4.20.

The residence time required for achieving a specified degree of equalization of temperature variation by means of *internal* heat transfer within the fluid is approximately proportional to the square of the channel size. This means that even in the case of true adiabatic operation, if a third-power scale-up ratio is used, the thermal homogeneity (or quality) of the extrudate in the larger extruder would be inferior to that in the smaller machine. This inhomogeneity would be aggravated if external heat transfer were also present.

In order to achieve the same degree of thermal homogeneity in the extrudate from two machines of different diameters, it is necessary to operate the larger machine at a slower screw speed or else to decrease the channel depth in the larger machine below that which would exist if the scale-up were geometric. A combination of both methods is a preferred alternative. One common approach is to increase the channel depth as the square root of the diameter scale-up ratio, and to lower the screw speed. The screw speed may be reduced by a factor as great as the square root of the diameter scale-up ratio.[25]

Irrespective of which approach is taken, the net effect is to decrease the capacity of the larger extruder to something below a cubic scale-up of the smaller machine.

In the case of a plasticating extruder, the bulk and solid-state properties of the feed particles determine to a large extent the increase in output attainable as a result of size scale-up. If the feed particles are hard and rigid, and if, upon melting, they form a low-viscosity fluid, as in the case of some nylons, internal shear is ineffective in generating heat, and conduction through the barrel must be relied upon to supply much of the energy required to melt the polymer. Heat transfer can thus become the controlling factor, and the ratio of attainable outputs may be limited to the square of the extruder size scale-up. Output may be limited to even lower factors in the case of precision extrusion, where stringent quality requirements in terms of thermal homogeneity are imposed on the extrudate.

For polymers which can undergo considerable deformation in the solid state, mechanical working is an effective means for introducing the energy required for plastication. Polyethylene is perhaps an outstanding example of a polymer in this category. If the energy input due to mechanical shear corresponds exactly to that required to maintain the desired melt temperature, the output and power can be increased in the limit as the cube of the geometric scale-up ratio of geometrically similar extruders. The exact scale-up attainable will again depend on the quality requirements imposed on the extrudate.

In the case of adiabatic extrusion, if maintenance of a fixed level in the quality of the extrudate is not required, a rate increase in proportion to the cube of the geometric scale-up factor may indeed be possible. Carley and McKelvey[20] presented the results of a successful tenfold scale-up from a 2- to a 20-in. polyethylene extruder on this basis. Power and capacity at a constant 15 rpm were 10^3 times larger in the 20-in. extruder, while the discharge temperature and pressure remained essentially the same.

From the preceding discussion, it can be seen that there is no easy or universal answer to the question, "How much production can I expect from a larger extruder?" The answer will depend, in a complex way, on the particular polymer and extruder design. To date, no rigorous approach to this subject has been made available, and recourse must usually be made to the generalizations of the type presented in the preceding paragraphs.

Instrumentation and Controls

Proper controls and instruments are required to ensure that the extruder delivers melt at the desired uniform temperature and rate. They also offer an important means for analyzing the performance of the extrusion equipment.

Temperature Measurement and Control. The melt temperature is governed by the energy put into the resin by the shearing action between the screw and the barrel, and by the heat conducted through the barrel. Control of the heat transferred through the barrel provides important flexibility for operation over a wide band of temperatures. Conducted heat also permits preheating the extruder barrel for easier start-ups.

The temperature-control system consists of a sensing element, a controlling element which interprets the information received from the sensing element, and a heating and/or cooling element which is regulated by the controller. In an extruder barrel there are usually several heating zones which are regulated by individual controllers. Thermocouple-actuated controllers are most common. Control systems actuated through thermistors and bimetallic strips are also used.

Barrel temperature-control thermocouples should be located so that the temperature at the inner surface of the barrel is maintained at the desired value with a minimum of fluctuation. The control instrument can regulate the temperature only at the location of the thermocouple. Consequently, if the control thermocouple were located at the outer wall of the barrel, there would be no indication of the true temperature at the inner surface of the barrel. Conversely, if the thermocouple were located near the inside barrel wall, it would indicate the temperature in this critical region as desired, but there would be temperature surges and temperature overriding because of the time required for heat to be conducted through the barrel from the heat source. Neither of these locations, therfore, would be entirely satisfactory for good control of temperature at the inner wall.

A compromise thermocouple location is about one third of the way into the barrel wall and in the center of each heating zone. An alternate method is to employ two thermocouples in each heating zone. One is located near the heat source, and the other near the inner barrel wall. The thermocouple nearer the heat source is connected to the controller, and, in the case of a barrel equipped with resistance heaters, it maintains the heater-band temperature at an even level. The deep-well thermocouple is used solely as an indication of the critical temperature at the inner barrel wall.

Temperature Controllers. There are several common types of controls used on extruders equipped with electrical resistance heaters.

Manual Control.—Manual control, as provded through the use of a variable power transformer, affords the simplest and cheapest type of temperature adjustment. Since temperature is not automatically controlled, it is difficult to correlate a voltage setting with the desired barrel temperature, particularly if screw speed, resin viscosity, or other factors influencing the mechanically generated heat inside the machine are altered.

On-Off Control.—With an on-off-type control, heaters are actuated when the temperature indicated by the thermocouple is lower than the instrument setting. This system causes some fluctuations in the barrel temperature, with a resultant variation in the melt temperature.

Time-Proportioning Control.—With time-proportioning-control action, power to the heater bands is turned on and off for periods of time which vary with the proximity of the indicated temperature to the instrument setting. This system permits a marked reduction of barrel temperature fluctuations as compared to the on-off-type control.

Voltage-Proportioning Control.—With a voltage-proportioning control, power to the heater bands is supplied continuously as with a variable transformer. The voltage increases when the temperature measured by the con-

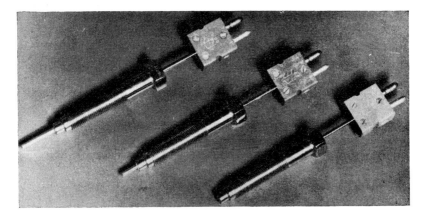

F𝙸ɢ. 4.41. Melt thermocouples.

trol thermocouple drops below the instrument setting, and decreases if the the set temperature is exceeded. Since this is a stepless control action, barrel temperature cycling is reduced to a minimum.

The various controls described above may also be employed to govern the temperature of heat-transfer media in jacketed barrels and to actuate the flow of cooling media when cooling is required.

Melt Thermocouples. It is important to know the temperature of the melt at the discharge end of the screw. This temperature to a large extent governs the behavior of the extrudate in the die and the take-off system. The design of a practical melt thermocouple (Fig. 4.41) has been described by Bernhardt.[9] Melt temperature is most conveniently measured by a thermocouple which is inserted into the melt stream and is connected to a measuring device, such as a potentiometer. Usually the best location for this melt thermocouple is in the die adapter near the end of the screw. In some instances additional melt thermocouples are installed in the die.

Melt thermocouples should not be used to govern temperature controllers, since the thermal lag between the heat source and the melt is excessive, and poor control action would result. Conversely, control thermocouples located in the barrel wall should not be relied upon as a measure of the melt temperature since the barrel-wall temperature is often significantly different from that of the melt.

Pressure Measurement and Control. The pressure of the polymer can be conveniently measured using a Bourdon-type gauge.[9] The gauges are usually installed in the die adapter. Sometimes gauges are installed both before and after the breaker plate and screens. A rise in pressure differential across the plate and screen assembly will then indicate when the screens become plugged.

To use Bourdon gauges for pressure measurements in molten thermoplastics, the entire Bourdon tube as well as the adapter fitting (Fig. 4.42) must be filled with high-vacuum silicone grease. The grease keeps molten polymer from entering the gauge and freezing there. The gauge should incorporate a capillary bleeder at the dead end of the Bourdon tube to bleed the air from this pocket, while the gauge is being filled with grease. The grease may conveniently be pumped into the assembly through a fitting in the adapter using a grease gun.

The pressure gauge and stock thermocouple, used together, simplify trouble shooting and are useful in describing operating conditions. Knowledge of the pressure of the adapter of the extruder is also helpful in carrying out extruder performance calculations.

With properly designed metering screws it is usually not necessary to maintain high back pressures at the head of the screw. For these screws, the delivery will be relatively independent of changes in the die restriction.

FIG. 4.42. Pressure gauge.

However, if it is desired to increase the amount of working which the resin received in the screw channel, particularly in the case where screws with relatively deep flights are used, it may be an advantage to increase the back pressure at the head of the screw by increasing the die resistance. This may be accomplished by installing a valve in the head of the extruder. Plug valves (Fig. 4.43), needle valves (Fig. 4.44), and modified forms of gate valves have been used successfully.[7, 44]

Screw Speed. The output of an extruder is influenced by the screw speed. Usually, the speed control is set by the machine operator at a given value, and speed uniformity of the screw is dependent only on the characteristics of the extruder drive. However, in some processes it may be desirable to vary the screw speed to counteract changes in pressure at the die. This can be done by feeding a signal from a pressure gauge, located near the die, back to the speed controller.

A tachometer is a convenient means for directly measuring the screw speed. It is especially useful in permitting rapid determination of screw-speed uniformity and facilitates accurate speed adjustments during start-up.

Drive Power. An ammeter-voltmeter combination (for d-c drive), or a wattmeter (for a-c drive), produces a continuous indication of motor load

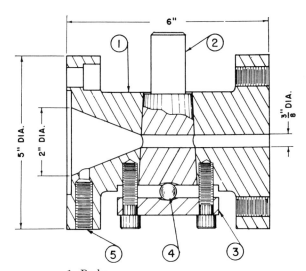

1. Body
2. Plug
3. Retainer plate
4. $\frac{1}{2}$ in diameter hardened ball
5. Stock thermocouple or pressure gauge fitting.

Fig. 4.43. Cross section of a plug valve.

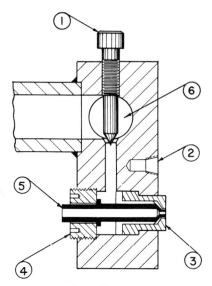

1. Flow adjustment needle
2. Thermocouple well
3. Die
4. Guide tip plug
5. Guide tip
6. Distribution manifold

Fig. 4.44. Cut-away view of needle valve used in multiple tubing die.

With these instruments it is possible to determine horsepower output for a given extrusion condition. This indicates the amount of working a thermoplastic material receives while in the extruder and thus helps establish operating conditions. These instruments are also useful in diagnosing troubles and preventing costly breakdowns. For example, one indication of bridging (the fusion of resin on the screw and consequent stoppage of feeding) is a sudden drop in the amperage drawn by the motor. Conversely, a sudden rise in motor current might indicate a plugged die or binding of the screw, thus prompting action to prevent damage to the equipment.

Recorders. Continuous recorders for any of the control variables discussed are advantageous for making a permanent record of the operating conditions. Such information is useful in determining if operating conditions are stable and to detect trends for trouble shooting.

DIE DESIGN

Definition of Extrusion Dies

While other shaping tools such as injection molds, stamping and forging tools, die-casting molds, wire-drawing dies, etc., are also spoken of as dies, the discussion here is limited to that class of tools through which plastic melts are forced under pressure to yield products in which only the dimensions perpendicular to the direction of flow are determined by the die.

Very simply, an extrusion die can be thought of as a shaped hole through which flows a steady stream of melt. The shape of the die determines the shape of the extrudate section, but the two may not be congruent, or even geometrically similar. Within this definition fall all the dies used on plastic extruders, dies for sheeting, pipe, gasketing, T-sections, etc. A mold is not a die within this definition, since a mold determines *all* the dimensions of the product.

Some extrudates are further shaped after extrusion, as in bottle blowing and sheet forming; these operations are discussed in later chapters.

Simplified Analytical Approach to Die Design

The flow of melt under pressure through a die may be calculated most simply by using the Newtonian flow equation:

$$q = \frac{kp}{\mu} \tag{146}$$

where k is defined for the several geometric shapes, shown in Fig. 4.45, as follows:

$$k = \frac{\pi R^4}{8L} \quad \text{circular orifice} \tag{147}$$

$$k = \frac{wh^3}{12L} \quad \text{slit} \tag{148}$$

$$k = \frac{\pi(R_0 + R_i)(R_0 - R_i)^3}{12L} \quad \text{annulus} \tag{149}$$

and where

$$p = \text{pressure drop through the die}$$

$$\mu = \text{viscosity of melt flowing through the die}$$

Calculations made in this simplified form must make use of the viscosity determined at the proper shear rate for the particular conditions.

Not only are these formulas useful for designing dies, but they can also be used to analyze the performance of existing dies. Even in complex dies, if the throughput and total pressure drop are known, it is possible to learn how this drop is distributed among the several parts. For each part the shear rate is calculated and the apparent viscosity found from the appropriate curve in part III. From this information the pressure drop in that part can be calculated. The sum of these pressure drops should be nearly equal to the observed total.

In designing a composite die, one can start with a rough guess as to the flow-influencing dimensions, then make calculations of the sort just described. If the apportionment of the pressure drop is poor, a new estimate is made, correcting the old dimensions in the direction that will improve performance. After a few times around, the dimensions found should be satisfactory. Dies of complex-shaped orifices do not lend themselves readily to this simple analysis and have usually been designed by repeated trial-and-adjust modifications of the orifice shapes.

As an example of the application of the above simple equations, consider a manifold-type sheeting die, Fig. 4.46. This is essentially a pipe with a slit along one edge. In the manifold the shear rate is $4q/\pi R^3$. In the die lips it is $6q/wh^2$, where R is the manifold radius, h is the slit opening, and w is the manifold length, all in inches, and q is the throughput in cubic inches per second. Since most dies are open to the air, the pressure drop p is equal to the gauge pressure in the head, in pounds per square inch. Reference must be made to an apparent viscosity curve such as Fig. 4.47, which gives the

CIRCULAR ORIFICE:

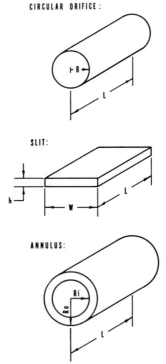

SLIT:

ANNULUS:

FIG. 4.45. Geometry of simple die passages.

apparent viscosity at any apparent shear rate for the material and temperature in question. Assume that $q = 2$, $R = 1.5$, $w = 24$, $h = 0.04$. The entire output enters the feed end of the die and starts to flow along the manifold, but all of it has gone out the slit before it reaches the other end.
Assume that half the total flow is a fair figure to represent the average volume
flow along the manifold. Then the shear rate in that part is

$$\frac{(4)(2)}{(2)(\pi)(1.5)^3} = 0.38 \text{ sec}^{-1},$$

corresponding on Fig. 4.47 to an apparent viscosity of 4.7 lb sec/sq in.
In the lips the shear rate is

$$\frac{(6)(2)}{(24)(0.04)^2} = 312,$$

corresponding to a viscosity of 0.186, less than 1/25th of the manifold
viscosity. With this information, the pressure drops can be computed.

Combining Eqs. (146) and (147), the average or mean pressure drop
p_m along the manifold is given by

$$p_m = \frac{8 q_m \mu_m w}{\pi R^4}.$$

Similarly, from Eqs. (146) and (148), the drop through the lips p_l is

$$p_l = \frac{12 q_l \mu_l L}{w h^3}$$

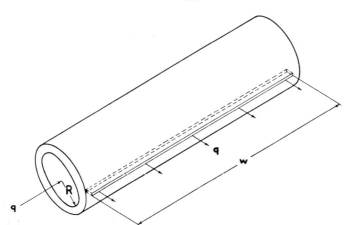

Fɪɢ. 4.46. Diagram of an end-fed manifold sheeting die. Land length of lips, L, is
measured in direction of small arrows emerging from lips. (*Courtesy Modern Plastics
Magazine*)

APPARENT VISCOSITY μ_d, LB$_F$ – SEC./IN.^{2}

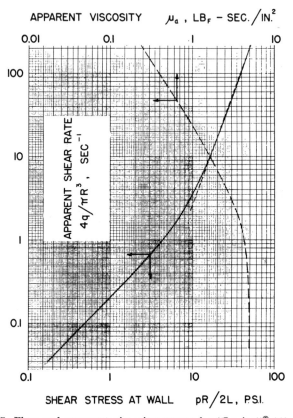

SHEAR STRESS AT WALL $pR/2L$, P.S.I.

FIG. 4.47. Flow and apparent viscosity curves for "Lucite"® 140 at 400°F.

Substituting the above data into these equations, and assuming the land length of the lips = 0.20 in., the two pressure drops are

$$p_m = \frac{(8)(1)(4.7)(24)}{(3.14)(1.5)^4} = 57 \text{ psi}$$

$$p_l = \frac{(12)(2)(0.186)(0.20)}{(24)(0.04)^3} = 580 \text{ psi}$$

These calculations show that the drop along the manifold is about 10 per cent of that across the lips. It is apparent that this die would deliver a film that is much thicker at the feed end than at the far end. To improve the uniformity of caliper would require that either the manifold radius be increased, the lip land length be increased, or both. If the land length is increased, the total pressure drop will increase also. Since the total pressure drop is only 637 psi, a considerable increase could be tolerated with most dies. An alternative, also resulting in a larger drop across the lips, is to reduce the aperture h and adjust the take-off mechanism to draw the film down less, if other considerations permit reduction of drawdown. Possible curtailment of output accompanying the increase in die resistance would also have to be considered before taking action, and this would require consideration of the operating characteristics of the extruder. The main point here is that this simple calculation has pinned down a serious defect in the design of this die and has suggested straightforward remedies for the defect.

More Fundamental Approach to Die Design

The use of the Newtonian flow equation becomes cumbersome for dies of complex geometry, and in it the viscosity term is correct only for those points at which the shear rate can be estimated accurately. Mathematical expressions in which the terms relating to the geometry of the passage and the viscosity may be continuously varied permit a complete analytical solution to the flow system. This integrated solution is obviously a closer approximation of the actual physical system than is a stepwise calculation.

Die-Design Problems. Die-design problems are of two kinds, chiefly (1) finding the combinations of dimensions that will give the desired production rate at a reasonable head pressure and (2) finding the die shape and dimensions that will impart the desired shape and size to the finished product. With regard to the second kind of problem, dies may be divided into two broad classes: (1) dies in which the melt flow is one-dimensional, i.e., where the velocity is changing in only one direction; (2) dies in which the flow is two-dimensional. In the one-dimensional-flow dies, which includes dies having circular, annular, and thin-slit cross sections, problems of adjusting the size and shape are easily solved by making an allowance for viscoelastic swelling of the emerging extrudate and/or by having an extrudate take-off device with adjustable drawdown.

With dies of the two-dimensional-flow class, which includes all other shapes, a number of forces are acting to distort the shape of the extrudate from that of the die. If the land length were everywhere the same, the thicker sections would flow much more rapidly than the thin ones. Usually, the drawn-off rate is everywhere the same; therefore, the thin sections emerge relatively too thin.

In this chapter the effects of compression recovery, viscoelasticity, and surface tension will not be treated quantitatively.* It is only for dies in

---

* Pao[55] has derived equations describing the two-dimensional flow of viscoelastic fluids, and it is possible that, with the aid of a high-speed computer, solutions to these equations for a number of shapes may be available some day. Such solutions, though necessarily specific to some particular set of conditions and dimensions, may provide a useful guide to design of dies for shapes.

which flow is one-dimensional that a reliable, quantitative design job can be accomplished. Approximate solutions will be attempted for one or two of the simpler two-dimensional cases, and some helpful suggestions can be made regarding the others. Fortunately, a great many of the commercially important dies fall into the first class.

Flow Behavior of Plastic Melts. The flow behavior of plastic melts is treated at length in Chap. 1, so it is reviewed only briefly here. All known thermoplastics exhibit non-Newtonian flow behavior at processing conditions; i.e., shear rate is not directly proportional to shear stress. Curves of apparent shear rate vs. shear stress for many materials are presented in Section III. Most of these curves are characterized by several features:

(1) Yield strength in shear at processing temperatures is essentially zero, so the curves pass through the zero-zero point.

(2) When plotted on log-log paper, most curves have a slope of 1 in the low shear-rate range; i.e., at low rates these materials are nearly Newtonian;

(3) The curvature is gentle, so that over a range of two or three orders of magnitude of shear rate the curves can be approximated well by straight lines. In addition, it has been observed experimentally[70] that many thermoplastic extrudates become wavy, rough, or torn if the applied shear stress exceeds about 100 psi. This upper working limit for stress can be raised perhaps threefold by tapering the approach to the die lips to an included angle of about 20 deg. *In designing any die, therefore, it is prudent to keep the shear stress well below this level of 100 psi.* Since tapering the inlet also prevents dead spots where melt might degrade, *it is recommended that the inlet be tapered wherever possible.*

The Reynolds numbers involved in plastic melt flow are far below the threshold of turbulence ($N_{Re} = 2,100$), so melt flow is always laminar. It is also usually safe to assume that the melt wets the walls of the die, and therefore the velocity at the wall is zero.

In turbulent flow of air and water, pressure changes in contraction and expansion owing to kinetic-energy changes (acceleration) may be substantial. However, in the usual ranges of melt flow, kinetic-energy effects are small, but the frictional losses associated with the convergent flow to produce the acceleration are quite sizable. The importance of pressure loss at inlets becomes obviously greater for smaller L/D values, since for a given flow rate the entrance loss will be constant and the land pressure loss will decrease with length. Under conditions of equal shear stress, the shear rates developed in tubes of different length-to-diameter (L/D) ratio are significantly unequal unless L/D exceeds about 20. Bagley[4] has recently proposed a simple formula, giving the tube length as a fixed term plus a number of diameters, which may be useful in designing dies when sufficient data are available to evaluate the constants.

The material entering the die, being under considerable pressure, is more dense than it is at atmospheric pressure. According to the equation of state,[65] the expansion amounts to about 0.7 per cent per 1,000 psi at 300°F and can be neglected.

Work (flow work $v\Delta p$) is done when melt is forced through a die by pressure. About 20 to 25 per cent of this work is absorbed by expansion of the polymer. The remainder appears as heat and causes an average temperature rise on the order of 3°C per 1,000 psi. The average figure does not tell the whole story, however; the work is concentrated most heavily in the regions of greatest shear rate, i.e., near the walls of the die. This reduces the viscosity in those regions, makes the velocity profile more pluglike,[14, 32, 69] and increases output by about 7 per cent per 1,000 psi. If anything, this greater tendency toward plug flow reduces distortion in two-dimensional-flow dies. The only practical difference it makes with one-dimensional-flow dies is an increase in rate. In shallow-flighted extruders—the kind recommended for high-pressure extrusion—the practical effect of this viscous heating will be a slightly reduced head pressure and increased capacity.

Power Law as a Basis for Die Design. As was observed in the preceding section, the log-log plots of shear stress vs. shear rate are nearly linear over limited ranges and can thus be approximated by the so-called power law, the equation for which is presented in Chap. 1, p. 29. The power law is reproduced here in its inverted form, since this form is easier to use in designing dies:

$$-\frac{dv}{dr} = \kappa \tau^{\nu} \tag{150}$$

where

v = the velocity of the fluid in the direction of flow at any point in the moving melt, (in./sec)

r = distance perpendicular to the flow direction increasing in the direction of increasing shear stress

κ = a flow constant for the melt that may be thought of as a fluidity. This κ is temperature dependent, changing much more rapidly with temperature than K, the consistency, defined on p. 29. Its units are $\text{in}^{2\nu}/(\text{lb}_F)^{\nu}(\text{sec})$. Most of the "activation energies" of flow reported in the literature for non-Newtonians refer to the temperature sensitivity of κ.

τ = the shear stress at any point r in the liquid, (psi)

ν = the "power" of the power law, a characteristic of each plastic. The exponent ν is equal to the average rate of change of log shear rate with respect to log shear stress over the stress range of interest and is therefore equal to $1/n$, as defined in Chap. 1. This exponent ν varies from 1 for Newtonian fluids to 4 or more for grossly non-Newtonian fluids and ranges between 1.5 and 3 for most of the commercially important thermoplastics. Most of the design equations in this chapter have been derived from Eq. (150).

Since, in a die of fixed dimensions, output seldom varies by as much as a factor of 10, the power law applicable to the range of interest will provide a good approximation of the true flow curve. A preliminary calculation will quickly establish the range. In some dies, such as sheeting dies with adjustable lips, it may be necessary to find dimensions that represent a good compromise for widely different shear rates. In this case the alternative is to find a number of paired values of κ and ν applicable to the different ranges, or to use a more general flow law.

Gee and Lyon[32] report that a two-term power law with three parameters, only one of which is temperature-dependent, closely describes the shear-stress–shear-rate dependence of plastic melts over the entire range from zero stress to the critical fracture stress. The equation is

$$-\frac{dv}{dr} = \frac{\tau}{\mu_0} (1 + C\tau^{\nu-1}) \qquad (151)$$

Where μ_0, the zero-shear viscosity (lb$_F$-sec/sq in.), is the temperature-dependent term and C is a constant.* Inspection of this formula shows that at low shear stresses, when the second term in parentheses becomes very small, the equation reduces to Newton's law of flow, while at high stresses it reduces to Eq. (150). Since Eq. (151) contains two terms involving the shear stress τ, its integrated forms are polynomials with nonintegral exponents. These are solved for the die dimensions by some iterative method of solution—Newton's method[64] is good here—that is more involved and takes a greater effort than the solutions of integrated forms of the simple power law. Only the two most important integrated forms of Eq. (151) will be presented in this chapter.

Use of the Power Law. As given in Eq. (150), the power law relates the point values of shear stress and shear rate, the so-called "true" values. However, in orifice rheometry wherein flow rate vs. pressure drop for melts flowing through circular holes is measured, it has been the custom to report the maximum shear stress, $pR/2L$, and the shear rate that would correspond to this if the material were Newtonian, $4q/\pi R^3$, or the "apparent"

* Evaluation of the constants from the flow curve (at any temperature) can be done simply and with fair accuracy by taking as μ_0 the average quotient of shear stress and shear rate at the three lowest measured stresses and letting ν be the average slope of the log-log plot over the last half decade of stress. Using these values, C is computed from the smoothed curve, taking five values over the entire stress range and averaging the results.

shear rate. The integrated forms of the power law and the fluidities κ (the fluidity based on true shear-rate data) and κ' (the fluidity based on apparent shear-rate data) differ slightly (for $\nu > 1$), depending on the value of ν and whether the corrected flow curve or the curve of apparent shear rate vs. maximum shear stress was used. On p. 252 the usual custom of plotting *apparent* shear rate vs. shear stress (both at the wall) has been followed, and *the integrated forms in this chapter are meant to be used with such unadjusted data.**

Apparent Viscosity. Although melt viscosity varies with shear stress, it is possible to use the appealingly simply Newtonian flow formula, providing the proper values of viscosity are inserted. Many die-design problems reduce to an equation in which everything is known but the land length and the viscosity.

The apparent shear rate is easily determined and permits the determination of the appropriate apparent viscosity from the graphs given in Part III. This viscosity is inserted in the design equation, and the land length is easily calculated. In those cases where some element of the equation other than land length is being sought, it is necessary to estimate the shear rate and determine the corresponding viscosity. This viscosity is inserted into the flow equation, and a second approximation to the flow rate and shear rate is obtained, which, in turn, leads to a revised estimate of viscosity. This process is repeated until successive values of the flow rate agree to within acceptable limits.

The apparent viscosity idea can be put to work in a little different way. As in Section III, the apparent viscosity μ_a is defined as the shear stress at the wall divided by the apparent shear rate. This definition can be stated thus:

$$\frac{4q}{\pi R^3} = \frac{1}{\mu_a}\left(\frac{pR}{2L}\right) \tag{154}$$

For materials obeying the power law

$$\frac{4q}{\pi R^3} = \kappa'\left(\frac{pR}{2L}\right)^\nu \tag{155}$$

* To illustrate the difference by a simple example, the flow through a hole of circular section is given by

$$q = \frac{\pi\kappa R^{\nu+3}p^\nu}{2^\nu(\nu+3)L^\nu} \tag{152}$$

where κ is used (152) and

$$q = \frac{\pi\kappa' R^{\nu+3}p^\nu}{2^{\nu+2}L^\nu} \tag{153}$$

where κ' is used. Equating Eq. (152) and (153), then $\kappa' = 4\kappa/(\nu+3)$.

Combining these two equations

$$\frac{1}{\mu_a} = \kappa' \left(\frac{pR}{2L}\right)^{\nu-1}$$ (156)

This statement is equivalent to writing the power law in the Newtonian form

$$-\frac{dv}{dr} = \frac{\tau}{\mu_a}$$ (157)

Note that the letter R in Eq. (155) is capitalized and stands for the radius of the die, whereas lower-case r signifies the variable radial distance. Equation (156), or its equivalent, may be substituted wherever apparent viscosity is needed in the integrated Newtonian flow equations.*

The two-term power law of Gee and Lyon is also given by Eq. (157), but the apparent viscosity is

$$\frac{1}{\mu_a} = \frac{1}{\mu_0} (1 + C\tau^{\nu-1})$$ (158)

Flow Through Thin Slits. A thin-slit die is a die in which the end effects of the slits on the flow rate can be neglected without causing serious error. If the width w is 20 times the depth h, the thin-slit flow equations are accurate to within about 2 per cent. The error increases to about 6 per cent and 14 per cent if the width-to-depth ratio is decreased to 10 and 5, respectively. Thin slits form an important class of one-dimensional-flow dies. Many dies approximate thin slits; blown-film dies, tubing dies, and dies for thin L-sections are examples.

The shear stress in a slit die is a maximum at the surface of the slit. At any distance r from the mid-plane, the stress is equal to pr/L, so at the wall, where $r = h/2$, the maximum stress is $ph/2L$. This is in every way analogous to $pR/2L$ for a circular die. The corresponding apparent shear rate at the wall is $6q/wh^2$, analogous to $4q/\pi R^3$.

Extruder-Die Interrelationships

The die is "married" to the extruder. The "better half" is the screw extruder to which the die is attached. Because the head pressure and throughput are common to both, the design and performance of the die and the extruder are closely linked. This interrelationship of extruder and die has been discussed in detail in the earlier portion of this chapter. Since this por-

---

* This method is not quite as accurate as the iterative method, since it is only as good as the fit of the power law to the data, whereas the other works directly with the curve. Where highest accuracy is wanted, this method gives an excellent estimate with which to begin iterating.

tion of the chapter treats die design alone, it will be assumed that the pressure-output characteristic of the extruder is known, and the flow rate through the die will be treated as a function of the gauge pressure and temperature of the entering melt.

In designing together an extruder and die, or in evaluating their joint performance, it is important to keep in mind that the apparent viscosity in the die may be an order of magnitude lower than that in the screw. The appropriate figure must be used for each, just as in the sample calculation previously given on p. 251.

Necessary Design Information

By now it is evident that a shear rate vs. shear stress curve (or some equivalent) for the temperature of interest is needed to establish the flow parameters on which the design equations are based. Such data for many materials are available in Section III. An exponential interpolation formula given in Chap. 1 permits the calculation of values for temperatures between those for which curves are plotted, and it is also useful for obtaining values near but outside the range of the existing data.*

Where there are only one or two measured rates in the range of interest, one can arbitrarily assume $\nu = 2.5$ and use the points to evaluate κ'. Where there are no data at all, or where they are meager, it may be more economical to pay the cost of having some measurements made than to run the risk of building an expensive unworkable die.

The density ρ_m to be used in the flow equations is that of the melt (rather than that of the solidified resin). Density is graphed as a function of temperature and pressure for the different materials in Section III; it may also be calculated directly from the equation of state given there. It is most con-

---

* One must be wary in applying the interpolation formula for K', the consistency, to κ', the fluidity. The temperature dependence of κ' may be expressed by an Arrhenius equation

$$\kappa' = A'e^{-E'/RT} \qquad (T \text{ in } °K)$$

Satisfactory values of A' and E' may be obtained by the following procedure: Calculate the average ratio R_a of the apparent shear rates at selected stresses in the range of interest for the two nearest temperatures at each stress, and also record shear rate and stress for the nearer temperature. Convert temperatures to °K. Then calculate $\kappa_1 = [\text{shear rate}/(\text{shear stress})^\nu]$ at the nearer temperature T_1. The terms E' and A' are given by

$$E' = \frac{4.57 T_1 T_2 \log_{10} R_a}{T_1 - T_2}$$

$$\log_{10} A' = \log_{10} \kappa_1' + \frac{E'}{4.57 T_1}$$

venient, in determining melt density, to use the mean pressure in the die lips, $p/2$.

Finally, the pressure p developed by the extruder at the desired output q is assumed to be known. Equations for calculating extruder output from screw dimensions, speed, and viscosity are given in earlier portions of this chapter. In general, therefore, a simultaneous solution of both the die-design problem and the extruder-design problem will have to be made.

Round-Rod Dies

The Poiseuille equation for flow through round holes is

$$q = \frac{\pi R^4 p}{8 \mu_a L} \tag{159}$$

As was mentioned, if the correct apparent viscosity is substituted in such equations, the results will reliably describe non-Newtonian melt flow. By combining Eq. (156) with Eq. (159), the modified Poiseuille equation for a melt obeying the power law is obtained:

$$q = \frac{\pi \kappa' R^{\nu+3} p^{\nu}}{2^{\nu+2} L^{\nu}} \tag{160}$$

Similarly, Eq. (158), the more versatile version of apparent viscosity by Gee and Lyon,[32] may be substituted into Eq. (160) to give a Poiseuille equation applicable over a wider range of shear stress for a given material:

$$q = \frac{\pi R^4 p}{8 \mu_0 L} \left[1 + C' \left(\frac{pR}{2L} \right)^{\nu-1} \right] \tag{161}$$

Expanded, this becomes

$$q = \frac{\pi R^4 p}{8 \mu_0 L} + \frac{\pi C' R^{\nu+3} p^{\nu}}{2^{\nu+2} \mu_0 L^{\nu}} \tag{162}$$

If Eq. (162) is compared with Eqs. (159) and (160), it is clear that the Gee-Lyon form is a linear combination of the Newtonian flow law and the power law. The group C'/μ_0 is equivalent in form and dimensions to κ', though the two are not likely to be equal.

In a round-rod die, since the finished rod diameter and the draw ratio are known, the radius R of the die is simply the radius of the finished rod times the square root of the draw ratio. Thus, only L remains to be established. This is easily done in the case of Eq. (160) by solving for L. In Eq. (162), however, there are two terms containing L, and since ν is not usually an integer, an iterative method of solution must be used.

Equations (159) and (161) make clear the relative importance of the several design factors that affect flow. From the standpoint of understanding this interplay of factors, the equations are indispensable. However, there are two much simpler methods of finding land lengths (and some other quantities).

The simplest is called the "flow-curve method," which works as follows: From R and q, the apparent shear rate $4q/\pi R^3$ is calculated. From the shear stress vs. shear rate plot for the material and temperature under consideration, the corresponding shear stress is read off. Since this is equal to $pR/2L$, it is simply divided *into* $pR/2$ to get L, the land length. Similarly, if p is sought and L known, the shear stress read off the curve is divided *by* $R/2L$. Note that this method uses the flow curve directly, avoiding errors of curve fitting to which power laws are subject.

The second method, the apparent-viscosity method, is similar. Having computed the apparent shear rate, the designer reads from a graph of apparent viscosity vs. shear rate the corresponding value. This is substituted into Eq. (159) and that equation is solved for L. Since the apparent viscosity curve is merely a replotting of the flow curve, the answers obtained by the two methods should be identical.

With either of these methods it is important to use a flow curve or apparent viscosity curve that was plotted for an orifice of about the same L/D ratio as the die being designed.

Sample Calculations for Round-Rod Die. Suppose that it is desired to extrude an acrylic rod with a finished diameter of 0.50 in. at a rate of 50 pph, a reasonable rate for a 2-in. extruder. The extrusion temperature is to be 400°F, and the draw ratio is 1.5. At this output the extruder to be used can develop 2,000 psi with general-purpose acrylic resin at 400°F head temperature.

The first step is to convert the output figure to cubic inches per second at the die. The applicable conversion is

$$q_w = 2.083q\,\rho_m$$

where

q_w = the mass flow rate in lb/hr

ρ_m = the melt density at the temperature and average pressure of the melt

in the die

The melt density for polymethyl methacrylate, calculated from the equation of state given for that material in Ref. 65, is 68.5 lb/cu ft. The output q then is 0.351 cu in./sec.

Flow-Curve Method. A graph of shear stress vs. apparent shear rate (a flow curve) for polymethyl methacrylate at 400°F is shown as the solid curve in Fig. 4.47. (These are not actual data but were computed from the formula and constants given by Gee and Lyon[32] for "Lucite" 140.) It is clear that one can enter Fig. 4.47 with either shear stress or shear rate to get the other (or to get apparent viscosity). In these calculations, since L is the unknown, shear rate is the more convenient. For a round die, apparent shear rate is $4q\pi R^3$, and in the example,

$$R = \frac{(0.50)(1.5)}{2} = 0.308 \text{ in.,}$$

so the apparent shear rate is

$$\frac{4q}{\pi R^3} = \frac{(4)(0.351)}{3.142(0.308)^3} = 15.3 \text{ sec}^{-1}$$

From Fig. 4.47, the shear stress corresponding to this shear rate is $pR/2L = 19.5$ psi. Since

$$\frac{pR}{2} = \frac{(2,000)(0.308)}{2} = 308 \text{ lb/in.,} \quad L = 15.8 \text{ in.,} \quad \frac{L}{R} = 15.8/0.308 = 51.$$

Thus, the critical dimensions of the die L and R of the orifice, have been established. This calculated die land length is too long to be practical, and a considerably shorter land length would undoubtedly be used. If it were desired to maintain 2,000 psi head pressure on the extruder—perhaps to increase the mixing achieved in the extruder—these calculations indicate that the use of screen packs or a valve for generation of back pressure would be necessary.

Apparent Viscosity Method. The dotted curve of Fig. 4.47 is a plot of apparent viscosity vs. shear rate (or stress) for polymethyl methacrylate at 400°F. Entering the graph with the calculated shear rate of 15.3 sec^{-1}, the corresponding viscosity is found to be 1.27 lb$_F$, sec/sq in. Substituting this and the pressure into Eq. (159) and solving for L.

$$L = \frac{(3.142)(0.308)^4(2000)}{(8)(1.27)(0.351)} = 15.8 \text{ in. as before}$$

Power-Law Method. Referring to Fig. 4.47, note that a straight line has been dashed in along the upper half of the shear-stress–shear-rate curve. This line approximates the curve closely over the range of shear rate from 8 to 1,000 sec^{-1}, the usual range of interest in the designing of rod dies. (Low shear stresses and rates would come into play if one were designing a die for a very large rod that was to be produced in a small extruder.)

The values of ν and κ' are obtained from this line as follows: Two well-spaced points on the *line* (stress$_1$, rate$_1$) at the lower end and (stress$_2$, rate$_2$) at the upper end are selected. The constants are given by

$$\nu = \frac{\log \left(\dfrac{\text{rate}_2}{\text{rate}_1}\right)}{\log \left(\dfrac{\text{stress}_2}{\text{stress}_1}\right)}$$

$$\kappa' = \frac{\text{rate}_1}{(\text{stress}_1)^\nu} \qquad \text{or} \qquad \kappa' = \frac{\text{rate}_2}{(\text{stress}_2)^\nu}$$

It is advisable to make both the computations indicated and average the results. Checking the constants by applying them in Eq. (155) to some middle-of-the-range point will turn up any errors in the calculations.

Applying these instructions to the dashed line of Fig. 4.47, the two points selected are (90, 1,000) and (10, 2.60). See footnote page 259.

$$\nu = \frac{\log \left(\dfrac{1,000}{2.60}\right)}{\log \left(\dfrac{90}{10}\right)} = 2.708$$

$$\kappa' = \frac{1,000}{90^{2.708}} = 0.00509$$

or

$$\kappa' = \frac{2.60}{10^{2.708}} = 0.00511$$

Average value of $\kappa' = 0.00510$ in.$^{5.416}$/sec, lb$_F$$^{2.708}$. Check: at

$$\frac{pR}{2L} = 40, \qquad \frac{4q}{\pi R^3} = 111,$$

which agrees with the value read from the line, and may be compared with 103 for the curve.

Applying these values to Eq. (160) and solving for L,

$$L = \left\{\frac{[3.142][5.10 \times 10^{-3}][(0.38)^{5.708}][(2 \times 10^3)^{2.708}]}{(2)^{4.708}(0.351)}\right\}^{1/2.708}$$

$$L = [(3.142)^{1/2.708}][(5 \times 10)^{1/2.708}][(10)^{-3/2.708}](0.308^{5.708/2.708})(2 \times 10^3)$$

$$\times \, [(2)^{-4.708/2.708}](0.351^{-1/2.708})$$

$$L = (1.525)(1.823)(0.0783)(0.0837)(2 \times 10^3)(0.2996)(1.472)$$

$$L = 16.1 \text{ in.}$$

This value compares unusually closely with the value of 15.8 obtained by the apparent viscosity method, because the dashed line of the power-law approximation happens to be almost coincident to the curve at the pertinent shear rate, 15.3 $\sec^{-1}$.

The following example is cited to illustrate how the L/D problem can be handled when the proper data are not available.

Bagley[4] showed experimentally that the shear stress for branched polyethylenes flowing through circular orifices could be represented by the equation

$$\tau_e = \frac{p}{2\left[\left(\dfrac{L}{R}\right) + n\right]} \tag{163}$$

where ·

τ_e = the effective shear stress, psi

p, R, L have the usual meanings

n = the effective length-to-radius ratio of an orifice whose actual length is zero. The value of n is about 5.

The term in the brackets is the effective L/R for the short orifice, and it is clear that, for any actual L/R over 40 ($L/D > 20$), the effective L/R is only slightly larger than the actual. A similar pattern of flow behavior has been noted with other plastics, and Bagley's equation will probably be found to be valid for them, too, although n may not be the same for all. Until more data become available, Eq. 163 should help to improve flow estimates and design calculations. It can be used to calculate land length or pressure drop, providing only that there is a flow curve available and that the L/R for that curve is known. Here is the procedure:

Let τ_n be the "nominal" shear stress, i.e., the stress plotted on the available flow curve. Let L/R for this curve = a. If land length is sought and p, q, and R are known, first compute the apparent shear rate, $4q/\pi R^3$ and read the corresponding τ_n from the curve. Then L is given by

$$L = R\left[\frac{p(a + 5)}{2a\tau_n} - 5\right] \tag{164}$$

If, on the other hand, L, R, and q are known for an existing die and the pressure drop p is wanted, the equation to use is

$$p = \frac{2a(b + 5)\tau_n}{(a + 5)} \tag{165}$$

where b = the actual L/R for the die.

Both of these equations are simply derived from Eq. (163); similar equations can be obtained for other quantities. Also, analogous expressions can be derived from Eq. (163) for the apparent viscosity method and for calculations involving slit dies.

Example: To illustrate the use of these equations, refer to the die for half-inch rod already discussed. Suppose $p = 400$ psi instead of the rather high value 2,000 psi. What will be the land length? Solution:

(1) $4q/\pi R^3 = 15.3$ sec^{-1}; from Fig. 4.47, $\tau_n = 19.5$ psi
(2) For Fig. 4.47, $L/R = 40$
(3) Substituting into Eq. (164)

$$L = 0.308 \left[\frac{400(40 + 5)}{2 \times 40 \times 19.5} - 5 \right] = 2.01 \text{ in.}$$

If the L/R factor had been ignored, and L had been calculated as on pp. 261–262, the value would have been 3.16 in. The error is over 50 per cent.

Slit Dies

Strip Dies. A strip die is a thin-slit die in which the melt pressure is the same over the whole slit width. Fig. 4.48 is a schematic diagram of a strip die that makes clear the essentials of the approach and the slit. The outside surface is simply a circular cylinder that will give uniform contact with band heaters. The dimensions, the width w, the depth h, and the slit length L are indicated on the sketch.

The basic power law relating true shear rate and stress is, of course, independent of the geometry of the die in which the flow happens to be occurring. The apparent shear rate at the wall, the stress at the wall, and the

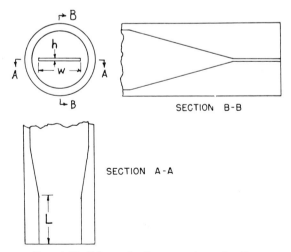

SECTION B-B

SECTION A-A

FIG. 4.48. Schematic diagram of a strip die.

apparent viscosity, however, *do* depend on the geometry. In other words, the flow curves in Section III, having been obtained from measurements on circular dies, differ slightly from the apparent shear rate vs. shear stress plots that would be obtained with the same materials at the same temperatures and equivalent L/h ratio in slit dies. Fortunately, the correction is small and is easy to make. In a slit die the apparent shear rate is given by $6q/wh^2$, and the stress at the wall is $ph/2L$. As with the round die, the apparent viscosity is defined as the ratio of stress to rate, and, for a material obeying the power law, it is given by

$$\frac{1}{\mu_a} = \kappa'' \left(\frac{ph}{2L}\right)^{\nu-1} \tag{166}$$

where the fluidity κ'' for the slit is related to the round-hole fluidity κ' by

$$\kappa'' = \frac{3(\nu+3)\kappa'}{4(\nu+2)} \tag{167}$$

The proof of this relationship is given in App. 1. Thus, to use the curves in Section III for designing slit dies, simply calculate ν and κ' as before and then, from Eq. (167), find κ''. For Newtonian materials, of course, κ'' and κ' are identical with κ, but for $\nu = 3$, $\kappa'' = 0.900\,\kappa'$. Inserting the apparent viscosity Eq. (166) into the Newtonian flow equation for a slit yields the design equation for non-Newtonians:

$$q = \frac{wh^3 p}{12\mu_a L} \tag{168}$$

$$q = \frac{\kappa'' wh^{\nu+2} p^{\nu}}{3L^{\nu} 2^{\nu+1}} \tag{169}$$

The apparent viscosity expression of Gee and Lyon also changes slightly, C' being replaced by C'', the two being related just as are κ' and κ'' by Eq. (167). The equivalent flow equation using this more widely applicable power law is

$$q = \frac{pwh^3}{12\mu_0 L} + \frac{C'' wh^{\nu+2} p^{\nu}}{3\mu_0 L 2^{\nu+1}} \tag{170}$$

On p. 261 methods were presented for using the flow curves and apparent-viscosity curves in Section III for calculations of flow through round-rod dies. These simple methods can also be used with slit dies, providing the calculated shear rate $6q/wh^2$ is multiplied by κ'/κ'' before entering the chart. Since this multiplying factor changes only slightly over the range of ν from 1.5 to 3, it will be satisfactory to use the mid-value 0.93. (Using the mid-value makes it unnecessary to determine the slope of the flow curve.) Since q, w, and h will usually have been set by production and dimensional requirements, $5.58\,q/wh^2$ is easily calculated.

As with the round-rod die, the L/D value for the flow curve should be close to that reached in the design of the strip die. For strip dies, if $L/h = 1.33$ times the L/D value on the flow curve, the residence times of the melt in both dies will be the same at equal shear rates.

Since there is virtually no difference between the calculations for a strip die and those for a round-rod die, except the matter of correcting the apparent shear rate, none will be given here.

Tubing Dies. Tubing may be defined as the product obtained from an annular die in which the outside radius R_o of the annulus is not more than three times the inside radius R_i. Since R_o/R_i is less than 1.3 even for extra-heavy pipe, pipe dies will be included in this definition. Excepted are blown film dies, in which the melt is distributed to the annulus by a pipe or channel, called a manifold. In tubing dies the melt pressure is the same at all points around the annulus, whereas this is usually not so in a manifold-type die.

If a cut is made along any one radius through the annulus, and the annulus is unrolled onto a plane surface, it becomes a slit die resembling the strip die referred to on p. 265, except for two features: (1) it has no end surfaces, and therefore it suffers from no end effects; (2) the side formed by the inner circumference is shorter than that formed by the outer circumference. This is taken care of by averaging the two side lengths, permitting the annulus to be treated as a slit whose depth $h = R_o - R_i$ and whose width $w = \pi(R_o + R_i)$, the mean circumference. The arithmetic-mean radius is not quite correct for a R_o/R_i ratio greater than about 3. At that value the error in the flow rate is only -1.5 per cent for a Newtonian melt and probably not much more for a non-Newtonian. An error of -7.0 per cent is obtained for a R_o/R_i ratio of 10. The exact flow-rate formula is derived in App. 2. A generalized treatment of flow through annuli is given by Frederickson and Bird.[30]

Making the substitutions indicated in Eqs. (168) and (169), the design formulas for tubing dies are obtained.

$$q = \pi \frac{(R_o + R_i)(R_o - R_i)^3 p}{12\mu_a L} \tag{171}$$

and

$$q = \frac{\kappa''(R_o + R_i)(R_o - R_i)^{\nu+2} p^\nu}{3L^\nu 2^{\nu+1}} \tag{172}$$

In using the flow-curve method, or in using the apparent viscosity method with Eq. (171), the apparent shear rate is given by

$$\frac{5.58q}{\pi(R_o + R_i)(R_o - R_i)^2}$$

and shear stress is

$$\frac{p(R_o - R_i)}{2L}$$

The removal of strips from the die is usually accompanied by some reduction in width and thickness. Similarly, tubing extrudates shrink in diameter as well as thickness if they are drawn away from the die without special precautions being taken. Usually, the central mandrel that forms the inner surface of the annulus is extended beyond the die to maintain the desired inside radius during take-off until the tubing has been chilled. The extension is water- and air-cooled, as in the die of Fig. 4.49, an offset-type die for tubing extrusion.[59] The cooling water must not be allowed to come into contact with the inner part of the mandrel. If it did, the extrudate would be rough, the inside dimension would be off, and the die might even freeze up completely. The principle illustrated in Fig. 4.49 can also be adapted with good effect to the extrusion of other shapes. The mandrel, which in this die is supported from the rear, can instead be supported by a "spider," or set of legs, that bridges the annular gap at several points.

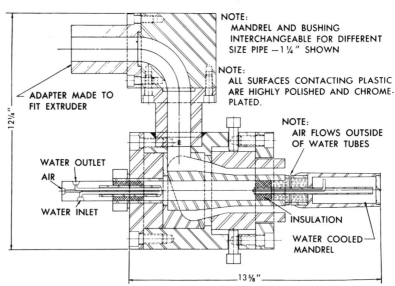

FIG. 4.49. Offset tubing die. (*Courtesy Modern Plastics Magazine*)

Spiders tend to leave weld lines on the product, however, and the circumferential strength along such weld lines may be so low as to reduce seriously the working pressure and service life of the pipe. The spider-type die has the occasionally valuable advantage that it does not require an offset or crosshead (right-angle turn of melt channel).

It appears that some ratio of L to h may be optimum for production of best-quality extrudates: Perkins[56] reported that, in experiments with pipe dies of different design, the optimum ratio of L to h was about 38 for polyvinyl chloride and "Kralastic" pipe, 47 for polyethylene and cellulose acetate butyrate.

Shape Dies Treated by Simple Strip Formulas. There is a whole class of shapes that are merely bent or composite strips, having the same thickness throughout. Any of the already discussed calculation methods may be applied to such shapes, the only problem being the determination of the appropriate slit width w. Ten such shapes are sketched in Fig. 4.50. Some of these will be discussed. Sketch 1 is of a half annulus, and the annulus formulas for tubing dies may be used.

The shape in Sketch 2 also has closed ends. Sketches 3 through 6 are all annuli without ends, and the only question is the figuring of the appropriate w and h. (For Sketch 7, $w = (R_o + R_i)(\theta + \sin\theta)$ where θ is the angle in radians defined by $\cos\theta = R_s/r$.) Although these slits have no ends, there are more or less abrupt changes in the direction of the velocity gradient at the corners, and there are undoubtedly some corner effects which will get worse as the w/h ratio for each branch decreases and as the corners get sharper. The same holds for the corners of "L's" and channels.

In all the shapes in Fig. 4.50 the slit depth or thickness h is constant throughout. Similar shapes having different depths in the several branches will be discussed later.

Wire-Coating Dies

Like tubing dies, wire-coating dies are annuli. However, the inside surface of the annulus is the wire to be coated, which is passing through the die at the lineal production speed. Wires coated by extrusion range from fine single strands to above 6-in.-thick composite cables, but the applicable equations are the same for all.

The wire passing through the melt drags some melt along by a drag-flow mechanism analogous to that discussed earlier in this chapter. The thin-slit method is only an approximation for calculating the drag flow q_d, because the drag originates at the inner surface which is considerably smaller than the outer area. For a Newtonian liquid and for $R_i = 0.9 R_o$ (equivalent to $w/h = 60$), the approximate formula yields a flow that is too high by 3.3 per cent. In order to obtain the same order of accuracy in the drag

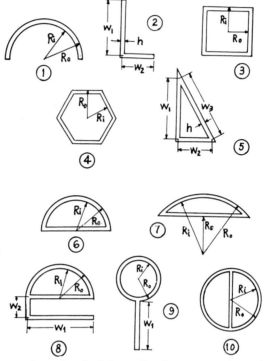

FIG. 4.50. Cross sections of typical shape dies that may employ strip-die formulas.

flow as in the pressure flow, exact drag-flow formulas must be used. If the wire were not moving, the pressure differential would force melt through the annulus at a rate given by the formulas for tubing dies. The total flow is the sum of both contributions, i.e.,

$$q = q_d + q_p$$

The drag-flow equation for a Newtonian fluid is

$$q_d = \pi v_w R_i^2 \left[\frac{\beta^2 - 1}{2 \ln \beta} - 1 \right] \tag{173}$$

where

$$\beta = \frac{R_o}{R_i}$$

and v_w = the wire velocity, in./sec, and that for a non-Newtonian fluid is

$$q_d = \frac{\pi v_w R_i^2 (1 - \nu)\beta^{3-\nu} - (3 - \nu)\beta^{1-\nu} + 2}{(3 - \nu)(\beta^{1-\nu} - 1)} \tag{174}$$

for $\nu \neq 1,3$. Inspection of Eq. (174) reveals that it is discontinuous and goes to infinity at $\nu = 1$ and 3. Equation (173) is given because the Newtonian case (i.e., $\nu = 1$) is of interest, but the case where ν is *exactly* 3 is rare. However, examination of the derivations of these equations in App. 3 will show how an equation for $\nu = 3$ may be derived, if desired. Note that there is no viscosity term in either of these equations.

Although the drag-flow contribution to the thickness of the coating may be considerable, it is the usual practice to assist it with some melt pressure. The flow arising from this pressure may be estimated by means of Eq. (171), using the flow-curve or apparent viscosity methods (which are only approximate in this case). The proper apparent shear rate is

$$\left(\frac{dv}{dr}\right)_{\text{wall}} = \frac{v_w}{R_o \ln \dfrac{R_o}{R_i}} + \frac{5.58 q_p}{\pi (R_o + R_i)(R_o - R_i)^2} \tag{175}$$

Usually, the land length will be wanted. To find it, calculate the drag flow q_d from Eq. (174) and subtract q_d from the output q to get the pressure flow q_p. The shear rate is calculated from Eq. (175), the flow curve consulted, and, using q_p, the land length is obtained from Eq. (171)

As with other extrudates, wire coatings may be drawn down as the coated wire emerges from the die. In this case the draw ratio DR is

$$DR = \frac{R_o^{\,2} - R_i^{\,2}}{(R_i + t)^2 - R_i^2} \tag{176}$$

where $t =$ the thickness of the finished coating. Given DR, t, and the wire radius R_i, the orifice radius is obtained by solving Eq. (176) for R_o:

$$R_o = \sqrt{(DR)[(R_i + t)^2 - R_i^2] + R_i^2}. \tag{177}$$

Manifold Sheeting Dies

Manifold sheeting dies are slit dies in which the slit is supplied with melt from a pipe, channel, or manifold that runs parallel to the slit. The manifold is connected to the extruder at one of the ends or at the center; however, it is quite correct to consider a center-fed die as equivalent to two end-fed dies of half length, operating in parallel. Schematically, such a die may be represented as in Fig. 4.46, though in practice it is considerably heavier-walled and more elaborate. The power-law theory for such dies was developed in Ref. 18, and its application was discussed in detail in Ref. 19; both references are readily available, and only the bare essentials will be given here. A slightly different approach, giving an approximate solution to the power law, is developed by Weeks in Ref. 71.

These dies differ from the strip dies discussed previously, in that there is some pressure drop along the manifold, so the available head forcing the melt through the slit is greater near the feed and smaller near the far end of the slit. If the slit dimensions are constant, this results in a lower extrusion rate at the far end than at the feed end (see example, p. 251).

It is common practice to compensate for the pressure drop, which is progressive along the slit, by three different methods. The first method is to increase the slit thickness with increasing distance from the feed end. The second method is to compensate for the pressure drop by increasing the temperature slightly along the slit, thus reducing viscosity and equalizing rates. It is difficult to achieve the proper adjustment by this method and furthermore erratic local temperature and stress profiles are induced.

The third method of compensating for the pressure drop involves the use of an adjustable restriction or dam between the manifold and the die lips, as illustrated in Fig. 4.51. Almost any desired portion of the available head pressure may be expended across the dam, and a uniform pressure can be set up along the whole length of the die lips.

In sheeting dies the melt temperature can be seriously affected by local variations in die temperature. The best policy is, therefore, to make certain that the die temperature is everywhere maintained as close as possible to the entering melt temperature. It is essential, therefore, to have well-fitted heaters and good control equipment, and to insulate thoroughly.

As was discussed previously, in the case where the channel and slit dimensions are fixed, the local extrusion rate at the feed point of the die will exceed that at the far end. The ratio of the flow at the far end to that at the feed point is called the uniformity index, hereafter referred to as UI.

The utility of the UI is to permit the design of a manifold die that will produce film or sheet of satisfactory and predictable uniformity of gauge

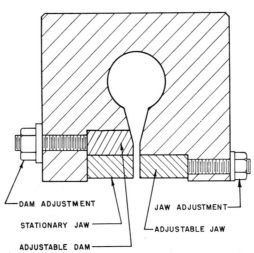

Fig. 4.51. Simplified diagram of a dam-type sheeting die (lengthwise section).

across its width. Sound die design should start with the UI required to produce an acceptable product.

In a manifold die, there is flow in two directions—along the channel and out the slit. The term for the slit width w is equal to the channel length, while the term L will denote the lip width of the slit, i.e., the "land length" in the direction of outflow. The design problem here is to find the proper values of L and the channel radius R that will give the desired UI. It will be seen from the equations that a UI of 1 is impossible to achieve, and, in general, the closer this value is approached, the more cumbersome the die becomes. Therefore the lowest acceptable UI should be chosen. This will be a value in the neighborhood of 0.95. The required equations are

$$L = \left(\frac{\kappa'' w h^{\nu+2}}{3q 2^{\nu+1}} \right)^{1/\nu} p \tag{178}$$

$$u = 1 - (UI)^{(\nu+1)/\nu} \tag{179}$$

$$\alpha = \frac{u^{\nu/(\nu+1)}}{w} \left(\frac{1}{\nu} + \frac{u}{2\nu+1} + \frac{u^2}{3\nu+2} + \frac{u^3}{4\nu+3} + \cdots \right) \tag{180}$$

$$R = \left[\frac{(\nu+3)h^{\nu+2}}{2\pi\nu(\nu+2)L^\nu \alpha^{\nu+1}} \right]^{1/(\nu+3)} \tag{181}$$

where

q = the volume rate of flow per branch of the die. In an end-fed die, this will be the extruder output; in a center-fed (or blown film) die, q will equal half the extruder output.

u and α are convenient functions of the UI, defined by the above equations

Since the shear stress in the relatively large channel is small compared to that in the die lips, the power law may not fit certain flow curves closely over the entire range involved here. If it is fitted to the high-stress portion, the design will be conservative, and vice versa. Where the fit is poor, the above equations can theoretically be rederived on the basis of the flow law of Eq. (151), but this promises to be very difficult. An alternative, which the reader may wish to investigate, is to fit the power law to the high range and find L from Eq. (178) and then, assuming $\nu = 1$, find R from the remaining equations. Since Eq. (178) is merely another form of Eq. (169), it is also possible to find L by the flow-curve method or the apparent viscosity method and then, assuming $\nu = 1$, find R from the last three equations. The procedure for using the above four equations is given in detail in Ref. 19. In another approach, the same equations can be used to calculate a design for a UI of 1.000 by varying L or h along the channel to compensate for the pressure drop. This also is explained in Ref. 19.

These equations apply also to blown-film dies, which are simply manifold dies in doughnut shape, if L is taken as *half* the mean circumference of the torus.

From these equations, it is evident that, as the die length w increases, for a given UI, R must increase, too. Since it is desirable to minimize R, it is almost always preferable to center-feed rather than end-feed the die. The design value of w is only half as great for a center-fed die as for an end-fed one. In some modern dies the feed stream is split several times, and there are many feed ports along the back of the manifold. If the splitting of the stream is properly done, this can reduce the channel radius with no loss of UI and can make the entire die lighter and more compact. Splitting the stream may introduce extra weld lines, however; particularly in the more elastic melts, such weld lines are often points of weakness.

Fan-Shaped Sheeting Dies

A horizontal mid-section of a fan-shaped ("fishtail") sheeting die is shown in Fig. 4.52. The principal reason for the existence of these dies is that they are more streamlined than crosshead sheeting dies, so it is easier to eliminate dead spots. They have therefore been used mostly with more heat-sensitive resins. While several approaches to the design of these dies are possible, only the simplest one will be considered here.

As with the manifold dies, one starts with the uniformity index, or UI

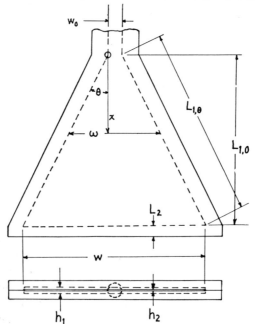

FIG. 4.52. Schematic diagram of a fishtail sheeting die.

the ratio of the local extrusion rate at the outside edge of the die to that at the center. Since the path from the feed entrance to the center of the die lips is shorter than that from the entrance to the edge, it is to be expected that if the lead-up space had the same depth throughout, the pressure at the center of the lips would be higher than that at the edge. The design equations determine the lead-up depth h_1 and the lip land length L_2, so that the required UI will be achieved. Let the half-angle of the fan be θ, the width of the slit be w, and the depth in the fan (lead-up) section be h_1. Let the head at the feed entrance be p, let the pressure drop across the lead up be P_1 (approximately, it ranges slightly from center to edge), and let the drop across the lips be P_2. The slit depth h_2 is the desired film thickness multiplied by the draw ratio, as with the other slit dies. The design equations are

$$\gamma = \frac{p_1}{p_2} = \frac{1 - (UI)^{1/\nu}}{\sec \theta - 1} \tag{182}$$

where $\gamma = W_e/w$, and W_e is an effective average slit width.

$$p_1 = \frac{\gamma p}{1 + \gamma} \tag{183}$$

$$h_1 \cong \left[\frac{15qw^{\nu-1} (\cot \theta)^\nu}{\kappa'' p_1^\nu} \right]^{1/(\nu+2)} \tag{184}$$

$$p_2 = p - p_1 \tag{185}$$

$$L_2 = \left(\frac{\kappa'' w h_2^{\nu+2} p_2^\nu}{3q2^{\nu+1}} \right)^{1/\nu} \tag{186}$$

For those who prefer the apparent viscosity method, the corresponding equations are

$$\gamma = \frac{p_1}{p_2} = \frac{1 - UI}{\sec \theta - 1} \tag{187}$$

$$p_1 = \frac{\gamma p}{1 + \gamma} \tag{183}$$

$$h_1 \cong \left(\frac{15q\mu_{a1} \cot \theta}{p_1} \right)^{1/3} \tag{188}$$

where μ_{a1} is evaluated for the apparent shear rate in the lead-up section. This shear rate (at the metal surface) is

$$15 \frac{q}{wh_1^2}$$

$$L = \frac{wh_2^3 p_2}{12\mu_{a2}q} \tag{189}$$

where μ_{a2} is evaluated for the apparent shear rate in the slit, i.e., $6q/wh_2^2$.

This design has the merit of being simple to execute in the machine shop, but it will usually make the volume of the lead-up section larger than it might be made if it were contoured so that the depths were slightly larger near the outer edges than at the center. This contouring cannot be calculated exactly for a non-Newtonian fluid, because the flow is two-dimensional, and the compound curvature of the surface would be difficult to machine accurately. The design scheme given here is relatively simple and should work with many plastics if the design is made for a resin having a relatively high value of ν.

Dies for Wedge Shapes

First, a subtle distinction should be noted. There are wedge-shaped dies and dies to produce wedge-shaped sections. The present discussion is limited to those dies whose maximum depth is about one tenth of the width or less. This corresponds to a wedge angle of only 6 deg or less, so the usefulness of these formulas is definitely limited.

Referring to Fig. 4.53, it is clear that the slit depth at any point z along a wedge-shaped die, with a wedge angle θ, is given by

$$h = z \tan \theta + h_0 \tag{190}$$

The land length L is assumed to be the same over the whole width. If we consider an elemental slice of width dz at point z, since it is in contact with moving melt at both boundaries, it is not troubled with end effects, and the strip equation, Eq. (169), can be applied. Substituting Eq. (190) and dz for h and w in Eq. (169), the element of output contributed by the dz-wide slice at z is

$$dq = \frac{\kappa'' p^\nu \, dz (z \tan \theta + h_0)^{\nu+2}}{3L^\nu 2^{\nu+1}} \tag{191}$$

This could be integrated to obtain the discharge equation of this wedge-shaped die, but interest here is in the variation of the discharge per unit

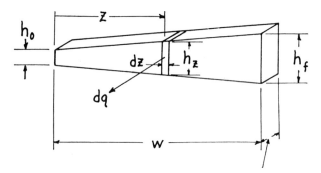

FIG. 4.53. Diagram of a wedge–shaped extrusion die.

length dq/dz with position z along the die. Dividing Eq. (191) by dz gives dq/dz, which is clearly not a linear function of z, even for the Newtonian case ($\nu = 1$). An extrudate from this die, drawn off uniformly, would have a disproportionately high flow rate at the wide portion of the wedge. This would cause concave upper and lower surfaces in the extruded shape, and the thickness ratio from one side to the other would be greater than the thickness ratio h_f/h_o of the wedge. If the extrudate is to be wedge-shaped, therefore, the die will have to be curved inward at the thick edge, or there will have to be some compensating variation of land length from one side to the other.

The unique design criterion for a wedge-section die is that dq/dz be linear in z, i.e.,

$$\frac{dq}{dz} = a + bz \tag{192}$$

where a and b are constants fixed by the shape of the desired wedge, the output rate, and the draw ratio. Consider first a die in which the land length L is constant and the slit depth h is to be varied to achieve Eq. (192).

$$\frac{dq}{dz} = \frac{\kappa'' p^\nu h^{\nu+2}}{3L^\nu 2^{\nu+1}} \tag{193}$$

If the right sides of Eqs. (192) and (193) are equated and solved for h, the resulting equation is

$$h = \left[\frac{3L^\nu 2^{\nu+1}(a + bz)}{\kappa'' p^\nu} \right]^{1/(\nu+2)} \tag{194}$$

Let $h_0 =$ the depth at the narrow end of the die, where $z = 0$ in Fig. 4.53. Then, from Eq. (194),

$$\frac{h}{h_o} = \left[\frac{(a + bz)}{a} \right]^{1/(\nu+2)} \tag{195}$$

This equation gives h in terms of z and h_o, but h_o and L are mutually dependent for the given dq/dz and pressure p. Let h_o equal the desired left-edge thickness of the emerging extrudate; then, since $dz/dz = a$ when $h = h_o$, it is possible to evaluate L from Eq. (193). From Eq. (195) a table of cuts to be made by the machinist may be set up.

Now consider a wedge-section die in which the slit depth h is the same everywhere, but the land length L varies, being greatest at the edge where the extrudate is to be thinnest. Again, by combining Eqs. (191) and (192) but solving for L, the result is

$$\frac{L}{L_o} = \left[\frac{a}{(a + bz)} \right]^{1/\nu} \tag{196}$$

In this case it might be wiser to let the slit depth h be equal to the *greatest* thickness of the emerging extrudate. If this value is inserted into Eq. (191) along with the condition that $dq/dz = a$ when $L = L_o$, Eq. (191) can be solved for L_o. Then Eq. (194) yields a table of cuts for use by the diemaker. Since flow rate is less sensitive to L than to h, and since L will usually be larger than h, varying the land length L will give better precision of extrusion for a given precision of machining.

The evaluation of the constants a and b in Eq. (192) requires explanation. Let t_1 be the thickness of the finished strip at the thinner edge, t_2 the thickness at the thicker edge. Let the width be W. The emerging extrudate has the dimensions t_1 (DR), t_2 (DR), and w, where w is the slit width and DR the draw ratio. (It is assumed here that all the DR was absorbed by a uniformly distributed change in thickness, so that $W = w$. However, if it is expected from previous experience that the width will be drawn down, too, w will be larger than W by the appropriate draw factor.) At the thin edge, dq/dz is given by $2t_1q/(t_1 + t_2)w$; at the thick edge,

$$\frac{dq}{dz} = \frac{2t_2q}{w(t_1 + t_2)}.$$

This leads to equations for a and b:

$$a = \frac{2qt_1}{w(t_1 + t_2)} \tag{197}$$

$$b = \frac{2q(t_2 - t_1)}{w^2(t_1 + t_2)} \tag{198}$$

The edges of the strip have been spoken of as though they will faithfully represent the edges of the die slit. Since the die edges do exert drag on the melt, the strip edges will emerge rounded rather than square cornered. Where close tolerances must be met on the edges, one can either extrude a little wider strip and trim the edges, or one can attempt to shape the die corners to compensate for the drag, a tricky business for which no equations are available.

The designer should not forget that the restrictions regarding L/h, which were discussed on pp. 258 and 269, apply equally to wedge sections.

There are also curved wedge shapes, e.g., gaskets, that taper gently but not linearly. Any gentle curve can be closely approximated by a series of short straight lines, and the ideas of the preceding articles can be applied to curved shapes, also. In another approach the variation of the thickness of the finished extrudate can be put in the form of an equation, e.g.,

$$\frac{dq}{dz} = f(z).$$

This equation can then replace Eq. (192), and an analogous series of subsequent equations can be derived for the particular shape desired.

Dies for Composite Shapes with Branches of Unequal Thickness

On p. 269, shapes composed of strips of equal thickness were discussed. The same basic method can be used to treat shapes made of strips of unequal thickness, of rods, and of wedges. It is impossible to avoid abrupt changes in the direction of flow (and the velocity gradient) in many of the commercially extruded shapes. At any such point there is local two-dimensional flow, so these junctions of different branches may be trouble spots. A wide range of strip thicknesses can be extruded from a single strip die by varying the draw ratio. (Plasticized vinyl film is sometimes drawn 20-fold.) In theory it might be possible to draw off a two-section strip of two distinct thicknesses from a die of a single slit depth but two land lengths. However, since the pressure drop is the same for all parts, the shear stress will be less in the longer-land section. This is bound to exaggerate any disturbance at the point where the strip thickness changes, so, in designing these dies for composite shapes, it is a good idea to try to maintain about the same shear stress

$$\left(\frac{ph}{2L}\right) \quad \text{or} \quad \left(\frac{pR}{2L}\right)$$

over the entire opening. Also, the lineal drawoff rate is the same at all points.

A good start would be arbitrarily to make all the L/R and L/h ratios the same for all branches of the shape, since this will equalize shear stresses throughout.

Tackle the round-rod branches first and determine L and R for each. Then go on to the strip and wedge branches, allowing perhaps 5 to 10 percent drawdown of *width*. The average velocity in each branch is calculated by dividing the q for that branch by its cross-sectional area. Let the take-off rate be equal to the highest of these velocities, then check the draw ratios in the other branches. If none is more than 3:1, the die will probably do a fair job. If there is too wide a disparity in draw, the equality in L/h must be upset to bring the draw ratios of the various parts more in line.

It is not easy to machine unequal land lengths into the different branches of a small shape die; nor is it easy to machine accurately a thin, wedge-shaped slit into a die face, and complexly curved slits may sometimes be needed. The work can often be eased by making the die of two or more pieces which are carefully fitted together before the orifice shaping is begun, then disassembled for that work.

Dies for Solid Shapes

By "solid shapes" is meant shapes having triangular, square, etc., cross sections which are too compact to be handled by the one-dimensional-flow formulas or simple modifications thereof. In solving the Navier-Stokes equations for two-dimensional flow, as required for these shapes, one must start with the boundary conditions, and these include the shape of the die opening. Since the solutions of these equations are usually Fourier series or Bessel functions containing exponential coefficients, working backward is difficult (if not impossible). A further difficulty stems from the fact that plastic melts are non-Newtonian. If one tries to apply the power law to the two-dimensional case, the partial differential equations become nonlinear with improper-fraction exponents. The published literature contains only the equations for flow of Newtonian liquids through holes of relatively simple shape—square, equilateral triangle, rectangle, ellipse, and a few others. Y. H. Pao[55] has presented differential equations for the three-dimensional flow of viscoelastic liquids, but so far no solutions for two- or three-dimensional flow have been presented. Some semiempirical relationships have been offered for polystyrene.[13]

Perhaps some benefit may be obtained from published solutions for Newtonian liquids, particularly where the shape desired is massive. The velocity distribution in the ellipse and rectangle (which includes the square) was first found by Boussinesq.[16] Flow in a rectangular or square channel may be calculated by the two-dimensional equation for pressure flow in an extruder screw channel presented earlier in this chapter.

An approximate distribution for the equilateral triangle was presented by Yardoff,[75] who cited an unidentifiable source. Yardoff's equation is

$$v = \frac{py[(y - \sqrt{3}\,d)^2 - 3x^2]}{4\sqrt{3}\,\mu\,dL} \tag{199}$$

where

$d =$ the semiside of the triangle; one of the sides is coincident with the x-axis from $-d$ to $+d$, and the altitude on that side lies on the y-axis and extends from the origin to $y = d\sqrt{3}$.

The maximum velocity, of course, is at the center of the triangle, whose coordinates are $(0, d/\sqrt{3})$. The triangle based on Yardoff's equation is sketched in Fig. 4.54, along with three curves of constant velocity (isovels) for $u = 0.9, 0.5,$ and $0.1\ u_{max}$. The dotted curve outside the triangle represents a die opening whose 0.1 isovel would be nearly triangular. (The effect of non-Newtonianism is to make the flow more pluglike, i.e., to make these isovels expand outward somewhat.) It seems fair to assume that if the 0.1 isovel is triangular, the extruded section will be closely triangular.

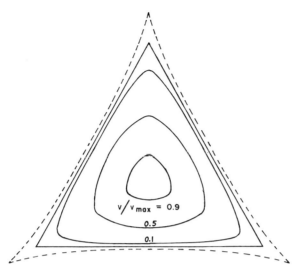

Fɪɢ. 4.54. Velocity distribution in a Newtonian liquid flowing through a triangular orifice.

For these shapes and more complex ones, it is possible that one of the "relaxation" methods which have been successful in determining temperature distributions during transient heat conduction in complex structures would enable one to find, in a reasonable time, a die shape that would give an 0.1 isovel of the desired extrudate shape.

A technique employing extended and water-cooled die lips, described in U.S. Patent 2,365,375, is also useful for maintaining control over the dimensions of solid shapes.

Mechanical Aspects of Die Design

In the previous discussions, the design of dies has been based only on considerations of the viscous flow of polymers. Mechanical problems in die construction must also be considered but are outside the scope of this book and belong more logically to machinery design. Examples of the mechanical problems encountered are distortions of the die parts, especially lips, arising from nonuniform thermal expansion, internal pressure, and the weight and strength of the component die parts.

In some extrusion shops, it is still a regular practice to shape the die cross section as judged appropriate from previous experience and to proceed from there by trial and error. The die is then installed, and a run is begun. Samples of the chilled extrudate are taken, and the dimensions are checked. Where the thickness is excessive, the corresponding points along the die lips are peened with hammer and punch, while the extruder is running, so as to close them slightly and reduce the section thickness. It is hoped that some day plastic flow will be understood well enough so that the crude method of peening extrusion dies will be eschewed by diemakers forever.

Where Do We Go from Here?

The biggest need at present is for usable methods of treating two-dimensional flow of non-Newtonian melts, including elastic effects.

The relaxation methods suggested above may offer a start in the right direction. To make these (or any other) methods useful, detailed flow data on the commercially important plastics must become available. It is to be hoped that such data will be considered by material suppliers to be just as important as the usually gathered physical-property data. Such data are necessary not only to die designers but to designers of almost all other types of equipment for making useful articles from thermoplastics. If dies are to be designed for the accurate production of complex shapes, the viscous heating and compressibility effects, discussed by Toor, Bird, Gee, and others, will have to be worked into the design methods. Even on the simpler dies, such as sheeting dies, the problem of dead spots has retarded the progress of extrusion of heat-sensitive materials, particularly unplasticized polyvinyl chloride. Where high die pressures are involved, it will probably be necessary to consider the increase of viscosity with hydrostatic pressure. It is clear that die design is not going to get simpler, and that if the design of dies for complex shapes is ever to become scientific, designers will have to become competent in the theory of viscous flow and the mathematics connected with it.

COOLING, TAKE-OFF, AND WINDUP EQUIPMENT

Molten plastic material issuing from an extruder may be in any of a wide variety of shapes and at various conditions of temperature and stiffness. Cooling, take-off, and windup equipment comprise those pieces of equipment which are used to cool, support, draw, further shape, windup, and otherwise handle the extrudate from the time it leaves the die until it is in the finished form. Because of the wide range of conditions encountered, these units are assembled to satisfy the particular needs of each extrusion operation. Several elements are common to most combinations, however. A brief explanation of the most widely used elements follows.

Cooling Equipment

The method by which the molten extrudate is cooled can directly affect the properties of the finished product. The following is a brief description of the common methods employed for cooling thermoplastics and a discussion of important considerations for maintaining an extrudate of uniform quality.

Quench Tanks and Cooling Troughs. Extrudates in the form of pipe, tubing, wire, film, and various other shapes are often cooled in a tank or a trough of water (Figs. 4.55, 4.56, 4.57). To ensure uniform cooling, it is important to have good water circulation and temperature control throughout the tank or trough. Provision must be made for removing or recycling

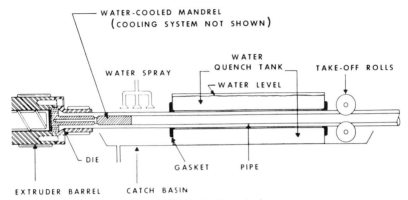

FIG. 4.55. Extrusion of pipe.

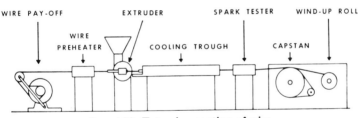

FIG. 4.56. Extrusion coating of wire.

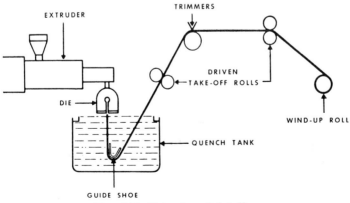

FIG. 4.57. Extrusion of flat film.

the water to prevent temperature build-up or localized hot spots where heat has not been carried away. Failure to observe these precautions can cause the finished product to vary in both physical properties and appearance.

Cooled Metal Rolls. Cooled rolls are often employed to provide cooling for films, coated substrates, and sheeting, as shown in Figs. 4.58 and 4.59. As with the quench tank, good water circulation and temperature control are necessary to ensure a uniformly cooled product. A cooled roll should be designed to allow a large volume of water to contact the inner surface of the roll at a high velocity, so that heat transfer can take place at a rapid rate. A roll that permits rapid heat transfer is shown in Fig. 4.60. An inner shell is placed within the main cooling roll to ensure that the water flow is adjacent to the inner surface of the outer shell. The inner shell is the heavier of the two in order to provide structural strength, while the outer shell is thinner to permit a high heat-transfer rate. The outer shell is sep-

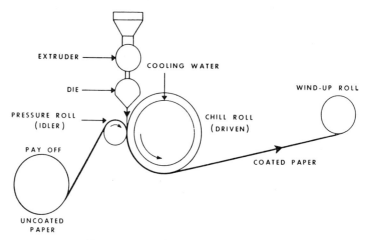

Fig. 4.58. Extrusion coating of paper.

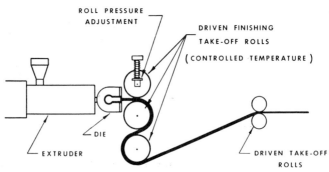

Fig. 4.59. Sheet extrusion.

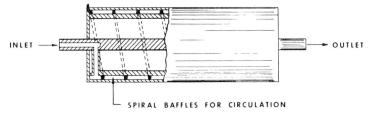

SPIRAL BAFFLES FOR CIRCULATION

INLET → OUTLET

FIG. 4.60. Cooled roll with spiral baffles.

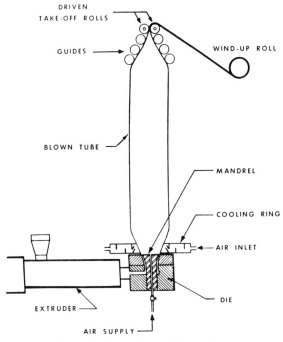

DRIVEN TAKE-OFF ROLLS

GUIDES →

WIND-UP ROLL

BLOWN TUBE

MANDREL

COOLING RING

AIR INLET

DIE

EXTRUDER →

AIR SUPPLY

FIG. 4.61. Extrusion of blown film.

arated from the inner by a spiral web which, in addition to supporting the outer shell, provides a path for positive circulation of the cooling water.

Air Cooling. Extrudates such as film and some shapes are also cooled by air (Fig. 4.61). Uniform cooling again is important, and good air circulation at a controlled temperature is required. With film, it is of importance to provide a high volume of air at low velocity. The low velocity avoids film vibration which would hinder uniform cooling.

Take-Off Devices

Take-off devices govern the linear rate at which the extrudate is removed from the die, and in this way they control the thickness or drawdown of the extrudate. Take-off devices therefore require accurate and sensitive speed controls. These driven rolls, belts, or capstans sometimes incorporate cooling devices, but their primary function is to govern the take-off rate of the extrudate.

Take-off Rolls and Belts. In many take-off systems the extrudate does not touch the driven take-off rolls until after it has gone through a cooling trough and the surfaces of the extruded shape have solidified (Figs. 4.55, 4.57, 4.61). In such a setup it is usually advantageous to use resilient take-off rolls made from rubber or some other elastomer. In many instances the roll surfaces are shaped to conform with the configuration of the extrudate being handled. Two or more take-off rolls may be used to grip the extrudate between them and draw it at the desired speed.

In many applications traction belts are used in place of rubber rolls. Belts provide greater contact area between the extrudate and the take-off device, and thus reduce the likelihood of slippage.

If the take-off rolls are to be used on uncooled resin directly after it comes from the die lips, the rolls are preferably made of metal and must be cooled to keep the extrudate from adhering to the rolls (Figs. 4.58, 4.59). Such rolls perform both a cooling and a take-off function. The finish of the rolls may be used to determine the surface of the extruded material. If an extrudate having high gloss is desired, the surface of the roll should be highly polished. Conversely, if a dull or matte finish is preferred, the surface of the metal roll may be altered by sandblasting, acid etching, or machining.

Conveyors. Belt or roller conveyors may be employed for guiding extruded shapes from the die. Cooling of the extrudate on the conveyor may be accomplished by air or water sprays along the length of the conveying belt.

Capstans. A capstan consists of a large metal wheel which imparts traction to a product, usually coated wire or monofilament, which passes around the wheel one or more times. A typical application of a capstan in a wire-coating process is illustrated in Fig. 4.56. The drawdown is determined by the speed of the capstan. A capstan may be run in water to provide additional cooling to the product.

Windup Equipment

For flexible materials such as film, tubing, wire, and some pipe, windup equipment is employed. The equipment may be designed to apply a constant tension to the web or a constant torque to the windup shaft. Some intermediate combination may also be used. Devices for achieving constant tension are shown schematically in Fig. 4.62 and constant-torque devices are shown in Fig. 4.63. A constant-tension drive is advantageous where a nonstretchable material such as coated paper or wire is involved, because it allows the formation of large, tightly wound rolls. For stretchable films,

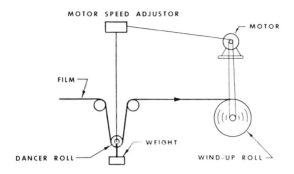

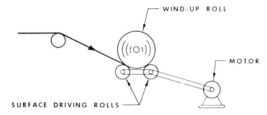

FIG. 4.62. Constant tension devices.

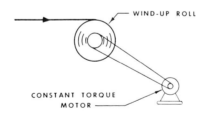

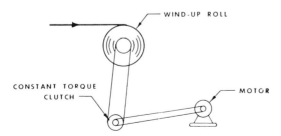

FIG. 4.63. Constant torque devices.

a constant-torque drive or modification thereof may be used in order to reduce the compressive effect of the outer layers of a large roll and to prevent the development of high pressures which might crush the core of the roll. Constant-torque windup units are usually limited to a 3:1 ratio of the roll to core diameters, because the film tension decreases with increasing roll diameter to the point where the outer layers become too loose to continue winding.

Heat-Transfer Calculations

An important aspect of the design of take-off equipment is to provide sufficient capacity to cool the melt at a rate equal to or greater than the pumping capacity of the extruder. Water, air, and chilled metal surfaces are the commonly used cooling media.

The application of the principles of heat transfer (discussed in Chap. 2) in the calculation of cooling capacities of take-off equipment is illustrated by the following examples. The first example is concerned with the design of a cooling-water trough to be used in a polyethylene pipe-extrusion process. The second example is a similar calculation applied to a chilled-metal forming box. The nomenclature of Chap. 2 is used in both of these calculations.

Design of a Cooling-Water Trough. In polyethylene pipe extrusions the temperature of the pipe leaving the end of the cooling-water trough must be low enough so that it can be coiled without suffering permanent deformation or set. This example shows the calculation of the length of trough required and the cooling-water requirements for a typical process. The design criterion is that there shall be sufficient length so that the maximum temperature in the pipe wall is 150°F when the pipe leaves the end of the trough.

Processing Conditions

Melt temperature. . . . . 330°F
Inside diameter of pipe. . . . . 1.0 in.
Pipe-wall thickness. . . . . 0.132 in.
Extrusion rate. . . . . 14 ft/min
Temperature of cooling water. . . . . 70°F

*Physical Properties of Polyethylene**

Specific heat. . . . . 0.70 Btu/lb-degF
Thermal conductivity. . . . . 0.15 Btu/hr-ft-degF
Density. . . . . 53.0 lb/cu ft
Thermal diffusivity†. . . . . 0.00404 sq ft/hr

* Average values for conventional polyethylene under the above processing conditions.

† Calculated with Eq. (47, Chap. 2).

The problem is primarily one of conduction heat transfer within the pipe wall and convection heat transfer from the pipe wall to the cooling water. The problem is simplified by considering the pipe a slab rather than a hollow cylinder. This procedure is commonly used with thin-walled cylinders and, while the pipe in this example cannot quite be considered thin-walled, the error introduced is quite small.

It is also assumed that heat transfer from the inner wall of the pipe to the stagnant air in the core is negligible in comparison to the heat transfer from the outer surface to the cooling water. The problem now becomes one of unsteady-state conduction in a slab with an adiabatic surface and with convective heat transfer at the other surface.

Consider a slab cooled uniformly from both surfaces. Since cooling occurs symmetrically about the mid-plane of the slab, there is no heat flow across the mid-plane, and it can be considered an adiabatic surface. Therefore, the problem is identical to one of heat conduction in a slab of twice the thickness and with convective heat transfer occurring at both surfaces at the same rate. The temperature distribution in the half plane of the new slab is identical to the temperature distribution in the pipe wall.

Solutions of this problem in unsteady-state conduction were discussed in Chap. 2, and charts for solving problems graphically were presented. However, before proceeding with the solution, it is necessary to examine the assumptions under which these solutions of the heat equation were obtained. The most important assumptions, for the present discussion, are that the convection coefficient h is a constant and that the initial distribution of temperature in the slab is uniform.

In this problem, as the pipe moves through the cooling trough, the surface of the pipe cools, and the convection coefficient changes. In other words, in the actual process the convection coefficient is a variable, while solutions of the heat equation are available only for the case in which the coefficient is assumed constant. One approach to the problem might be to make a stepwise calculation assuming h constant in each step. However, this cannot be done with the existing charts, as the assumption of an initial uniform temperature was made in their derivation. As the pipe cools, the temperature distribution in the wall becomes quite nonuniform. The most reasonable approach to the problem is to estimate an "effective" or average convection coefficient and then use it in the existing solutions.

Consider now the calculation of the convection coefficient h. Because the pipe moves through the water very slowly and because the water itself is not in violent motion, it is reasonable to assume that the mechanism of heat loss is natural convection. Natural convection from horizontal cylinders was discussed in Chap. 2, where it was shown [see Eq. (77), Chap. 2] that two dimensionless groups—the Prandtl number and the Grashoff number—control the process. Both of these groups are temperature-dependent, and it is customary to evaluate them at the temperature T_m, defined by the following equation:

$$T_m = T_s + \tfrac{1}{2}\Delta T \tag{200}$$

where

T_m = mean "film" temperature

T_s = surface temperature

T_f = bulk temperature of fluid

$\Delta T = (T_s - T_f)$.

The general equation [Eq. (77), Chap. 2], which applies to all fluids, can be written in the following form for the special case where the fluid is water:

$$h = C(\Delta T/D)^{1/4} \tag{201}$$

where

h = convection coefficient (Btu/hr-sq ft-degF)

$\Delta T = [T_s - T_f]$ (degF)

D = diameter of cylinder (ft)

and the values of the coefficient C are given in Table 4.1 below.

Assuming an average or effective value of the surface temperature, the effective convection coefficient is readily calculated from Eq. (201).

Example: Assuming the average value of T_s to be 90°F and the bulk temperature of the cooling water as 70°F, the mean temperature of the film is 80°F, and the value of h is given by the calculation

$$h = C(\Delta T/D)^{1/4} = (22)[(20)/(0.105)]^{1/4} = 82 \text{ Btu/hr-sq ft-degF}$$

The design criterion—that the maximum temperature in the pipe wall shall not exceed 150°F—is now applied. The maximum temperature occurs at the inside surface of the pipe wall. The chart in Fig. 2.4 of Chapter 2 is used to obtain the solution.

The dimensionless temperature Y, defined by Eq. (55), Chap. 2, is obtained by the following calculation:

$$Y = \frac{T - T_f}{T_i - T_f} = \frac{150 - 70}{330 - 70} = 0.308$$

TABLE 4.1. VALUES OF THE COEFFICIENT C OF EQ. (201)

T_m(°F)	C
80	22
100	27
120	30
140	33
160	36

The parameter N, defined by Eq. (57), Chap. 2, is given by the calculation

$$N = \frac{ah}{k} = \frac{(0.011)(82)}{(0.15)} = 6.0$$

where a represents the thickness of the pipe wall.

The dimensionless time ϕ is obtained from Fig. 2.4. Its value is 0.80, from which the required residence time in the cooling trough is calculated.

$$\theta = \frac{a^2\phi}{\alpha} = \frac{(0.011)^2(0.80)}{(0.00404)} = 0.0240 \text{ hr}$$

Since the pipe moves through the trough at a rate of 14 ft/min, the length of trough required to give a residence time of 0.0240 hr is readily found by the following calculation:

$$L = (0.0240)(60)(14) = 20.2 \text{ ft}$$

Similar calculations were carried out for other assumed surface temperatures. The results of these calculations are summarized in Table 4.2.

The next step is to determine which of the assumed temperatures is most reasonable to use.

Example: If an effective surface temperature of 90°F is assumed, then the convection coefficient h will have a value of 82 Btu/hr-sq ft-degF, and in a trough which is 20 ft long the inside surface of the pipe will be at a temperature of 150°F as it leaves the trough. The temperature of the outer surface can be calculated using Fig. 2.3 of Chap. 2, as follows:

$$\phi = \frac{\alpha\theta}{a^2} = \frac{(0.00404)(0.0240)}{(0.011)^2} = 0.80$$

$$N = \frac{ah}{k} = \frac{(0.011)(82)}{(0.15)} = 6.0$$

The value of Y, as read from Fig. 2.3 of Chap. 2, is 0.07 and the surface temperature is given by the following calculation:

$$T_s = (0.07)(330 - 70) + 70 = 88°F$$

Similar calculations were carried out for other positions corresponding to shorter residence times. The results of these calculations are shown in Fig. 4.64. Note that the surface temperature drops rapidly from its initial value of 330°F, and, for the last 10 ft of the trough, its average value is a little

TABLE 4.2. SUMMARY OF CALCULATIONS

T_s(°F)	T_f(°F)	T_m(°F)	ΔT(°F)	h(Btu/hr-sq. ft.-degF)	θ(hr)	L(ft)
90	70	80	20	82	0.0240	20.2
130	70	100	60	132	0.0204	17.1
170	70	120	100	167	0.0195	16.4
210	70	140	140	198	0.0186	15.6
—	—	—	—	∞	0.0156	13.1

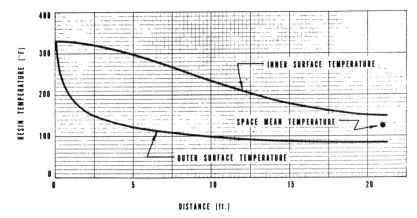

Fɪɢ. 4.64. Pipe temperatures as a function of position in the cooling trough.

higher than the assumed value of 90°F. For the first half of the trough the
average temperature is much higher than the assumed value. The net
result is that the actual value of h is slightly higher than the 82 Btu/hr-
sq ft-degF, and the required trough length is somewhat less than 20 ft.

The above calculation has assumed that the cooling water is maintained
at a constant temperature of 70°F. Actually, the heat removed from the
pipe will cause the cooling-water temperature to rise and thus reduce
somewhat the cooling rate. It appears reasonable, therefore, to specify a
length of approximately 20 ft for the cooling trough.

Figure 4.64 also shows the temperature of the inner surface of the pipe
as a function of position in the cooling trough. Note that there is a much
more gradual decrease in temperature, as in this case the heat must be
conducted through the pipe wall before it is dissipated to the cooling
water.

The final question in the design of the trough concerns cooling-water
requirements.

Example: The water enters the trough at a temperature of 70°F. Assuming an allowable temperature rise of 10°F, what is the required flow rate?

Since the dimensions of the pipe, the density of the polyethylene, and the linear
speed of the pipe through the trough are known, the mass flow rate is readily calculated. It is 6.45 lb/min. The polyethylene enters the trough a *uniform* temperature of
330°F. Let $\bar{T}$ be the space mean temperature, defined by Eq. (62), Chap. 2, of the
polyethylene leaving the trough. The rate at which heat is dissipated from the pipe
is given by the equation

$$\Delta H = (6.45)(0.70)(330 - \bar{T}) \tag{202}$$

where the units of ΔH are Btu/min.

Let Q represent the volumetric flow rate of cooling water (expressed as gallons per minute), and take the density of water as 8.34 lb/gal. The heat absorbed by the cooling water is given by the equation

$$\Delta H = (Q)(8.34)(1)(10) \qquad (203)$$

Combining Eqs. (202) and (203) and solving for Q gives the following result:

$$Q = (0.054)(330 - \bar{T}) \qquad (204)$$

The space mean temperature is calculated using the method presented in Chap. 2. The applicable equation is Eq. (65), Chap. 2, which can be written in the form

$$\bar{Y} = He^{-M^2\phi} \qquad (205)$$

where

$$\bar{Y} = \frac{\bar{T} - T_f}{T_i - T_f} \qquad (206)$$

H and M are functions only of the parameter N and are plotted in Fig. 2.5 of Chap. 2. The values of ϕ and N, as calculated previously, are

$$\phi = 0.80 \qquad N = 6.0$$

The values of H and M obtained from Figure 2.5 are

$$H = 0.98 \qquad M = 1.4$$

Substituting into Eq. (205) gives

$$\bar{Y} = (0.98)e^{-(1.4)^2(0.80)} = 0.204$$

and the space mean temperature, as calculated with Eq. (206), is

$$\bar{T} = (0.204)(330 - 70) + 70 = 123°F$$

The cooling-water requirement, as calculated with Eq. (204), is

$$Q = (0.054)(330 - 123) = 112 \text{ gpm}$$

Cooling with a Chilled Metal Surface. In some polyethylene pipe-extrusion processes a chilled-metal forming box is used to "freeze" a thin skin on the molten pipe so that it will not deform during transit to the cooling trough. The following example shows the calculation of the length required to form a skin of 0.015 in. thickness having a maximum temperature of 200°F, assuming that the processing conditions and the physical properties of the polyethylene are the same as in the first example.

In this case it is assumed that there is negligib'e resistance to heat transfer between the surface of the forming box and the surface of the pipe. This is equivalent to assuming an infinitely large heat-transfer coefficient—that the surface of the pipe instantaneously assumes the same temperature as that of the metal with which it comes into contact. It is to be expected that this condition will arise only when the two surfaces are in intimate contact. If, for example, an air film should form between them, the thermal resistance might become important.

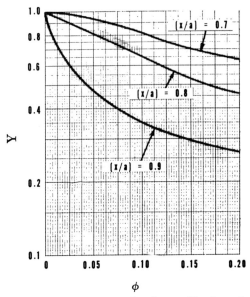

FIG. 4.65. Solutions of the heat equation for small values of ϕ and negligible surface resistance.

It is apparent that a relatively short residence time ϕ is required. Under these conditions and for the case where the parameter N is infinitely large, it is impossible to obtain accurate results using the conventional Gurney-Lurie chart. Furthermore, the first-term approximation upon which Eq. (60, Chap. 2) is based is no longer valid and cannot be used. The solution of the problem is based on Fig. 4.65, which is a special chart prepared for the case $N = \infty$ and for small values of ϕ. The parameter (x/a) is a dimensionless number giving the position of the point in the slab. The calculation is shown below.

$$(x/a) = \frac{(0.118)}{(0.133)} = 0.89$$

$$Y = \frac{T - T_f}{T_i - T_f} = \frac{(200 - 70)}{(330 - 70)} = 0.50$$

The value of ϕ is found from Fig. 4.65 to be approximately 0.04. The residence time is given by the following calculation:

$$\theta = \frac{a^2\phi}{\alpha} = \frac{(0.011)^2(0.04)}{(0.00404)} = 0.00122 \text{ hr}$$

and the required length is

$$L = (14)(60)(0.00122) = 1.02 \text{ ft}$$

APPENDIX A

Fluidity and corrected average fluidities for round orifices and slits

Given: The melt obeys the power law; i.e., the true shear rate and stress at any point are related by

$$-\frac{dv}{dr} = \kappa \tau^{\nu} \tag{A1}$$

"Apparent" flow constants κ' and κ'' are defined by

$$\frac{4q}{\pi R^3} = \kappa' \left(\frac{pR}{2L}\right)^{\nu} \qquad \text{for round holes} \tag{A2}$$

and

$$\frac{6q}{wh^2} = \kappa'' \left(\frac{ph}{2L}\right)^{\nu} \qquad \text{for thin slits} \tag{A3}$$

In circular holes, $v(R) = 0$. Integrate Eq. (A1) with respect to r and substitute Eq. (A4) to get the velocity distribution in a round hole:

$$v = \frac{\kappa p^{\nu}(R^{\nu+1} - r^{\nu+1})}{2^{\nu}L^{\nu}(\nu + 1)} \tag{A5}$$

$$q = \int_{o}^{R} 2\pi r v \, dr \tag{A6}$$

$$q = \frac{\pi \kappa p^{\nu} R^{\nu+3}}{2(\nu + 3)L^{\nu}} \tag{A7}$$

Solve Eq. (A7) for

$$\frac{\kappa p^{\nu} R^{\nu}}{2^{\nu} L^{\nu}} = \kappa \left(\frac{pR}{2L}\right)^{\nu}$$

and substitute the result for the right side of Eq. (A1)

$$-\left(\frac{dv}{dr}\right)_{r=R} = \frac{\kappa pR}{2L} = \frac{(\nu + 3)q}{\pi R^3} \tag{A8}$$

But by definition of Eq. (A2),

$$\kappa' \left(\frac{pR}{2L}\right)^{\nu} = \frac{4q}{\pi R^3}$$

Therefore

$$\kappa = \frac{(\nu + 3)\kappa'}{4} \quad \text{and} \quad \kappa' = \frac{4\kappa}{\nu + 3} \tag{A9}$$

Similarly, for slits

$$v \text{ at } \frac{h}{2} = 0 \tag{A10}$$

$$v = \kappa_p{}^\nu \left(\frac{h^{\nu+1}}{2^{\nu+1}} - r^{\nu+1} \right) \tag{A11}$$

and

$$q = 2 \int_o^{h/2} wv \, dr \tag{A12}$$

$$q = \kappa \frac{wh^{\nu+2}p^\nu}{2^{\nu+1}(\nu + 2)L^\nu} \tag{A13}$$

The shear rate at the wall is

$$-\frac{dv}{dr}\bigg]_{r=(h/2)} = \kappa \left(\frac{ph}{2L} \right)^\nu = \frac{2(\nu + 2)q}{wh^2} \tag{A14}$$

Note that for $\nu = 1$,

$$-\frac{dv}{dr}\bigg]_{r=(h/2)} = \frac{6q}{wh^2} \tag{A15}$$

But by the definition, Eq. (A3),

$$\kappa'' \left(\frac{ph}{2L} \right)^\nu = \frac{6q}{wh^2}$$

Therefore

$$\kappa = \frac{(\nu + 2)\kappa''}{3} \quad \text{and} \quad \kappa'' = \frac{3\kappa}{\nu + 2} \tag{A16}$$

Equating κ in Eqs. (A9) and (A16),

$$\kappa'' = \frac{3(\nu + 3)\kappa'}{4(\nu + 2)}. \tag{A17}$$

APPENDIX B

Derivation of exact equation for flow of Newtonian liquid through a circular annular channel

Given: Inside radius of channel $= R_i$

Outside radius of channel $= R_o$

Radius to any thin annular element $= r$

Thickness of element $= dr$. Over this thickness the stress increases by an amount $d\tau$.

Forces acting on the element are the pressure differential p in the direction of flow (z direction), the inner shear stress τ acting in the same direction and opposed by the outer stress $\tau + d\tau$. The sum of the forces (at equilibrium) in the z direction is

$$-2\pi r p \, dr - 2\pi r L \tau + 2\pi L (r + dr)(\tau + d\tau) = 0 \tag{B1}$$

$$-rp \, dr - rL\tau + rL\tau + rL \, d\tau + L\tau \, dr + L \, dr d\tau = 0 \tag{B2}$$

Ignore the second-order product $dr d\tau$. Then

$$-rp \, dr + rL \, d\tau + L\tau \, dr = 0 \tag{B3}$$

For Newtonian liquids in pressure flow

$$\tau = -\mu \frac{dv}{dr} \tag{B4}$$

$$d\tau = -\mu \frac{d^2v}{dr^2} \, dr \tag{B5}$$

$$-pr \, dr - \mu L r \frac{d^2v}{dr^2} \, dr - \mu L \frac{dv}{dr} \, dr = 0 \tag{B6}$$

$$\frac{d^2v}{dr^2} + \frac{1}{r}\frac{dv}{dr} = -\frac{p}{\mu L} \tag{B7}$$

Let

$$\frac{dv}{dr} = v'.$$

Then Eq. (B7) becomes

$$\frac{dv'}{dr} + \frac{v'}{r} = -\frac{p}{\mu L} \tag{B8}$$

This is a linear differential equation of the first order for which $e^{\int dr/r}$ is an integrating factor.

But $e^{\int dr/r} = r$.   Therefore,

$$v' = \frac{1}{r}\int -\frac{pr}{L} \, dr + \frac{C_1}{r} = \frac{dv}{dr} \tag{B9}$$

$$v = -\frac{pr^2}{4\mu L} + C_1 \ln r + C_2 \tag{B10}$$

This is the basic equation for velocity distribution in cylindrical holes. If the boundary conditions

$$R_i = 0, \qquad R_o = 0, \qquad \frac{dv}{dr}\bigg]_{r=0} = 0$$

are applied, the familiar Poiseuille equation is obtained. In the annulus the appropriate boundary conditions are

$$v(R_i) = 0 \tag{B11}$$

$$v(R_o) = 0 \tag{B12}$$

$$0 = -\frac{pR_o{}^2}{4\mu L} + C_1 \ln R_o + C_2 \tag{B13}$$

$$0 = -\frac{pR_i{}^2}{4\mu L} + C_1 \ln R_i + C_2 \tag{B14}$$

Subtract Eq. (B13) from Eq. (B14) to get

$$-\frac{p}{4\mu L} (R_o{}^2 - R_i{}^2) + C_1 \frac{R_o}{R_i} = 0 \tag{B15}$$

and

$$C_1 = \frac{p(R_o{}^2 - R_i{}^2)}{4\mu L \ln \left(\dfrac{R_o}{R_i}\right)} \tag{B16}$$

Substitute Eq. (B16) into Eq. (B13) to get

$$C_2 = \frac{p}{4\mu L} \left[R_o{}^2 - \frac{(R_o{}^2 - R_i{}^2) \ln R_o}{\ln \left(\dfrac{R_o}{R_i}\right)} \right] \tag{B17}$$

Substitute Eqs. (B16) and (B17) into (B10) to get the annular velocity distribution:

$$v = \frac{p}{4\mu L} \left[R_o{}^2 - r^2 + \frac{(R_o{}^2 - R_i{}^2) \ln \left(\dfrac{r}{R_o}\right)}{\ln \left(\dfrac{R_o}{R_i}\right)} \right] \tag{B18}$$

The discharge is given by

$$q = \int_{R_i}^{R_o} 2\pi r v \ dr \tag{B19}$$

$$q = \frac{\pi p}{2\mu L} \int_{R_i}^{R_o} \left\{ R_o{}^2 r - r^3 + \left[\frac{(R_o{}^2 - R_i{}^2)}{\ln \left(\dfrac{R_o}{R_i}\right)} \right] r \ln \frac{r}{R_o} \right\} dr \tag{B20}$$

Take the last part first:

$$\int_{R_i}^{R_o} \left(r \ln \frac{r}{R_o} \right) dr = \left[\frac{r^2}{2} \ln \frac{r}{R_o} - \frac{r^2}{4} \right]_{R_i}^{R_o} = \frac{R_i^2}{2} \ln \frac{R_o}{R_i} - \frac{(R_o^2 - R_i^2)}{4} \quad \text{(B21)}$$

Now perform the rest of the integration and collect similar terms to get

$$q = \frac{\pi p}{8\mu L} \left[R_o^4 - R_i^4 - \frac{(R_o^2 - R_i^2)^2}{\ln\left(\frac{R_o}{R_i}\right)} \right] \quad \text{(B22)}$$

Note that as

$$R_i \to 0, \qquad q \to \frac{\pi p R_o^4}{8\mu L}$$

This may be compared with the approximate Eq. (171) of the text:

$$q = \pi \frac{(R_o + R_i)(R_o - R_i)^3 p}{12\mu L} \quad \text{(171)}$$

$$q = \frac{\pi p}{8\mu L} \left[\frac{2}{3} (R_o + R_i)(R_o - R_i)^3 \right]$$

Let $\beta = R_o/R_i$; then Eqs. (B22) and (171) become

$$q = \frac{\pi p R_i^4}{8\mu L} \left[\beta^4 - 1 - \frac{(\beta^2 - 1)^2}{\ln \beta} \right] \quad \text{(B23)}$$

and

$$q = \frac{\pi p R_i^4}{8\mu L} \left[\frac{2}{3} (\beta + 1)(\beta - 1)^3 \right] \quad \text{(B24)}$$

The exact and approximate factors in the brackets are listed below for various β.

β	Exact	Approx.	Relative error, %
1.1	0.001400	0.001400	
1.2	0.011731	0.011733	
1.5	0.2089	0.2083	−0.2
2.0	2.016	2.0000	−0.8
3.0	21.745	21.333	−1.9
5.0	266.11	256.00	−3.8
10.0	5,742.5	5,346.0	−6.9

APPENDIX C

Drag flow in wire-coating dies

Given: A wire of radius R_i, concentric with a hole of larger radius R_o, is drawing out melt as it passes through the hole at a rate v_w in./sec. There is no applied pressure differential, but the melt completely fills the annulus.

Unless R_o and R_i are nearly equal, a large error will result if the annulus is treated as two parallel plates of average width $\pi(R_o + R_i)$ and separation $R_o - R_i$. Drag flow (of a Newtonian liquid) through such a pair of plates is given by

$$q = \frac{\pi v_w R_i{}^2 (\beta^2 - 1)}{2} \tag{C1}$$

where

$$\beta = \frac{R_o}{R_i}$$

Case 1. Newtonian Liquids

To drag out liquid there must be a pull T on the wire. This force acts on a shear surface of $2\pi R_i L$. At any distance r into the melt there is a new surface $2\pi r L$. Since this slug is bounded by R_i and r and is in equilibrium, the opposing shear stress at r must also develop a total force T. Therefore

$$\tau = \frac{T}{2\pi r L} \tag{C2}$$

$$-\frac{dv}{dr} = \frac{\tau}{\mu} = \frac{T}{2\pi \mu r L} \tag{C3}$$

$$v = -\frac{T}{2\pi \mu L} \ln r + C_1 \tag{C4}$$

At $r = R_o$, $v = 0$; at $r = R_i$, $v = v_w$.

$$0 = -\frac{T}{2\pi \mu L} \ln R_o + C_1 \tag{C5}$$

$$C_1 = \frac{T \ln R_o}{2\pi \mu L} \tag{C6}$$

$$v_w = \frac{T(\ln R_o - \ln R_i)}{2\pi \mu L} = \frac{T \ln \dfrac{R_o}{R_i}}{2\pi \mu L} \tag{C7}$$

$$v_w = \frac{T \ln \beta}{2\pi \mu L} \tag{C8}$$

$$T = \frac{2\pi \mu L v_w}{\ln \beta} \tag{C9}$$

$$v = \frac{-v_w \ln r}{\ln \beta} + \frac{v_w \ln R_o}{\ln \beta} = \frac{v_w \ln \left(\dfrac{R_o}{r}\right)}{\ln \beta} \tag{C10}$$

$$q_d = \int_{R_i}^{R_o} 2\pi r v \; dr \tag{C11}$$

$$q_d = \frac{2\pi v_w}{\ln \beta} \int_{R_i}^{R_o} \left(r \ln \frac{R_o}{r} \right) dr \tag{C12}$$

$$q_d = \pi v_w R_i^2 \left(\frac{\beta^2 - 1}{2 \ln \beta} - 1 \right) \tag{C13}$$

If the term in brackets is compared with the corresponding term from Eq. (C1), viz., $(\beta^2 - 1)/2$ for various β, the following table gives the errors.

β	Exact	Approx.	Relative error, %
1.1	0.1017	0.1050	+3.2
1.2	0.2067	0.2200	+6.4
1.5	0.5414	0.6250	+15.4
2.0	1.1640	1.5000	+23.3

Case 2. Melt Obeying Power Law

The force balance is the same as for the Newtonian case. Equation (C3) becomes

$$-\frac{dv}{dr} = \kappa \left(\frac{T}{2\pi L} \right)^\nu r^{-\nu} \tag{C14}$$

The same boundary conditions apply, and the velocity distribution becomes

$$v = \frac{v_w (R_o^{1-\nu} - r^{1-\nu})}{(R_o)^{1-\nu} - (R_i)^{1-\nu}} \tag{C15}$$

for $\nu \neq 1$. Applying Eq. (C11) to Eq. (C15) and integrating,

$$q_d = \frac{\pi v_w R_i^2 [(1 - \nu)\beta^{3-\nu} - (3 - \nu)\beta^{1-\nu} + 2]}{(3 - \nu)(\beta^{1-\nu} - 1)} \tag{C16}$$

for $\nu \neq 1, 3$.

The same procedure can be used to find u and q for $\nu = 3$. Note that the shear stress at any point is given by Eq. (C2) and (C9):

$$\tau = \frac{\mu v_w}{r \ln \beta} \tag{C17}$$

The corresponding shear rate is given by

$$-\frac{dv}{dr} = \frac{v_w}{r \ln \beta} \tag{C18}$$

Both are greatest for $r = R_i$.

NOMENCLATURE

Any consistent system of units may be used in the preceding extrusion equations. The only restriction imposed on choice of units is that the screw-rotation speed be expressed in revolutions per unit time rather than, for example, degrees or radians per unit time.

The nomenclature employed in the foregoing section on extrusion is listed below.

a Ratio of pressure flow to drag flow along the z-axis [with negative sign introduced to make a normally positive; refer to Eq. (32) and related discussion].

b Axial channel width.

b Constant in viscosity-temperature relationship $(°K^{-1})$.

C Constant in the Gee-Lyon power law. (See also κ, κ', κ'')

C_p Specific heat at constant pressure. (For most polymers C_p and C_v can safely be assumed equal.)

c Ratio of the transverse pressure flow to drag flow as measured along the x-axis (with negative sign introduced as with a).

D Inside barrel diameter or, if flight land clearance is neglected, outside screw diameter.

DR Draw ratio.

e Axial flight width.

e Base of natural logarithms.

F_d Drag-flow shape factor given by Eq. (7) for full screw channels or by Eq. (50) for partially empty screw channels; dimensionless.

F_p Pressure-flow shape factor given by Eq. (10), dimensionless.

F_{cd} Channel curvature factor for drag flow given by Eq. (53); dimensionless.

$F_{\mu d}$ Viscosity correction factor for drag flow given by Eq. (47); dimensionless.

$F_{\mu p}$ Viscosity correction factor for pressure flow given by Eq. (48); dimensionless.

F'_d $F_d F_{\mu d} F_{cd}$.

F'_p $F_p F_{\mu p}$.

f The fractional extent to which a screw channel is filled with fluid.

f Coefficient of friction.

h Inside barrel radius minus screw root radius or, if flight land clearance is neglected, the screw-channel depth.

h Slit depth of a slit die.

J Ratio of the flight land clearance to the channel depth.

k Die constant defined by Eq. (98) $(length^3)$.

L Axial length of screw.

l Distance measured along the auxiliary l-axis increasing in the die-ward direction. (This is not an independent coordinate but is related to z by $l = z \sin \phi$.)

M Adiabatic extrusion constant defined by $M = \mu_i b \epsilon / \rho C_p$.

N Screw-rotation speed in revolutions per unit time.

n Number of screw channels (or flights) in parallel.

n Ratio of effective length to radius of an orifice whose actual length is zero.

p Pressure.

q Volumetric flow rate.

q_w Mass flow rate $(= \rho q)$.

R Radius.

R The ratio of the fluid viscosity at the screw inlet to that at the die, dimensionless.

r Radial distance.

s Land width measured perpendicular to flight face.

t Screw lead $(= \pi D \tan \phi)$.

t Temperature.

t Thickness.

T Absolute temperature.

U Velocity of barrel relative to screw.

UI Uniformity index.

V Volume or specific volume of a fluid.

v Velocity.

w Die-slit width (long dimension perpendicular to flow).

w Channel width measured perpendicular to flights, i.e., along the x-axis [Refer to Eqs. (14) through (16).].

x Distance measured along the x-axis.

y Distance measured along the y-axis.

Z Power.

z Distance measured along the helical z-axis.

GREEK LETTERS

α Drag-flow constant defined by Eq. (23) (length^3).

α Constant for slit die, defined by Eq. (180).

β Pressure-flow constant defined by Eq. (24) (length^4).

β R_o/R_i in tubing and wire-coating dies.

γ Shear rate (time)$^{-1}$.

γ Ratio of viscosity at barrel surface to screw root.

δ Flight land clearance, i.e., the radial clearance between the flight and barrel.

ϵ Screw power constant defined by Eq. (128)

θ Angle of movement of a solid plug in the feed zone.

θ Time

κ Fluidity based on true shear-rate data.

κ' Fluidity based on apparent shear-rate data.

κ'' Fluidity for a slit die.

λ Latent heat of fusion.

μ Viscosity.

μ_a Apparent viscosity.

ν Exponent of the power law.

π 3.1415. . . .

ρ Density.

τ Shear stress.

ϕ Helix angle measured at the flight crest ($= \arctan t/\pi D$).

ψ Dissipation function for viscous shear energy.

SUBSCRIPTS

b Barrel.

c Circumferential.

D Die.

d Drag flow.

i Inlet.

i Inside.

L Land clearance.

m Mean.

o Outside.

p Pressure flow.

s Screw.

w Mass rate.

w At the wall.

x, y, z Directed along the appropriate respective axis.

ACKNOWLEDGMENTS

The assistance of J. M. McKelvey, Washington University, in preparing the sample problems illustrating the design of extrudate cooling equipment is greatly appreciated.

E. C. Bernhardt, E. I. du Pont de Nemours & Co., Inc., assisted greatly in the organization and preparation of this chapter in addition to his responsibilities as Editor.

REFERENCES

1. Anonymous, "General Purpose Extrusion-Molding Machine," *Brit. Plastics*, **29**, 442 (1956).

2. Anonymous, "New Machine with Screw Preplasticizer," *Modern Plastics*, **29**, 115 (Dec. 1951).

3. Atkinson, T. E., and Owen, D. G., "Some Aspects of the Screw Extrusion of Thermoplastics," *Trans. Plastics Inst. (London)*, **21**, 40 (1953).

4. Bagley, E. B., "End Correction in the Capillary Flow of Polyethylene," *J. Appl. Phys.*, **28**, 624 (1957).

5. Baigent, K., "Multi-Screw Extruders," *Trans. Plastics Inst. (London)*, **24**, 134 (1956).

6. BECK, E., "High Speed Screw Type Extruders," *Kunststoffe*, **46**, 18 (1956); "Extrusion with High Speed Screws," *Kunststoffe*, **47**, 250 (1957); "Practical Experiences in the Case of Extrusion with High Speed Self-Regulating Screws," *Plastverarbeiter*, **1**, 19 (1957) all in German.

7. Beck, H., "Kunststoffverarbeitung-Spritzgiessen," p. 112, Munich, Carl Hanser Verlag, 1957.

8. Bernhardt, E. C., "Calculating Extruder Performance," *Modern Plastics*, **32**, 127 (Feb. 1955).

9. Bernhardt, E. C., "Stock Thermocouples, Pressure Gauges, and Rupture Disks for Use on Plastics Extruders," *SPE Journal*, **11**, 25 (Nov. 1955).

10. Bernhardt, E. C., "A New Development in Extraction-Extrusion—the Vacuum Extruder Screw," *SPE Journal*, **12**, 40 (Mar. 1956).

11. Bernhardt, E. C., "Valved Extrusion," *SPE Journal*, **13** (Feb. 1957).

12. Bernhardt, E. C., and McKelvey, J. M., "Analysis of Adiabatic Plastics Extrusion," *SPE Journal*, **10**, 419 (Mar. 1954).

13. Beyer, C. E., and Towsley, F. E., "Flow of Polystyrene Through Rectangular Channels," *J.Colloid Sci.* **7**, 236 (1952).

14. Bird, R. B., "Viscous Heat Effects in the Extrusion of Molten Plastics," *SPE Journal*, **11**, 35 (Sept. 1955).

15. Booy, M. L., private communication to P. H. Squires, June 11, 1957.

16. Boussinesq, M. J., "Sur l'Influence des Frottements dans les Mouvements Reguliers des Fluids," *J. mathematique pures et appliquees*, series 2, **13**, 377 (1868).

17. Carley, J. F., "Operating Characteristics of Extruders," *SPE Journal*, **9**, 9 (Mar. 1953).

18. Carley, J. F., "Flow of Melts in 'Crosshead'-Slit Dies; Criteria for Die Design," *J. Appl. Phys.*, **25**, 1118 (1954).

19. Carley, J. F., "Design and Operation of Crosshead Sheeting Dies," *Modern Plastics*, **33**, 127 (Aug. 1956).

20. Carley, J. F., and McKelvey, J. M., "Extruder Scale-Up Theory and Experiments," *Ind. Eng. Chem.*, **45**, 989 (1953).

21. Carley, J. F., Mallouk, R. S., and McKelvey, J. M., "Simplified Flow Theory for Screw Extruders," *Ind. Eng. Chem.*, **45**, 974 (1953).

22. Carley, J. F., and Strub, R. A., "Basic Concepts of Extrusion," *Ind. Eng. Chem.* **45**, 970 (1953).

23. Colwell, R. E., "Applications of Extrusion Theory," presented at the 13th Ann. Nat. Tech. Conference of the SPE, January, 1957; *Tech. Papers*, **3**, 15 (1957).

24. Darnell, W. H. and Mol, E. A. J., "Solids Conveying in Extruders," *SPE Journal*, **12**, 20 (Apr. 1956).

25. E. I. du Pont de Nemours & Co., Inc., Polychemicals Dept., Information Bulletins: X-70, "'Alathon' Polyethylene Resin—Extrusion"; X-40c, "'Zytel' Nylon Resin—Extrusion."

26. Eccher, S., and Valentinotti, A., "Experimental Determination of Velocity Profiles in an Extruder Screw," *Ind. Eng. Chem.*, **50**, 829 (1958).

27. Fisher, E. G., "Modern Views on Extrusion Machinery," *Trans. Plastics Inst. (London)*, **24**, 143 (1956).

28. Fisher, E. G., "Single Screw Extruders," *Trans. Plastics Inst. (London)*, **24**, 125 (1956).

29. Fisher, E. G., "Extrusion of Plastics," London, Iliffe & Sons, Ltd., 1958.
30. Frederickson, A. G., and Bird, R. B., "Non-Newtonian Flow in Annuli," *Ind. Eng. Chem.*, **50**, 347 (1958).
31. Gaspar, E., "Problems and Trends in European Extruder Design," *SPE Journal*, **12**, 23 (Oct. 1956).
32. Gee, R. E., and Lyon, J. B., "Nonisothermal Flow of Viscous Non-Newtonian Fluids," *Ind. Eng. Chem.*, **49**, 956 (1957).
33. Gore, W. L., "Principles of Plastics Screw Extrusion," *SPE Journal*, **9**, 6 (Mar. 1953).
34. Gore, W. L., and McKelvey, J. M., "Theory of Screw Extruders," Vol. III, "Rheology; Theory and Applications," Eirich, F. R. (ed.), New York, Academic Press, Inc., to be published in 1958.
35. Grant, D., and Walker, W., "Plastics Progress," Morgan, P. (ed.), "Problems of Mixing in Extrusion," pp. 245–253, Iliffe & Sons, Ltd., 1951.
36. Gray, A. N., "Autogenous Extrusion," *Rubber Age (N.Y.)*, **79**, 286 (1956).
37. Jepson, C. H., "Future Extrusion Studies," *Ind. Eng. Chem.*, **45**, 992 (1953).
38. Kennaway, A., and Weeks, D. J., "Extrusion Problems and Screw Design," in "Polythene," Renfrew, A. and Morgan, P. (eds.), pp. 285–305, London, Iliffe & Sons, Ltd., 1957.
39. McAdams, W. H., "Heat Transmission," pp. 34–38 and 178, New York, McGraw-Hill Book Company, Inc., 1954.
40. McKelvey, J. M., "Design of Screws for Polyethylene Extrusion," *SPE Journal*, **9**, 12 (Mar. 1953).
41. McKelvey, J. M., "Experimental Studies of Melt Extrusion," *Ind. Eng. Chem.* **45**, 982 (1953).
42. McKelvey, J. M., "Analysis of Adiabatic Plastics Extrusion," *Ind. Eng. Chem.*, **46**, 660 (1954).
43. Maddock, B. H., "Fundamental Mechanisms in Polyethylene Extrusion," *SPE Journal*, **12**, 49 (Oct. 1956); 50 (Nov. 1956).
44. Maddock, B. H., "Factors Affecting Quality in Polyethylene Extrusion," *Modern Plastics*, **34**, 123 (Apr. 1957).
45. Maddock, B. H., "How to Predict Extruder Performance with Polyethylene," *Plastics Technol.*, **3**, 385 (1957).
46. Maillefer, C., "An Analytical Study of the Single Screw Extruder," *Brit. Plastics*, **27**, 394 (1954).
47. Mallouk, R. S., and McKelvey, J. M., "Power Requirements of Melt Extruders," *Ind. Eng. Chem.*, **45**, 987 (1953).
48. Meskat, W., "Theory of the Flow of Material in Worm Machines, Part I" *Kunststoffe*, **45**, 87 (1955) (in German).
49. "Modern Plastics Encyclopedia Issue," "Extruding Machines," Vol. 36, No. 1A-1958, p. 1112, New York, Breskin Publications, Inc.
50. Mohr, W. D., and Mallouk, R. S., private communication to P. H. Squires, Sept. 20, 1957, to be published.
51. Mohr, W. D., Saxton, R. L., and Jepson, C. H., "Theory of Mixing in the Single-Screw Extruder," *Ind. Eng. Chem.*, **49**, 1857 (1957).
52. Mori, Y., and Ototake, N., "Mechanism of Flow through a Compression-Type Screw Extruder," *Chem. Eng. (Tokyo)*, **19**, 9 (1955) (in Japanese).
53. Mori, Y., Ototake, N., and Igarashi, H., "Screw Extrusion Processes for Forming Plastic Materials," *Chem. Eng. (Tokyo)*, **18**, 221 (1954) (in Japanese).
54. Pai, Shih-I, "Viscous Flow Theory; I, Laminar Flow," Princeton, N. J., D. Van Nostrand Co., Inc., 1956.

55. Pao, Y. H., "Hydrodynamic Theory for the Flow of a Viscoelastic Fluid," *J. Appl. Phys.*, **28**, 591 (1957).
56. Perkins, R. S., "Extrusion Dies for Plastic Pipe," *SPE Journal*, **12**, 47 (Aug. 1956.
57. Perry, J. H., "Chemical Engineers' Handbook" p. 473, New York, McGraw-Hill Book Company, Inc., 1950.
58. Pigott, W. T., "Pressures Developed by Viscous Materials in the Screw Extrusion Machine," *Trans. ASME*, **73**, 947 (1951).
59. Robbins, K. O., "Extrusion Dies and Take-off Equipment," *Modern Plastics*, **33**, 125 (Dec. 1955).
60. Rogowsky, Z. (now Rigby, Z.), "Principles of the Screw Extrusion Machine," *Engineering*, **162**, 358 (1956); also *Proc. Inst. Mech. Engrs. (London)*, **156**, 56 (1957).
61. Rowell, H. S., and Finlayson, D., "Screw Viscosity Pumps," *Engineering*, **114**, 606 (1922); **126**, 249 (1928).
62. Sackett, R. D., "Viscosity Data for Extruder Flow Equations," *SPE Journal*, **12**, 32 (Oct. 1956).
63. Simonds, H. R., Weith, A. J., and Schack, W., "Extrusion of Plastics, Rubber and Metals," New York, Reinhold Publishing Corp., 1952.
64. Sokolnikoff, I. S., and Sokolnikoff, E. S., "Higher Mathematics for Engineers and Physicists," 1st Ed., p. 97, New York, McGraw-Hill Book Company, Inc., 1941.
65. Spencer, R. S., and Gilmore, G. D., "Equation of State for High Polymer," *J. Appl. Phys.*, **21**, 523 (1950).
66. Squires, P. H., "Screw-Extruder Pumping Efficiency," *SPE Journal*, **14**, 24 (May 1958).
67. Squires, P. H., and Galt, J. C., unpublished work, June, 1958.
68. Strub, R. A., "The Theory of Screw Extruders," *Proc. Second Midwestern Conference on Fluid Mechanics*, Ohio State University, pp. 481–494, 1952.
69. Toor, H. L., "The Energy Equation for Viscous Flow," *Ind. Eng. Chem.*, **48**, 922 (1956).
70. Tordella, J. P., "Melt Fracture—Extrudate Roughness in Plastics Extrusion," *SPE Journal*, **12**, 36 (1956).
71. Weeks, D. J., "Some Aids to the Design of Dies for Plastics Extrusion," *Brit. Plastics*, **31**, 201 (1958).
72. Whitcut, H. M., "Extrusion Equipment," *Rubber & Plastics Age*, January, 1957, p. 56.
73. Willert, W. H., "Injection Molding Apparatus," U.S. Patent 2,734,226 (Feb. 14, 1956).
74. Willert, W. H., "Heating Systems for Extrusion Cylinders," *SPE Journal*, **13**, 122 (June 1957).
75. Yardoff, O., "Mecanique des Fluides—Sur les Ecoulements a la Poiseuille," *Compt. rend.*, **223**, 192 (1946).
76. Yoshida, T., Hayashida, K., Kobayashi, K., and Tenaka, H., "A Method for Graphical Representation of Screw Characteristics," *Chem. Eng. (Tokyo)*, **21**, 366 (1957) (in Japanese).

5. INJECTION MOLDING

G. B. Thayer, B. S.	Co-ordinator; Mold Design
J. W. Mighton, B. S.	Co-ordinator; Introduction; Granule Feed
R. B. Dahl, B. S.	Heating Cylinder Design; Nozzles
C. E. Beyer, B. S.	Role of Temperature, Pressure and Time; Moldability

The Dow Chemical Company

INTRODUCTION

Injection molding is one of the major methods of fabricating thermoplastics. The process provides economical rapid production of high-quality precision parts from a wide selection of plastic materials.

This chapter discusses the function and design of molding equipment, the molding cycle, and moldability. Injection molding was developed as an art, because many of the complex problems encountered required extensive and continuing research to solve theoretically. Recently, however, insight into the process, gained through experimentation, has resulted in better agreement between the theory of molding and the art. The section entitled "Role of Pressure, Temperature, and Time in Injection Molding" covers much of the still-evolving theoretical approach to injection molding.

The Injection Molding Machine

Basically, injection molding is a simple cyclic process in which plastic granules are heated until they are melted. The melt is then forced into a mold where it cools and resolidifies to produce a part of the desired shape. Machines range from small automatically operated units with capacities of 1 oz to large 300-oz machines equipped with "preplasticators." Typical machines are shown in Figs. 5.1, 5.2 and 5.3. Conventional-type machines are used most widely in the industry but a smaller number of the preplasticating type find use for special moldings, such as large-area parts or where high-speed injection is required. A brief description of the conventional molding machine components follows (Fig. 5.4).

(*Courtesy Reed-Prentice Div. Package Machinery Co.*)

Fig. 5.1. Conventional 4-oz molding machine.

(*Courtesy Watson-Stillman Div. Farrel-Birmingham Co., Inc.*)

Fig. 5.2. Conventional 16-oz. machine.

Feed Mechanism. The feed mechanism is usually mounted in conjunction with the plastic storage hopper and meters out a constant amount of material for each cycle.

Injection Plunger. The plunger, or ram, activated by hydraulic pressure, advances the plastic through the heating cylinder, nozzle, and into the mold.

(Courtesy Hydraulic Press Mfg. Co.)

FIG. 5.3. Preplasticating 200-oz. machine.

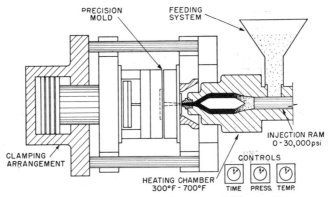

FIG. 5.4. Components of injection molding machine.

Heating Cylinder. The heating cylinder uniformly softens the plastic and provides a passage for the ram to inject the material into the mold. Modern machines have from two to six zones of electrical heater bands which are individually controlled for proper temperatures. A torpedo or spreader is located internally to give improved heat transfer to the plastic granules.

Nozzle. The nozzle is the connecting passageway between the cylinder and the mold. The contact surface between the mold and cylinder is usually small, to minimize heat conduction from the cylinder. Many different nozzles have been designed for use with general molding techniques and for special applications. Some nozzles may require small heater bands and a means of temperature control to maintain the proper plastic temperature.

Mold. The mold contains cavities which are filled with plastic during injection, thereby producing a part having the desired shape.

The molten plastic enters the mold cavities from the heating-cylinder nozzle through the sprue, runners, and gates. The sprue is the passage between the nozzle of the molding machine and the runners in the mold. This is usually a tapered cylindrical passageway. The runners carry the plastic laterally across the mold to the gates, which are generally short and restricted passages through which the resin flows from the runners into the mold cavities. Most molds are designed for temperature control, since one of their basic functions is to remove heat from the plastic.

Clamp. The clamp is the "press" portion of the machine which holds the mold tightly closed during injection and cooling. The opening of the clamp separates the mold to allow removal of the plastic article. The clamping force is usually provided by a hydraulically operated toggle or a straight hydraulic cylinder.

Hydraulic System. The hydraulic system in the molding machine provides the force for moving the component parts during operation. This system consists of pumps, high-pressure lines, hydraulic valves, solenoid valves, and timers. Two pumps are used; one delivers high pressure at low volume and the other high volume at low pressure. This dual system permits rapid motion of the clamp and ram at the beginning of the stroke, and a slower motion at much higher pressure at the end of the stroke. Not only the pumping capacity of the system but also the dependence of delivery losses on the pressure developed by the pump are characteristics of the hydraulic system. The influence of the performance of the hydraulic system on the injection-molding operation has been the subject of a detailed study.[8]

Controls. Nine major controls are available to the molding-machine operator. They govern the following: (1) the amount of plastic introduced in the cylinder, (2) the pressure applied to the plunger, (3) the plunger speed, (4) the temperature of the heating cylinder (and nozzle if controlled), (5) the temperature of the mold, (6) the plunger forward time, (7) the mold closed time, (8) the clamping force, and (9) the mold open time. Other controls may be provided, depending on the manufacturer's design or the intended use of the machine.

Means of controlling the plastic feed will be discussed later in more detail.

The amount of pressure applied to the injection plunger is controlled by a hydraulic relief-valve adjustment.

Plunger speed is usually controlled by a flow valve in the hydraulic line to the injection cylinder.

Plastic temperature is one of the more critical variables and, therefore, special attention is paid to the control of the heating cylinder. Controlling pyrometers are used with thermocouple or resistance-wire sensing elements mounted in the wall of the heating cylinder. The pyrometers should have some anticipatory characteristics to reduce temperature cycling. The newer saturable core-reactor controllers produce a minimum of temperature cycling. If heater bands are required on the nozzle, their temperature is usually controlled with a variable transformer or one of the methods used on the heating cylinders.

Mold temperature control is best achieved through the use of an auxiliary unit. Basically, the unit consists of a liquid circulating system and means of adding or removing heat from the liquid.

The cycle controls require timers that are precise, sensitive to fractions of a second, and readily adjustable for accurate control of the plunger-forward, mold-closed, and mold-open times.

Adjustment of the clamping force on a machine having a straight hydraulic-ram clamp is accomplished by a relief-valve adjustment. With a toggle clamping system it is necessary to adjust the large nuts on the tie bars, so that when the mold closes, the toggle will be in the locked position and exert the proper pressure.

The Molding Cycle

Skill at control settings and their proper adjustment determines the quality of the finished article. Most of these controls are so interrelated that a simple adjustment is not possible; e.g., when the plastic temperature is increased, the mold may flash unless injection pressure is reduced. At higher temperatures the gate freezes more slowly, and a longer plunger-forward time might be necessary to prevent sinks or voids.

There are two kinds of controls available to the injection-molding-machine operator; a set of primary controls affects the quality of the molding by directly controlling the pressure and temperature. The secondary controls indirectly affect the primary controls.

A molding of good quality is one free from warpage, sinks, bubbles, scoring, cracks, etc. It can be made only if the correct amount of plastic is injected into the mold at the proper pressure and temperature. Other defects that may appear in moldings are discussed on pp. 360 through 363.

The Plastic Temperature Cycle. To describe the molding process in more detail, it is convenient to follow the plastic through the machine and show the temperature, pressure, and time variables in the formation of the molding.

The plastic granules placed ahead of the plunger are usually at room temperature. As the plunger moves forward, it forces the plastic into the heating zone and advances previously heated material out of the heating cylinder. Many "shots" are usually in inventory in the cylinder to allow adequate time for uniform heating. The plastic temperature rises rapidly at first but eventually increases at a lower rate as it is advanced through the cylinder. When the machine is on a normal cycle, the average plastic temperature at the nozzle end has approached the inside wall temperature of the cylinder, but it never attains it, because of insufficient time.

Upon entering the mold, the plastic immediately begins to cool, even during filling of the cavity. Cooling continues until the part is rigid enough to allow ejection without distortion. After removal from the mold, the plastic cools to room temperature, completing the temperature cycle.

The Mold-Pressure Cycle. The subdivision of the molding cycle into the steps of Fig. 5.5 is based on consideration of the pressure on the polymer in the mold. The vertical axis is the pressure scale, and the horizontal axis is the time scale. The *dead time* (1) is the time before the polymer starts flowing into the mold. In the next period (2) the material is *filling* the cavity. As soon as the cavity is filled, the pressure increases rapidly, and *packing* (3) occurs. At this stage plastic flow into the cavity is at a very slow rate. The compressibility of the plastic allows some flow during pressure build-up. Also, as the plastic cools in the mold, it occupies less volume, which allows more to enter. When the ram is returned, the gate is usually still relatively fluid in the case of a large gate and a thick part. Owing to pressure differences, reverse flow, or *discharge*, (4) will occur. Further cooling causes *sealing* (5) at the gate of the cavity, and no further flow in or out

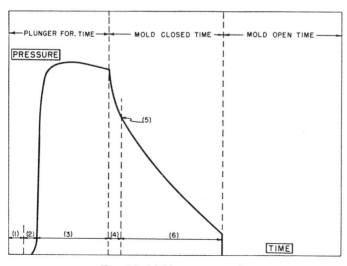

Fig. 5.5. Mold-pressure cycle.

of the cavity is possible. With smaller gates, sealing occurs faster, and common practice is to time the ram to return after sealing, thus preventing discharge. The remaining pressure in the cavity decays during the *sealed cooling* (6) until the mold is opened. Usually, there is pressure remaining in the cavity just before part ejection. Too high a residual mold pressure can cause sticking, scoring, or cracking.

GRANULE FEED

Metering of the plastic granules from the storage hopper into the machine is necessary to control the amount of material which is forced into the mold. If too few granules are fed into the cylinder, the cavity will not completely fill, and the result will be an incomplete molding, or short shot. Even if the feeding is just a trifle short, there will not be enough pressure built up during the packing step to make up for the contraction of the polymer on cooling. The surface of the piece may shrink from the sides of the mold, producing objectionable sink marks. Too much feed in the machine will increase the granule column (cushion) in front of the ram, and thereby cause lower pressures in the cavity.

Granule-Feed Methods

There are several methods used to measure the proper amount of feed.

Volumetric Feed. Granules are allowed to fall from the hopper into a box or chute which can be adjusted to measure the desired volume. This volume of plastic then drops into the heating cylinder in front of the ram. Volumetric feeding is the conventional technique found on most standard molding machines.

The precision of volumetric feeding is adequate for many moldings. However, when a more difficult, complicated part is involved or higher-speed operation is encountered, the method falls short of the required accuracy. Slight changes in granule geometry, surface lubrication, or static attraction could cause significant changes in the weight of the measured volume. Thus, while improvements in volumetric feeding have been made, other methods are necessary for greater accuracy.

Weigh Feed. With weigh feed, the granules are carefully weighed on a precise automatic scale and dropped into the heating cylinder. The amount of granules is not influenced by geometry or lubrication changes, and a much more uniform feed can be expected for each cycle. The weigh-feeder unit is actuated by the position of the plunger, so that it will always drop the granules at the proper time. Besides the primary weight control, most of the feeders have other controls which adjust the speed of operation and accuracy.

The technique of weighed-starved feeding is to place an exact amount of plastic in the cylinder ahead of the injection plunger which displaces the correct amount of material so as to just fill the mold cavity. This method minimizes the possibility of excess pressures in the cavity. The plunger can then remain forward until the gate solidifies. Thus discharge from the cavity is prevented, without the possibility of excessive packing.

Preplasticator. A preplasticator is an auxiliary heating cylinder in which the granules are melted. The plunger of the preplasticator forces the molten resin into the shooting cylinder, from which the plastic is injected into the mold. Machines equipped with preplasticators offer the advantages of lower injection pressure, higher rate of injection, lower cylinder temperature, increased heating capacity, and larger shot capacity.

In addition, this method permits accurate measurement of the material feed by volumetric means. A limit switch or mechanical stop is located on the "shooting" ram so that the preplasticator ram can force only the desired amount of plastic into the injecting cylinder. Since the material is melted and forced at the same pressure and temperature every cycle, many of the variables associated with other feeding methods are eliminated. Thus the molding machine with a preplasticator can provide excellent feed control.

Effect of Granule Size, Shape, and Treatment

In the early days of injection-molding thermoplastics, granule geometry and granule lubrication were varied on a trial-and-error basis in an effort to develop molding powders of good feeding characteristics. More recently, definite relationships have been established between the granule variables and frictional heat generation, air entrapment, pressure transmission, and heating rate.

Lubrication. Granule surface lubrication reduces the pressure loss through the molding machine, allows the granules to compact better, eliminates friction burning, and allows faster plunger travel. Figure 5.6 indicates the effect of external lubricant on the pressure loss in the nonfluid zone. Too little lubrication allows some compaction of the granules but does not reduce the friction between the granules and the wall. This increases the pressure loss. Additional lubricant reduces the pressure loss. However, with clear, uncolored materials there is a limit to the amount of lubricant which can be used, because excessive amounts might cause hazing and streaking in the molded piece.

Geometry. The size and shape of granules are important factors in compaction and air entrapment. If the granules are too large, air entrapment is likely to be a problem. When air is carried through the heating cylinder into the mold, it becomes a major cause of silver streaking or bubbles. Granules which are too small have been observed to melt quickly along the cylinder wall and be compacted in such a fashion as to trap air

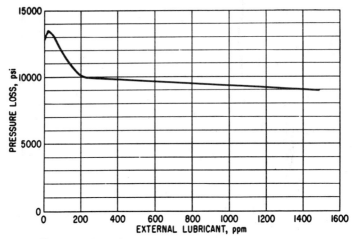

FIG. 5.6. Granular pressure loss *vs*. external lubricant.

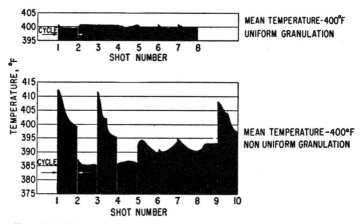

FIG. 5.7. Effect of granulation uniformity on plastic temperature.

within a plastic mass which will not release it and carry it into the mold. The small granules have been found to be good for dry-blend coloring because of their large surface-to-volume ratio.

The shape of the granules is also directly related to the flowability and the apparent density, or bulk factor. A wide variety of shapes have been used to achieve good pourability, small angle of repose, and small bulk factor. To sum up, the shape is chiefly important in getting the material into the heating cylinder, while the size and external lubrication affect the molding performance.

Uniform granulation is as important as size, shape, and external lubricant. Granulations with wide ranges of size distribution have shown high pressure loss and poor temperature uniformity at the nozzle. Temperature variation of the plastic measured at the nozzle with uniform and nonuniform granulation is shown in Fig. 5.7.

Drying. Some molding materials have a tendency to absorb moisture from the air, and in some cases moisture will condense on the outside of granules. These plastics must be dried to remove the moisture which would otherwise cause minute bubbles or silver streaking in the molded pieces. An oven fitted with trays and shelves or a hopper drier are the two principal drying methods used.

By drying, or preheating materials, the temperature of the granules introduced into the heating cylinder will be raised considerably above room temperature. Thus, because less heat has to be added by the heating cylinder, its melting capacity will be increased.

THE HEATING CYLINDER

The heating cylinder is the heart of the injection-molding machine. Here, the plastic is softened so it can be formed into the shape of the mold cavity. The temperature and pressure of the plastic as it leaves the nozzle are two of the most important variables which determine whether a good molding will be made. At present, unfortunately, these two variables are seldom measured directly.

Theoretical Considerations

Temperature Measurements. Early in the development of the injection-molding machine, it was discovered that, because of the low thermal conductivity of plastics, the heating surface in the cylinder had to be very large and the thickness of the plastic layer being heated had to be very small. The principal method of achieving these conditions was to introduce a spreader or torpedo into the heating cylinder. A typical heating cylinder, without construction details, is shown in Fig. 5.8a. The plastic enters Zone A in the form of hard, cold granules. These granules are compacted and heated, and the material eventually leaves the nozzle as a viscous fluid. All conditions between these two extremes exist in the heating cylinder.

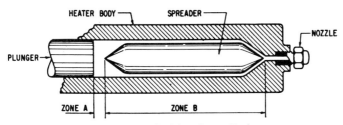

Fig. 5.8a. Typical heating cylinder.

The major absorption of heat by the plastic takes place between the spreader and the heater body. For the calculation of the theoretical heating efficiency of a heating cylinder, the plastic can be considered to be in the shape of a tube, as in Fig. 5.8b. Because of the simple geometric shape of the plastic in this region, the equations of heat transfer for an infinite slab can be applied, neglecting end effects. It should be remembered that, although most of the heating cylinder has this shape, the spreader must be supported in the cylinder. As a result, the equations will not be 100 per cent accurate, and the calculations are made only to indicate the possible range of performance.

The plastic will leave the nozzle with an average temperature T_a which is usually much lower than the temperature of the cylinder walls. The temperature of the plastic leaving the nozzle of a given cylinder will depend upon (1) the temperature of the cylinder walls or heater temperature, and (2) the contact time or production rate. In the injection-molding machine the plastic is pushed into the heating cylinder at some initial temperature T_o. This is either the temperature of the room or the temperature of the hopper.

As the plastic moves through the heating cylinder, the temperature rises. This temperature increase can be expressed as $T_a - T_o$, and it is directly proportional to the amount of heat absorbed by the plastic. If the plastic remained in the heating cylinder long enough, it would eventually come very close to the temperature T_i of the cylinder walls. Thus the maximum possible temperature rise can be expressed as $T_i - T_o$ and would be proportional to the maximum amount of heat the plastic could acquire. The ratio of the actual amount of heat absorbed to the theoretical or maximum amount has been called the heating efficiency and expressed as

$$E = \frac{T_a - T_o}{T_i - T_o} \tag{1}$$

The temperature of the plastic leaving the nozzle T_a is not perfectly uniform throughout the entire mass but varies from a minimum temperature T_m to the temperature of the cylinder wall T_i. As noted previously, T_a is the average temperature of the melt, and the temperature distribution

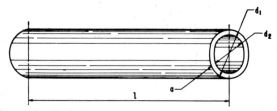

Fig. 5.8b. "Infinite slab" of plastic in Zone B.

spread will be $T_i - T_m$. This shows that the smaller the temperature variations in the plastic, the higher will be the value of the heating efficiency (Fig. 5.9). Therefore, E is not only a measure of the average temperature of the polymer as it leaves the nozzle but is also an indication of the temperature uniformity. Note that since this heating efficiency contains the ratio of plastic temperature rise to maximum temperature rise, it is independent of the control temperature. Thus any efficiency rating of the heating cylinder does not require a qualifying control temperature but may be used at any temperature.[2]

The heating efficiency can be measured at several different throughput rates, and a graph of heating efficiency vs. output rate can be drawn. This heating efficiency curve can be an effective means of comparing the performance of heating cylinders. A typical curve is shown in Fig. 5.10.

Since the maximum production rate of a molding machine is ambiguous and will depend on the heater temperature, the material, and the complexity of the mold, it is almost impossible to choose a maximum output that will have any meaning. An arbitrary standard such as 80 per cent efficiency has proved practical. At this value the plastic will be fairly uniformly heated and will be in the range of output rates used for standard-quality moldings with an acceptable level of strains.

The output rate of a given heating cylinder will depend upon two factors: (1) the size of the cylinder, and (2) the basic design of the cylinder. To evaluate the plasticating capacity of the design, it becomes necessary to correct for the effect of the dimensions on the output rate. To do this, it is necessary to go back to the equations of heat conduction and separate these two variables.

The theory of heat transfer through a flat slab has been well established. The quantity of heat taken up by a slab of plastic depends upon (1) the

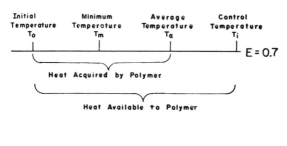

Fig. 5.9. Effect of temperature distribution on heating efficiency, E.

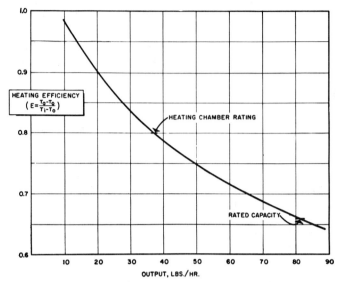

FIG. 5.10. Efficiency curve for comparing heating cylinder performance.

thermal diffusivity of the polymer, (2) the contact time or inventory time in the cylinder, (3) thickness of slab, and (4) temperature difference between heating surface and layer of plastic.

The thermal diffusivity is a product of the three thermal properties of the polymer: the thermal conductivity K, specific heat C, and density ρ, and equals

$$\alpha = \frac{K}{C\rho} \tag{2}$$

This value is reasonably constant over the temperature range considered.

The average contact time can be expressed in terms of the dimensions of the heating cylinder and other terms commonly used in injection molding. The contact time is equal to the inventory weight V_p, in ounces, divided by the shot weight W, in ounces, and multiplied by the total cycle t_c, in seconds. This may be written as

$$t = \frac{V_p t_c}{W} \tag{3}$$

The output of plastic through the heating cylinder q, in pounds per hour, may be introduced, since it is equal to shot weight divided by total cycle.

$$q = \frac{225W}{t_c} \tag{4}$$

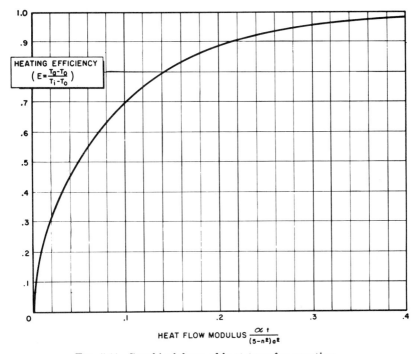

FIG. 5.11. Graphical form of heat transfer equation.

A factor of 225 converts ounces per second to pounds per hour. Substituting in Eq. (2) results in

$$t = \frac{225V_p}{q} \tag{5}$$

From the heat-transfer equation, the ratio of actual temperature rise to the wall temperature can be given in terms of the thermal diffusivity, contact time, and slab thickness. Since this equation is rather complicated, it is given in graph form in Fig. 5.11. From this graph the value of

$$\frac{\alpha t}{a^2}$$

can be found for any value of E. This equation can be expressed functionally as

$$E = f\left(\frac{\alpha t}{a^2}\right) \tag{6}$$

and will apply to an infinite slab heated from both sides. If the torpedo were not supplying heat, the result would be a slab heated from only one side, which would effectively double the thickness of the slab. In this situation the denominator is changed, and the equation becomes

$$E = f\left(\frac{\alpha t}{(2a)^2}\right) \qquad (7)$$

In the injection-molding heating cylinder, heat is usually supplied through the heater body to one side of the slab. However, heat is conducted into the spreader through the connections with the heater barrel. The amount of heat going into the spreader will depend primarily on the amount of contact surface between the spreader and the heater barrel. In general, unless an internally heated spreader is used, the spreader temperature will be less than the barrel temperature, the amount of heat supp ied to the plastic will be somewhere between that given by Eqs. (6) and (7), and the number of sides heating the slab will be something less than two. If a coefficient n is introduced, which is a measure of the effectiveness of the spreader in supplying heat to the plastic, Eqs. (6) and (7) can be written[6] as

$$E = f\left(\frac{\alpha t}{(5 - n^2)a^2}\right) 1 \leq n \leq 2 \qquad (8)$$

When the heating efficiences are measured at various output rates, a curve can be drawn similar to that in Fig. 5.12. By comparing this curve with the

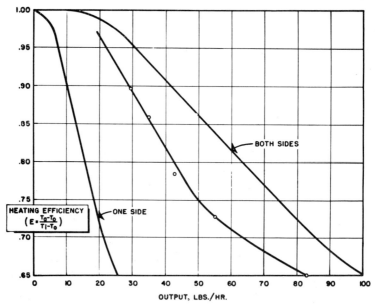

FIG. 5.12. Effect of spreader on efficiency.

two theoretical curves calculated from Eqs. (6) and (7), the value of n can be found.

Using Eq. (8) and choosing a particular value for the heating efficiency, for example $E = 0.8$, then it is possible to set

$$\frac{\alpha t}{(5 - n^2)a^2} = K_R \tag{9}$$

where K_R is a constant that is determined by the value of E that has been chosen.

The surface area of the slab of plastic in the heating cylinder

$$S = L\pi(d_1 + d_2) \tag{10}$$

and the volume

$$V = \frac{L\pi(d_1^2 - d_2^2)}{4} \tag{11}$$

so that the surface-to-volume ratio is

$$\frac{S}{V} = \frac{4\pi L(d_1 + d_2)}{L\pi(d_1^2 - d_2^2)} = \frac{4}{d_1 - d_2} = \frac{2}{a} \tag{12}$$

From Eq. (5) the contact time at rated output in the heating cylinder is the volume divided by the rated output.

$$t = \frac{225 V_p}{Q_R} \tag{13}$$

Eq. (9) becomes

$$\frac{225\alpha V_p}{(5 - n^2)Q_R} \cdot \frac{S^2}{4V^2} = K_R \tag{14}$$

and

$$Q_R = \frac{225\alpha S^2}{4K_R(5 - n^2)V_p} \tag{14}$$

or

$$Q_R = K\frac{S^2}{V} \tag{15}$$

From this relationship it is possible to determine the influence of size on the rated output. By calculating the (surface)^2-to-volume ratio and dividing the equation by S^2/V, a value of K will be obtained. This value of K will depend upon the value of E chosen, the material, and the effectiveness of the particular design in heating the polymer. With the same material and at a constant E, the factor K will be a measure of the performance of the particular design of heating cylinder. It has been found on further calculations that this holds for a cylindrical tube of plastic as well as for a slab.

Resistance to Flow and Pressure Loss. It is desirable to design injection heating cylinders which offer the least resistance to the flow of polymer. For a given ram pressure, a cylinder with a low resistance to flow permits faster injection into the mold, with resulting improvements in physical properties of the molding, and cycle economies.

As the plastic material is forced through the heating cylinder, it meets resistance to movement, resulting in lower plastic pressure at the nozzle than at the plunger face. Most of the resistance to flow occurs in the granular zone, with the remainder occurring in the semifluid and fluid regions. Because of the poor pressure transmission of the granules, some pressure loss is encountered even at the end of the injection cycle, after the flow has stopped.

The resistance to flow in the injection cylinder can be measured with a special fixture containing a variable restriction to simulate the effects of back pressure exerted on the cylinder by the mold passages. Figure 5.13 shows such an installation used for measuring the pressure in the nozzle. The resin flows along the passage marked by the dotted line. The opening of this passage is adjustable.

Tests to measure the pressure loss or the resistance to flow along the cylinder have been conducted with this equipment, using a constant cycle and running at the rated shot capacity of the machine. The resistance to flow equals the pressure loss divided by the flow rate. Figure 5.14 is a plot of pressure drop against the ram pressure.

If this graph is viewed in terms of *fluid* flow through a channel, the behavior is not as would be expected. It is known that the flow rate will de-

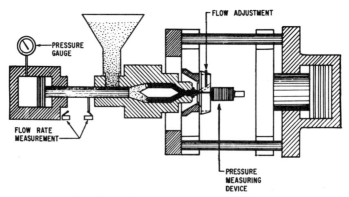

Fig. 5.13. Pressure measuring apparatus.

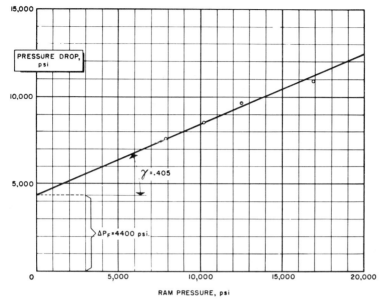

Fig. 5.14. Pressure loss in the heating cylinder.

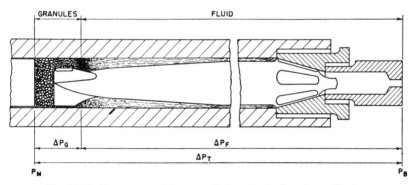

Fig. 5.15. Two types of flow conditions in the heating cylinder.

pend upon the pressure differential along the channel, and that when this differential is changed, the flow rate will also change. The points on Fig. 5.14 were taken at the same flow rate. Consequently, the resistance to flow might be expected to remain constant. In actual practice, however, the resistance to flow through the heating cylinder, at the same flow rate, is found to vary with the ram pressure or the hydrostatic pressure on the polymer. To find a rational explanation, it is necessary to look further into plastic movement inside the heating chamber.

Figure 5.15 shows that there are two distinct types of flow conditions existing in the heating chamber: one is the movement of the granules through the rear portion of the heating chamber; the other is the viscous flow of the molten polymer.

The total resistance to flow of a cylinder is made up of the resistance to flow in the granular section, where the resistance varies directly with the static pressure in the zone, and the resistance to flow in the fluid section, where the resistance is independent of pressure.

The polymer starts through the heating cylinder as cold granules at room temperature, and as it advances, its temperature increases. Once the material is molten, its viscosity will also vary along the length of its flow path. Because of the temperature variations, there is no one value of viscosity that can be assigned to the polymer in the heating chamber. An integrated viscosity value could probably be computed as some function of the temperature distribution in the cylinder. Since the machine is run at uniform conditions at all times, the temperature distribution was considered to be a constant.

The resistance to flow through the granular zone will be dependent on the coefficient of friction between the cylinder wall and the granules, the surface area in contact with the granules, and the applied force.

Spencer, Gilmore and Wiley[19] found that under steady flow conditions the frictional effects of polystyrene granules in a steel cylinder could be expressed by the following relationship:

$$P_d = P_m e^{-4uL_0/D} \qquad (16)$$

where e is the base of the natural logarithms $= 2.718$, P_m is the ram pressure, P_d is the pressure at the forward moving end of the granular zone, L_0 is the length of the uncompacted granules, D is the diameter of the granular zone, and u is the coefficient of friction between the polymer and the steel.

Assuming that these conditions approximately represent the kinetic conditions, the pressure loss through this granular zone would be expressed as

$$P_m - P_d = (1 - e^{-4uL_0/D})P_m \qquad (17)$$

The exact values of the constants are not known for heating cylinders. The quantity

$$(1 - e^{-4uL_0/D})$$

is set equal to some constant γ which is a measure of the frictional drag on the granules. So

$$P_m - P_d = \Delta P_G = \gamma P_m \qquad (18)$$

and the pressure drop or the resistance to flow through the section of the cylinder filled with granules is simply proportional to the ram pressure. The total pressure loss in the heating cylinder will be the sum of the loss through the granules, which is pressure-dependent and the loss through the molten polymer or fluid zone, which is independent of pressure.

$$\Delta P_T = \Delta P_G + \Delta P_F \tag{19}$$

or

$$P_m - P_b = \gamma P_m + \Delta P_F \tag{20}$$

where P_b is the back pressure exerted on the heating cylinder by the resistance to flow in the mold passages and ΔP_F is the pressure loss in the fluid zone.

When the total pressure loss is plotted as a function of the ram pressure, the result should be a straight line with a slope of γ and an intercept on the ordinate equal to the fluid pressure loss agreeing with experimental result (Fig. 5.14). Values of γ and ΔP_F can be easily calculated from these data. By multiplying γ by the desired ram pressure, the pressure drops through the granules and through the molten polymer are known, and the total pressure drop in the cylinder will simply be the sum of these.

When the total pressure loss is plotted as a function of the ram pressure, from Eq. (20) the result is a straight line with the slope γ proportional to the frictional resistance and the y intercept proportional to the viscous resistance. Because the flow conditions existing in the heating chamber differ widely from those in a viscometer, this development has not been carried further.

The properties of the polymer will have a large effect upon the pressure losses through the heating cylinder. In the unmelted zone, such variables as the amount of external lubricant and granule size and shape will affect the pressure losses, while in the viscous or molten zone the viscosity and shear dependence of the material will affect the pressure losses.

The question of how much external lubricant to put on the granules will probably be one of long standing.[20] A very small amount will affect the compaction of the granules; a little more will help the flow (see Fig. 5.6). The frictional component of the resistance to flow drops rapidly until the lubricant concentration reaches 200 ppm. Beyond this there is not much change.

The size of the shot or length of the granular plug will also affect the slope of the pressure-drop curve, as shown in Fig. 5.16. As the shot size increases, the slope also increases to a critical granule length. Beyond this, enough molten polymer has formed next to the wall so that it acts as a fluid lubricant. This would indicate that the frictional resistance to flow will also depend somewhat on the melting temperature of the polymer,

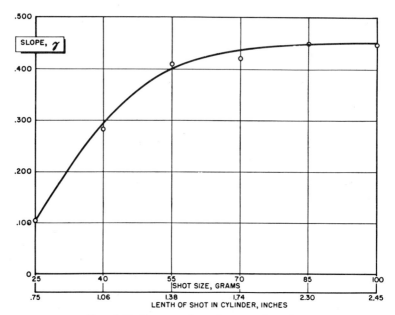

FIG. 5.16. Pressure-drop slope *vs.* shot size.

and the sooner it becomes fluid the shorter will be the length of the granular plug. This also indicates that the frictional resistance to flow (as much
as 80 per cent of the total resistance to flow in the heating cylinder) is
concentrated in a very short space directly in front of the plunger.

Heating-Chamber Design

The first requirement for the heating chamber is to heat the plastic
charge to a uniform temperature. The cylinder is primarily a heat-transfer
device. The job of designing the cylinder is complicated by two properties
of the plastic: (1) its low heat transfer coefficient, and (2) the tendency for
molecular breakdown when the plastic is locally overheated. The second
requirement is that the pressure loss in the heating cylinder should be kept
to a minimum. These two objectives are sometimes in conflict, as will be
shown later. In an ideal heating chamber the entire shot travels through as
a unit, with no part remaining under heat longer than absolutely necessary. For design purposes, speed or flow velocity should be as uniform as
possible in all parts of the heater.

To determine the flow pattern in the heating cylinder, a simple test is
made. The machine is purged on a constant cycle, using clear plastic. One
shot of dark-colored material is introduced into the feed, followed by successive shots of clear material. The material extruded from the nozzle is

carefully laid out and allowed to cool. Cross-sectional wafers can then be cut from the rod and examined.

The first cylinder considered is one of conventional design (shown in Fig. 5.15). The spreader in this cylinder is not fixed but floats against the nozzle retainer. Some heat is transferred to the spreader by this seat and by fins necessary to keep the spreader nose centered.

The wafer cut from the extruded rod shows three dark streaks of color that have moved ahead of the main part of the colored shot (illustrated in Fig. 5.17). The positions of these three streaks correspond to the position of the guide fins at the rear of the spreader. The cold plastic granules passing next to the fins heat up rapidly and become fluid. Temperature measurements indicate that the material passing next to the fins can be as much as 45°F hotter than the main mass of material, as illustrated in Fig. 5.18. Calculating the ratio S^2/V (see p. 323) for this cylinder, a performance factor $K = 0.023$ to 0.025 is obtained. In a cylinder of this type, where guide fins are necessary in transferring heat to the plastic, they decrease the uniformity of the plastic temperature.

Better results are obtained by mounting the spreader on an intregal flange about halfway along its length (Fig. 5.19). Heat flows most rapidly to the plastic just after it enters the chamber, which requires that the entering nose of the spreader needs by far the most heat. This type of mount places the heat source closer to the unmelted plastic and results in a K actor 0.028 to 0.032. The plastic is carried through the flange by a ring of

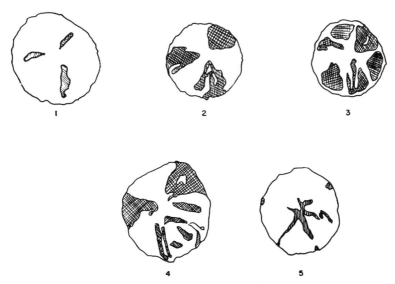

Fɪɢ. 5.17. Wafers cut from rod show flow pattern around spreader.

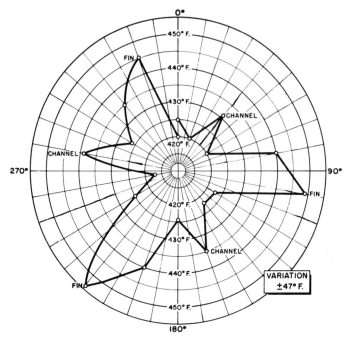

FIG. 5.18. Temperature variation of plastic caused by cylinder fins.

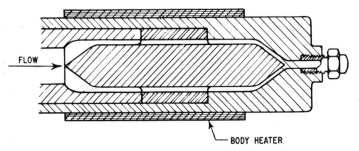

FIG. 5.19. Central flange supported spreader.

drilled holes, suitably streamlined. The struts formed by this operation are an obstacle to flow, which is not serious if the incoming plastic has softened. If the smooth nose is not long enough, or if an especially slow-melting plastic is used, high resistance to flow will result.

The most effective way to heat a spreader is to generate heat within it. This is usually done with electricity, although circulating oils, or vapor such as steam, can be used. If possible the heater wattage should be concentrated near the upstream end of the spreader, and the control thermocouple placed where temperatures will be highest (Fig. 5.20). Heaters with adequate internal heat show K factors up to 0.051. A serious disadvantage of this type of spreader is the tendency to "silver streak." This occurs when air, normally present between granules, is carried over the spreader nose and trapped between the spreader and cylinder wall. When the spreader is relatively cool, the air has an opportunity to escape along the spreader. This is not by any means the only cause of streaking, nor is a heated spreader always to be blamed. A straightforward way to increase heating-chamber performance is to increase the S^2/V ratio by increasing surface, decreasing volume, or both. The aim is to accomplish these ends without undue resistance to flow, or other undesirable results. It is an accepted fact that the resistance to flow is minimized by proportioning the chamber so that the cross-sectional flow area around the spreader nose is at least equal to that of the ram.

The limitation to this design is a mechanical one. As the diameter is increased, the stresses on the fastenings which hold the spreader are increased, as is the thickness of the barrel needed to withstand the pressures within.

As the plastic moves into the chamber and becomes more fluid, it is possible to decrease the spreader cylinder clearance to improve heat transfer. This should be done with caution since a decrease in diameter size will result in a higher resistance to flow, and any increases in heating performances may be counteracted. The heating chamber can be made very long, but the increase in heating performance is offset by a greater resistance to flow, and the larger volume of plastic might be under heat for an excessively long time. Another disadvantage of the long heater is the problem of supporting the spreader and keeping the chamber with its nozzle in alignment.

The rate of heat flow can be increased substantially if the material which has been in contact with the hot surface is removed and mixed with the cooler material. In one such scheme the torpedo consists of a series of fins which are arranged so no fin is directly behind any other fin (Fig. 5.21). The resulting strong erosion of the heated material from the hot fin by the cold plastic gives a high efficiency.

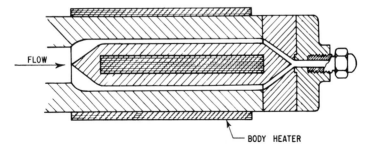

FLOW

BODY HEATER

FIG. 5.20. Internally heated spreader.

FIG. 5.21. Fin torpedo.

Other successful heating chambers have been built without spreaders, the heating surface being obtained by complex-shaped flow passages. A simple heater is made by cutting slots into the barrel (Fig. 5.22). The material in this type of heater tends to channel through the center of the chamber. Incorporating a small pin or spreader to block the channel will improve performance but must be carefully fitted to avoid entrapment of plastic. Another design is made by drilling many holes in a solid block of steel (Fig. 5.23). This heater is efficient but requires much care in the streamlining of the hole entrances, and there is a tendency to pass unmelted plastic through the center holes.

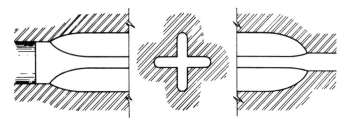

FIG. 5.22. Slotted cylinder.

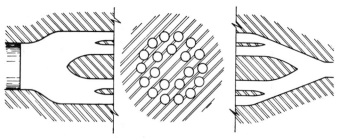

FIG. 5.23. Hole cylinder.

Conventional heating chambers, of the type discussed thus far, heat the plastic by straight conduction. The plastic which is in contact with the heated metal surface approaches the temperature of the metal, and heat is transferred through this resin to the plastic which is farther away. The poor conductivity of plastics is illustrated by the time required to heat slabs of varying thickness. If the average temperature of polystyrene were to be raised from room temperature to 450°F, using a wall temperature of 500°F, it would take the following times:

Slab thickness, inches	Time, seconds
$\frac{1}{2}$	921.0
$\frac{1}{4}$	230.0
$\frac{1}{16}$	14.0
$\frac{1}{32}$	3.6

This points out how time-consuming it is to "soak" the polymer in a thick section to obtain a uniform temperature.

When plastic first contacts the heater wall, heat transfer occurs at a high rate. If this heated layer can be removed during each cycle and replaced with cool material, the high transfer rate can be maintained. This is the design objective of the "melt extraction" or "polyliner" type of heating chamber.[1, 12]

The separation of melt is usually accomplished by inserting a conical or straight perforated sleeve into the heater barrel (Fig. 5.24). The sleeve has grooves cut into its outside surface to convey the plastic to the nozzle.

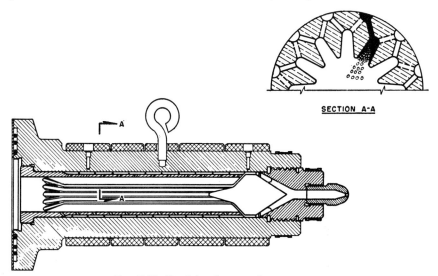

SECTION A-A

FIG. 5.24. Straight sleeve melt extractor.

In some designs the sleeve is closed on the downstream end, with holes placed appropriately, to block the passage of the solid center and allow melted material to move through. While a much higher rate of heat transfer is obtained, the melt-separation type of chamber is not exempt from the necessity of having enough heat-transfer surface. The surface can be calculated by using the same technique as before, except that the plastic thickness is calculated by assuming that each shot removes from the hot surface a uniform layer of melt. Thus thickness $= \dfrac{\text{volume}}{\text{surface area}}$. Then the time necessary to heat this thickness of plastic to an efficiency of 0.90 is calculated. This procedure, repeated for many combinations of surface area, shot size, and cycle, results in the curves of Fig. 5.25. It is possible to run this type of cylinder at much higher than standard rates, as the performance figures of these two cylinders indicate.

The conical model has only one third the surface area of the straight model, yet it shows about the same heating efficiency. The reasons for this are twofold: (1) The network of passages which carry the plastic away from the primary heating surface are small in cross section and serve to heat the material thoroughly. (2) The very high pressure differential necessary to push the cool plastic into the passages represents energy which is put into the plastic and must appear as heat. This is shown by the comparison of pressure loss in Fig. 5.26. The foregoing data on pressure loss should not be construed to mean that the straight cylinder has a marked su-

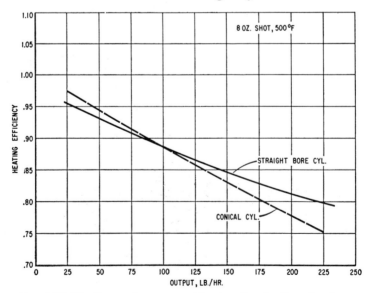

FIG. 5.25. Heating performance-melt extraction heating chambers.

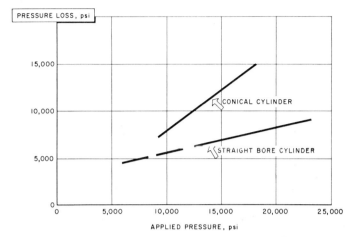

Fɪɢ. 5.26. Pressure loss-melt extraction cylinders.

periority over the conical model. The angle should be calculated so that the granular volume replaces an amount equal to the layer of the melt. The result of proper design decreases pressure loss and provides a more effective cleaning of the softened plastic from the primary surface.

An important advantage in the melt-separation heating cylinders is that the cold centered column of plastic affords an ideal route for the escape of air or volatile matter as driven off from the melting plastic.

Temperature Control

Injection-molding heating cylinders are usually supplied heat by electric heater bands, clamped on the outside surface of the heating cylinder. The use of oil or steam as a heat source has been used, but with limited success. Depending on machine size, most cylinders have two or three zone controls.

The demand for heat is not the same all over the heating cylinder.[7, 13] Most notably, a large amount of heat is needed in the back where the hot barrel contacts a water-cooled feed sleeve. Where the unheated plastic first comes in contact with the heating surface, a high flow of heat occurs. Figure 5.27 indicates the demand variation along the barrel for a cylinder 24 in. long. Thermocouples located every 2 in. along the cylinder length gave the temperature profiles in this figure. This points out that the thermocouple is effective in controlling the temperature in its immediate vicinity, which includes a distance of $1\frac{1}{2}$ in. from the couple. Moving the rear thermocouple farther back (as shown by arrows in Fig. 5.27) causes high mid-barrel temperatures. Generally, the best longitudinal location is in the center third of the control zone.

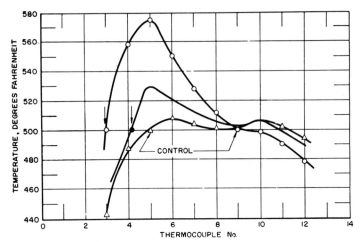

Fig. 5.27. Effect of control location.

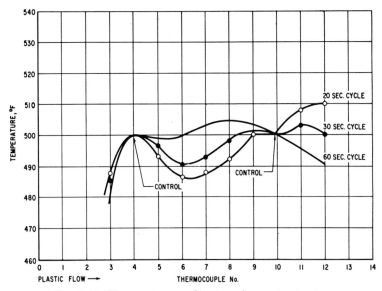

Fig. 5.28. Temperature profile at various output rate.

An increase in cycle or output rate will change the demand pattern, as shown in Fig. 5.28. The zone of relatively cool plastic will extend farther into the chamber, causing more demand in the center, and the temperature is depressed in that area. This increase in demand is not felt at the nose, and the increased "on" time results in high front-zone temperatures.

Placing a reflective cover around the heating cylinder results in a 25 per

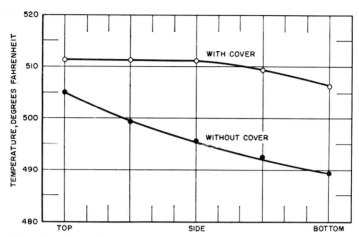

FIG. 5.29. The effect of a tight fitting cover on temperature variation around the cylinder.

cent power saving. In addition, the temperature variation from the top to to the bottom of the cylinder is reduced, as indicated in Fig. 5.29. This variation is caused by cool air contacting the bottom, flowing around the sides, and forming an eddy of hot air on top. For this reason, it is recommended that the thermocouple be located on top to minimize hot spots.

The thermocouple should be located near the mid-point of the barrel thickness. If it is mounted too close to the heater bands, it will not sense the temperature at the critical inside barrel surface, and low plastic temperatures may result. A deep thermocouple would measure most accurately the temperature to be controlled. However, the thickness of the metal between heater band and control induces a time lag in the system, which allows temperature overshoots. The combination of a deep and shallow thermocouple hooked in parallel gives an average temperature. This system reacts quickly to changes in conditions and results in marked improvement in control action.

Nozzles

The design of the injection-molding-machine nozzle is critical from the standpoint of pressure and temperature considerations. It is essential to avoid unnecessary resistance to flow and to maintain uniform plastic temperatures in this region. It is not recommended to add or take away heat at the nozzle but merely to prevent the plastic from chilling after it has been heated in the cylinder.

The use of a standard nozzle (Fig. 5.30) with a long taper constitutes a higher-than-necessary resistance to flow.

Free-Flow Nozzles. The free-flow nozzle was designed to reduce the resistance to flow (Fig. 5.31). The resistance to flow through the orifice is minimized by keeping the land length short ($\frac{1}{8}$ in.).

Reverse-Tapered Nozzles. Reverse-tapered nozzles, as shown in Fig. 5.32, have found wide use in molding crystalline polymers. Such polymers (e.g., nylon) have relatively sharp and high melting points. These resins either may tend to drool from the nozzle between shots, if the nozzle is kept hot, or may tend to freeze in the nozzle, if too much heat is lost to the sprue bushing. The reverse-tapered nozzle makes it possible to extract chilled material from the nozzle tip with ease, and avoids the need to raise the nozzle temperature to the point where drooling might become a problem.[15]

Ball-Check Nozzles. When restricted gates are employed, the filling time is longer than that for a larger gate. The gate, however, seals fast and permits the use of a shorter plunger dwell time.

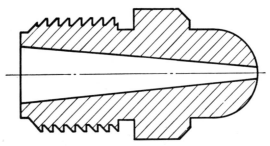

Fig. 5.30. Standard type injection nozzle.

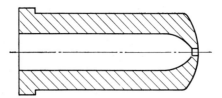

Fig. 5.31. Free-flow nozzle.

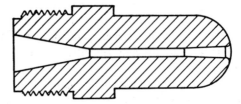

Fig. 5.32. Reverse-tapered nozzle.

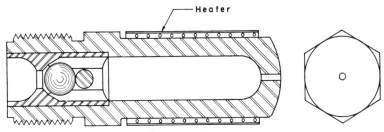

Fiu. 5.33. Ball-check nozzle.

Restricted gating is not always practical with large moldings, but fast sealing and short plunger dwell times can be achieved by a ball-check nozzle, as shown in Fig. 5.33. This nozzle is merely a mechanical sealing device which permits plastic to flow around the ball into the mold. When the plunger is returned, the ball is pushed back, preventing discharge. A slight amount of discharge must occur in order to push the ball back to its seat. This type of nozzle is not streamlined, which gives the disadvantages of higher resistance to flow and longer color-change times.

Extended Nozzles. The use of a nozzle extended to the cavity improves cycle time and reduces shot weight compared to conventional nozzles, since the sprue is essentially eliminated. This nozzle is particularly suited for automatic molding operations, because sprue trimming is not required. Cycle improvements are due to shorter mold passages (slight improvement in fill time and possible lower plastic temperature) and faster cooling time without the relatively thick sprue. Figure 5.40 shows a design of the nozzle as used in thin-wall container molding.

It is important to keep the contact area of the nozzle with the mold at a minimum. Chilling of the nozzle can occur rapidly, and it is necessary to provide nozzle heaters with accurate temperature control. Extended nozzles should be of rigid construction, and the alignment of the nozzle with the mold is critical. Nozzles of this general type can be used in hot-runner and manifold-nozzle molds (Fig. 5.40).

Mixing Nozzles. Mixing nozzles are designed to provide mixing of the heated plastic primarily in dry-blend color operations. A restriction, in the form of an insert, is placed in the nozzle which disrupts the flow pattern, resulting in better color mixing. Figure 5.34 shows a simple mixing nozzle with breaker-plate inserts. There are other nozzles, such as a pineapple, screw, or melt-extractor type, which work well. The extra restrictions in the nozzle naturally cause some additional resistance to flow.

THE INJECTION MOLD

The function of the mold is to form a molded shape within specified dimensional tolerances with satisfactory surface finish and physical prop-

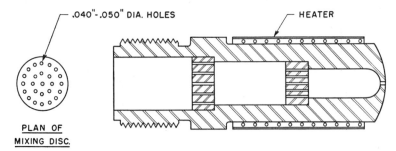

Fɪɢ. 5.34. Color mixing nozzle.

erties, and with satisfactory permanence of dimensions, finish, and properties. The mold must perform economically, with amortizable original cost
and satisfactory tool life. The mold must be safe for the operating person-
nel, and it must present a minimum hazard of tool damage.

The degree of functional perfection must be established for each mold
and function in the planning stage. The degree of perfection cannot be
stated as a general rule, nor can minimum standards be established for
general use.

Theoretical considerations aim to define perfection in function which is
not usually attainable in practice. Theory provides the engineer with information to aim his design in the proper direction. He has to decide,
upon the basis of the requirements of the application, just how great a
degree of perfection will be required.

The design of the mold must aim to provide the degree of perfection required in all functional aspects and in all construction features. Construction considerations are as important as function and design, and they
should be included in the planning of the mold in proportion to their importance.

The following considerations usually enter in the planning stages to be
evaluated before construction beings:
  (1) Durability
  (2) Strength
  (3) Economy
  (4) Convenience of operation
  (5) Rigidity
  (6) Materials of construction

Parts of the Mold

Figure 5.35 is a photograph of a conventional type of injection mold,
and Fig. 5.36 is a view of this mold showing six subassemblies of parts.
Principal mold parts are indicated by their commonly used names.

The Mold Cavity. The mold cavity forms the soft plastic into the desired shape, and it is usually the first part which is considered in designing the mold. The plastic is under sufficient pressure to produce stresses from 10,000 to 180,000 psi in the mold-cavity metal. This causes considerable deformation, which is not harmful provided the stress is within the elastic limit of the mold material. When the dimensional tolerance of the part is very critical, the mold material must be stiff and the section modulus must be high to prevent deformation which interferes with production of parts within this tolerance limit.

The dimensions of the mold cavity must be larger than those of the finished part because of shrinkage of the molded plastic upon cooling. The total effect of the various factors which control shrinkage is difficult to compute, and mold engineers have come to rely upon accumulated experience to determine shrinkage allowances. Some typical mold shrinkage allowances are shown to indicate the range:

Cellulose acetate—0.004 to 0.008 in. per inch

Methyl methacrylate—0.003 to 0.008 in. per inch

Nylon—0.005 to 0.040 in. per inch

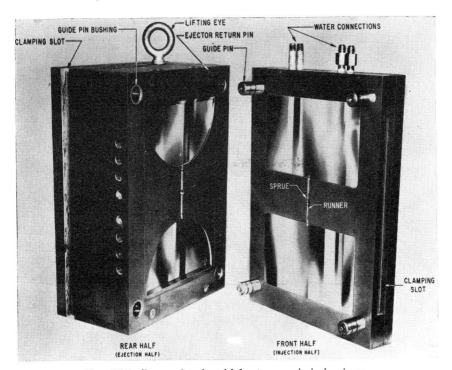

Fig. 5.35. Conventional mold for two semi-circle pieces.

Polyethylene—0.005 to 0.040 in. per inch
Polystyrene—0.003 to 0.008 in. per inch

A practical rule is to allow limits of plus or minus 0.001 in. per inch on the finished product to make up for variations in mold shrinkage which cannot be controlled by the molder except at extremely high cost.

The crystalline plastics exhibit extremely wide shrinkage ranges, because they contract in volume considerably with crystallization. The degree of crystallization of a plastic during its cooling time in the mold varies, depending upon a number of factors. Sometimes unmelted plastic is forced into the mold, and because it is already crystallized, it shrinks only the amount dictated by simple thermal contraction. This is probably the principal cause of unpredictability of shrinkage of the crystalline plastics. Another factor which has been found to be important is the amount of restraint. A polyethylene or a nylon part may shrink as little as 0.005 in. per inch when molded in a thin cylindrical part. The inner core of the mold prevents shrinkage of the plastic to the dimension it would naturally assume if the core were not present. In such cases the crystallization may have gone as far as it goes ordinarily, but the shrinkage stresses relax as the plastic "cold flows" to the larger dimension because of the restraint set up by the core.

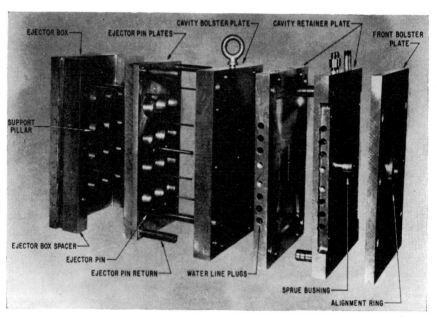

FIG. 5.36. Parts of a conventional mold.

The surface-finish requirements of most injection-molded articles call for smooth and lustrous qualities. Luster is directly related to the surface finish of the mold. Surface finish of the mold cavity is a matter of polishing the metal and maintaining the surface in good condition. Hardened steel is probably the most difficult material to polish, but it has the advantage of taking a very high luster and being relatively free from damage by abrasion. A thin layer of chromium helps prevent rusting and provides more permanent luster when electroplated on the surface of the highly polished steel mold.

Softer metals may be polished reasonably well, but they are subject to upsetting or permanent deformation which may cause waviness, even though the luster remains bright.

The surface appearance of injection-molded articles is affected also by a number of operating conditions, such as plastic temperature, mold temperature, injection speed, and the presence of contaminants in the plastics, such as air or steam. These surface defects are not associated with the surface finish of the mold.

Control of the surface temperature of injection molds is an important requirement.[9, 21] Mold cavities and cores must be kept at the correct temperature during operation to assist dimensional accuracy of the finished parts, to assist filling and cooling, and to help maintain the inherent engineering properties of the plastic material in the finished part. Copper and aluminum alloys are metals of high thermal conductivity, and they are employed in some cases to obtain uniform temperature distribution. They are not very useful, however, for injection molds, because they are not stiff enough and are usually too soft for long mold life. The thermal conductivity of plastics is so much less than that of metals that it is of no great advantage to select special metals for mold construction which have higher thermal conductivity than steel.

When the hot plastic enters the mold, the mold temperature increases and then decreases as the cooling water takes the heat away. A cyclic temperature change of the order of 20°F or greater occurs under ordinary molding conditions. Temperature cycling cannot be avoided, but it should be held within reason. Occasionally, heat must be added to portions of a mold to maintain them at a high enough temperature for filling the cavities.

Sprues. The sprue should be kept as small as is practical. Large-diameter sprues require a long time to cool, and in many cases large sprues have been observed to make the molding cycle far longer than that which would be dictated by the thickness of the section of the molded part. If the sprue is large, it must be cooled sufficiently so it will not tear apart when the mold opens and the runner section or the sprue ejector pulls the sprue out of the bushing. When the sprue has to be long to reach through a thick mold, the taper requirements usually cause the diameter to be large where the sprue is connected to the runner. Mold practice has evolved short sprues in conjunction with long nozzles which can reach far into the mold. This allows a relatively small-diameter sprue of short length to be used. Such a sprue is illustrated in Figs. 5.37 and 5.38 in conjunction with a three-plate mold. Observations have shown the sprue need not be greater than $\frac{1}{4}$ in. diameter for most thermoplastics, provided other parts of the feeding system and the flow in the mold are correctly made. The sprue is usually not responsible for a great proportion of the total resistance to flow which occurs in the feed system.

Runners. The runners which feed the various cavities should have a cross-sectional shape which allows for free passage of the plastic. The resistance to flow in the runner system increases with the length. Rigorous and fundamental analyses of the flow through runners and gates, allowing

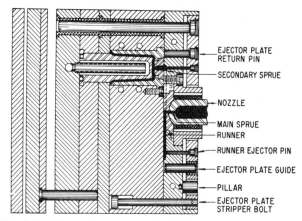

FIG. 5.37. Three-plate positive-runner ejector mold (closed).

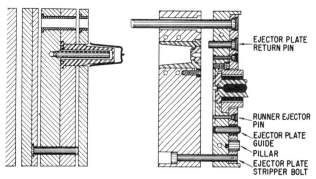

FIG. 5.38. Three-plate positive-runner ejector mold (ejection of part from mold).

for cooling and changes in shear stress, have been carried out and reported in the literature.[5]

A full, round cross-section runner is recognized as the most efficient shape for a runner passageway from the standpoint of having maximum flow area with minimum skin area for chilling the runner. Chilling of the runner skin has become less and less of a consideration in the design of injection molds with faster injection speed and shorter mold fill time. Again practical considerations in machining the mold and in ejecting the runner have brought about modified runner shapes, as shown in Fig. 5.39.

The runners in Fig. 5.39 may be defined in dimension by reference to their width. Generally, they are not wider than $\frac{5}{16}$ in. for nearly all thermoplastics molding work. They range down to about $\frac{1}{8}$ in. in width, and to as little as $\frac{1}{16}$ in. for short distances. The resistance to flow along the runners may be controlled by the runner size. Since it is desirable to have all mold cavities fill simultaneously and uniformly, control of runner size offers a convenient means for balancing the flow to multiple cavities. (Control of flow through variation of gate size will be discussed later.)

In some specialized types of molding work, the molds are built essentially without runners, or with runners which remain molten.[14] When the runner is kept molten, the mold is called a hot runner mold. Figure 5.40 illustrates three types of molds which feed the plastic essentially directly from a nozzle into the cavity. The upper view at the center shows a single-cavity arrangement in which the nozzle of the heating cylinder reaches far into the mold and the plastic is fed into the cavity through a short, small-diameter sprue. The lower left-hand view shows a multiple-nozzle arrangement in which two or more cavities are fed by nozzles which are attached to the heating cylinder. The lower right-hand view shows a manifold hot-runner design in which the runner system is part of the mold and is kept

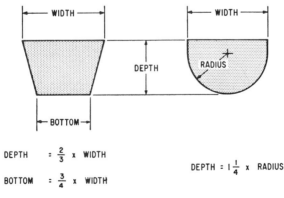

FIG. 5.39. Runner cross sections.

hot. The chief advantage of these systems is the elimination of the need for regrinding the plastic runners and remolding this material.

In addition, a hot-runner mold requires a smaller amount of melt per shot than an equivalent cold-runner mold. Consequently, the injection time is reduced, and the cycle may be speeded up, particularly if the machine is operating near the melting capacity of the heating cylinder.

Molds of the design shown in Fig. 5.40 are often difficult to set up and run under equilibrium conditions. They should be considered only for large-scale mass production under automatic or nearly automatic conditions. It is sometimes difficult to maintain the area of the molded part near the sprue or gate in a flat nonwrinkled condition, because the hot nozzle may raise the mold wall temperature too high for proper cooling. This results in wrinkling or otherwise distorting the area of plastic immediately adjacent to the gate. Exact pressure control is required to operate this type of mold, because there is no section of the feed system which actually can solidify sufficiently to seal off between the mold cavity and the hot plastic in the feed system.

Gates. The gate in an injection mold is one of the most important features of the mold. It generally has high resistance to flow, which must be adjusted to the proper magnitude. As the plastic flows into the cavity, the pressure in the cavity is at a low level until the mold is filled. At this

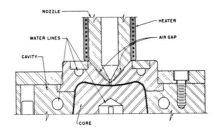

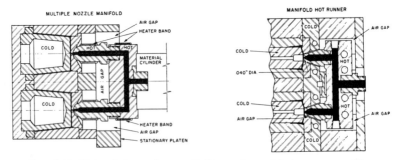

Fig. 5.40. Extended nozzle, manifold nozzle, and hot runner molds.

time the pressure builds up rapidly in the cavity to equal that which can be transmitted from the end of the injection plunger through the heating cylinder and feed system. This pressure, if not controlled by some means, will usually be greater than is desirable. After the mold is full and under pressure, it is desirable to have the gate solidify to the point where it will not allow the still-hot plastic to flow back out of the mold when the injection plunger is withdrawn. This solidification should be instantaneous as soon as sufficient material has been fed into the mold. Of course, the solidification is not instantaneous, but solidification time should be kept to a minimum without having the gate be so small as to interfere with filling the mold.

The gate land, as illustrated in Fig. 5.41, is the key to flow control into the mold in conventional restricted-type gates.[3] Generally, the width of the gate may be anything up to the width of the runner. Wider gates usually offer no advantage. The only advantage in having the gate narrower than the runner is in the convenience and ease of degating (separating the molding from the runners). It is preferable to have the gate width from three fourths to the full width of the runner. The depth of the gate generally has been established at 0.4 to 0.6 times the thickness of the section of the molded article where the gate is attached. The minimum gate-land length should be equal to the thickness of the gate.

In a multiple-cavity mold it is desirable to balance the flow of plastic so that all the cavities fill simultaneously. If flow stops in any cavity, it might not start again if the gate is severely restricted, because the plastic

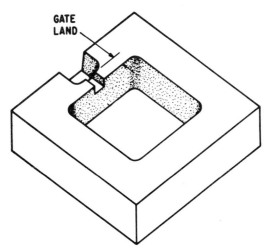

GATE
LAND

FIG. 5.41. Gate land.

in the gate section may solidify to the point where the available pressure is insufficient to cause resumption of flow.

One exception to the general practice of gate design, as described above, is the use of fan gates. This type of gate is wider than the runner and in the shape of a fan, with the wide part of the fan connecting to the molded piece. Fan gates are particularly useful in reducing stress at the gate area of large, flat molded parts, when it is not feasible to control the stress by other means.

Empirical methods of gate balancing have established the principle that the length of gate land on the cavities nearest the sprue should be twice as great as the length of gate land on the cavities farthest from the sprue. The length of land for cavities in between should be in proportion to the distance away from the sprue. This rule of thumb has been established by a great deal of practical observation, and it works rather well. Some mold designers prefer to balance the flow by means of runner width or by runner width combined with gate-land-length control.

Orientational and Packing Strains. Plastics are generally considered to be long-chain molecules with random orientation. During the filling portion of the mold cycle, the molecules will depart from their original state and orient in the direction of flow. As the material comes in contact with the cold mold wall (layer B, Fig. 5.42), it chills rapidly. The plastic layer A is still moving, although it is chilling also. Frictional forces are high between layers, and these forces stretch or orient the plastic in the direction of flow. The result is frozen orientational strain.[17] This type of strain can be minimized by filling the mold more rapidly and by using higher mold temperatures.

Packing more plastic into the filled mold at the end of the injection cycle causes further orientation of material nearer the center of the part thickness. The resulting high packing strain in the gate region can be minimized by high injection speeds, rapid gate freezing, shorter plunger dwell

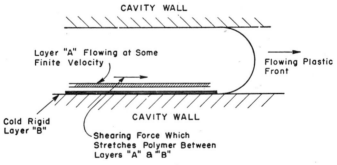

Fig. 5.42. Formation of frozen orientational strain.

time, and lower packing pressures. Weigh feeding, which places the correct amount of material in the cavity, will reduce these strains.

Mold Construction

The hydraulic pressure in an injection mold may be as low as 500 psi or as high as 12,000 psi. Generally, the pressure reaches about 4,000 psi at some time during the mold filling cycle. This pressure, multiplied by the number of square inches in the mold, may be an enormous force. Distortion and displacement of the mold parts result from unbalanced pressures and from high pressures.

Thin-walled moldings in the range of 0.012 to .035 in. thick are common. Containers of these thicknesses are molded by the millions. It is essential that the mold parts remain in perfect alignment to assure uniform wall thickness in these container molds. This may be illustrated by an example:

If a container is to be molded having a wall of 0.060 in., and the core shifts 0.010 in., the thin side of the molded part will be 0.050 in. thick and the thick side will be 0.070 in. thick. It is not difficult to fill even the thinner side of this part, and a practical or useful container can be made in a mold which permits this much core shifting. If, however, the part is to be made with a 0.035 in. wall thickness, and the core shifts 0.010 in., the thin side will be 0.025 in. thick and the thick side will be 0.045 in. thick. The thicker side has nearly twice the dimension of the thin side, and this difference is enough to cause extreme difficulty in molding. The injection pressure required to fill the mold would be that for a wall of 0.025 in. rather than for a wall of 0.035 in. This means that a core shift also requires much higher injection-molding pressure when other things are equal.

A comparison of mold rigidity has been made on two similar molds. One, as illustrated in Fig. 5.37, is a multiple-cavity mold aligned by the guide pins only. The total core shift, including a very small amount of bending, was 0.009 in. under ordinary injection-molding conditions. A single-cavity mold, as shown in Fig. 5.43, allowed the core to shift 0.0025 in. The single-cavity mold was built much more rigidly by means of a tapered cone on the core, which enters the cavity and aligns the core rigidly in place. The mold shift was decreased by a factor greater than 3 by employing the improved design.

The improvement in design also included a much more massive cavity block and core block. Not only is it necessary to use materials that are stiff, but the section modulus of the cavity and core must be made large through the use of thick metal cross sections. The difference in thickness of the two mold designs is obvious when the illustrations are examined closely. It is recommended that the thickness of metal around the cavity be at least 1/2 in. per inch of diametral dimension.

It is possible to reduce deformation of a mold cavity by surrounding it with a heavy steel retainer plate or chase. The retainer plate reinforces the cavity after the cavity has deformed enough to provide a large bearing area between the outer surface of the cavity block and the inner surface of the retainer. However, considerable deformation takes place before this happens. A microscopic examination of the contact between the two faces would very likely show a very small area of contact as the parts are fitted normally and when they are not under pressure. When the plastic pressure begins to cause the cavity to expand, the cavity first expands through the open space between it and the retainer, and as more and more of the faces of the cavity come in contact with the container, resistance is built up by deformation of the cavity and the retainer surfaces. After considerably more deformation, the retainer is stressed sufficiently to resist the force of the expansion of the cavity. In many cases in which the mold is constructed too lightly, the reinforcing action of the retainer occurs far too late in the molding cycle. So much deformation has occurred that the cavity is out of shape, and the part is not molded to correct dimensions. In some extreme cases the deformation is so great that the part cannot be released from the mold.

Materials for Molds. Many types of ferrous and nonferrous metals are used in the construction of injection molds. Ease of machinability sometimes determines the selection of a given metal. Ease of obtaining a cavity with a minimum of machinability may also be a determining factor.

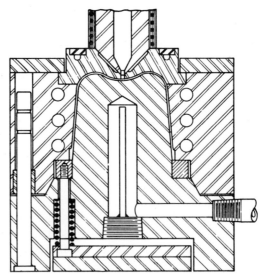

Fɪɢ. 5.43. Single-cavity automatic mold.

Corrosion resistance sometimes is considered when corrosive plastics are used or when a humid atmosphere prevails in the region of the molding plant. Economy in processing mold parts may dictate the use of an easy-machining metal, or a long run often decides the selection of a hard, long-wearing material. Preventing warping of large pieces sometimes is a dominant factor in the selection of metals for use in building the mold. The performance requirements of the mold under consideration determine the selection of the material of construction. It is impossible to make general rules for specification of materials for mold parts.

Practically all kinds of steel are used. Low-carbon steel and nickel-alloy–low-carbon steel are used for mold cavities which are hobbed, i.e., made by forcing a hardened metal master into the cold cavity blank. Alloy steels of many descriptions are used for mold parts that are machined by cutting. These may be water-, oil-, or air-hardening steels, or precipitation-hardening steels.

Wrought metals, such as cold-rolled steel or hot-rolled steel, are used for many mold parts. Cast metal is not sufficiently high in tensile strength and cleanliness for most mold requirements. In some cases, however, cast stainless steel has been used successfully for mold cavities which may be difficult to machine or finish because of the complex nature of the shape of the cavity.

Mold plates for retainers or bolsters or ejector-pin plates, spacers, and pillars are usually hot-rolled machinery steel. Hot-rolled steel, being much less highly stressed at the surface, can be machined with less danger of warping. In many cases, alloy-steel backup or bolster plates are used in a hardened condition so they will not become upset owing to the constant reversal of stress as the mold part is pushed against the retainer or backup plate during the molding cycle. Soft, hot-rolled backup plates have been observed to be upset by as much as $\frac{1}{32}$ in. after a long period of use. The hardened plates deform about the same amount under the load, but they do not yield. The hardening raises the yield point and prevents permanent deformation. It is not necessary to harden such plates, e.g., to the very high degree required for the cavity surfaces.

Water-hardening steels are not likely to be used except in the form of drill rod, which is used for ejector pins, return pins, and possibly dowels. Water-hardening steel is subject to cracking or warping in complex shapes, and it is avoided for this reason. Oil-hardening steels are often used for cavity and core parts, because they can be heat-treated readily and quenched in a variety of ways to produce hardness, elongation, toughness, and other blends of properties. Air-hardening steels are used for parts which require maximum insurance against warpage or cracking during the quenching process. Precipitation-hardening steels are hardened through prolonged heating and are usually hardened to the limit of machinability before they are cut into the form of mold cavities or cores. They are not heat-treated after machining, and heat-treating damage therefore is avoided.

Large mold-cavity blanks which cannot be made from regular sizes of rolled stock have to be forged into approximately the shape and size required. Forging may produce considerable stresses. Forged mold-cavity blanks should be stress-relieved before they are machined, and they should be stress-relieved further after they are machined within about $\frac{1}{8}$ in. of their final dimensions. The double stress relief, when performed thoroughly and properly, goes a long way toward eliminating disastrous cracking or warping in the final heat-treating process.

Many nonferrous metals are used in making mold cavities, and for some purposes they are entirely adequate. Generally, nonferrous alloys can be made into mold cavities of complex shape very economically by casting or pressing. In some cases they are adequate metals for short runs or for sampling, although, when mold pressures are high, their utility is questionable. For example, beryllium copper may be hardened to approximately 45 Rockwell "C," which is sufficient for most injection-molding requirements. However, the metal is only two thirds as stiff as steel and it will deform one and one half times as far as steel under equal pressure.

Aluminum and magnesium are extremely easy metals to machine. These metals are often used for sample molds, because they can be machined quickly when a sample mold is needed, without the delay of the longer processing time required for steel. These metals are considerably less stiff then beryllium copper and in some cases not stiff enough for injection-molding use at all. Of course, they cannot be hardened to a satisfactory hardness for long runs of injection molding.

Low-melting, soft metals, such as "Kirksite," Wood's metal, and lead, have been used for injection molds only under extremely specialized circumstances, as they cannot withstand high injection pressure and prolonged use.

ROLE OF PRESSURE, TEMPERATURE, AND TIME IN INJECTION MOLDING

Equation-of-State

Important in determining the quality of a molded part are pressure, average temperature, and density of the polymer in the mold, just before the mold is opened. In general, it is well to know the values of these quantities as a function of time, after the mold has been filled. Knowing the geometry of the mold, the temperature at which the polymer enters the mold, and the mold temperature, the average temperature of the piece

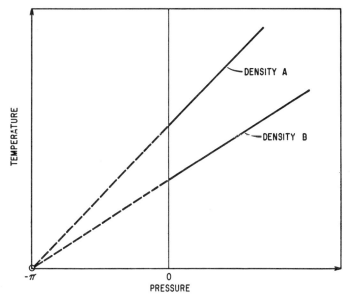

Fig. 5.44. Pressure-temperature diagram.

may be computed as a function of time from heat-conduction equations. This may involve approximations, but a sufficiently accurate answer can be obtained in most cases, leaving the pressure and density to be determined as functions of time. Fortunately, it is not necessary to measure both of these quantities, inasmuch as they are related through the equation-of-state which has been found to hold for amorphous polymers.[16]

$$(P + \pi)(V - \omega) = RT$$

where P is the pressure, V the specific volume, T the average temperature, and π, ω, and R are constants determined for many of the common polymers.

The equation-of-state indicates that, when density is held constant, pressure is a straight-line function of the temperature. This leads to a very convenient graphical representation, illustrated in Fig. 5.44, where temperature is plotted against pressure. When density is held constant, the temperature and pressure vary along a straight line, the slope of which depends upon the density. All such straight lines pass through a single point, located at $P = -\pi$ and $T = 0°K$. This type of plot is useful in analyzing data on conditions inside a mold.[18]

Pressure-Temperature Diagram

Reliable techniques for measuring and recording the pressure cycles in the mold cavity and at the nozzle have been described by P. D. Kohl.[11]

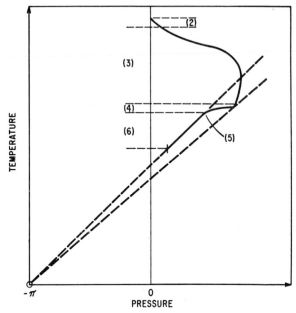

Fɪɢ. 5.45. P-T diagram of injection molding cycle.

In a typical mold pressure cycle, if time is expressed in terms of temperature (calculated from heat-conduction data), the replot results in a temperature vs. pressure curve. The various steps can be shown on Fig. 5.45:

(1) Dead time
(2) Filling
(3) Packing
(4) Discharge
(5) Sealing
(6) Sealed cooling

The proper conditions for opening the mold can be established on this pressure-temperature diagram. First of all, the piece must be rigid enough to hold its shape, which means that the polymer temperature must drop to at least some value T_s. The mold is controlled at some lower temperature, and the molding cannot be cooled below this temperature while in the mold. On the pressure scale the residual mold pressure P_r must be less than some maximum value to avoid scoring or breaking the molding when the mold is opened. On the other hand, in a mold containing a core, a negative minimum pressure may be defined beyond which sticking on the core will occur. Also, on most moldings (except very thin sections) sink marks and bubbles will appear if the mold pressure goes too low. The two pressure and temperature limits define an area within which the mold

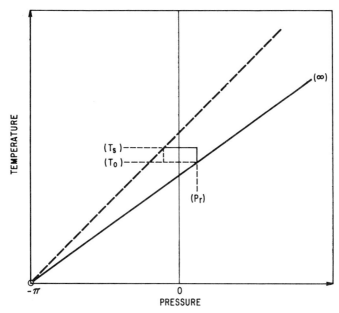

FIG. 5.46. P-T diagram of mold opening conditions.

should be opened. During cooling, this region is approached along a constant-density line, as illustrated in Fig. 5.46. This figure shows the limits of density in the mold to make good parts.

The weight of polymer in the mold, and consequently the constant-density line along which the pressure and temperature decrease, will be determined by the pressure and temperature at which the gate seals. These cooling lines show that the gate sealing point will be the place where the curve deviates from this straight line. The temperature-pressure plot around the sealing point for a number of plunger-forward times is shown in Fig. 5.47. The relationship between the various sealing points is approximately a linear variation of temperature with pressure. The position of this sealing line will depend largely upon the mold wall temperature, polymer setup temperature, and gate dimensions.

The optimum conditions for opening the mold will be determined by the pressure and average temperature in the mold at the time the gate seals. The sealing line may be approached in several different ways, depending upon the combination of settings on the controls. The three variables in determining the sealing point will be (1) the polymer temperature as it enters the mold, (2) the peak mold pressure, and (3) the packing time.

Some of the various ways of approaching the sealing line are shown in Fig. 5.48. Line 1 shows a low mold pressure, and the plunger is kept for-

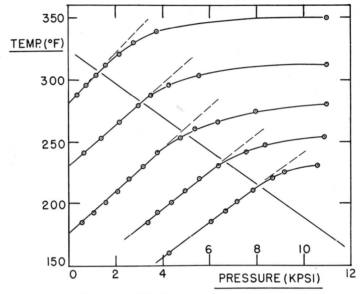

FIG. 5.47. P-T diagram of mold sealing.

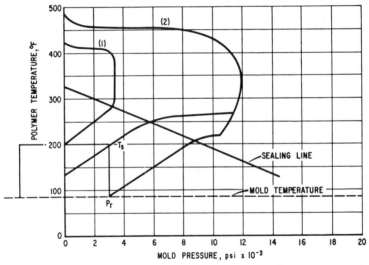

FIG. 5.48. P-T diagram of changes in plastic temperature and plunger forward time.

ward until the gate seals. When the sealing line is reached, the pressure and temperature will follow the sealed cooling line, regardless of whether the plunger is still held forward. The more conventional method is shown by Line 2, where the plunger maintains the pressure in the mold by packing an additional amount of material in the mold. When the polymer reaches the proper sealing temperature, the plunger is released, and the mold discharges down to the pressure that the polymer in the gate will hold at that temperature. Any additional packing time will increase the weight of polymer in the mold.

Effect of Weigh Feeding. A technique to help obtain correct pressure and temperature in the mold is weigh feeding. When properly adjusted, weigh feeding places the correct amount of material in the mold, and the mold pressure will not exceed that required for a good molding at the time the gate seals. As long as the plunger-forward time is sufficient to allow the gate to seal and prevent discharge, all of the moldings will have the same weight. The pressure and temperature in the cavity will approximate the cooling curve given by the equation-of-state for that weight of material (Fig. 5.49).

As long as the plunger is held forward until pressure and temperature cross the sealing line, a good molding will result; but if the plunger-forward time is too short, as shown by the dotted line, there will be some material discharged from the mold, giving a molding that is lighter than desired. This situation leads to more trouble than just one light molding. Since the one molding is too light, but the proper weight is being fed into the machine for each shot, there will be too much polymer in the machine for the next shot.

Effect of Nozzle Valves. The ball-check nozzle, or any other nozzle or gate valve, mechanically seals any desired pressure and temperature in the

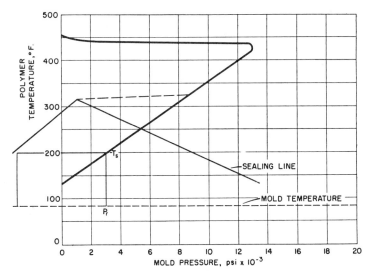

FIG. 5.49. P-T diagram of weigh feeding.

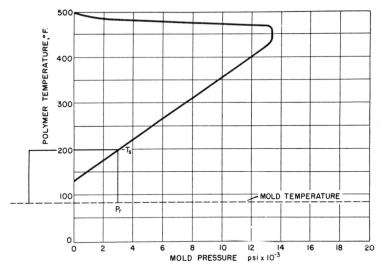

Fɪɢ. 5.50. P-T diagram with a ball-check nozzle.

mold. Since, in any molding operation, the temperature of the plastic and the rate of cooling may vary, the gate may not always seal at the same point in the molding cycle. The ball-check nozzle seals the mold when the plunger releases its pressure and makes the quality of the molding independent of the gate sealing time. The mold can therefore be sealed at a higher pressure and temperature, thus allowing higher injection pressures and faster filling of the mold. With the ball-check nozzle the sealing point can be anywhere along the line given by the equation-of-state for the correct weight that will produce a good molding.

In Fig. 5.50 the mold is filled at some pressure and temperature determined by the injection pressure and heater controls. During the plunger-forward time there is packing into the mold the same as in conventional molding. But as soon as the plunger returns, the gate is sealed by the ball-check nozzle at a pressure and temperature higher than in conventional molding but along the cooling line that will give a good molding.

Moldability

Moldability Definition. The word "moldability" has been rather loosely used at times. From a molder's point of view, a simple, general definition of this property of a polymer has been offered: "Moldability is a measure of the speed and ease with which a polymer can be fabricated to a certain given specification."

The term "given specification" refers to acceptability criteria. These specifications will vary with application and material and must be set up for any moldability determination.

Moldability Theory. The paramount interest of the molder is to produce acceptable pieces as rapidly as possible. Bearing this obvious but important fact in mind, emphasis must be placed upon the length of time
consumed by a single molding cycle, or "cycle time." The first step in determining optimum molding conditions is to establish the requirements
that must be met by the molded article.

Acceptability can best be defined negatively: defects are required to be
absent, or at least kept below some level. The criteria set up will vary from
part to part, but many will be common to most production runs. Typical
acceptability criteria could be:

(1) Rigidity
(2) Release
(3) Minimum blemish
(4) Conformity to mold
(5) Minimum frozen orientation consistent with conformity

On the pressure-temperature plot, Requirement 1 means that the average temperature of the piece when the mold is opened must be not greater
than some effective softening temperature T_s. Of course, in molding heavy
sections this condition may be violated successfully by immersing the
piece in a cold bath as soon as it is removed. This should be regarded as
strictly an emergency procedure, however, as there is a tendency to form
sink marks or bubbles. Requirement 2 means that the pressure in the mold
when it is opened must not be greater than the characteristic release pressure P_r.

Since it would be inefficient to cool the piece below the temperature T_s,
it is only necessary to consider the area between the constant-density lines
which reach the temperature limit T_s at $-P_r$ and $+P_r$, as shown in Fig.
5.51.

Requirement 3 concerns the filling of the mold and specifies a maximum
fill time above which the polymer will not fill the mold properly for acceptable surface finish. There is also a minimum fill time below which the
machine cannot operate. The peak mold pressure and polymer temperature for these two filling times are also shown on the pressure-temperature
plot as f_B and f_m. From the limiting cycle concept, the cooling line which
passes through the temperature limit T_s will give the minimum cooling time,
and also the pressure and temperature along f_m will give the minimum fill
time. There is still some leeway in the variables peak mold pressure, polymer temperature, and packing time. There are also some further limitations
such as degradation of the polymer with too much heat, maximum machine
pressure available, and mold temperature.

The pressure and temperature plot shown is for only one point in the
mold. Since the mold pressure and plastic temperature will vary from point
to point in the mold, the conditions in the mold at any point must fall

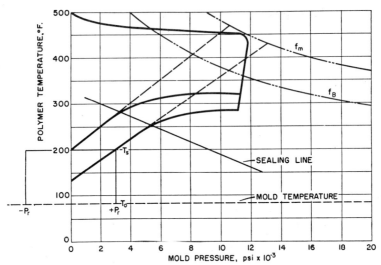

Fig. 5.51. P-T diagram at limiting cycle conditions.

within these limits. For a very complicated mold the conditions of pressure and temperature at some point may be outside these limitations, leading to localized sink marks, scoring, or surface blemishes.

If the constant-density lines are extended beyond the sealing line, it will be noted that the density of the polymer is at times higher than required, and the excess polymer is discharged out of the mold. This flow in and out of the mold will cause additional frozen orientation in the piece. To minimize this frozen orientation consistent with Acceptability Requirement 5, such things as bottoming the plunger, weigh feeding, and the ball-check nozzle will effectively start the sealed cooling portion of the cycle much sooner than the sealing line.

Analysis of Variables in the Injection-Molding Operation and the Solution of Molding Problems. Since time is very important in injection molding, the emphasis must be placed on the length of time consumed by a single molding cycle. In terms of the molding-machine operation, the cycle is customarily broken down into (1) plunger-forward time, (2) mold closed, and (3) mold-open time. This breakdown, while convenient for setting the controls of the machine, is not suitable for analytical purposes. Instead, the cycle should be divided in terms of what happens to the polymer: (1) dead time, (2) fill time, (3) packing time, (4) discharge, (5) sealing, and (6) sealed cooling time. Along with the correct time sequence for a good molding, the molder must also have the proper temperature and pressure sequence. During filling, the polymer must be sufficiently molten and have enough pressure behind it to fill the mold quickly and conform to the shape of the cavities. During the packing and discharge period, the pressure and temperature of the polymer are controlled so that at the instant the gate freezes off, or seals, the correct amount of material will be in the mold. The cooling period further reduces the temperature and pressure to a point where the molding can be removed easily from the mold without distorting. Thus, any analysis of the molding cycle must be based on all three of the major variables in the molding cycle—pressure, temperature, and time.

The molding cycle and the three major variables (pressure, temperature, and time) are determined by three sets of conditions or variables: (1) machine variables, (2) mold variables, and (3) polymer variables. Each of these three sets of variables can be adjusted through a wide, but not unlimited, range. In the solution of molding problems, it is logical to examine and correct each set of variables in the above order.

To show how this method of analysis is used in solving problems, assume that a molder is starting up a new mold. When a new mold is placed in a press, the molder uses his past experience on similar molds to set up an approximate cycle. If the moldings are not perfect on this cycle, he will vary the pressure, temperature, and time sequences by adjusting the machine conditions until he produces good pieces. In the solution of a molding problem, adjustments are first made in the machine variables:

Pressure:
  Ram pressure
  Shot weight
Temperature:
  Heater temperatures
  Nozzle temperature
  Granule drying temperature (if dryer is used)
Time:
  Plunger-forward time
  Cooling time
  Mold-open time
  Plunger speed

These conditions are simple to change, but their influence on the quality of the molded piece is not always direct. All of the above variables are interrelated; e.g., the temperature of the heaters will also determine the pressure transmission through the heating cylinder. The cycle time as well as the heater temperature will dictate the temperature of the plastic.

If the molder fails to make acceptable pieces by changing the machine conditions, he should examine the design of the mold. Changes in the following variables could be made:

Pressure-Controlling Variables:
  Sprue and runner design
  Gate size and location

Section thickness
Length of flow path
Temperature-Controlling Variables:
Mold temperature
Cooling lines (temperature uniformity)
Length of flow path
Time-Controlling Variables:
Fill time: See Pressure-Controlling Variables
Cooling time: See Temperature-Controlling Variables

All changes of the mold affect the temperature, pressure, and time sequences in the mold, and, as can be seen from the above lists, these interrelationships are difficult to calculate and to predict.

Most molding problems can be solved by varying the machine conditions in the manner previously discussed. A few more problems can be solved by additional changes of mold conditions, but there will be some remaining problems on which these approaches will be unsuccessful. These are the problems that may be caused by polymer properties. Some of the polymer characteristics or conditions which affect the quality of a molded piece are:

Flow Characteristics:
Viscosity
Shear dependence of viscosity
Thermal Properties:
Specific heat
Heat of fusion
Thermal conductivity
Crystallization induction time
Granulation:
Granulation size and shape
Granulation lubrication

A comprehensive chart to serve as a guide to the solution of molding problems according to this approach is presented in Table 5.1.

Injection-Molding Equation. This background in the variables of injection molding leads to consideration of the effect of polymer properties (e.g., melt viscosity, coefficient of friction) which influence the fill time, and other properties (thermal diffusivity, softening point, etc.) which influence the cooling time. The minimum sum of filling time and cooling time will give a measure of the speed at which moldings can be made. An approach to determining the influence of polymer properties on moldability can be made by setting up an equation showing the relationships between polymer properties and the molding cycle. Because of the complexity of the injection-molding industry, equations cannot cover all molding situations. In fact, to obtain a practical equation, the molding cycle must be simplified and a number of assumptions made.

TABLE 5.1. SOLUTION OF INJECTION-MOLDING PROBLEMS

Moldability Problem	Injection-Molding Cycle	Molding Variables	Limitations
What is the molding problem?	What molding condition causes the problem?	What can be changed to get the correct molding cycle to eliminate the problem?	What limits changes in the molding variable?
Increased production	Dead time	A. Machine variables	A. Machine variables
Short shots	Fill time	Heater temperature	Control limits
Poor ejection	Plastic temperature	Granule feed	Size of machine
Weld lines	Packing pressure	Plunger pressure	Machine design
Surface finish	Packing time	Plunger speed	
Silver streaks	Weight density	Plunger-forward time	
Cracking or crazing	Gate sealing	Mold-closed time	
Sink marks	Cooling time	Mold-open time	
Warpage	Residual pressure	Nozzle temperature	
Dimensional control		B. Mold variables	B. Mold variables
		Mold temperature	Use of part
		Cooling lines	Strength of part
		Section thickness	Piece design
		Volume of mold	Mold design
		Sprue, runner, and gate design	
		Number of cavities	
		C. Polymer variables	C. Polymer variables
		Melt viscosity	Polymerization condition
		Non-Newtonian constant	Tensile, impact strength
		Heat-distortion temperature	Granulation, lubrication
		Thermal properties	
		Viscosity vs. temperature	
		Orientation	
		Compressibility	
		Granulation	
		Density	
		Lubrication	

The equation-of-state which relates pressure, temperature, and density shows that if the weight of material placed in the mold is controlled, the correct mold pressure will result. By using a very accurate weigh feeder, the packing and discharge steps become fixed and can be safely ignored. The equation then need be concerned only with the filling and cooling of the polymer.

With this simplification, the injection-molding cycle becomes a function of only two independent variables—temperature and time. (The third variable, pressure, has been replaced by density, which is controlled by the weigh feeder and is no longer an independent variable.) The next step is to relate temperature and time. This is done by finding the time required to fill the mold and the time required to cool the polymer as a function of temperature. The starting point of our equation is the temperature and available pressure of the plastic as it enters the mold.

The total cycle time is

$$\text{Total cycle} = \text{dead time} + \text{fill time} + \text{cooling time}$$

$$t_{cy} = d + f + c \tag{21}$$

The fill-time equation is

$$f = \beta \eta P_B^{-\alpha} \tag{22}$$

where

$$f = \text{fill time}$$

$$\eta = \text{viscosity at zero shear}$$

$$P_B = \text{nozzle pressure}$$

$$\beta \text{ and } \alpha = \text{constants}$$

Temperature corrections to the viscosity can be made from the equation

$$\text{Log}_{10}\eta_0 = \text{Log}_{10}\eta_0^* + k(T + T^*)$$

$$0.434\, Ln_e\eta_0 = 0.434\, Ln_e\eta_0^* + k(T + T^*) \tag{23}$$

$$\eta_0 = \eta_0^* e^{k'(T+T^*)} \tag{24}$$

where

$$\eta_0 = \text{melt viscosity at } T$$

$$\eta_0^* = \text{melt viscosity at } T^* = 225°C$$

$$k = \text{constant}$$

$$k' = \frac{k}{0.434}$$

and Eq. (22) becomes

$$f = \beta\eta_0 e^{k'(T-T*)} P_B{}^{-\alpha}$$

If we wish to express this equation in terms of ram pressure, Eq. (22) would become

$$f = \beta'\eta_0(1 - \gamma)^{-\alpha} P_m{}^{-\alpha} \qquad (25)$$

Using both the temperature and pressure correction, the complete fill-time equation would be

$$f = \beta\eta_0 e^{k'(T-T*)}(1 - \gamma)^{-\alpha} P_m{}^{-\alpha} \qquad (26)$$

The cooling of a plastic slab can be approximated by the equation

$$\text{Log } \theta = -\frac{4.24\alpha'^2 t}{a^2} + \text{Log}_{10}\, 0.81 \qquad (27)$$

$$\alpha' = \text{thermal diffusivity}$$

$$t = \text{time variable}$$

$$\text{Log}_{10}\, 0.81 = \text{constant**}$$

$$4.24 = \text{constant**}$$

where

$$\theta = \frac{T_t - T_m}{T - T_m}$$

$$T_t = \text{polymer temperature at any time } t$$

$$T_m = \text{mold temperature}$$

$$T = \text{initial polymer temperature}$$

The cooling time in the mold would then become

$$c = \frac{-a^2}{4.24\alpha'^2}\left(\text{Log } \theta - \text{Log } 0.81\right) \qquad (28)$$

In both the fill-time and cooling-time equations, T is the temperature of the plastic as it enters the mold. The point at which we have an accurate measurement of plastic temperature is at the nozzle of the heating cylinder. Further simplification of the moldability test can be obtained by eliminating the sprues and runners and bringing the tip of the nozzle right up to the mold cavity. Thus the nozzle temperature, which is easily measured, now becomes the same as the temperature of the plastic as it enters the mold. In the cooling-time equation T_t is the average temperature of the

** Equation derived from H. S. Carslaw and J. C. Jaeger, "Conduction of Heat in Solids," Oxford University Press, New York, 1947.

plastic as the mold is opened. There are two conditions which determine the point at which the mold can be opened: (1) The mold pressure must be at the proper level, preferably zero. (2) The average plastic temperature must be low enough so that the molded piece will not warp. In the moldability test the first condition is controlled by the weigh feeder. Experiments on cooling in the mold have shown that the temperature required to prevent the molding from distorting is very close to the apparent heat-distortion temperature. This warpage temperature will vary somewhat owing to the residual strains in the molding and will, therefore, depend upon the initial plastic temperature and the mold temperature. As a first approximation, the heat-distortion temperature T_{HD} can be used with a fair degree of accuracy. For greater accuracy, the maximum average temperature of the molding to prevent warpage can be measured by special methods.

The injection-molding-cycle equation is

$$t_{cy} - d = \text{plunger-forward time} + \text{mold-closed time}$$

$$= \text{fill time} + \text{cooling time} \tag{29}$$

$$= \beta' \eta_0 e^{k'(T-T^*)} (1 - \gamma)^{-\alpha} P_m^{-\alpha}$$

$$+ \frac{a^2}{4.24\alpha'^2} \left(\log 0.81 - \log \frac{T_{HD} - T_M}{T - T_M} \right)$$

A specific example of polystyrene molded in a certain machine and mold is given in the appendix at the end of this chapter.

To verify completely this equation would be a formidable task, if at all possible. It would be almost impossible to find polymers which differed only in melt viscosities or only in heat-distortion temperatures. As a whole, the agreement of the equation with molding experience is quite good, if the boundary conditions imposed by the molding machine are inserted. There are two big omissions from this equation: (1) the cooling of the polymer while the mold is filling and its effect on the fill time, and (2) the orientation produced in the molding while filling and how it affects the cooling time.

The linear terms f and c are well defined by the equation. To be accurate, the equation should have four terms:

$$t_{cy} = f + c + f_c + c_f \tag{30}$$

where f_c and c_f denote the cooling during filling, and the effect of filling (orientation) on cooling. The amount of the change in the cycle caused by these two cross-product terms will vary with section thickness. On very thin moldings the amount of cooling during filling and orientation will be much greater than in a thick-section mold. So, for very thin moldings the equation, or moldability test, that does not recognize these cross-product terms will give misleading results.

Moldability Evaluation

The purpose of a moldability test is to measure the molding charatceristics of a polymer using a minimum of polymer. The test must be arranged so that it will rate the polymer as closely as possible to the rating that would be obtained from a complete evaluation in commercial use. The moldability test should give a measure of the performance of the polymer in the field. Because of the wide ranges of applications, molds, and machines, the truly complete evaluation would demand that the polymer be run on every mold and in every molding machine.

According to the definition of moldability, two factors must be measured: (1) the speed, and (2) the ease with which a piece can be fabricated. The first item, speed, would place the emphasis on the cycle time. The best test that has been devised to measure speed is the minimum-cycle test. The second item, ease, would put the emphasis on the pressures and temperatures required to fill the mold. The test for ease of filling is the molding-area diagram. The minimum-cycle test will give the shortest possible cycle of the polymer for the mold in which it is being tested. On the other hand, the molding-area diagram will measure the pressure and temperature required to mold a piece on a given cycle. Occasionally, the results of these tests will contradict each other. A material which flows into the mold easily may take a long time to cool and may require a longer cycle than another material with a higher viscosity. An example of this is shown in some moldability data on polyethylene:

Material	Cylinder temperature	Injection pressure to fill at minimum cycle	Minimum cycle
Polyethylene A	451°F	15,000 psi	28 sec
Polyethylene B	438°F	14,500 psi	30 sec

In this instance the material which fills the mold at the lowest temperature and pressure takes longer to cool and has a longer minimum cycle.

Molding-Area Diagram. A molding-area diagram is developed by plotting the cylinder temperature and injection pressure at which a material may be molded in a test mold. As indicated, there are only two molding variables—cylinder temperature and injection pressure. The molding cycle, mold temperature, etc., are held constant, and of course the same machine, mold, and technique are used for all materials in any one evaluation. The technique consists of gradually increasing the pressure at constant temperature until the mold cavity is just full and increasing further until

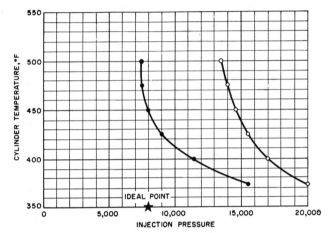

Fig. 5.52. Typical molding area diagram.

it sticks or flashes. The short-shot point and stick point are recorded on a graph. The cylinder temperature is then increased by a specific amount, and a new set of points is found. The process is repeated until, because of our test conditions, the temperature limitations of the material are reached.

A typical diagram produced by this method is shown in Fig. 5.52. The graph is a plot of the cylinder temperature against injection pressure. At 375°F it was found that the part was just full at 15,500 psi, and at 20,000 psi the part stuck in the cavity. At 25°F intervals of cylinder temperature, these short and stick points are found and recorded. By connecting all the short-shot points and all the stick points, there are two curves which are called the short-shot line and the stick line. The area between these two lines is known as the molding area, in that full parts may be molded at any of the combinations of injection pressure and cylinder temperature that fall within the area. The molding-area diagram shows the minimum and maximum temperature-pressure combinations, under set conditions, at which the material can be molded in a test mold.

Molding-area diagrams of different materials can be compared visually by superimposition or by a numerical rating method. The numerical rating would take into consideration the size of the area as well as its distance from "ideal point" (e.g., 350°F at 8,000 psi for polystyrene).

Minimum Cycle. A second test incorporated in the study of moldability is the determination of the minimum cycle for producing satisfactory parts. A range of logical mold- and cylinder-temperature combinations are investigated to determine the maximum speed at which a material may be molded. The mold shot size should not be greater than 75 per cent of the machine capacity in order to avoid exceeding the plasticating rate of the heating cylinder. Many shots at any one set of conditions are required to assure temperature equilibrium. The minimum molding temperature from the molding-area diagram is used as a basis for the minimum-cycle determination. The cycle used in plotting the molding-area diagram is kept as a starting point, and booster time is added to facilitate filling. The material is weigh-fed into the cylinder. Minimum plunger-forward time is first determined, while maintaining a constant cycle by adding any time removed from the plunger-forward timer to the mold-closed timer and keeping mold-open timer constant. After this is determined, the mold-closed time is reduced, thereby reducing the over-all cycle. The end point in both of these determinations is reached when satisfactory parts are no longer produced. This is repeated for several selected mold temperatures. After these mold temperatures are explored, the cylinder temperature is increased by 100°F, and another set of mold temperatures is investigated. The selection of cylinder-temperature and mold-temperature combinations is based on the usual practice of using a low cylinder temperature with high mold temperatures or a high cylinder temperature with low mold temperatures.

This is a reliable test which shows the speed with which the mold may be filled and how fast the material sets up in the mold. Because emphasis is always on satisfactory parts, the parts are evaluated for shrinkage, silver streaking, black streaking, cracks, gas traps, etc.

Selection of Molds. In selecting a mold for moldability testing, the first concern must be whether any of the special problems such as inserts, variable thickness, bosses, etc., should be included. Usually, these are not included, and the molds are made to resemble as many typical applications as possible. Problems associated with unusual molds must be studied separately. The general-moldability mold can be described in two ways: (1) by the ratio of the piece weight to the shot size of the machine, and (2) by the ratio of the thickness to the surface area. When the weight of the piece approaches the shot capacity of the machine, or the number of pounds per hour of polymer approaches the heating capacity, there will be moldability problems caused by variations in shot size and by insufficiently heated material. Moldability molds should be designed for a shot size of no more than 75 per cent of the machine capacity.

The term "thin or thick section molding," is best described as the thickness-to-surface ratio a/S. The molds, when classified as to section thickness, can be considered to fall into three categories: thin section, where $a/S \sim$ 0.0004; medium section, where $a/S \sim 0.001$; and thick section, where $a/S \sim 0.003$.

Using the section-thickness classification, one may predict how the four terms of the moldability equation will change with section thickness under similar machine conditions.

Thin section	Medium section	Thick section
a/S 0.0004 (calculated)	a/S 0.001 (calculated)	a/S 0.003 (calculated)
f long	medium	short
c short	medium	long
f_c large	medium	small
c_f large	medium	small

In the very thin section mold, the filling time and cooling time are about equal. A large portion of the cooling occurs during filling, making it difficult to avoid a short shot. The pressures and temperatures required to fill the mold will be greatly influenced by the cooling of the polymer in the mold. In a thin section, the orientation will have a large influence on the cooling time because of the reduced heat-distortion temperature. Also, the filling time is a very large portion of the total cycle time. The minimum cycle is a measure primarily of the ability of the polymer to fill the mold easily and of the orientation produced by filling.

In a medium-section mold, the filling characteristics are similar to those of a thin-section mold and are affected somewhat by cooling during filling. The minimum cycle is a measure primarily of cooling. The orientation and the filling will have some effect on the minimum cycle.

In a thick-section molding, the molding-area diagram will indicate primarily the flow of polymer into the mold. The cooling during filling will be insignificant. The minimum cycle will measure primarily the cooling in the mold. The fill time and orientation are insignificant.

Each of the moldability tests will measure all four terms. The importance of the terms in each test will depend upon the section thickness of the molding. The following itemization is a summary of the above paragraphs giving the importance of the four terms in moldability testing.

	Thin	Section Thickness Medium	Thick
Molding-area diagram			
Important	f_c	f	f
Less important	f	c_f	
Insignificant	c and c_f	c and f	c, c_f, and f_c
Minimum cycle			
Important	c_f and f	c	c
Less important	c and f_c	c_f and f	
Insignificant		f_c	f, f_c, and c_f

The results of each of these tests will have a different meaning depending on the section thickness of the mold.

To analyze the molding behavior completely, four things must be known about the polymer:

(1) Filling characteristics—f—the ability of the polymer to fill the mold easily with minimum plastic temperatures and pressure

(2) Cooling characteristics—*c*—the ability of the polymer to "set up" or become rigid as fast as possible

(3) Orientation —*c$_f$*—the ability of the polymer to be molded with minimum residual strains

(4) Cooling during filling—*f$_c$*—the ability of the polymer to resist becoming rigid until the mold is filled.

A polymer which performs well in one section thickness may be entirely unsuitable for another. A polymer for thin-section molding should have the following characteristics:

> *f*–easy flowing
> *c*–not too significant
> *c$_f$*–low orientability
> *f$_c$*–slow cooling during filling

In terms of the polymer and molding variables this means:

> *f*–low melt viscosity
> –highly non-Newtonian
> –high plastic temperature
> –low frictional drag
> –high mold temperature
> *f$_c$*–low thermal diffusivity
> –low heat distortion
> –high mold temperature
> *c$_f$*–low orientability
> –high mold temperature
> –high plastic temperature

On the other extreme, a polymer for thick sections must meet the following conditions:

> *f*–not significant
> *c*–fast setup
> *f$_c$*–not too significant ⎫
> *c$_f$*–not too significant ⎬ these produce only skin effects

In terms of polymer and machine conditions this means:

> *c*–high heat-distortion temperatures
> –high thermal diffusivity
> –low plastic temperature
> –low mold temperature

Between these extremes, the polymer requirements will vary with section thickness.

APPENDIX

Injection-Molding-Equation Evaluation

In referring to the injection-molding equation described earlier in this chapter, the following values of the variables and constants were evaluated for a specific mold with polystyrene. These values were:

$$\beta' = 8 \qquad T_m = 65°C \qquad P_m = 20K \text{ psi}$$

$$\eta_0 = 34{,}000 \text{ poise} \qquad T_{HD} = 77°C \qquad T = 230°C$$

$$1 - \gamma = 0.64 \qquad a = 0.070 \text{ in.} \qquad \alpha = 3.5$$

Using these values as a reference, calculations were made of the fill times and cooling times for a wide variation of each variable, holding all others constant. The calculated cycle for this set of values is:

$$\text{fill time } f = 3.16 \text{ sec}$$

$$\text{cooling time } c = 13.11 \text{ sec}$$

$$f + c = t_{cy} - d = 16.27 \text{ sec}$$

This, plus 6 sec dead time, gives the over-all calculated cycle of 22 sec.

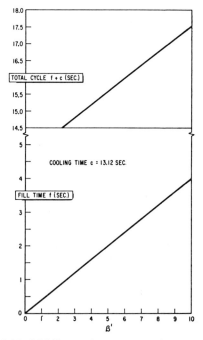

FIG. 5.A1. Molding cycle *vs.* geometrical constant.

This value compares very well with the measured cycle of 21 sec. Figures 5A1 through 5A9 show the change in fill time, cooling time, and total cycle with β', melt viscosity η_0, frictional drag γ, non-Newtonian constant α, mold temperature T_m, plastic temperature T, section thickness a, ram pressure P_m, and the temperature at which the piece can be removed from the mold T_{HD}.

β' **Fig. 5A1.** β' is a geometrical constant of the fill-time equation. Its value will depend upon the size of the molding, the section thickness, and the mold temperature. The exact dependence is not known, but it does decrease with increasing thickness and increasing mold temperature. Thus, the calculations of these values will be accurate only for the cooling time, since β' is not given as a function of these two variables in the equation.

η_0 **Fig. 5A2.** η_0 is the zero shear melt viscosity measured at 225°C. The fill-time equations reflect the effect of melt viscosity, or molecular weight, but since the molecular weight should affect the heat-distortion temperature, there may be a slight change in cooling time.

γ **Fig. 5A3.** γ is a measure of the frictional drag on the granules in the cold zone of the heating cylinder. Thus a change in the value of γ will change the amount of pressure available to force the plastic in the mold.

P_m **Fig. 5A4.** P_m is the pressure applied by the ram at the rear of the heating cylinder.

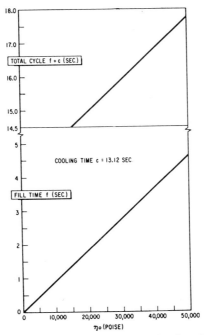

Fig. 5.A2. Molding cycle *vs.* melt viscosity.

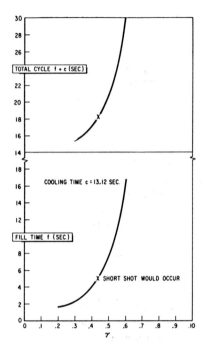

FIG. 5.A3. Molding cycle *vs*. frictional drag.

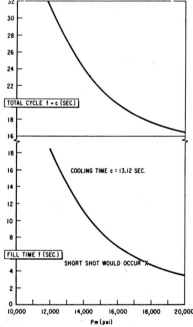

FIG. 5.A4. Molding cycle *vs*. ram pressure.

α **Fig. 5A5.** α is another number that expresses the non-Newtonian characteristics of the materials. It is similar to the $1/k$ value commonly used. $\alpha = 1$ is a Newtonian plastic, and higher values give the deviation from Newtonian flow.

T_m **Fig. 5A6.** T_m is the temperature of the mold.

a **Fig. 5A7.** The calculations of section thickness a show a larger increase in cooling time than was obtained with larger section thicknesses. The reason may be that it is necessary to harden only a skin of finite thickness to hold the piece rigid. The mass average polymer temperature may be above the heat-distortion temperature for the thicker moldings.

T **Fig. 5A8.** The calculations of the fill time and cooling time for different plastic temperatures T agree with previous experience. These calculations also give the characteristic U shaped curve which has been observed on several different molds.

T_{HD} **Fig. 5A9.** T_{HD} is the average plastic temperature at which the molding can be removed from the mold. In these calculations, the heat-distortion temperature of 77°C was used. At different mold temperatures the change in the amount of orientation in the molding will change this temperature.

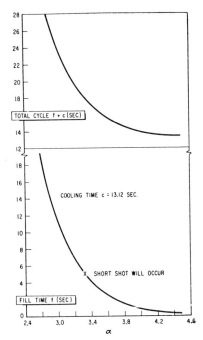

FIG. 5.A5. Molding cycle *vs.* non-Newtonian constant.

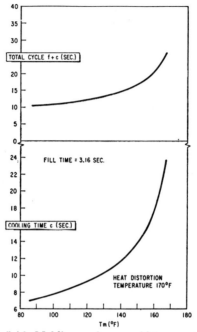

FIG. 5.A6. Molding cycle *vs.* mold temperature.

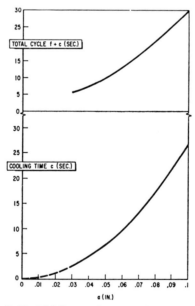

FIG. 5.A7. Molding cycle *vs.* section thickness.

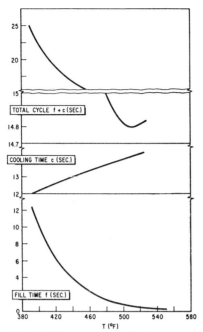

FIG. 5.A8. Molding cycle *vs.* plastic temperature.

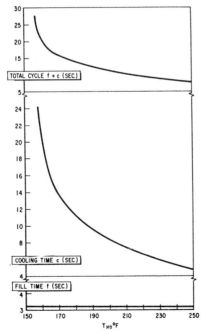

FIG. 5.A9. Molding cycle *vs.* heat distortion temperature.

REFERENCES

1. Bernhardt, E. C., and Paggi, L., "Polyliner Improves Injection Molding," *Modern Plastics*, **33**, 109 (*Feb*. 1956).
2. Beyer, C. E., and Dahl, R. B., "Measurement of Heating Capacities of Injection Molding Machines," *Modern Plastics*, **30**, 124 (*Sept*. 1952).
3. Bostwick, R., and Joslin, C. A., "Restricted Gating," *Modern Plastics*, **31**, 125 (*Oct*. 1953).
4. Farris, R. N., and Meeks, P. J., "Importance of Mold Rigidity in Injection Molding," *Plastics Technol.*, **3**, 371 (1957).
5. Gee, R. E., and Lyon, J. B., "Non-isothermal Flow of Viscous Non-Newtonian Fluids," *Ind. Eng. Chem.*, **49**, 956 (1957).
6. Gilmore, G. D., and Thayer, G. B., "Some Design Considerations for Injection Molding Heating Chambers," *Trans. ASME*, **75**, 903 (1953).
7. Griffiths, L., "Temperature Control in Injection Moulding," *Brit. Plastics*, **27**, 134 (*Apr*. 1954).
8. Hahn, O. M., "The Hydraulic System and Polymer Flow in Molding," *SPE Journal*, **13**, (*July* 1957).
9. Imig, C. S., "Mold Temperature Effects in Polyethylene Molding," *Modern Plastics*, **34**, 149 (*Dec*. 1956).
10. Kern, "Process Heat Transfer," 1st Ed., New York, McGraw-Hill Book Company Inc., 1950.
11. Kohl, P. D., "Pressure Measurement in Injection Molding by Use of Ejector Pins," *Plastics Technol.*, **3**, 629 (1957).
12. Maccaferri, M., and McKee, R. B., "The Maccaferri Injection Molding Heating Chamber," *SPE Journal*, **12**, 11 (*Feb*. 1956). Discussion appeared in *SPE Journal*, **12**, 55 (*May* 1956).
13. Morse, A. R., "Effects of Thermocouple Location and Wattage Control on Injection Cylinder Temperatures," *Plastics Technol.*, **1**, 277 (1955).
14. Moslo, E. P., "Runnerless Injection Molding," *Modern Plastics*, **32**, 119 (*Apr*. 1955).
15. Paggi, L., "Molding Cycles—Nozzle Design," *SPE Journal*, **13**, 42 (*May* 1957).
16. Spencer, R. S., and Gilmore, G. D., "Equation of State for High Polymers," *J. Appl. Phys.*, **21**, 523 (1950).
17. Spencer, R. S., and Gilmore, G. D., "Residual Strains in Injection Molded Polystyrene," *Modern Plastics*, **28**, 97 (*Dec*. 1950).
18. Spencer, R. S., and Gilmore, G. D., "Role of Pressure, Temperature and Time in the Injection Molding Process," *Modern Plastics*, **27**, 143 (*Apr*. 1950).
19. Spencer, R. S., Gilmore, G. D., and Wiley, R. M., "Behavior of Granulated Polymers Under Pressure," *J. Appl. Phys.*, **21**, 527 (1950).
20. Toor, H. L., and Eagleton, S. D., "Plug Flow and Lubrication of Polymer Particles," *Ind. Eng. Chem.*, **84**, 1825 (1956).
21. Whitlock, C. H., "Mold Temperature Control," *Modern Plastics*, **31** (*Oct*. 1953).

GENERAL REFERENCES

Beyer, C. E., "Pressure Control for Injection Molding Machines," *Plastics Technol.*, **3**, 459 (1957).

Beyer, C. E., Dahl, R. B., and McKee, R. B., "Temperature and Pressure Measurements in the Injection Machine Heating Cylinder," *Modern Plastics*, **32**, 127 (*Apr*. 1955); **32**, 110 (May 1955); **32**, 127 (June 1955).

Gaspar, E., "Basic Features Influencing the Performance of Injection Molding Machines," Plastic Progress, 1951, Iliffe & Sons.

Gilmore, G. D., and Spencer, R. S., "Photographic Study of the Polymer Cycle in Injection Molding," *Modern Plastics*, **27**, (*Apr.* 1951).

Toor, H. L., and Eagleton, S. D., "Energy Conversions in the Flow of High Polymers: Applications to Injection Molding," *J. Appl. Chem.*, **3**, 354 (1953).

Tordella, J. P., "Melt Extrusion of Polyethylene," *SPE Journal*, **6**, 9 (*May* 1953).

6. CALENDERING

D. I. Marshall, Ph. D.

Union Carbide Plastics Company
Division of Union Carbide Corporation

THE CALENDERING PROCESS

Calendering is the formation of a continuous sheet of controlled size by the squeezing of a softened thermoplastic material between two or more horizontal rollers.

The process was developed in the early days of the rubber industry and grew, along with the industry, to its status as an important art connected with the manufacture of rubber products. Today, the paper, linoleum, rubber, metals, and plastics industries all use rolling operations to form or treat sheets. Examples of plastics being calendered today include the vinyl chlorides, vinyl chloride-acetate copolymers, polyethylene, cellulose acetate, coumarone-indene, and many others. Synthetic-resin floor products have recently grown into a large segment of the calendering industry.

The manufacture of flexible polyvinyl chloride film and sheeting accounts for most of the production in the plastics calendering industry. Particular attention has been paid to high-speed production of thin films of uniform gauge. Films less than 0.002 in. thick are now being produced in widths up to 6 ft and at speeds up to 300 ft/min within thickness tolerances of 0.0001 in. Such close control requires a high degree of engineering in the design and operation of the equipment. The success to date indicates that calendering has progressed a long way toward becoming a science instead of an art.

Outlined in Fig. 6.1 is a typical calendering layout for production of these materials, incorporating some of the newer developments. The layout consists of a Banbury mixer for fluxing the charge and a two-roll mill to sheet the Banbury product. A more-or-less continuous strip from the rolls is fed through a metal detector into a four-roll calender. A modification replaces the metal detector with a screw extruder, which screens out contamination and feeds the molten material at a controlled temperature to the calender. Alternatively, a preblend may be fed directly to the calender in some cases. In the next stage the film passes through three successive nips which further mix it and reduce it to a prescribed gauge. Transfer from one roll to the next is accomplished by some combination of temperature differential, speed differential, and surface-finish differential. The film is then stripped by a smaller, higher-speed roll which can be used to stretch the sheet and give further thickness reduction. The surface finish of the sheet may be controlled by the finish on the rolls preceding the stripper, or an embosser may be added to the train following the stripper, after which the sheet passes over cooling drums which cool it rapidly without further straining.

In this chapter we shall point out how the properties of the thermoplastic materials should be considered in the design of the calender. The emphasis is placed on the problem of relating flow properties to pressure between the rolls and the effect on sheet profile control. Methods of compensating for the deflection of the rolls under pressure will be taken up at some length, and other mechanical design features will be touched upon.

Figure 6.2 illustrates conditions of flow existing in the region of the nip of a pair of calendering rolls. It is assumed that the material is incompressible and that it sticks to one roll as it approaches and leaves the area of elevated pressure.

The width of the sheet changes at each nip in inverse proportion to the decrease in thickness. It is assumed, further, that the rolls are traveling at equal speed, and that the increase in width occurs before the material reached the point of peak pressure h_1. At point h_1 the derivative of pressure with respect to X is zero, so that the forces are balanced in the X direction, and there is no acceleration at this point. Similarly, there is no acceleration at point h_2. Between these two points the material accelerates and decelerates, its average velocity being inversely proportional to h. Under these conditions h_1 must be equal to h_2. If the material were compressible, h_1 would be less than h_2. Even under conditions of incompressibility, and regardless of whether the deformation in shear is elastic or not,

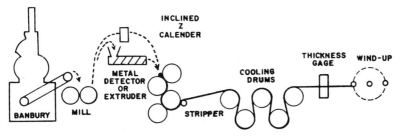

FIG. 6.1. Parts of calender layout for plastic film production.

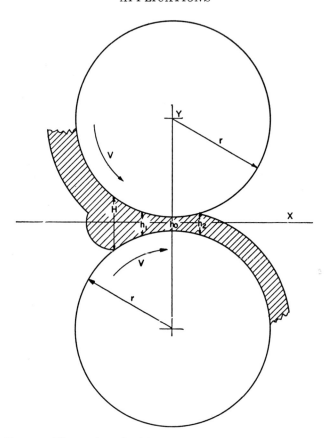

Fɪɢ. 6.2. Illustration of rolling process and coordinate system.

it is clear that the thickness h_2 must be greater than the nip h_0. At h_0 the surfaces of the material touching the rolls move with the speed of the rolls, while the material at the X-axis actually moves through the nip at a greater velocity. This increase in thickness will be determined by the flow characteristics and compressibility of the material, but not by elasticity in shear.

DESIGN PROBLEMS IN THE CALENDERING UNIT

One of the first problems that arose when rubber calenders were introduced into the plastics industry was that of maintaining uniform temperature across the face of the rolls. To improve this situation the drilled roll was developed to replace the former hollow-core type. Figure 6.3 shows details of the two types of rolls. The drilled roll increased the effective width of the hot part of the roll by reducing the separation between hot water and roll surface. Further improvement in surface-temperature uniformity was obtained by circulating hot oil, at controlled temperature, through the bearings.

It has recently been shown by Bergen[4] that rolls may be drilled even closer to the surface than has been customary, without causing serious localized stresses. Therefore, further improvements in heat transfer are possible, giving more uniform surface temperatures and more effective heating or cooling.

Another problem that appeared in calenders of the three-roll type or inverted-L four-roll type, where three rolls were mounted in-line, was that of stabilizing the rolls. Until recently, sleeve bearings were invariably used, which, for proper lubrication, required appreciable clearance. This permitted the rolls to move when the load fluctuated. The instability was particularly serious with the center roll, which had roughly equal loads on each side. Three developments have helped to overcome this instability. Preloading, also called "pullback" and "zero clearance," employs a loading mechanism to pull the roll against one side of its bearing. The tapered roller bearing was another development which permitted tight bearing settings without harming lubrication. Thirdly, the Z arrangement of the rolls was developed as a means of isolating the separating forces and reducing the tendency toward instability.

Gauge control is the exacting requirement of modern calendering. Variations in the contour across the sheet and variations along the sheet caused by instability of the roll in its bearing or by eccentricity of the roll with respect to its bearing shaft must be controlled within narrow limits. Various methods have been devised for controlling the crown in the sheet caused by the flexure of the rolls as a result of pressure developed in the nip. The determination of this pressure and the methods of compensating for the flexure of the rolls will be discussed in detail later in this chapter. The

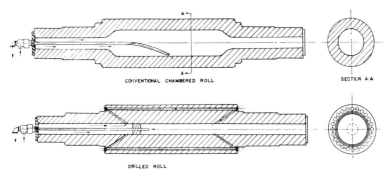

CONVENTIONAL CHAMBERED ROLL   SECTION A-A

DRILLED ROLL

Fig. 6.3. Cross sections comparing the old and new methods of controlling surface temperature. (Drawing by Adamson United Co.)

various dimensional factors must be collectively capable of holding the film gauge within 0.0001 in. if acceptable thin film is to be produced.

Other important design problems arise in connection with the stretching and cooling of the sheet. Any stretching necessary should be done while the sheet is in a hot state. If the cooled sheet were stretched, excess shrinkage would result after the film was unwound from the roll. It is generally more practical to freeze in the strains put in by the stripper than to anneal them, because temperatures higher than stretching temperatures are required to anneal all strains from the vinyl chlorides. High-temperature strains can be frozen in to give a stable sheet, whereas low-temperature strains cannot and should therefore be avoided.

MEASUREMENT OF PRESSURE AND ROLL-SEPARATING FORCE

Squeezing of material between the rolls develops pressure which bends or deflects the rolls and affects the profile of the sheet being formed. Prediction of the roll-separating forces to be expected is an important aid to the design of a calender for profile control. Furthermore, the prediction methods are useful for predicting what range of materials can be processed on an existing calender. The following section describes measurement and calculation of separating forces and applications of results.

Experimental Measurements

Several methods have been reported for directly measuring the pressure or force separating a pair of rolls. These have given results which have helped to test the equations, making it possible to set up calculation procedures. The methods of measurement are described below.

Pressure-Sensitive Insert in Rolls. The technique for measuring the distribution of pressure as the material moves through the nip of the rolls was developed by Bergen and Scott.[5] A pressure-sensitive device inserted into the roll body contained a resistance-wire strain gauge to transform force into an electrical signal which was recorded on a strip chart. The pressure profiles thus obtained were compared with those computed by several equations. Figure 6.4 shows the results of comparing measured with computed pressure profiles. Since viscosity was unknown, in order to calculate the pressure profile it was necessary to normalize the equations by an empirical method. This was done, in the case of the Ardichvili equation, by setting the peak pressure equal to the measured value, and, in the case of the Gaskell equation, by setting the pressure at the nip equal to the corresponding measured pressure value.

The measured pressure profiles can be integrated by measuring the areas under the curves, thus yielding values for separating force. With the method

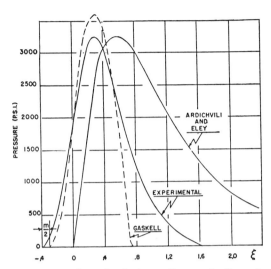

6.4. Pressure distribution for calendering a thermoplastic resin, compared with solutions of several equations. (After Bergen and Scott[5])

of normalization used, the separating-force results were similar for the different profiles illustrated in Fig. 6.4. No direct comparison of the accuracy of these equations for predicting absolute pressure values could be made in this case because of the absence of independent apparent viscosity values.

Measurement of the Strain on Take-Up Screws. Direct measurement of the force tending to separate a pair of rolls is obtained by measuring the load on the bearings. Results have been reported based on Carey's method, which uses resistance-wire strain gauges on the take-up screws of a two-roll mill.[6] This method has permitted the measurement of force values, which can be used in several ways. A comparison may be made of separating-force values from different plastics, for example. These force values may then be used to obtain an apparent viscosity value, or to scale up or down to other roll sizes when suitable formulas are to be found. Formulas for these calculations will be discussed in sections to follow.

Hydraulic Loading Mechanisms. Recently, calenders have been fitted with hydraulic mechanisms for adjustment of the positions of the rolls. These mechanisms, also called gauging devices, can work in either direction, but when they are used directly against the roll separating force, a pressure indicator on the hydraulic system gives a measure of the separating force. This value provides a source of engineering data on full-scale equipment for use in the design of similar equipment. Gooch[11] has reported data on the relation between separating force and sheet thickness for a 28- by 66-in. calender roll measured by this method. The stock was a plasticized polyvinyl chloride compound. The force was found to be described approximately by the relation

$$F = 476{,}000 \, t^{-1.13} \tag{1}$$

where

$F =$ the force in pounds
$t =$ the sheet thickness in thousandths of an inch

This relation, based on measured values between 0.001 and 0.004 in., indicates a very profound influence of sheet thickness on the separating-force value.

CALCULATION OF PRESSURE AND SEPARATING FORCE

The problem of calculating pressure profiles and roll separating forces has been treated by different approaches. One of the earliest of these was that of Ardichvili.[1] Eley[7] treated the problem in a different manner, but he obtained similar equations with different constants. A third treatment in which non-Newtonian flow was considered was that of Atkinson and Nancarrow.[2] Experimental confirmation of their method has not yet appeared. A very realistic analysis in terms of the conditions of flow existing on each side and through the nip was made by Gaskell.[10] Further work by Paslay[13] covered the application of viscoelastic data to the pressure-profile calculation; because elastic constants are not generally available for polymer melts, this work is of little practical use at this time.

Calculation methods with a claimed accuracy of 5 per cent have been worked out for separating force in the cold rolling of steel.[15] In the case of plastics calendering, no comparable accuracy is possible at the present state of progress. Useful semiquantitative results can be obtained, however, and there exist good possibilities for improving the methods in the future.

The Gaskell Equation

Gaskell has considered the hydrodynamic problem in the rolling system assuming Newtonian flow. He has pointed out that the pressure developed by the squeezing of the material past the nip of a pair of rolls actually must carry beyond the nip, regardless of whether the material is elastic or not. He showed that equations can be developed to described flow conditions through the nip, and pointed out that it is feasible to do so for a Bingham body as well as for a Newtonian fluid.

Based on general hydrodynamic equations and several approximating assumptions, the following pressure profile was developed:

$$p = \frac{3\mu V}{2h_0 \delta} \left\{ \left[\frac{-1 + \xi^2 - 5\xi_1^2 - 3\xi_1^2 \xi^2}{(1 + \xi^2)^2} \right] \xi - \left(\frac{1 + 3\xi_1^2}{1 + \xi_1^2} \right) \xi_1 \right. $$

$$\left. + (1 - 3\xi_1^2)(\tan^{-1} \xi + \tan^{-1} \xi_1) \right\} \qquad (2)$$

where ξ, the dimensionless variable describing the distance in the X direction relative to the roll radius and nip opening, is defined by:

$$\xi = x/\sqrt{rh_0}$$

and

$$\delta = \sqrt{h_0/r}$$
μ = viscosity of a Newtonian fluid
h_0 = the roll separation at the nip
r = radius of the rolls
V = velocity of the roll surface

Figure 6.2 contains a graphic representation of these variables. Derivation of Eq. (2) is given in the appendix of this chapter.

Equation (2) is very cumbersome to integrate to a force value and also has other shortcomings arising from simplifying assumptions. While it rationally treats the exit side of the nip, it does not consider the position of the entrance plane, and it does not converge to $p = 0$ for the larger range of possible values for ξ_1. Therefore, the simplified calculation method to be described is considered more useful. With modern computation methods it may be possible to improve the Gaskell treatment of the problem, and the latter may eventually replace the present method.

The Ardichvili Equation

Assuming that $p = 0$ at $X = 0$ (coordinates as in Fig. 6.2), Ardichvili was able to develop a differential equation describing the pressure profile which was easily integrated to yield an analytical expression for the separating force. His treatment may be regarded as a special case of the Gaskell treatment, giving results which differ only slightly from those obtained in the more rigorous case. As before, it is assumed that the two rolls are of equal diameter and are turning at equal speed. The plastic is assumed Newtonian and the process isothermal. It is further assumed that there is no slip on the metal surface, that movement of the material in the Y and Z directions can be neglected, that inertia forces are insignificant, and that there is no eddying.

From basic hydrodynamic equations an expression for the change in p with changes in X was derived. The result is

$$\frac{dp}{dX} = 12\mu V \left(\frac{1}{h^2} - \frac{1}{h^3} \right) \tag{3}$$

This equation can be integrated if dX is expressed in terms of h. From simple geometry it is evident that

$$h = h_0 + 2(r - \sqrt{r^2 - X^2}) \tag{4}$$

On expanding the radical and dropping higher terms, Eq. (4) becomes

$$h \simeq h_0 + X^2/r \tag{5}$$

Solving for X and differentiating, we obtain an expression which may be substituted into Eq. (3). Now Eq. (3) can be solved; however, the analytical solution is very involved. Ardichvili made the further simplifying assumption that

$$h_1 = \tfrac{4}{3} h_0 \tag{6}$$

The expression for p after insertion of Eq. (6) into the integrated form of Eq. (3), was simplified to

$$p = 4\mu V \frac{\sqrt{r(h - h_0)}}{h^2} \tag{7}$$

The total force F is

$$F = w \int_{h_0}^{H} p \, dx \tag{8}$$

where w is the length of roll covered by the sheet.

Equation (8), after substitution therein of Eqs. (7) and (5), can be integrated to

$$F = 2\mu_a V r w \left(\frac{1}{h_0} - \frac{1}{H} \right) \tag{9}$$

Equation (9) yields values for the separating force when an appropriate viscosity value is known, providing a convenient method of calculating separating force based only on operating conditions and viscosity values. When separating-force values have been measured, however, the relation can be solved for μ_a, and the viscosity value so obtained can be used in other calculations involving other roll sizes, roll velocities, and nip openings, within known limits of applicability.

Since plastic materials are non-Newtonian and viscoelastic, the question of selecting the right viscosity value becomes very complex. Common graphs of apparent viscosity vs. shear rate based on capillary-flow measurements and the Poiseuille relation may be used for this purpose. One can also make a correction to take into account the influence of time under shear and end effects.

Calculations Based on the Ardichvili Equation

The methods of estimating viscosity values suitable for use in the Ardichvili equation will now be described. Viscosity may be estimated either from a separation-force measurement and used for scale-up, or it may be estimated from capillary-flow measurements using data provided in the Processing Properties section of this book. In either case it is necessary to determine a shear rate for the calendering operation corresponding to the shear rate in capillary flow to which viscosity is related. A shear-time number is needed, also, for both the calendering operation and the capillary in which viscosity was measured. This number lumps the time-dependent elastic effect and the end effect together to give a general correction factor. It is defined on the basis of residence time in the passage.

Scale-up Calculation of Separating Force. When a separating-force value on a given plastic is known, a viscosity value may be computed directly from Eq. (9). This method of obtaining viscosity avoids some of the uncertainty of estimating it directly from capillary-flow data on the same or a similar material. The scale-up procedure, however, requires that the viscosity be adjusted from the shear rate in the measuring rolls to that in the operation of the rolls being designed.

Dexter and Marshall[6] derived the expression for apparent shear rate based on the Ardichvili treatment corresponding to apparent shear rate in capillary flow. This rate has its maximum at the roll surface at the point of the nip.

The expression is

$$\text{Apparent shear rate} = \frac{2V}{h_0} \tag{10}$$

After computing a viscosity value from Eq. (9) and two shear-rate values from Eq. (10), one may refer to the viscosity–shear-rate graphs in the Processing Properties section to find a plastic similar to the one being considered. On selecting the curve having the viscosity nearest that measured in the rolls, a line may be drawn parallel to this curve and describing the viscosity–shear-rate relation for the sample under study (see Fig. 6.6). From this line and the second shear-rate value, the viscosity for the second rolling condition is located. The temperature correction may then be made if the two rolling operations were not performed at the same temperature. This correction is made on the basis of known plots of viscosity vs. shear rate at several temperatures. Finally, it is necessary to make an adjustment for the time under shear and the end effect.

The time under shear and the end effect can be combined into a single adjustment factor which Bagley[3] has called an end correction. This factor can be regarded as being caused by time effects with the same results. Based on the time under shear, the correction for the rolling process is approximated as the time required to pass from point h_1 through the nip to point h_2. The surface velocity of the rolls is taken as an approximation for the rate of transfer through this region. From these approximations and Eq. (6), an expression is derived.

$$t_s = \frac{2X_1}{V} \tag{11}$$

where X_1 represents the distance from h_0 to h_1. On the basis of Eqs. (6) and (5), X_1 may be put in terms of r and h_0. Then Eq. (11) becomes

$$t_s = \frac{2}{V} \sqrt{rh_0/3} \tag{12}$$

On combining Eqs. (10) and (12), the time under shear reduces to

$$t_s = \frac{2.31}{\gamma} \sqrt{r/h_0} \tag{13}$$

where γ is the apparent shear rate.

It is evident from Eq. (13) that the time under shear is a function of the shear rate and a dimensionless number. Since apparent viscosity has already been related to shear rate, the effect of shear time at constant shear rate may be included by relating a correction factor to the dimensionless

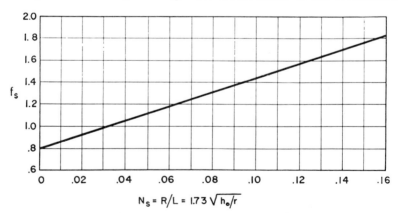

FIG. 6.5. Plot of shear-time adjustment factor, f_s vs. shear-time number, N_s, for adjusting viscosity to new N_s. Standard $N_s = 0.0312$.

number $2.31\sqrt{r/h_0}$. It is convenient, however, to obtain a linear relationship between the apparent viscosity and the shear-time number. This can be done by using the reciprocal of the above quantity. It is a further convenience to multiply this value by 4, making it equivalent to the ratio R/L for circular capillaries. On the basis of a most typical R/L value, one can conveniently choose a standard shear-time number and relate viscosity at other values of this number to the viscosity at this standard value. The relationship then becomes

$$f_s = a + bN_s \tag{14}$$

where

f_s = the adjustment factor for adjusting from standard N_s (0.0312) to any N_s value

a, b = constants ($a = 0.8$, $b = 6.4$)

N_s = shear-time number

$$\left(N_s = \frac{R}{L} = 1.73\sqrt{\frac{h_0}{r}}\right)$$

The constants of Eq. (14) have been determined from data at high shear rates reported by Bagley[3] and by Dexter and Marshall.[6] The standard condition has been chosen at $R/L = 0.0312$, because this is a common ratio used in capillary viscometry. For convenience in calculating, Eq. (14) has been plotted in Fig. 6.5.

Example 1:

A 30 per cent plasticized vinyl compound is rolled on an 8-in.-diameter mill producing a sheet 15 in. wide. The temperature is 170°C, the roll speed is 50 ft/min, and the sheet thickness is 0.016 in. The bank is 0.5 in. wide, and the separating force is 6,000 lb. What separating force would be expected for a 32-in.-diameter calender making 0.006 in. sheet in a width of 90 in., at a speed of 100 ft/min and at 170°C?

Solution: It is necessary first to estimate the viscosity using Eq. (9). The quantities needed are

$$h_0 = \tfrac{3}{4}\, h_2 = 0.012 \text{ in.}$$

$1/H$ may be dropped since it is only 2.4 per cent of $1/h_0$

$$V = \frac{(50)(12)}{(60)} = 10 \text{ in/sec}$$

$$r = 4 \text{ in.}$$
$$w = 15 \text{ in.}$$
$$F = 6{,}000 \text{ lb}$$

Substitution into Eq. (9) gives $\mu_a = 0.06$ lb sec/sq in. for the two-roll milling process. To convert this to the appropriate viscosity for the calender-

TABLE 6.1. DATA FOR DEFINING VISCOSITY VALUES

Roll Size	Apparent shear rate $\frac{2V}{h_0}$, sec^{-1}	Shear-time number $N_s = 1.73 \sqrt{h_0/r}$
8-in. mill	1,670	0.095
32-in. calender	8,900	0.0292

ing process, the two shear-rate values and the values for shear-time number are needed. These are computed as described in a previous section. The results are given in Table 6.1.

From data on viscosity *vs.* shear rate, we estimate, as described above, that the increase in shear rate to 8,900 sec^{-1} will reduce the viscosity from 0.06 lb sec/sq in. to 0.0185, as shown graphically in Fig. 6.6. Similarly, by use of Fig. 6.5, it is found that the decrease in N_s will lower the viscosity further, by a factor of 0.99/1.41. Using this new viscosity value of 0.0130, the separating force for the calender is calculated to be 166,000 lb.

Calculation Based on Extrusion Plastometer Flow Data. The separating force for a calendering operation may be calculated from extrusion plastometer capillary-flow data obtained from the same or a very similar compound. In this case one estimates the apparent viscosity for the rolling operation by computing the shear rate and the shear-time number for the calendering process. The viscosity value applicable to these conditions is obtained from the flow charts.

Example 2:

Find the separating force for the calendering operation in Example I without the aid of the separating-force value from the smaller mill.

Solution: Determine the shear rate and the shear-time number as above. From capillary-flow charts, find the viscosity value for the plasticized vinyl compound at 170°C and at the computed shear rate. Use Fig. 6.5 to adjust from $N_s = 0.0312$ to $N_s = 0.0292$. The viscosity is 0.0134 at 8,900 sec^{-1}, and corrected for N_s it becomes 0.0133. This value is then used in Eq. (9) to yield a separating force of 163,000 lb.

Comparisons of Calculated and Measured Separating-Force Values. Separating-force values measured on an 8-in. by 16-in. mill with the strain-gauge method and on a larger calender with the hydraulic gauging device are given in Table 6.2. The values listed as measured for the 28-in. by 66-in. calender actually were obtained with Eq. (1). This relation was obtained from measurements while calendering a commercial polyvinyl chloride compound in the low-thickness range. The computed column lists results obtained by the method based on Eq. (9).

The calculation predicts the separating-force value to a useful degree of accuracy in many cases, particularly where only relative levels of separating force are required. As indicated by the data in the table, the accuracy is good except in the case of one value at 0.001 in. thickness, where Eq. (9)

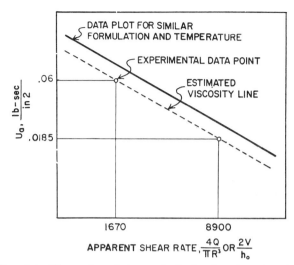

Fig. 6.6. Illustration of the method of estimating viscosity.

and Eq. (1) are at variance. Equation (9) indicates separating force to change with the negative first power of nip opening, all other factors being constant. Equation (2) reveals a measured negative 1.13 power. But with the non-Newtonian viscosity, a negative power less than 1 is expected. The observed negative 1.13 power may indicate that the material is nearly Newtonian at the shear rate encountered, or possibly that an important temperature effect has been neglected. The apparent shear rate in this case is in the range of 40,000 sec^{-1}, which is an unexplored region of shear rate, requiring large extrapolations to obtain viscosity values. At these shear rates, there is uncertainty also in estimating the average temperature. Further, the bank size tapers from a maximum at the center to zero at the edge of the sheet in calendering, whereas the calculation has assumed a constant bank size. It is clear that there is room for improvement in methods of obtaining apparent viscosity values and in methods of calculating the separating-force values. Further experimental studies are needed also for verification of future computation methods.

Applications of Separating-Force Values. Obviously, calculated or measured separating-force values would be helpful in the design of a calendering unit requiring close gauge and contour control. With knowledge of the range of materials to be calendered in a given installation and the approximate flexural modulus of the roll, the amount of crown and the required range of crossing and/or bending can be predicted. While the detailed crown contour cannot be obtained, certain conclusions can be drawn, such as an estimation of the smallest acceptable roll diameter that will avoid excessive crown adjustment.

TABLE 6.2. MEASURED AND COMPUTED SEPARATING FORCE

Plastic material	Per cent plasticizer	Thicknesss, thou- sandths	t, °C	Roll size, inches	Load in pounds Measured	Computed
Polyvinyl chloride with dioctyl	30	20	170	8 × 16	5,250	5,450
phthalate	36	20	170	8 × 16	4,050	3,800
Polyethylene	—	20	130	8 × 16	6,120	5,900
Phenolic novolac	—	20	125	8 × 16	11,600	13,900
Commercial polyvinyl chloride	~32	4	~170	28 × 66	100,000	106,000
Commercial polyvinyl chloride	~32	1	~170	28 × 66	476,000	146,000

Separating force values can also be applied to existing units. If a new material is to be processed or if a present material must be processed at thinner levels or at greater speeds, separating-force calculations give estimates of required crown settings. If limitations in the machine are known, the calculated values can warn of the danger of overloading equipment at some point. The decision can be made whether thinner sheets rolled at greater speeds, or sheet stretching should be used. The decision may be that a more easily processed compound is needed, in which case the separating-force calculation helps to estimate the amount of plasticizing or the reduction in molecular weight required. Considerable savings can be expected over trial-and-error procedures in many cases.

METHODS OF ADJUSTING SHEET PROFILE

The pressure that forces rolls apart applies stresses to rolls, bearings, and frame which can be easily taken into account in the design of the machine. The effect of the flexed roll on sheet contour, however, must be compenpensated by elaborate means when close gauge tolerances are required. To compensate for this roll deflection and make possible the production of flat or controlled profile sheets, it is necessary to provide flexibility in profile adjustment. There are numerous ways of compensating, the usual ones being roll crown, roll crossing, and roll bending. If the nature of the load deflection of a roll is known, it should be possible, by some combination of these methods, to design a calender that will produce a perfectly flat sheet. Such a machine would be good only for one product, however, making it impractical for general-purpose installations. Because adjustment methods are imperfect, some accuracy must be sacrificed for the sake of flexibility.

The Deflection of Calender Rolls

The load on a calender roll should cause a deflection which is predictable from the equations for bending of structural members. In practice this becomes difficult, because the roll is not uniformly loaded, nor is it of uniform cross section. Ardichvili[1] has treated in some detail the problem considering the distribution of moments of area over the different sections.

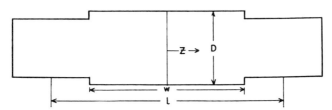

FIG. 6.7a. Symbols for deflection and bending equations.

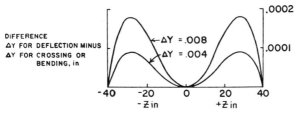

FIG. 6.7b. Computed ox-bow contour for compensation of the above roll by crossing or bending.

For our purposes, however, it should suffice to approximate the total deflection in order to predict the amount of crown to be used and the amount of flexibility that one should add by means of crossing or bending.

Based on the assumption of uniform loading and cross section, Seanor[14] has reported an equation for the total deflection of a roll over its width w. The symbols used are defined in Fig. 6.7a. The relation is

$$\Delta y_1 = \frac{(12l - 7w)f}{384EI_x} \tag{15}$$

Δy_1 = the change in roll separation caused by the deflection
l = length between bearings
f = load per unit of width
E = modulus of rigidity
I_x = second moment of area

The distribution of this deflection over the width of the roll is given by

$$\Delta y = \Delta y_1 \frac{8(6wlZ^2 - 3w^2Z^2 - 2Z^4)}{(12l - 7w)w^3} \tag{16}$$

In the design of equipment it is necessary to incorporate facilities for accurately compensating such a deflection.

Roll Crown

The most common method of compensating for roll flexure has been the practice of using crowned rolls. On a crowned roll, the roll diameter in the center of the roll is slightly greater than at the edges. The use of crowned rolls permits the exact compensation of any given deflection but has the disadvantage of lack of flexibility. It was a practice in the rubber industry to produce a crown on rolls by applying a coating of water glass, which was renewed when a change in the crown was needed. The common practice in the newer plastics industry has been to use rolls manufactured with a fixed crown and to manipulate operating conditions when adjustments are needed. Since viscosity, nip opening, and roll speed all enter into the load expression, any method of adjusting one of these provides flexibility in the amount of deflection.

If it is desired to increase the load on the rolls, an increase in speed, a decrease in temperature, or a decrease in plasticizer content may help. These may also be used in reverse to decrease the roll load. A fourth method of decreasing load is to use a larger nip opening and to stretch the sheet to obtain the desired thickness. Local heating by infrared lamps has also been tried.

Obviously, some of the above methods would appreciably alter production rates, and there would be various limitations on their use. In fact, the adjustments that can be made by these methods are seldom adequate. The result is that other methods of obtaining flexibility in contour correction have been developed.

Roll Crossing and Roll Bending

Roll crossing or roll skewing are names applied to the practice of slightly rotating the axis of one roll in the x-z plane. This increases the nip opening at the ends of the rolls relative to that at the center, giving the effect of increasing the roll crown. Roll bending is the technique of applying a bending moment at each end of a roll which subtracts from, or adds to, the deflection arising from the separating force. Bending is accomplished with a second bearing on each roll neck loaded with a hydraulic cylinder. The method of roll crossing was developed in Europe and introduced into this country following World War II. It has been widely used in modern installations. The bending method has been developed more recently.

According to the idealized equations these two methods give virtually identical results which nearly cancel the load-deflection contour. If the adjustment gets large, the difference between the adjustment and the deflection becomes significant. Therefore, it is usually necessary to put a crown on the rolls and to supplement the crown by the adjustment feature.

Gooch[11] has reported the equation for the change in contour resulting from a given amount of crossing. The exact equation for the increase in clearance Δy, when the axis of one roll is skewed with respect to the other axis by moving each end of the roll an amount C_1, is

$$\Delta y = \sqrt{C_1^2 \left(\frac{2Z}{w}\right)^2 + D^2} - D \qquad (17)$$

where

$$D = \text{diameter of the roll}$$

For a given correction Δy_1 at the end of the roll, the correction contour described by Eq. (17) can be approximated with insignificant error by the relation

$$\Delta y = \Delta y_1 \left(\frac{2Z}{w}\right)^2 \qquad (18)$$

For the case of roll bending, consider a bending moment M applied at each end of a roll. The equation for the deflection due to these bending moments is given by Seanor.[14] The deflection of the ends of the roll with respect to the center is

$$\Delta y_1 = \frac{Mw^2}{8EI_x} \qquad (19)$$

This deflection will be distributed along the roll in the identical manner described by Eq. (18). For the ideal roll, therefore, the two methods give the same correction contour.

If the correction by bending or crossing is large, then significant differences between the contour correction, as given by Eq. (18), and the load deflection, as given by Eq. (16), will be encountered. This difference results in a sheet contour known as an oxbow, which is illustrated in Fig. 6.7b.

Consider a roll 80 in. long deflected by uniform loading and bent or crossed to make the clearance at the center again equal to that at the edge. The net result is shown on the plot for 0.004 in. and 0.008 in. total deflection. The difference between the load deflection, as computed by Eq. (16), and the bending or crossing deflection, as computed by Eq. (18), was 0.00018 in. This is a serious gauge nonuniformity in terms of very thin films, and it illustrates that bending or crossing must be kept at a low level.

The actual contour of a sheet will not be identical to that in Fig. 6.7b, because we are not dealing with an ideal roll; neither is it uniformly loaded, nor is the value for the second moment of area in the deflection relationships explicitly known. The bending contour will differ from the crossing contour because of this, but only more experience will reveal whether one gives a significantly better contour than the other. A pertinent point is the fact that bending can either increase or decrease contour correction, so that smaller adjustments from the average crown are needed when bending is used in both directions, in place of crossing which is restricted to one direction. However, the oxbow contour can be compensated by proper roll contouring, which diminishes the oxbow problem with roll crossing, and either device is suitable for installations in which a wide range of materials is processed.

Bending increases or decreases bearing loads, however, and may be limited in some cases by this consideration. Large bending forces may tend to overload bearings, or, if the bending load opposes the separating force, it is limited to the separating-force value. The latter fact would be serious, particularly in the case of sleeve bearings where motion is permitted by the clearance if the bending load approached the separating force. The practical limit in most cases would be 0.002 or 0.003 in. of bending. The roll-bending feature is relatively simple to install on existing calenders. Recently, a new device for crossing the rolls on existing calenders has been developed, in which changes are made in the connecting gears and bearings without

(*Courtesy Adamson United Co.*)

Fig. 6.8. Inverted-L calender with hydraulic cylinder for bending mounted on neck of bottom roll.

changing the rolls or frames.[12] These provide convenient means for improving the useful range of units having no provision for adjustment.

Figure 6.8 shows an inverted-L calender with both roll crossing and roll bending. The cylinder for bending the bottom roll is readily visible under the roll neck.

FURTHER BASIC CONSIDERATIONS

Stock Temperature

The temperature of the material during its travel between calendering rolls is of great importance for several reasons: (1) The operating conditions for obtaining a smooth sheet may be very sensitive to temperature. (2) Estimating bending loads requires knowledge of the viscosity, which is sensitive to temperature. (3) Some plastics, such as those containing vinyl chloride resin, tend to suffer thermal decomposition. (4) It has been shown that excessive temperature rise within the sheet owing to mechanical working may encourage the formation of blisters in the product.[9] It is important therefore, to know temperatures and also residence times. The temperature problem in calendering, however, is a difficult one, and practical working solutions of proved accuracy have not yet been worked out.

The mean temperature of the material at a given position on the X-axis is often considerably higher than the temperature of the rolls. One can readily show this by a heat balance or by measurement in the bank with a needle pyrometer. A calculation based on a power value gives an indication of energy available, but this will not show the temperature rise because the thin sheet permits rapid conduction to the roll. Relations for heat build-up and the temperature profile in the Y direction have been derived by Eley[8] and by Finston;[9] however, no experience with their use in engineering of calenders has been reported. The methods of estimating viscosity and shear rate described in this chapter cannot be recommended for calculation of heat build-up because heat calculations require more accurate information than is required for pressure calculations.

It is feasible to use the equations for nonsteady-state heat flow to estimate the temperature in a sheet in contact with a roll surface of a different temperature. It can thus be determined how long a sheet remains in contact with a calender roll before approaching the roll temperature. The calculation methods also would be of value in the design of cooling trains, where the cooling rate must be controlled and the amount of drum surface required to accomplish a given amount of cooling must be determined.

Torque and Horsepower

The torque required to rotate a roll against the material is the integral of the product of shear stress times roll radius over the entire area of contact of the material on the roll. No actual applications of this torque value have been reported, but it can be performed based on Gaskell's treatment of the hydrodynamic problem (see Appendix). The horsepower, also, could be estimated as the product of torque and angular velocity. The accuracy of these predictions is not known, and designs are usually based on experience with similar installations.

STEPS IN THE DESIGN OF A CALENDERING LAYOUT

In setting out to design a calendering layout, the following are some important questions to be faced:
(1) Range of materials to be processed and thickness range required
(2) Maximum width required
(3) Required production rates
(4) Separating forces to be expected
(5) Operating-temperature ranges
(6) Power requirements
(7) The amount of cooling train needed

Usually, a wide versatility in thickness range and materials is required. Particularly, the calendering of thin films demands good stability and rigidity of rolls, as well as accurate roll crown and good contour adjustment. Roller bearings may be preferred for zero clearance settings and accurate crown grinding. Crossing, bending, or both will be required, the amount to be estimated from expected separating-force and deflection values.

In considering separating force for the case of vertically stacked rolls, the weight of the roll must be considered. An average roll-crown value is 0.0065 in., and 0.010 in. by crossing is often allowed. In order to keep oxbow sheet contours at a minimum, the range of roll-crown adjustment should be small. This condition may be satisfied by the use of large roll diameters. The largest diameter consistent with sound economics will provide the most satisfactory operation.

Operating temperatures and power requirements are estimated from experience with similar installations. It is good practice to use a small stripping roll which can be mounted close to the take-off roll. The reason for this is that the shortest stretch distance gives the highest strain rate for a given speed differential, thus permitting higher stripping forces at lower stretch levels. Cooling requirements are controlled by the thickest sheets to be made.

A four-roll unit is preferred over three rolls for plastics because of increased working in the extra nip. The Z arrangement has the advantage of isolated separating forces. In this arrangement the fourth roll can be

(Courtesy Farrell Birmingham Co.)
FIG. 6.9. Inclined-Z calender with individually driven rolls.

crossed, or bending moments can be applied to the third and fourth rolls. Figure 6.9 shows a new type of Z arrangement which is set on an incline to give greater accessibility to the third roll from which the sheet may be stripped.

The calendering units shown in Figs. 6.8 and 6.9 both have universal joints on the drives. These are necessary for the case where roll crossing is used. The jointed drive shafts also permit separating drive gears from the rolls (unit drive), thus providing important maintenance advantages. Figure 6.9 shows separate drive motors for each roll. This provides a wide range of speed differentials which may be needed to aid mixing and sheet transfer.

APPENDIX

Derivation of the Gaskell Equation

The Gaskell equation Eq. (2) is derived on the basis of the same coordinate system as that shown in Fig. 6.2, with the exception that h_1, h_0, and h_2 are not used. Instead of h, the distance between the surfaces of the two rolls, we use t, the distance from the x-axis to a roll surface. We then let the corresponding values t_0, t_1, t_2, and t represent the same positions on the

x-axis as h_0, h_1, h_2, and h. Further, we use dimensionless variables ξ, η and δ, where

$$\xi = x/\sqrt{2rt_0} = \pm\sqrt{t/t_0 - 1}$$

$$\eta = y/\sqrt{2rt_0}$$

and

$$\delta = \sqrt{2t_0/R} \tag{A1}$$

The assumptions made in this derivation are essentially the same as those mentioned for the Ardichvili derivation, except that we now let the material fill the rolls to the point t_2, whereas Ardichvili had assumed that it pulled away at the point t_0. This is the basic difference between the two derivations.

By the definition of viscosity, the shear stress τ can be expressed as

$$\tau = \mu \frac{dv}{dy} \tag{A2}$$

Further, by basic hydrodynamics, the change in stress with y may be written

$$\frac{d\tau}{dy} = \frac{dp}{dx} \tag{A3}$$

Differentiating Eq. (A2) and combining with Eq. (A3), we have

$$\mu \frac{d^2u}{dy^2} = \frac{dp}{dx} \tag{A4}$$

Two integrations of Eq. (A4) with the conditions $v(t) = v(-t) = V$, give

$$u = V + \frac{1}{2\mu} \frac{dp}{dx} (y^2 - t^2) \tag{A5}$$

The total flow Q is the integral of vdy between the limits $-t$ and $+t$. Integrating from Eq. (A5) and substituting t_1 for $Q/2V$, we have

$$\frac{dp}{dx} = \frac{3\mu V}{t^2} (1 - t_1/t) \tag{A6}$$

We can now substitute Eq. (A6) in Eq. (A5) and obtain the velocity

$$v = \frac{V}{2} \left[\frac{3y^2}{t^2} (1 - t_1/t) - 1 + 3t_1/t \right] \tag{A7}$$

From simple geometry it is seen that

$$y = \pm t = \pm(t_0 + r - \sqrt{r^2 - x^2}) \tag{A8}$$

Expanding the radical and dropping higher terms, we have

$$y = \pm t = \pm (t_0 + x^2/2r) \tag{A9}$$

On the basis of Eq. (A9) and the dimensionless variables ξ and δ, we substitute into Eq. (A6) to obtain

$$\frac{dp}{d\xi} = \frac{6\mu V}{t_0 \delta} \left[\frac{\xi^2 - \xi_1^2}{(1 + \xi^2)^3} \right] \tag{A10}$$

Integration of Eq. (A10) gives

$$p = \frac{3\mu V}{4 t_0 \delta} \left\{ \left[\frac{-1 + \xi^2 - 5\xi_1^2 - 3\xi^2 \xi_1^2}{(1 + \xi^2)^2} \right] \xi + (1 - 3\xi_1^2) \tan^{-1}\xi + C \right\} \tag{A11}$$

We must now evaluate ξ_1 and C. These are obtained from the conditions at the exit. From Eq. (A10), ξ_1 must equal ξ_E when $dp/d\xi = 0$, and this condition exists at the exit where the shear stress has vanished and $v = V$. Also at this point $p = 0$ and, by Eq. (A11), the constant C becomes

$$C = (1 - 3\xi_1^2) \tan^{-1}\xi_1 - (1 + 3\xi_1^2)\xi_1/(1 + \xi_1)^2 \tag{A12}$$

Inserting Eq. (A11) into Eq. (A12), one arrives at Eq. (2).

REFERENCES

1. Ardichvili, G., "An Attempt at a Rational Determination of the Cambering of Calender Rolls," *Kautschuk*, **14**, 23 (1938).
2. Atkinson, E. B., and Nancarrow, H. A., "Rheology and Thermoplastics," *Plastics Inst. (London) Trans.*, **19**, 23 (1951).
3. Bagley, E. B., "End Corrections in the Capillary Flow of Polyethylene," *J. Appl. Phys.*, **28**, 624 (1957).
4. Bergen, J. T., "Analysis of Localized Stresses in Drilled Calender Rolls," *Proc. Soc. Exptl. Stress Anal.*, **IX**, No. 2, p. 13 (1952).
5. Bergen, J. T, and Scott, G. W., "Pressure Distribution in the Calendering of Plastic Materials," *J. Appl. Mechanics*, **18**, 101 (1951).
6. Dexter, F. D., and Marshall, D. I., "Calculation of Roll Separating Forces in Calendering and Milling of Plastics," *SPE Journal*, **12**, 17 (*Apr.* 1956).
7. Eley, D. D., "Theory of Rolling Plastics, I Calculation of Roll Pressure," *J. Polymer Sci.*, **1**, 529 (1946).
8. Eley, D. D., "Theory of Rolling Plastics, II Thermal Effects," *Ibid*, **1**, 535 (1946).
9. Finston, M., "Thermal Effects in Calendering Viscous Fluids," *J. Appl. Mechanics*, **18**, 12 (1951).
10. Gaskell, R. E., "The Calendering of Plastic Materials," *J. Appl. Mechanics*, **17**, 334 (1950).
11. Gooch, K. J., "Designing Better Calenders," *Modern Plastics*, **34**, 165 (*July* 1957).
12. Gooch, K. J., private communication.
13. Paslay, P. R., "Calendering of a Viscoelastic Material," *J. Appl. Mechanics*, **24**, 602 (1957).
14. Seanor, R. C., "Roll Bending Applied to Rubber and Plastic Calenders," Am. Soc. Mech. Engrs. Paper No. 56-A-176.

15. Whitton, P. W., "Computation of Force and Torque in Cold Rolling by Modern Theory," *J. Appl. Mechanics*, **23,** 307 (1956).

ADDITIONAL READING

1. Brown, Joseph, "Plastics Calendering—Types of Machines and Layouts," Plastics Progress, London, Illiffe & Sons, 1951.
2. Garvin, G. S., Chap. XVI in Schildnecht, C. E. (Ed.), "Polymer Processes," New York, Interscience Publishers, Inc., 1956.
3. Johnson, E. H., Chap. IV in Seaman, R. G., and Merrill, A. M. (Eds.), "Machinery and Equipment for Rubber and Plastics," Vol. I, New York, India Rubber World, 1952.
4. Jukich, M., "Roll Bending—A New Tool for Controlling Gage in Vinyl Calendering," *Modern Plastics*, **33,** 138 (*Aug.* 1956).
5. Kulgren, G. V., "Modern Calender Processing Equipment," *India Rubber World*, **120,** 323 (1949).
6. "Modern Plastics Encyclopedia," recent annual issues Plastics Catalogue Corp., Bristol, Conn.
7. Seanor, R. C., "Calendering Equipment and The Plastics Industry," *Technical Papers*, 12th Annual National Technical Conference, Vol. II, Soc. Plastics Engrs., Greenwich, Conn.
8. Wuest, E. F., "Calendering of Vinyl Sheeting," *Technical Papers*, 12th Annual National Technical Conference, Vol. II, Soc. Plastics Engrs., Greenwich, Conn., 1956.

7. MIXING AND DISPERSING PROCESSES

J. T. Bergen, M. S.

Armstrong Cork Company

INTRODUCTION

General Considerations

In the processing of thermoplastic materials, very frequently it is desired to combine intimately the resin matrix with other ingredients such as colorants, chemicals, plasticizers, fillers, and pigments. The process by which this is accomplished is referred to as mixing, and the desired product of the mixing process is a uniformly blended physical mixture of resin and other ingredients.

The process of mixing developed as an art in the rubber industry, and, as originally applied in plastics processing, was borrowed almost directly from rubber technology. During the past 10 years or so, improvements in technique and changes in machine design have been directed toward the mixing process for thermoplastics specifically. This period also has seen the beginnings of the development of theories fundamental to the mixing process.

Nevertheless, the mixing and dispersion processes—terms to be defined later—remain among the least understood phases of the processing of thermoplastics. The fundamental concepts, as they exist today, are very thoroughly discussed by W. D. Mohr in Chap. 3 of this volume. It is the purpose of this present chapter to consider the major types of plastics mixers in current use—roll mill, internal mixer, and extruder—in the light of these basic concepts. It will become evident to even the casual reader that these mixing and dispersing devices cannot be completely described in fundamental terms; however, it is hoped that the discussion, as far as it can be carried, will contribute to a better understanding of some of the underlying principles, at least, and that the technology of this phase of thermoplastics processing may become a little clearer.

The Mixing Process

As stated in Chap. 3, the object of a mixing process is to alter the original distribution in space of a non-random or segregated mass, and thereby increase the probability of finding a particle of any one component at any particular point, so that an acceptable spatial probability distribution is achieved. Although this definition deals with particles of a component, the concept may be extended to particle concentration occurring within a sample volume suitably small in terms of the total continuum. The problem is that of determining how to deform the initial continuum in order to achieve this desired probability distribution, in the absence of diffusion or other random molecular motions.

The Dispersing Process

An additional complication arises if it is found that the ultimate particles are not independent of one another, but instead exert interparticulate forces leading to agglomerations of particles. Some finite force must be exerted on such agglomerates to allow them to mix. The consideration of these forces, or stresses, constitutes the problem of dispersion processes.

Mixing and Dispersing in Thermoplastics

In mixing and dispersing processes for thermoplastics, the thermoplastic material is considered essentially a fluid, and descriptions of these processes are restricted to this physical state. Furthermore, the flow conditions under which these processes are carried out fall well into the laminar-flow region, far removed from the domain of turbulent flow of fluids. The further restriction of incompressibility of thermoplastics permits deformation of such materials only by means of shear.

Thus the problem of mixing in thermoplastics is that of subjecting such materials to laminar shear deformations in such a manner that an initially non-random distribution of ingredients approaches randomness on some arbitrary scale of comparison. Furthermore, the problem is usually complicated by the fact that the ingredients do exhibit interparticulate forces, so that the stresses accompanying the deformation must be considered, as well as the deformation process itself.

Status of Mixing and Dispersing Theory

In recent years, considerable progress has been made in establishing fundamental concepts of the mixing process,[1, 8, 17, 19, 26] though applications of these concepts have not yet become widespread, except for certain simple types of mixers on an experimental basis, or in the case of the screw extruder.[20]

Considerably less effort has been expended toward fundamental understanding of the dispersion process; a single recent paper attacks this problem directly.[3] A great deal of empirical information exists regarding the mixing and dispersing of solids in rubber and plastics (e.g., Refs 4, 5, 6, 15, 16, 18, 21, 24, 25), although the conclusions drawn from most of this work are restricted to the particular systems studied.

THEORETICAL CONSIDERATIONS

Laminar-Flow Mixing

The general theory of mixing, as discussed by Mohr (Chap. 3), considers an initially non-random or segregated mass of two components, which mass is to be deformed by a laminar or shearing deformation process. The object of this shearing process is to mix the mass in such a way that the statistical variance of some property of a group of samples taken from the mass is minimized, i.e., ultimately tending to zero. The shearing process is generalized, i.e., it is not limited to any particular kind of shearing action or mixing device, but applies to all such devices.

Three principles are given by the general theory of mixing:

(1) The interfacial area between the components must be greatly increased in the mixing process.

(2) Elements of the interface must be distributed uniformly throughout the mass being mixed.

(3) The mixture components must be distributed so that in any (characteristic) volume element the ratio of the components is the same as that of the whole system.

The first and second statements obviously require, for any particular mixing process or device, that the hydrodynamics of flow within the device be described completely. Also, further elaboration of these statements leads to these further conclusions:

(1) The optimum initial orientation of the interface between components should be normal to the flow lines or streamlines within the device.

(2) *All* the streamlines of flow should lead to a region (or regions) of maximum shear.

Finally, the third statement implies that:

(3) The scale of sampling (or "scale of scrutiny" of Danckwerts[8]) must be large in terms of the ultimate particle size.

Within the framework of these criteria, this chapter will consider, in so far as is possible, the flow patterns and shearing characteristics of several widely used mixing devices, in order to evaluate them in terms of the ideal mixing process.

Limitations on the Application of Mixing Theory

Since mixing theory, as it now stands, is generalized, it is desirable to point out some of the limitations which must be recognized in applying these concepts to actual plastic materials and present mixing devices:

(1) The application of the theory is limited to purely viscous (Newtonian) materials because of limitations of present hydrodynamic theories, while actual plastic materials are viscoelastic, plastic, or otherwise non-Newtonian. However, the qualitative concepts which hold for simple viscous bodies are of great value in furthering the understanding of the mixing of real materials.

(2) It is assumed that no van der Waals or other interparticle forces exist.

(3) The initial orientation of the components is assumed to be known. Actually, this is almost never true in practice.

(4) The mixing process is assumed to be isothermal. This assumption is definitely not valid, since the viscosity of most plastic materials is sufficiently high so that the energy dissipation during a mixing process is considerable.

These general limitations make it impossible, for the present, to apply rigorously the conclusions of the theory of intensive mixing to real problems in a quantitative manner. The major gap in this technological application lies in our inability to describe the rheological behavior of the complex plastic materials used in practice. Also, the hydrodynamic flow within actual mixing devices is very complex, and the solution of these problems has been developed for only a few cases.

However, it is well to reiterate that the application of qualitative and semi-quantitative concepts serves to throw considerable light on the process of mixing. In this respect, considerable progress has been made in recent years.

Measurement of the Degree of Mixing

Since any discussion of mixing implies some criterion or measure of the material being mixed, in terms of the degree of mixing, methods for measuring the amount of mixing achieved in a given mass will be reviewed briefly.

A fundamental description of a mixture has been derived by Danckwerts[3] and Lacey.[17] These authors are considered by Mohr in Chap. 3. They describe a mixture in terms of the statistical deviation of a suitable number of samples of the mixture from the mean. However, the size of the samples to be taken depends upon some length, volume, or area which is characteristic of the mixture or its properties. For example, if color is the property (and mixing is accomplished by shearing, not diffusion) and the visual impression of color homogeneity is the measure, the characteristic length is the resolving power of the eye, say 0.001 in. A mixture which is completely mixed by this measure exhibits no color streaks greater than 0.001 in. in thickness. If, however, a spectrophotometer which integrates over, say, a 1-in.-diameter circle were used to measure color uniformity, the streaks could be, say, 0.1 in. thick, and the color value for any given series of samples would appear uniform to the spectrophotometer.

Likewise, the intensity of color difference between streaks would affect the resolving power of the eye—or the spectrophotometer—and, hence, the characteristic length.

The actual means used to measure the degree of mixing achieved are varied. In commercial practice this is usually done by means of visual inspection for color homogeneity, color comparison, and inspection of the mass for specks, streaks, or spots of unmixed filler or resin. This highly subjective criterion has been used to evaluate experimental mixing studies.[15, 16, 24] Changes in physical properties, such as tensile strength, modulus, or density, are frequently used to evaluate the degree of mixing.[24] It is likely that these properties are affected during various mixing processes by such extraneous processes as polymer degradation, thermal effects on the mixture, etc., so that observed changes do not strictly evaluate the mixing process as such.

Some of the more fundamental measures include changes in rheological properties,[19] chemical reactions,[17] and electrical conductivity.[27] The latter measures approach most nearly the idealization of the measurement of the basic criteria of mixing.

The electrostatic charges induced during the mixing of solids into rubber have been reported as a measure of the mixing process.[13]

The only direct measure of a basic criterion of mixing is the "striation thickness" proposed by Mohr (Chap. 3), though this property is measurable at present only under certain conditions, and more work needs to be done to widen its application to mixtures of plastics in general.

Thus there exists no universally accepted standard of performance of the mixing process, nor is there any generally applicable technique for evaluating thoroughness of mixing. For the present, each case must be considered in the light of the nature of the material being mixed, the significant properties to be considered, and the scale of scrutiny to be applied.

CURRENT MACHINES FOR MIXING AND DISPERSING

The machines employed today for mixing and dispersing thermoplastics fall into three categories—roll mills, internal mixers, and extruders.

The roll mill usually is in the form of the two-roll mill. It consists of two parallel rollers, rotating in opposite directions, placed close to one another with the roll axes lying in a horizontal plane, so that a relatively small space or nip between the cylindrical surfaces exists. The thermoplastic material, upon being placed in the nip, is seized by friction forces between itself and the rollers and is caused to deform and flow through the nip, in the direction of roll motion. As will be shown later, the nature of flow within the region of the nip is quite complex. If liquid plasticizers or finely divided solid ingredients are also placed in the nip, the shearing action in the nip causes such ingredients to be incorporated into the resin matrix.

Usually, by adjusting the temperature of the rollers, the resinous material can be caused to adhere to one of the rollers in the form of a relatively thin sheet. For this reason the rollers are hollow cylinders into which a heating or cooling medium may be introduced. The rollers usually are rotated at different speeds to facilitate the formation of a sheet or band upon one of them. During the course of mixing, the band is frequently cut and manually pulled loose from the roller. The gap between the rollers generally may be adjusted manually by means of hand- or motor-driven screws.

Roll mills vary greatly in size, from very small laboratory machines with rollers of about 1 in. in diameter, driven by a fractional-horsepower motor, to very large mills with rollers of nearly 3 ft in diameter and 7 or 8 ft in length, driven by motors upwards of 100 hp. A typical two-roll mill of production size is shown in Fig. 7.1.

Special-purpose roll mills are available with three, four, or five rolls, in which the material is caused to pass from one nip to the next, in succession. Likewise, rollers may be arranged in pairs within a single frame, as many as

(Courtesy of Farrel-Birmingham Corp.)

FIG. 7.1. Two-roll mixing mill.

four pairs of rollers, each independently adjustable in clearance, being employed. The material is led through the various pairs in tandem, providing a cascade arrangement of two-roll mills for continuous mixing.

Internal mixers employ the principle of a cylindrical container, or shell, within which the materials to be mixed are deformed by rotating blades or rotors. In most cases the shell actually consists of two adjacent cylindrical shells with a rotor describing an arc concentric with each section of the shell. The rotor-blade tips clear the cylindrical segment of the shell by a small amount. The motion of the blade thus causes the mixture to be sheared between its tip and the shell. In turn, the blades interact between themselves to cause folding or "shuffling" of the mass in a complex manner. This shuffling is further accentuated by arranging the blade helically along the axis of the rotor, imparting motion to the mass in the third, or axial, direction. Frequently, the blade is divided into two helices of opposite direction of pitch in order to further the shuffling of components within the mixture.

Finally, the shell and rotor are cored or otherwise provided with means for heating or cooling for the purpose of controlling the temperature of the batch.

A very common type of internal mixer is the Banbury (named for its inventor), a cross section of which is shown in Fig. 2. The rotor blades here

(*Courtesy of Farrel-Birmingham Corp.*)

FIG. 7.2. Section of Banbury internal mixer.

are elliptical in cross section, and they rotate, as indicated, within the closed chamber. A pneumatically operated upper ram serves to close the chamber after the batch is introduced. It is this ram which causes the mixture to be confined within the mixer shell, and which greatly facilitates the flow of the mixture between the blade tip and the shell where the most intensive shearing action occurs.

These mixers range in size from laboratory models, with a capacity of about 2 lb of mixture, and powered by about 10 hp, to machines of approximately 100 to 150 lb capacity driven by motors upwards of 100 hp.

In other cases the rotor blades are Z-shaped arms instead of the elliptical design shown in Fig. 7.2, while still further variations are naben and fishtail blades. A more complete description of such mixers is given by Quillen,[21] and exhaustive engineering detail for a large number of internal mixers is contained in a book by Seaman and Merrill.[23]

The thermoplastic mixture discharged from the internal mixer is usually in the form of large shapeless lumps; it is frequently convenient to roll these lumps into sheet form by means of a two-roll mill. For this purpose a mill is placed beneath the internal mixer. Experience has indicated that this mill may also perform additional mixing and dispersing, i.e., the internal mixer and mill function efficiently in a cascade arrangement. See Fig. 7.3.

The internal mixer and the two-roll mill, singly and in combination, account for the majority of installed mixing and dispersing equipment. The third class of mixer, the extruder, though not primarily designed as a mixing device, is finding increasing applications in cases where mixing and extruding may be performed simultaneously. Machines which employ the extrusion-screw principle and which are specifically designed as mixing machines have been available for some time, and improved designs continue to appear. The functioning of the screw extruder is thoroughly covered in Chap. 4.

Two-Roll Mixing Mills

The two-roll mill is the earliest form of thermoplastics mixer in use today, having been employed for more than a century in rubber mixing. Until about 30 years ago, it was the primary intensive mixing device for both rubbers and plastics, when internal and screw-type mixers began to supplant it. Two-roll mills still play an important part in plastics processing. Although primarily a batch-type mixer, the two-roll mill is sometimes used as a continuous mixer in which the stock is fed onto one end of the rollers and withdrawn in a relatively narrow strip from the opposite end.

The problem of describing the shear characteristics of the milling process can be pictured by referring to solutions of the hydrodynamic problem of the calender, which is discussed in the preceding chapter of this book. The pertinent characteristics of the hydrodynamic flow in the mill are then considered in the light of the conclusions following from the general theory of

(Courtesy of Farrel-Birmingham Corp.)
FIG. 7.3. Banbury internal mixer installed on platform over two-roll mill.

mixing. In this manner, advantages and shortcomings of the two-roll mill as an intensive mixer may be considered. The role of geometric and material factors in determining the engineering characteristics of the mixing machines is also discussed.

This analysis presumes the plastic materials to be Newtonian fluids, and even for simple Newtonian fluids this mathematics of the calendering process is quite complex; an analysis of this problem for a material of non-linear flow behavior has not yet been feasible. However, the behavior of various plastic materials in the calendering process has been found to approximate that of a Newtonian fluid.[2] Therefore, the description of the flow of a viscous fluid in the two-roll mill is sufficient as a first approximation to warrant its use.

Flow Streamlines in the Milling Process. The milling process is pictured in Fig. 7.4. The rolls act upon a thin, flowing wedge of the material which is simultaneously compressed and forced to flow through the space

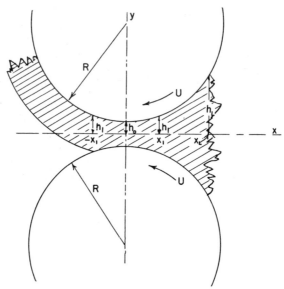

FIG. 7.4. Geometric representation of a two-roll mill.

between the rolls, usually referred to as the "roll nip" or nip. The rolls of radius R, separated by a distance $2h_o$, rotate in opposite directions with a velocity U; the thickness of the wedge is $2h_R$ at entrance and $2h_L$ at exit. The analysis of the hydrodynamics of this process is given by Gaskell,[11] who points out that the streamlines are obtained by integrating the stream function

$$\psi = \int u \, dy \qquad (1)$$

where $\psi = $ constant is a streamline, u is the velocity in the x direction, and finding v, the velocity in the y direction so that the hydrodynamic continuity equation $\partial u/\partial x + \partial v/\partial y = 0$ is satisfied.

We employ Gaskell's dimensionless variables ξ and η, where

$$\xi = x/\sqrt{2Rh_o} = \pm\sqrt{h/h_o - 1} \; ; \qquad \eta = y/\sqrt{2Rh_o} \qquad (2)$$

The velocity in the x direction u is given by

$$u = 3U/2 \left\{ \left[\frac{\xi^2 - \xi_1^2}{(1 + \xi^2)^3} \right] \frac{4\eta^2}{\delta^2} + \frac{2 - \xi^2 + 3\xi_1^2}{3(1 + \xi^2)} \right\} \qquad (3)$$

Here ξ_1 is the value of ξ at the nip exit and δ, a geometric constant, equals $\sqrt{2h_o/R}$.

If Eq. (3) is substituted into Eq. (1), and the indicated integration is

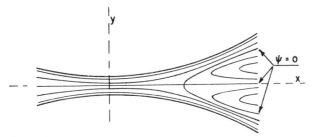

Fɪɢ. 7.5. Streamlines within the nip area of a two-roll mill, for equal roll speeds.

performed, and, with the boundary condition that $\psi = o$ for u, $v = o$, we have

$$\psi = \frac{Uh_o\mu}{\delta}\left[\frac{4\eta^2(\xi^2 - \xi_1^2)}{\delta^2(1 + \xi^2)} + \frac{2 + 3\xi_1^2 - \xi^2}{1 + \xi^2}\right] \tag{4}$$

If Eq. (4) is plotted for a series of values of ξ and η, the streamline flow pattern shown in Fig. 7.5 results. Here the material is seen to flow more or less parallel to the roll surfaces in the region of the roll surfaces, the roll surface itself being a streamline. Toward the center of the upstream region of the wedge, backflow occurs. For the case of a finite wedge, this backflow would take the form of two closed vortexes, as can be observed upon watching the "rolling" nip of a mill with equal-speed rolls.

The material leaving the nip adheres to either roll, is carried around the roll, and contacts the vortex portion of the wedge to pass through the nip again just as it had before.

The velocity distribution, Fig. 7.6, is obtained by plotting Eq. (3) for a series of values of ξ [where ξ_1 is determined from $\xi_1 = \sqrt{Q/2h_oU - 1}$ for a typical value of Q, in Eq. (3)]. The backflow is evident, and, upstream from a point ξ_1, the center of the wedge follows the material near the roll surfaces. Beyond ξ_1 the center begins to lead the material near the roll surfaces, but at $-\xi_1$ the velocity becomes uniform again, and the milling process is completed.

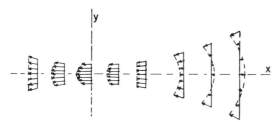

Fɪɢ. 7.6. Velocity profiles within the nip area of a two-roll mill, for equal roll speeds.

Figure 7.6 enables one to visualize how the material is sheared in passing through the roll nip.

The shearing stress is given by

$$\tau = y\, dp/dx = \frac{6\mu U}{\delta h_o}\, \eta \left[\frac{\xi^2 - \xi_1^2}{(1 + \xi^2)^3} \right] \tag{5}$$

where μ is the viscosity of the material. Thus the shear stress is zero for $\eta(y) = 0$, and it increases linearly to a maximum value at the roll-surface boundary. Figure 7.7 illustrates the distribution of maximum shearing stress in the nip.

Symmetrical Two-Roll Milling as a Mixing Process. The description of some of the features of the hydrodynamics of the symmetrical two-roll mill may now be used to consider the milling process in the light of the ideal mixing process.

(1) The interfacial area is increased in milling very slowly for part of the material. In Fig. 2 the streamlines $\psi = 0$ form a closed system which passes through regions of very small velocity gradient in the region of backflow. Beyond the stagnation point the velocity gradient is always zero for $\psi = 0$. Thus, for this ideal symmetric case, certain interfacial areas will be increased very slowly compared to those lying on streamlines passing through regions of large velocity gradient.

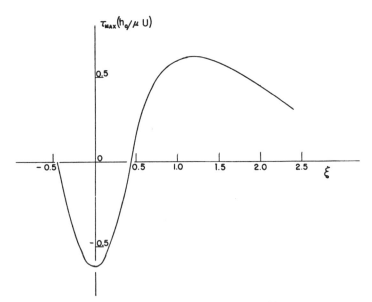

FIG. 7.7. Distribution of maximum shearing stress within nip area of a two-roll mill, for equal roll speeds.

(2) Elements of the interfacial area will not be distributed throughout the mass; once an interface becomes oriented along a streamline, it will continue along that line, since no flow across streamlines is possible.

(3) The distribution of volume elements throughout the mass will not be uniform, because of the closed streamlines and because of the absence of any appreciable flow in the Z or axial direction. Even if we presume that the components are distributed perfectly uniformly along the axis of the rolls, the former condition will cause the mixture always to include undistributed interfaces.

Thus, taken by itself, the symmetrical milling process is not a particularly good mixing process, since it would never result in satisfactory mixing.

Nonsymmetrical Two-Roll Milling as a Mixing Process. In the preceding discussion the two-roll mill was considered completely to be symmetrical; the velocity and temperature were the same for each roll, and the material was allowed to flow in an undisturbed manner.

In practice, however, the roll velocity and temperature are purposely made different, ostensibly as a means for improving the mixing action of the mill.

For the case of unequal roll speeds U_1 and U_2, the same analysis used by Gaskell is followed, with the exception that the double integration of Eq. (3) in that paper is performed between the limits $u(h) = U_1 > u(-h) = U_2$, so that we obtain

$$u = \frac{3U_o}{2}\left[\frac{\xi^2 - \xi_1^2}{(1 + \xi^2)^3}\frac{4\eta^2}{\delta^2} + \frac{2 - \xi^2 + 3\xi_1^2}{3(1 + \xi^2)} + \frac{4\lambda\eta}{3\delta(1 + \xi^2)}\right] \qquad (6)$$

where

$$U_o = (U_1 + U_2)/2; \qquad \lambda = \frac{U_1 - U_2}{2U_o}$$

In deriving this equation it is again assumed that $Q = 2U_oh_1$, so that

$$\frac{dp}{dx} = 3\mu U_o(h - h_1)/h^3$$

The shearing stress now becomes

$$\tau = \int y\frac{dp}{dx} = \frac{6\mu U_o}{\delta h_o}\left[\frac{\eta(\xi^2 - \xi_1^2)}{(1 + \xi^2)^3} + \frac{\lambda\delta}{6(1 + \xi^2)}\right] \qquad (7)$$

If Eqs. (6) and (7) are compared with their symmetric counterparts, Eqs. (3) and (5) respectively, it will be seen that an additional term appears on the right for each of the unsymmetric equations. These terms serve to "warp" the symmetric stress distribution and velocity profile, as

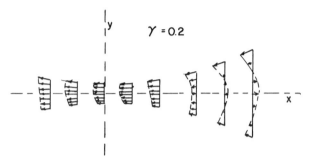

FIG. 7.8. Streamlines within the nip area of a two-roll mill, for unequal speeds. The ratio of roll speeds is 1.22:1.

illustrated in Fig. 7.8. The stream function, derived exactly as for the symmetric case, is now

$$\psi = \frac{U_o h_o \eta}{\delta} \left[\frac{4\eta^2(\xi^2 - \xi_1^2)}{\delta^2(1 + \xi^2)^3} + \frac{2 + 3\xi_1^2 - \xi^2}{1 + \xi^2} + \frac{2\lambda\eta}{3\delta(1 + \xi^2)} \right] \qquad (8)$$

It is seen that one streamline $\psi = 0$ still lies along $\eta = 0$, with the backflow being "crowded" toward the slower roll.

Most important is the conclusion that now the streamlines all lead through regions of finite shear deformation beyond the stagnation point, which will result in increased shear deformation as compared to the symmetric case. Thus there is theoretical justification for employing different roll speeds in two-roll milling. However, the streamlines are still closed, so that even differential-speed, two-roll milling per se will not fulfill the requirements for an ideal mixer, since interfaces oriented along a given streamline will continue to follow that streamline as before.

Practical Consideration in Two-Roll Milling. In the foregoing description of the milling process as an ideal mixing process, two conditions tend to detract markedly from two-roll mill performance—the existence of closed streamlines and the absence of any transfer of material along the axis of the rolls. In practice, these objections are overcome by the technique known as "cutting-down" or "quartering." The mill operator cuts slabs of the mixture (which is necessarily a plastic material) from the roll, folds or turns them, and introduces them again into the nip at a different position along the roll axis. In this way the closed streamlines are disturbed, and axial transfer of material is achieved. If this procedure is repeated frequently and in a random manner, statistical shuffling of the material begins to take place, and eventually the mass will be blended, while a statistically large number of the interfaces will have been subjected to relatively large shear deformations and uniform distribution. Thus, the cutting-down procedure is an essential part of two-roll milling, if it is to be considered a satisfactory mixing process.

If the mill is to be used as a continuous mixer, some auxiliary cutting-down or plowing device seems to be necessary to disrupt the closed streamlines.

Thus far the material to be mixed has been considered as a simple viscous fluid. Actually, it is almost always a rubbery or plastic mass exhibiting complex rheological behavior. A detailed description of the hydrodynamics of milling of such complex materials is not possible without a rheological equation-of-state for the material under consideration. Even then, the mathematics for the milling process would indeed be formidable.[10] However, the qualitative considerations discussed above may be supplemented with some quantitative results to allow dealing with actual problems.

In achieving a desirable mixture of a solid filler in a plastic, it is frequently necessary to apply not only an adequate amount of shear deformation and suitable blending or shuffling, which constitute the mixing process, but also to overcome the interparticle forces or van der Waals' forces between the particles. This latter process has been defined as dispersion. If the shear stress to which any agglomerate of particles is subjected is less than that necessary to overcome interparticle forces, no dispersion will result.

The shearing stress given by Eq. (7) is seen to depend on the several parameters μ, U_o, h_o, $\delta = \sqrt{2h_o/R}$ and λ (a function of the differential roll speeds). The term within brackets is dimensionless, hence is the same for all sizes of mills, assuming λ to be constant. Hence, the factors affecting shear stress are μ, U_o, R, and h_o. In general, τ will increase as $R^{1/2}$ and $h_o^{-3/2}$; i.e., shear stresses increase slowly with increased roll radius, and much more rapidly as the roll separation $2h_o$ is decreased.

Now the integral of the shear stress [given by Eq. (7)] over the roll surface, which is torque T per unit of roll length, is

$$T = R \int_{-x_1}^{x_R} \tau(\pm h)\, dx$$

$$= \frac{3\mu U_o R}{\delta} \left\{ \left[\frac{2\lambda}{3} \pm (1 - \xi_1^2) \right] (\tan^{-1} \xi_R + \tan^{-1} \xi_1) \right. \tag{9}$$

$$\left. \pm \frac{(\xi_1 + \xi_1\xi_R^2 + \xi_R + \xi_1^2\xi_R)}{1 + \xi_R^2} \right\}$$

Considering the term within brackets to be constant for a given λ or roll speed differential, the torque is also a function of h_o, R, μ, and U_o. Experimental measurements of torque vs. U indicate that torque is essentially independent of U, a phenomenon likewise observed for roll separating force.[2] Apparently, the term $U\mu$ is constant for a given plastic material, within the range of roll speed encountered in practice.

Likewise, for plastic materials, the ratio of sheet thickness to roll separation, h_1/h_o, and hence ξ_1, is very nearly constant for the range of values of h_o usually encountered in the milling of plastics. Since the maximum shearing stress occurs at h_o, Eqs. (5) or (7) may be used to scale up results obtained with a laboratory mill to predict the characteristics of a production-size mill.

Furthermore, experience has shown that the ratio of entering thickness of the wedge $2h_R$ to the roll separation $2h_o$ is approximately constant for a given material being milled under given milling conditions. This enables the torque and power requirements of a production mill to be predicted from data taken from a laboratory-size mill.

Typical Problems in Milling Plastics. *Equal Shearing Stresses.* When plastic materials are compounded in the laboratory, it is frequently desirable to specify milling conditions for a larger production-size milling machine to ensure that equal dispersing forces are exerted by the larger machine.

The variables in Eq. (7) are ξ_1, h_o, R, U_o, μ, and λ. As stated previously, the product μU_o is constant; the size of both the experimental and large mills is usually fixed, hence R' and R'' are not arbitrary (primes and double primes referring to small and large units, respectively). Finally ξ_1 is essentially the same for either unit. Hence the only variable is $2h_o$, the roll separation. Assume the roll speed differential to be identical for each unit.

Experimental Data. The experimental milling conditions which yielded a satisfactory dispersion of a solid filler in a plastic matrix were found to be as shown in Table 7.1. It is desired to produce the same material with a production mill under the conditions as given in Table 7.2. The maximum shearing stress, given by Eq. (7) occurs at $\xi_o = 0$, $\eta = \delta/2$

$$\tau_{\max} = \frac{6\mu U_o}{\delta h_o} \left| \frac{\lambda}{2} (-\xi_1^2) + \frac{\delta\lambda}{6} \right| = \frac{3\mu U_o}{h_o} \left[\frac{\lambda}{2} - \xi_1^2 \right]$$

or, rearranging,

$$\tau_{\max}/3\mu U_o(\lambda/2 - \xi_1^2) = \frac{1}{h_o'} = \frac{1}{h_o''}$$

That is, $h_o' = h_o''$ and the roll separation must be the same for either mill to achieve the same maximum shearing stress in each case.

Equal Batch Temperature. Suppose that it is desired to specify the roll-surface temperature of the larger mill so that the average batch temperature is the same as that observed for the experimental mill.

The only additional experimental information required is the average temperature of the material leaving the nip of the experimental mill after milling is completed. This was found to be 150°F.

The problem is to equate the heat generated by viscous resistance to flow

TABLE 7.1 (6-in. by 14-in. Mill)

Roll diameter $(2R')$	6 in.
Sheet width (W')	12 in.
Sheet thickness $(2h_L)$	0.070 in.
Front roll-surface temperature (T_o)	75°F
Front roll-surface speed U_1'	450 in./min
Average roll-surface speed U_o'	400 in./min
Roll separation $2h_o$	0.050 in.

TABLE 7.2 (20-in. by 60-in. Mill)

Roll diameter $(2R'')$	20 in.
Front roll-surface speed U_1''	750 in./min
Average roll-surface speed U_o''	660 in./min
Sheet width W''	59 in.

to the heat transferred to the roll from the sheet through the arbitrary temperature difference which is to be determined.

The energy, in arbitrary units, generated by viscous friction, is the product of torque and roll speed; from Eq. (9) for torque,

$$q = 2\pi N_o T = \frac{12\pi\mu U_o R N}{\delta} [f(\xi_1, \xi_R)]$$

where q is the power, or rate of energy dissipation for an average rate of roll rotation N_o, per unit of roll length. Since μU_o, and $f(\xi_1, \xi_R)$ have already been taken to be constant, there results

$$q = A N_o \sqrt{R^3/2h_o} \tag{10}$$

where

$$A = 12\pi\mu U_o[f(\xi_1, \xi_R)]$$

The sheet adhering to the front roll, rotating at a speed N_1, is considered a thick slab of initial temperature T_a suddenly brought into contact with a surface at T_o. The slab properties are: thermal conductivity k and thermal diffusivity a. The heat transferred in time t, per unit area, is*

$$Q = \frac{2k(T_a - T_o)}{\sqrt{a\pi}} \sqrt{t}$$

The rate of heat transfer is thus†

$$\frac{dQ}{dt} = -\frac{k(T_a - T_o)}{\sqrt{a\pi}} t^{-3/2} = q''$$

* See Schack, Partridge, and Goldsmith, "Industrial Heat Transfer," New York, John Wiley & Sons, Inc., 1933.

† The preceding equation is valid since the ratio $\dfrac{h_1}{\sqrt{at}} > 0.6$, i.e., for $a = 3 \times 10^{-3}$ sq ft/hr, $h_1 = 0.050$ in., $t < 0.01$ hr, or N must be greater than 1.6 rpm.

This rate is per unit of area. To keep it consistent with the rate of energy dissipation given by Eq. (10), which is energy per inch of roll length, multiply by the area represented by a unit length of roll:

$$q = q'(2\pi R) = 2\pi R \frac{k(T_a - T_o)}{\sqrt{a\pi}} t^{-3/2}$$

Finally, t in this equation is the time required for one revolution of the roll, which is $1/N_1$, thus

$$q = 2\pi R \frac{k(T_a - T_o)}{\sqrt{a\pi}} N_1^{3/2} = KRN_1^{3/2}(T_a - T_o) \qquad (11)$$

where

$$K = 2\pi k/\sqrt{a\pi}.$$

Since the rate of energy dissipation [Eq. (10)] must equal the rate of heat transfer [Eq. (11)],

$$AN_o\sqrt{R^3/2h_o} = KRN_1^{3/2}(T_a - T_o)$$
$$(T_a - T_o) = (A/K)N_o/N_1^{3/2}(1/\delta) \qquad (12)$$

Since A and K are the same for either mill, we take the ratio

$$\frac{(T_a - T_o)'}{(T_a - T_o)''} = \frac{(N_o/N_1^{3/2})'}{(N_o/N_1^{3/2})''} \frac{\delta''}{\delta'} \qquad (13)$$

where the primes denote the experimental mill; the double primes, the large mill.

Referring to Table 7.1, Table 7.2, and temperature of the stock leaving the nip of the experimental calender $T_a = 150°F$, the expression above is to be solved for T_o'':

$$T_o'' = -47°F$$

This required roll temperature for the large mill cannot be satisfactorily met, since the minimum T_o'' attainable is about $+50°F$. One possible alternative in Eq. (13) is to adjust N_1'' and N_2''. Setting $(T_a - T_o)'' = 100$, Eq. (13) becomes

$$(N_o/N_1^{3/2})'' = 0.436 \qquad (14)$$

Recalling that

$$N_o'' = \frac{N_1'' + N_2''}{2}$$

and

$$N_1'' = 1.30 N_2''$$

Eq. (14) yields

$$N_1'' = 2.1 \text{ rpm}$$

This solution is unrealistic since now the capacity of the mill is entirely too low, and the mill would be unable to supply the mixture at the rate required.

Thus, if the criteria of equal shearing stress and equal temperature for experimental and large-scale mills were to be maintained, it follows that the large mill must provide either an inordinate amount of cooling for the usual speed and capacity conditions, or a drastic reduction in capacity must be accepted if normal cooling conditions are to be allowed.

This dilemma was met by sacrificing a tolerable amount of shearing stress, and hence degree of dispersion, which allowed an increase in roll separation $2h_o$ from 0.050 to 0.180 in. (about $\frac{3}{16}$ in.) and an increase in resulting sheet gauge from 0.070 to 0.25 in. Thus, the value of shearing stress, being inversely proportional to h_o, was reduced in the large mill by a factor of more than 3, while the allowable roll speed is computed as follows:

From Eq. (13)

$$\frac{(T_a - T_o)'}{(T_a - T_o)''} = \frac{75}{100} = \frac{(N_o/N_1^{3/2})'}{(N_o/N_1^{3/2})''} - \frac{\delta''}{\delta'} = \frac{0.276}{(N_o/N_1^{3/2})''}$$

Also, as before,

$$N_o'' = \frac{N_1'' + N_2''}{2} = \frac{N_1'' + 0.77N_1''}{2}$$

Thus

$$N_1'' = 7.2 \text{ rpm}$$

The large mill was modified to operate at this speed, with a roll separation of about $\frac{3}{16}$ in. and with a roll temperature in the region of 50°F. Experience has shown that with these conditions the batch can be milled without thermal damage and with less than ideal, but satisfactory, dispersion, as observed visually.

In conclusion it should be pointed out that the average mix temperature referred to here does not represent the maximum temperature actually encountered, since large temperature gradients occur within the wedge.[10] The analysis of the problem above was successful in this respect, because the value of the peak temperature rise encountered in the milling process and the average temperature rise are more or less directly related.

Also, this problem serves to explain the common complaint that it is difficult to achieve the same degree of dispersion of solid fillers with large-scale mills as is possible with laboratory-scale equipment. In the problem given above, the limitations of mix temperature forced a sacrifice in degree of dispersion. In other instances, limitations of available power, machine-design considerations, or mill capacity may lead to the necessity of increasing roll separation $2h_o$ in order to render the milling process practicable for larger mills. This is accompanied by a corresponding decrease in maximum shearing stress. If the shear stress necessary to achieve deagglomeration of particle clumps is of the order of magnitude of the shearing stress developed by the mill, the diminished stress obtained in practice with the larger mill could well be reflected in poorer dispersion of solid fillers in the mixture from the larger mill.

Internal Mixers

Internal mixers have been developed empirically; evidently, present designs evolved from earlier machines on the basis of experience. To the author's best knowledge, no hydrodynamic analysis of an intensive mixer has been published. This is perhaps due to the extreme difficulty of deriving a complete description of the flow within an internal mixer, even for an ideal viscous fluid. The difficulty is magnified further for actual plastic materials which are not ideal rheologically. In the region of intensive shear between the blade and chamber wall (Fig. 7.9), the approximation of an ideal viscous fluid is relatively acceptable; elsewhere, in regions of very small shear rate or shear stress, the plastic and elastic properties of real materials predominate. The transport pattern in this case, even with closed streamlines, cannot readily be analyzed. Actually, the streamlines are not closed; the volume of the chamber varies erratically, because under certain circumstances the materials press against the ram to raise it, so that the

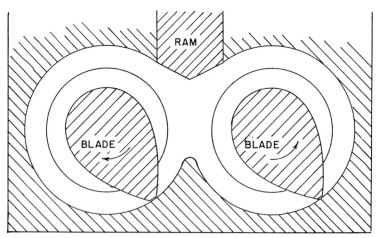

Fig. 7.9. Section of Banbury blade and shell.

transport pattern becomes a sort of shuffling process which is erratic or statistical in nature.

Intensive Shear in Internal Mixers. In App. A the hydrodynamics of the shearing of a viscous fluid between the blade tip and chamber wall is derived. In this derivation the following assumptions are involved: (1) The material is a viscous fluid of constant coefficient of viscosity; (2) the clearance between the blade and wall h is supposed to vary slowly with x (Fig. 7.A.1); (3) the radius of curvature of the chamber is large with respect to the clearance h; and (4) the process is isothermal.

Two configurations of the blade tip are considered: (1) The tip is parallel to the chamber wall, i.e., $h = $ constant; and (2) the clearance varies linearly with X so that $h = h_o(1 - Cx)$ where C is a constant.

For the first configuration, a "channel" of constant width, the distribution of velocity u is given by

$$u = U(1 - y/h_o) \tag{15}$$

That is, it varies linearly from $u = 0$ for $y = h_o$ (at the chamber wall) to $u = U$ for $y = o$ (at the blade surface) where U is the peripheral speed of the blade tip. The shearing stress is

$$\tau = \mu \, du/dy = -\mu U/h_o = 2\mu Q/h_0^2 \tag{16}$$

That is, it is constant across the channel since $h_o = $ constant. Also, the power (per unit blade length) is the product of total drag on the blade and its velocity:

$$P = U \int_o^L \tau \, dx = \mu U^2 L/h_o \tag{17}$$

The shear strain γ experienced by the material in passing through the channel is from Eq. (A14):

$$\gamma = L/(h_o - y) \tag{18}$$

This is equal to L/h_o at the chamber wall and increases toward infinity at the blade tip where $y = h_o$. However, this material, subjected to infinite shear, always adheres to the blade tip, and thus a high value of γ is of little value in mixing if associated with a very small value of outflow velocity. Therefore, a factor shear output S may be defined,

$$S = \gamma(y) \int_o^h u(L, y) \, dy \tag{19}$$

which is the product of the shear-strain function in y, $\gamma(y)$, and the integral of the differential volume flow over the limits of y. For the case of the constant-clearance blade, we substitute Eqs. (15) and (18) into Eq. (19) and obtain

$$S = \int_o^h U(1 - y/h)(L/h - y)\, dy$$

$$S = UL$$

Thus the shear output is directly proportional to blade speed and blade-tip width. Furthermore, this shear output acts per unit time, on a volume of material $Q = \frac{1}{2} U h_o$, so that the specific shear output σ (shear output per unit volume) is

$$\sigma = S/Q = 2L/h_o \tag{20}$$

This relationship states that the specific shear output of an internal mixer of constant-depth channel is increased by increasing the blade width or decreasing the channel depth.

Linearly Decreasing Channel Depth. The case of the constant-depth channel discussed above may be compared with a similar mixer of variable channel depth, for which the taper α or ratio of inlet depth h_o to outlet depth h_L is 2. This case is analyzed in App. A, where it is shown that for a taper greater than 2, undesirable backflow near the entrance of the channel will result.

Shearing stress τ_h at the blade surface, for the tapered-channel mixer, is [Eq. (A29)]

$$\tau_h = \frac{2\mu Q}{h_o^2} \left(\frac{1}{1 - \beta\rho} \right)^2 \tag{21}$$

in which

$$\beta = \frac{\alpha - 1}{\alpha}; \qquad \rho = x/L$$

The corresponding equation for the straight channel is [Eq. (16)]

$$\tau_h = 2\mu Q/h_o^2 \tag{22}$$

In the second term on the right of Eq. (21), the factors β and ρ are always less than or equal to unity; thus for constant Q and h_o, the shear stress is greater for the tapered channel. In this instance, for $\rho = X/L = 1$, and $\beta = \alpha - 1/\alpha = \frac{1}{2}$, the term $1/(1 - \beta\rho)^2 = 4$, and the shearing stress would be increased fourfold at the exit with a tapered channel compared to the straight channel.

Specific Shear Output, σ. For the straight channel this is [Eq. (20)]

$$\sigma = 2.0\, L/h_o$$

while for the tapered channel, from Eq. (A28),

$$\sigma = 3.57 \ L/h_o$$

The tapered channel thus produces about 75 per cent greater specific shear output than does the straight channel.

Power, P. The power P, per unit length of blade, for the straight channel, is, from Eq. (A12),

$$P = 4\mu Q^2 L/h_o{}^3$$

and for the tapered channel, from Eq. (A30),

$$P = 15.5 \ \mu Q^2 L/h_o{}^3$$

hence the tapered channel requires nearly four times as much power, for equal volume rate of flow, as the straight channel.

In summary, for equal volume rate of flow Q and equal blade-to-chamber wall clearance h_o, the tapered-channel mixer produces about 75 per cent greater shear output, about four times greater shear stress, and requires about four times as much power as the equivalent straight-channel mixer.

The Internal Mixer as an Ideal Mixing Device. In terms of laminar-flow mixing theory, the internal mixer fulfills all the important requirements of this theory, at least in some degree. As is evident in the analysis discussed above, the shear stress and shear rate in the region between the blade tip and the chamber wall are more or less uniform; in Eqs. (A14) and (A25) the shear strain is nowhere zero in the channel between the blade and chamber wall. Since the streamlines outside this region cannot be satisfactorily analyzed, no unequivocal conclusion may be drawn in this respect. However, it is a fact that the blade as a whole is usually given a helical shape, and that the blades are usually rotated at different speeds. This indicates that the designers of these devices have recognized the need for obtaining a distribution of component interfaces, and of the components themselves, throughout the mass. The streamlines within the chamber are constantly changing, as the phase relationship of the blades changes, at least in a cyclical manner. Thus, any particle eventually will reach a streamline which will carry it through the region of large shear, although in the meantime other particles may have traveled through this region many times.

So in this respect the internal mixer tends to approach the ideal, as opposed to the two-roll mill which, left to its own devices, never would. On the other hand the time—and hence energy—required to achieve a satisfactory degree of mixing, is certainly much greater than for an ideal mixer. The fact that the internal mixer is able to deform the more or less tough, very viscous materials encountered in thermoplastics processing in a way which fulfills, at least to a reasonable degree, the criteria for an ideal mixer explains its wide acceptance in this respect. In the absence of a fundamental analysis of the complete flow problem in such mixers, few conclusions can be drawn for the present as to just how efficient they are in terms of the ideal, or as to what steps can be taken to improve their efficiency. In general, increasing the rate of rotation of the blade will tend to decrease the elapsed time required for satisfactory mixing. Also, changing the shape of the channel will yield greater shear output, as illustrated by the example cited above for a tapered channel as compared with the uniform channel. This likewise will decrease the time of mixing.

Either of these steps leads to greater power requirements per unit of mix produced, so that the advantage of greater capacity must be weighed against this greater economic cost.

Practical Considerations of Internal Mixers. The hydrodynamic description of internal mixers thus far has considered the mixture to be a Newtonian fluid, and the process to be isothermal. Furthermore, mixing has been considered a shear-displacement process independent of shear stress.

Actually, the thermoplastic materials met with in practice are markedly non-Newtonian and viscoelastic, to the extent that the quantitative application of viscous theory is seriously limited. Likewise, the assumption that the process is isothermal is quite unreal. These effects are illustrated in Fig. 7.10, which presents the relationship between rate of rotation of a Banbury mixer, and the power required, for a given rubber stock as reported by Jones and Snyder.[16] The speed was varied over a fourfold range, and the results were reported as the total energy required to achieve suitable dispersion, together with the time at each speed. The average power was calculated by dividing energy by time of mixing. The power P was found, by hydrodynamic analysis, to be related to blade speed U and viscosity μ, in Eq. (A12):

$$P = 4\mu U^2 L/h_o = \text{const. } (\mu U)(U) \tag{23}$$

where L is the blade width or "land" and h is the clearance between blade and wall. (It is assumed here that the channel of the subject Banbury is of uniform depth.) Equation (23) calls for a quadratic relationship between power and blade speed, which is indicated in Fig. 10 by the dashed line, using the data for 69 rpm to establish the constants of Eq. (23). If, however, the factor μU is taken to be constant, the solid line results, which exactly fits the data. Thus, just as was the case for the two-roll mill, the term μU is virtually constant over the range of speeds usually encountered. Consequently, in actual practice, torque at the blade shaft is independent of speed.

The shear stress, Eq. (21), (with $\beta = 0$) is

$$\tau = 2\mu Q/h_o^2 = \mu U/h_o^3$$

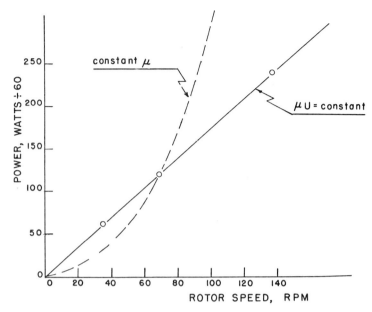

Fɪɢ. 7.10. Power *vs.* speed for Banbury mixing of rubber. (Data from Ref. 16.)

where the term μU is now constant. Thus it appears that shearing stress in an internal mixer is independent of all other variables, for a given mixture, except blade clearance, and further that the shearing stress is very sensitive to the clearance. The results of Jones and Snyder[16] seem to refute this conclusion, since the degree of dispersion (measured subjectively by visual examination of the mixture for undispersed specks of zinc oxide) was increased with an increase in speed from 35 to 69 rpm. However, a further increase to 137 rpm resulted in a somewhat poorer dispersion by this criterion. Evidently, extraneous effects, other than simply shear stress, were involved. Further study of this question is required, particularly by means of a mixing criterion which is a measure of shearing stress alone. It is certainly reasonable to conclude, however, that shearing stress is virtually independent of rotor speed.

The question now arises as to how the effectiveness of an internal mixer can best be improved. Comes[7] describes recent developments in Banbury-mixer design which involve higher speed and greater ram pressure. Higher speeds are reported to improve mixing most for softer materials, while higher ram force appears to improve mixing most for harder (tougher) materials. These conclusions are reasonable in the light of the comments above, particularly if the following is considered.

In the analysis of the flow of a viscous fluid in the channel of an intensive mixer, the material was assumed to adhere everywhere to the blade and to the chamber walls. Actual thermoplastic materials will exhibit this behavior only in the case of soft, very fluid materials. As the elastic or plastic behavior of the material becomes more pronounced, the phenomenon of "slip" flow sets in—i.e., the material will flow in shear along a confining surface only as long as the shearing stress does not exceed some limiting value (see Ref. 9, p. 659 ff.). Thus the material within the confines of the channel of the mixer may, under appropriate circumstances, simply slide along with the blade as an elastic solid, undergoing no shear. The tensile forces developed in the material just leaving the channel may lead to tensile failure at that point. Furthermore, since the material elsewhere in the chamber is behaving elastically, finite stress is necessary to displace it in order to fill in the void left behind the moving blade. If the entire chamber were rigidly enclosed, this stress would appear as a pressure distribution on the enclosure boundaries, or chamber walls. However, the ram is restrained only in so far as the force developed by the pneumatically loaded ram piston allows. If the integral of pressure, along the surface of the ram, exceeds the piston load, the ram will be forced out until these forces are balanced; i.e., until the material begins to deform or flow so as to fill the void either clockwise around the blade or counterclockwise through the channel. This phenomenon is frequently observed with intensive mixers as "bumping" or "bouncing" of the ram, provided the chamber is nearly completely filled.

Now, if the material rheologically approaches a Newtonian fluid, the normal pressure p will be relatively small, and, in addition, the tendency for slip within the channel will be relatively slight. Thus the important factor in the mixing of "soft" materials, aside from channel depth h_o, will be the velocity U which determines the rate of shear displacement. Since the ram is loaded sufficiently to render it a rigid confine, increasing U improves the mixing.

If, however, the material approaches an elastic solid in rheological behavior, the normal stress can become sufficient to displace the ram, while slip (flow) in the channel will be more pronounced. While slip flow occurs, the mixing process ceases. With a constant load on the ram, stress maxima sufficient to "bump" the ram will increase with increasing blade speed; slip flow and interruption of shear displacement will become more frequent, and the mixing process will be only slightly enhanced. On the other hand, an increase in the ram load will decrease the incidence of slip flow in the channel, with correspondingly fewer interruptions of the mixing process. Thus, for hard, tough materials, improvement in mixing will best be realized by increasing the ram force.

In either case, the power requirement will increase; for soft materials the increase in power will be directly proportional to the increased speed, while for hard materials the average power level will rise owing to the fewer interruptions of shear deformation within the channel.

It will be observed that the power or torque requirements of an internal mixer will fluctuate over a rather wide range. This is due in part to the constantly varying engagement between the blades and chamber walls, because of the helical orientation of the blades along their axis and to their "phase" relationships. If the fluctuations in torque were solely due to such engagement and phase fluctuations, a regular pattern of torque variation should appear. However, such is not the case; the torque usually appears to fluctuate very erratically, a manifestation of the occurrence of slip flow in an irregular manner.

"Scale-Up" Experiments. Since the internal mixer cannot be analyzed rigorously at present, it is necessary to evaluate mixing problems experimentally. When small-scale mixers are employed to arrive at such factors as sequence of addition of components, temperature range, mixing time, etc., it is helpful to consider some of the scale factors involved. Although the foregoing hydrodynamic description of the flow and intensive shear in an internal mixer is by no means complete or exact, the principles are nevertheless useful as an approximation to the important scale factors involved in extrapolating laboratory results to large-scale machines.

For example, the shear stress, given by Eq. (16), is

$$\tau = -\mu U/h_o$$

Since it has been shown that the term μU is constant, to achieve equal shear stresses in different internal mixers, the clearance h_o between blade and chamber wall should be the same in all cases.

Likewise, the total shear deformation per unit time γ_θ is the product of shear deformation per revolution, given by Eq. (18), and the rate of rotation N:

$$\gamma_\theta = N\gamma = NL/(h_o - y) \tag{24}$$

Since h_o, and hence $h_o - y$, is identical for the mixers to be compared, the product NL should be identical for the mixers, where L is the width, or "land" of the blade tip.

Thus, for appropriately scaled mixers, the clearance h_o and the product NL should always be the same. Table 7.3 illustrates some comparisons for several Banbury mixers.

The factors h_o and NL are relatively constant, although they indicate that some difference in the performance of these mixers may be expected.

TABLE 7.3. COMPARISON OF h_o AND NL FOR THREE SIZES OF BANBURY MIXERS

Mixer Size	Chamber Volume, cu. in.	h_o	Approximate Values of		NL
			N	L	
B	103	⅛ in.	120	¼ in.	30
3A	4,315	³⁄₁₆ in.	56	½ in.	28
11	14,940	³⁄₁₆ in.	40	1 in.	40

FIG. 7.11. Extruder mixer for plastics.

In general, the smaller value of h_o associated with smaller, laboratory-scale mixers probably accounts for the common observation that such mixers tend to produce better dispersions than their larger counterparts, since the smaller h_o leads to larger shear stress. However, much more experimental work is necessary before a complete description of this sort may be drawn. The picture of dispersing and mixing in internal mixers, presented above, represents only a beginning toward a fundamental understanding of what is yet very much an art.

Single-Screw Extruders

Although it was developed as a forming device for thermoplastics, the single-screw extruder (Fig. 7.11) also functions as a mixing device, owing to the laminar-flow deformation to which the mixture is subjected upon passing through the machine. For a more complete description of extrusion equipment, the reader is referred to Chap. 4.

The extruder, as such, is not primarily employed as a mixer; it is frequently convenient, however, to add ingredients to the resin during melt extrusion and thereby to utilize the mixing action of the extruder. It is quite common for colorants to be added to extruded products in this way. The colorant and resin are metered into the feed hopper as required, and, with a proper arrangement of the extrusion machine, a suitably colored extrudate may be obtained.

Frequently, reclaimed scrap stocks of differing color are mixed satisfactorily in the extruder when suitable metering of such materials to the extruder feed hopper is provided. Alternatively, a master batch, or premixed concentrate, of colored thermoplastics may be fed to the extruder simultaneously with the resin to be colored; in this instance the extruder functions as an auxiliary mixer.

There is very little published information on the use of the extruder as a mixing device; the applications of the principles of mixing to the extruder remain very largely an art. It is encouraging to note that the theory of mixing in the single-screw extruder has been considered by Mohr, Saxton, and Jepson in a recent paper.[20] The results of this analysis, in the light of the theory of mixing, and the theory of extrusion developed in Chap. 4, serve to illuminate the role of the extruder as a mixing device for thermoplastics.

Mixing in the Single-Screw Extruder. The mixing which a given volume of polymer receives may be expressed in terms of the total amount of shear to which it is exposed.[20] This total shear equals the product of the shear rate and the residence time in the extruder. It is a measure of the relative displacement of one particle with respect to its neighbor.

The total amount of shear in an extrusion operation can be increased by diminishing the channel depth of the screw, by letting the helix angle approach 0 or 90 deg, or by increasing the amount of pressure flow and leakage flow through increased die restriction.

The total amount of shear to which a particular element of liquid polymer is exposed depends upon its initial position in the screw channel. The flow path, and thus both the residence time and the shear rate, vary according to the initial position of the material in the cross section of the screw channel. The material near the center of the channel receives less mixing than does that near the screw surface or the barrel wall. The principal reason for this is the shorter residence time of the material near the center of the channel. Examination of the figures in Chap. 4, illustrating the velocity distributions within the screw channel, bears this out. It is also important to note that no motion of material backward along the screw axis ever takes place. Hence, single-screw extruders provide no "turnover" and little bulk mixing in the axial direction.

In the paper by Mohr, Saxton, and Jepson,[20] two equations describing the amount of shear in planes parallel and perpendicular to the screw axis are derived. These equations express the amount of shear in terms of the position of the particle in the channel depth (y-axis).

$$M_{\lambda c} = \frac{L}{h}\left(F_V - \frac{F_T}{1-a}\right) \tag{25}$$

$$M_{UC} = \frac{L}{h}\left(\frac{F_V}{\tan\phi} + \frac{F_T\tan\phi}{1-a}\right) \tag{26}$$

where

$M_{\lambda c}$ = amount of shear parallel to the screw axis
M_{UC} = amount of shear perpendicular to the screw axis
L = length of the screw
h = channel depth of the screw
ϕ = helix angle of the screw
α = ratio of pressure flow to drag flow in down-channel plane

TABLE 7.4. VALUES FUNCTIONS F_v AND F_t

$\frac{y}{h}$	F_v	F_t
0.050	17.527	−21.679
0.100	7.880	−8.527
0.150	4.796	−4.171
0.200	3.309	−1.983
0.250	2.441	−0.648
0.300	1.870	0.264
0.350	1.461	0.936
0.400	1.149	1.458
0.500	0.675	2.225
0.600	0.278	2.754
0.750	−0.446	3.155

F_v and F_t are dimensionless functions of the reduced height in the channel y/h, where y is the height in the channel measured perpendicular to the screw root (Table 7.4).

To determine the average amount of shear in the screw channel, it would be necessary to integrate these equations over the cross-sectional area of the screw channel.

Many types of special mixing heads or torpedoes have been designed as attachments to the end of extruder screws. Their primary purpose is to increase further the amount of shear to which the extrudate is exposed and to cross-blend the somewhat non-uniformly mixed material leaving the screw channel. Some of these devices are illustrated among the screw designs in the introductory part of Chap. 4.

Screw Mixers

Several modifications of the single-screw extruder have been devised to improve the mixing action of these machines. Some double-screw and triple-screw extruders[23] feature an arrangement of intermeshing screws which tend to break up the continuous streamlines along which material that receives relatively little mixing may travel. The same fundamental laminar-flow mixing process occurs, however, between the screw and the barrel, as in the case of a single-screw extruder. Since the barrel does not entirely encompass each screw, the complete hydrodynamic analysis of flow for such extruders often becomes extremely complicated, although the principles resulting from the analysis for the single-screw case would apply qualitatively.

Another form of screw mixer is the pug mill,[21] also known as the German mixer in the linoleum industry.[25] In this device the screw is a series of radial spokes arranged helically on the screw shaft. The spokes are spaced apart axially to mesh with fixed spokes attached to the barrel. As the screw rotates, the sequential engagement of rotating and fixed spokes causes the

(*Courtesy of Baker Perkins, Inc.*)

FIG. 7.12. "Ko-Kneader" continuous mixer.

material to advance axially by small increments, meanwhile undergoing shear between the fixed and rotating spokes. This device develops intensive shear between the spokes, but it is limited by relatively large torque resulting from the considerable area over which intensive shear occurs. It fails to meet the criteria for ideal mixing in that there is no flow radially, since the streamlines tend to be parallel to the axis from inlet to outlet. Furthermore, the axial shear is relatively small, so that the material travels through the chamber more or less as it would through a large pipe.

Yet another type of screw mixer is the "Ko-Kneader"[21] shown in Fig. 7.12, which, like the pug mill, consists of an interrupted screw which meshes with blades fixed to the barrel. In this mixer the screw is oscillated axially, so that the fixed blades clear the gaps in the rotating interrupted screw while the screw moves forward and backward alternately. The helical pitch of the screw transmits an over-all axial motion to the material. The oscillating motion leads to forward-and-backward motion which tends to reduce greatly the deficiency of unidirectional motion previously mentioned in connection with the single-screw extruder.

In this device intensive shear is not continuous, and the clearances necessary to allow the axial oscillation of the screw may reduce the effective shear stress; also, the large area over which appreciable shear stresses operate leads to resultant torque requirements which limit the viscosity or toughness of thermoplastic materials capable of being mixed in this device. As a mixer, however, the "Ko-Kneader" appears to possess the advantages of the single-screw extruder while overcoming its disadvantages with respect to closed streamlines and unidirectional flow. Its evaluation must, for the present, be based upon experimental observations for each particular case since no theoretical description of the hydrodynamics of flow is available.

Thermoplastic materials may exhibit slip flow in screw extruders in the same manner as was described for internal mixers. This is probably the principal reason that tough or highly filled mixtures lead to low extruder "efficiency" which is related to q_0/q_D , the ratio of actual output to theoretical output. Under this circumstance the shear-stress and shear-strain distribution deviates widely from that derived for a Newtonian fluid which adheres everywhere to the confining surfaces. Since this situation has not yielded to analysis, it appears that a quantitative evaluation of an extruder mixer is best accomplished through direct experimentation with the particular mixture of interest.

CONCLUSION

Commercial machines for mixing and dispersing thermoplastics appear to fall into three general types, based respectively on the principle of the two-roll mill, the internal mixer, and the screw extruder mixer. A hydrodynamic analysis of the flow conditions obtaining in each of these types is developed and interpreted in terms of the ideal mixing process for laminar-flow mixing. The internal mixer appears to fulfill most nearly all of the basic criteria for ideal mixing, although its efficiency in power and time, in relation to the ideal mixer, is evidently fairly low. Of all mixers, the internal mixer is the most massive and costly, while the two-roll mill is the least. Extruder mixers range between these two extremes, approaching the size and cost of the internal mixer as their design becomes more complicated in order to overcome the limitations which are inherent in the more simple single-screw extruder when used as a mixer. The extruder-type mixer is unique in that it is inherently a continuous mixer, whereas the two-roll mill and the internal mixer are basically adapted to batch-type operation.

The two-roll mill has one great advantage in its versatility with regard to ease of varying shear rate and shear stress merely by adjusting the clearance between the rolls; the other general types allow variation in shear rate only by varying the speed of rotation, since changes in clearance of the channel involve major mechanical alterations.

Thus, each type is best suited for particular applications in practice. The technology of mixing and dispersing has not yet reached the point where problems can be solved from a fundamental approach alone; each case must be considered, to some degree, in the light of experimental or empirical data. The fundamental approach will be expanded along two lines—a more complete description of the complicated rheology of the thermoplastic materials met with in practice, and a more complete description of the mechanics of flow of these materials within the existing mixing device itself. At the present time, work is continuing along both of these avenues.

APPENDIX A

Flow Past the Blade Tip of an Internal Mixer*

If the radius of curvature of the chamber wall is large compared to the clearance (t) between the blade tip and chamber wall, the wall may be considered straight, Fig. 7.A-1.† The blade is moving past the wall with

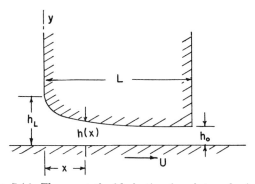

Fig. 7.A1. Flow past the blade tip of an internal mixer.

velocity $-U$. Gaskell[11] shows that the volume rate of flow (per unit axial length of blade) is, for a channel of constant depth h_o,

$$Q = h/2U - h^3/12\mu \; (dp/dx) \tag{A1}$$

where μ is the coefficient of viscosity of the material and p is the pressure

* This analysis is taken from privately communicated work by W. Prager and J. K. Talbot, Brown University, Providence, R. I.

† The velocity of the blade is here taken to be zero and that of the wall U, since this keeps the coordinate system fixed with respect to the blade, considerably simplifying the analysis. This convention does not affect the results of the analysis, however.

which is a function of x. The x-component of velocity u at a point is[11]

$$u = U(1 - y/h) - h^2/2\mu(dp/dx)(y/h - y^2/h^2) \tag{A2}$$

and the distribution of shearing stress τ is

$$\tau = -\mu U/h - h/2(dp/dx)(1 - 2y/h) \tag{A3}$$

Equations (A1), (A2), and (A3) are correct for a channel of constant depth. They are approximately correct for a channel of varying depth, provided the depth varies slowly with x.

Solving Eq. (A1) for dp/dx,

$$dp/dx = 6\mu(U/h^2 - 2Q/h^3) \tag{A4}$$

Now the pressure (beyond a uniform, arbitrary pressure) vanishes at both the entrance $x = 0$ and exit $x = L$, so that,

$$\int_0^L (dp/dx) \, dx = 0$$

and with Eq. (A4):

$$\int_0^L 6\mu(U/h^2 - 2Q/h^3) \, dx = 0$$

or

$$U = 2Q \int_0^L (h^2/h^3) \, dx = 2Q(H_3/H_2) \tag{A5}$$

where

$$H_n = \int_0^L dx/h^n \tag{A6}$$

Equation (A5) gives the blade velocity as a function of the arbitrary volume rate of flow, with the functions H_2 and H_3 representing the shape of the channel. These are functions in h, and, in turn, x.

Thus the shear stress, from Eqs. (A3), (A4), and (A5), becomes

$$\tau = 6\mu Q/h^2 - 8\mu Q/h(H_3/H_2) - 12\mu Q/h(y/h)(H_3/H_2 - 1/h) \tag{A7}$$

and for $y = h$, the shear stress is

$$\tau_h = 6\mu Q/h^2 - 8\mu Q/h(H_3/H_2) \tag{A8}$$

The total shearing force F on the blade surface is

$$F = \int_0^L \tau_h \, dx = 2\mu Q[4H_1(H_3/H_2) - 3H_2]$$

and the power (per unit axial length of blade) is

$$P = 4\mu Q^2 (2H_1 H_3^2 / H_2^2 - 3H_3) \tag{A9}$$

It is desirable to know the shear strain to which the material is subjected in passing through the channel. Since h varies slowly with x, as a first approximation it will be assumed that the path a particle follows is constant at $z = y/h$. The velocity may be rewritten from Eqs. (A1), (A2), (A4), and (A5) as

$$u = 2Q/h[3z(1 - z) + (1 - 4z + 3z^2)hH_3/H_2] \tag{A10}$$

This velocity u is experienced by the particle as it passes through the channel of depth h; at this point it experiences a shear-strain rate $du/dy = (1/h) \, du/dz$. The particle advances an infinitesimal distance dx in a time dx/u, experiencing a shear strain $d\gamma$ which is

$$d\gamma = 1/h(dx/u)(\partial u/\partial z) = 1/h(\partial \log u / \partial z) \, dx$$

The total "natural" shear strain experienced by the particle is the summation of these infinitesimal shears between $x = 0$ and $X = L$,

$$\gamma(z) = \int_o^L 1/h \frac{\partial \log u}{\partial z} \, dx = \frac{\partial}{\partial z} \int_o^L (1/h) \log u \, dx \tag{A11}$$

since h depends only on x.

Thus it is required to state u as a function of x (or z) in order to evaluate $\gamma(z)$ in Eq. (A11).

Constant Channel Depth

For the constant channel depth, $h = h_o$, the volume rate of flow becomes

$$Q = Uh_o/2$$

so that from Eq. (A4)

$$dp/dx = 0$$

and from Eq. (A2)

$$u = U(1 - y/h_o) = U(1 - z)$$

The shearing stress τ_h becomes, from Eq. (A3),

$$\tau_h = -\mu U/h_o$$

and the power transmitted at the blade $y = h$ is simply

$$P = U \int_o^L \tau_h \, dx = \mu U^2 L/h_o \tag{A12}$$

Finally, the shear strain γ becomes, from Eq. (A11),

$$\gamma = 1/(h_o)\partial/\partial z \int_o^L \log u\, dx$$

$$\gamma = 1/(1 - z)(L/h_o)$$

(A13)

and, since $1 - z = 1 - y/h_o$,

$$\gamma = L/(h_o - y)$$

(A14)

Linearly Decreasing Channel Depth

Now consider that the channel depth varies linearly from h_o at $x = 0$ to h_L at $x = L$ so that

$$h = h_o(1 - Cx)$$

(A15)

$$h_L = h_o(1 - CL)$$

(A16)

Let

$$\alpha = h_o/h_L \qquad (\alpha \geqq 1)$$

so that Eq. (A16) becomes

$$1/\alpha = 1 - CL; \qquad C = \beta L$$

where

$$\beta = \alpha - 1/\alpha$$

Further let

$$\rho = x/L$$

so that Eq. (A15) becomes

$$h = h_o(1 - \beta\rho)$$

(A17)

Since $H_n = \int_o^L dx/h^n$ [Eq. (A6)], the ratio H_3/H_2 in Eq. (A5) becomes

$$H_3/H_2 = \alpha + 1/2h_o$$

(A18)

Thus the velocity distribution may be rewritten from Eqs. (A2), (A4), and (A5) to be

$$u = (2Q/h)(1 - z)[3z + (1 - 3z)h(H_3/H_2)]$$

With Eqs. (A17) and (A18) this becomes

$$uh_o/Q = (1 - z)[6z/(1 - \beta\rho) + (\alpha + 1)(1 - 3z)]$$

(A19)

This is now differentiated with respect to z, to obtain

$$h_o/Q(\partial u/\partial z) = \frac{6(1 - 2z)}{1 - \beta\rho} - 2(\alpha + 1)(2 - 3z) \tag{A20}$$

The derivative $\partial u/\partial z$ vanishes when z assumes the value

$$z^* = \frac{3 - 2(\alpha + 1)(1 - \beta\rho)}{3[2 - (\alpha + 1)(1 - \beta\rho)]} \tag{A21}$$

We now let z assume all values outside the range 0 to 1, i.e., we wish to find values of the right-hand function of Eq. (A21) which satisfy this condition. This is met if

$$1.5 \leq (\alpha + 1)(1 - \beta\rho) \leq 3$$

This means that the velocity u will be a monotonically decreasing function of z for all ρ, $0 < \rho < 1$ if

$$(\alpha + 1)(1 - \beta) = \alpha + 1/\alpha \leq 1.5$$

and

$$\alpha + 1 \leq 3$$

that is,

$$\alpha \leq 2 \tag{A22}$$

A channel decreasing in depth sufficiently rapidly will lead to enough pressure to cause backflow near the channel entrance. This phenomenon will be avoided if, in Eq. (A19),

$$6z/(1 - \beta\rho) + (\alpha + 1)(1 - 3z) < 0 \tag{A23}$$

The first term on the left-hand side of Eq. (A23) is always positive; to make it as small as possible and, at the same time, to make the second term as large as possible in absolute value, set $\rho = 0$, $z = 1$; Eq. (A23) then may be solved for α, viz.,

$$\alpha > 2$$

Equations (A22) and (A23) show that the velocity u will be a monotonically decreasing function of z for all ρ between 0 and 1, and that backflow will not occur if $\alpha \leq 2$; i.e. if the channel depth at the entrance is no more than twice that at the exit.

The infinitesimal shear strain, as in the case of the constant channel depth, is

$$d\gamma = 1/h[(1/u)\partial u/\partial z] \, d\rho \tag{A24}$$

The terms u and $\partial u/\partial z$ are given by Eqs. (A19) and (A20), so that the differential equation Eq. (A24) may now be written

$$d\gamma = \frac{L\, d\rho}{h_o(1 - \beta\rho)} \cdot \frac{6(1 - 2z) - 2(\alpha + 1)(2 - 3z)(1 - \beta\rho)}{(1 - z)[6z + (\alpha + 1)(1 - 3z)(1 - \beta\rho)]}$$

This equation can best be integrated by substituting

$$\zeta = 1 - \beta\rho$$

and the integral equation becomes

$$\gamma(z) = \frac{L}{\beta h_o(1 - z)} \int_{1-\beta}^{\beta} \frac{6(1 - 2z) - 2(\alpha + 1)(2 - 3z)\zeta}{[6z + \zeta(\alpha + 1)(1 - 3z)]\zeta}\, d\zeta$$

$$\gamma(z) = \frac{-L}{\beta h_o}\left[\frac{1 - 2z}{z(1 - z)}\log(1 - \beta)\right. \tag{A25}$$

$$\left. + \frac{1}{z\,(1 - 3z)}\log\frac{6z + (\alpha + 1)(1 - 3z)}{6z + (\alpha + 1)(1 - 3z)(1 - \beta)}\right]$$

For the channel of constant depth, $\alpha = 1$, $\beta = 0$, Eq. (A25) is in indeterminate form and must be evaluated by L'hopital's rule, whereupon it reduces to Eq. (A11).

Since it has been shown that backflow results for $\alpha > 2$, the maximum shear strain without backflow results from

$$\alpha = 2$$

$$\beta = \alpha - 1/\alpha = \tfrac{1}{2}$$

and

$$\gamma(z) = 2L/h_o\left[\frac{1 - 2z}{z(1 - z)}\log 2 - \frac{1}{z(1 - z)}\log^2\frac{(1 - z)}{1 + z}\right] \tag{A26}$$

The specific shear output is defined by Eqs. (18) and (19). Since $h_L = h_o/\alpha$, the specific shear output σ is the integral, from $z = 0$ to $z = 1$, of the following expression:

$$d\sigma = \frac{1}{\alpha}\frac{uh_o}{Q}|\gamma|\, dz$$

Employing the expressions for u, Eq. (A19), and $|\gamma|$, Eq. (A26), the differential shear output is

$$d\sigma/dz = \frac{L}{h_o} \cdot \frac{3(1 + z)}{z}\left[\frac{1 - z}{1 - 3z}\log 2\frac{1 - z}{1 + z} - (1 - 2z)\log 2\right] \tag{A27}$$

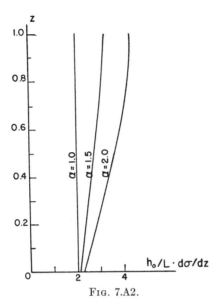

FIG. 7.A2.

Figure 7A.2 shows a plot of $d\sigma/dz$ as a function of z for the case of $\alpha = 1$ (constant channel depth) and $\alpha = 2$ (2:1 taper). For $\alpha = 1$, $d\sigma/dz$ is constant, while for $\alpha = 2$ it increases somewhat with z. Graphical integration of the curves of Fig. 7A.2 yields

$$\sigma = 2.0 \ (L/h_o)$$

for the case $\alpha = 1$ and

$$\sigma = 3.57 \ (L/h_o) \tag{A28}$$

for $\alpha = 2.0$

From Eq. (A8) the shearing stress at the blade becomes

$$\tau_h = \frac{2\mu Q}{h^2} = \frac{2\mu Q}{h_o^2} \left(\frac{1}{1 - \beta\rho}\right)^2 \tag{A29}$$

To compute the power from Eq. (A9), note that since

$$H_n = \int_o^L dx/h^n \qquad \alpha = h_o/h_L$$

$$H_n = \frac{\alpha^{n-1} - 1}{(n-1)ch_o^n} = \frac{L}{(n-1)h_o^n} \cdot \frac{\alpha^n - \gamma}{\alpha - 1}$$

Thus

$$H_1 = \frac{\log \alpha}{c h_o} = \frac{L}{h_o} \cdot \frac{\alpha \log \alpha}{\alpha - 1}$$

$$H_2 = L/h_o^2 \cdot \frac{\alpha^2 - \alpha}{\alpha - 1}$$

$$H_3 = \frac{L}{2 h_o^3} \cdot \frac{\alpha^3 - \alpha}{\alpha - 1}$$

And the power is, for $\alpha = 2$,

$$P = 15.5 \frac{\mu Q^2 L}{h_o^3} \tag{A30}$$

NOMENCLATURE

a Ratio pressure flow to drag flow, q_p/q_d .

a Thermal diffusivity.

h Channel depth; roll separation.

k Thermal conductivity.

L Channel length; blade-tip width.

N Rate of rotation.

p Pressure.

P Power.

q Rate of energy dissipation, per unit roll length.

q_p Pressure flow in an extruder.

q_D Drag flow in an extruder.

q_0 Observed flow in an extruder.

Q Rate of heat transfer per unit area.

R Radius.

t Time.

T Temperature.

u Velocity at a point, x direction.

U Velocity.

v Velocity at a point, y direction.

w Width of extruder channel.

z Dimensionless length, y/h.

α Ratio of channel depth at entry h_L to channel depth at exit h_o .

β $(\alpha - 1)/\alpha$.

γ Shear strain.

γ Function of roll velocities $\dfrac{2(U_1 - U_2)}{U_1 + U_2}$.

δ Dimensionless ratio $\sqrt{2 h_o/R}$.

ζ $1 - \beta p$.

η Dimensionless length, $y/\sqrt{2Rh_o}$.

μ Coefficient of viscosity.

ξ Dimensionless length, $x/\sqrt{2Rh_o}$.

ρ Dimensionless length, x/L.

σ Specific shear output.

τ Shear stress.

ϕ Helix angle of extruder screw.

ψ Stream function.

REFERENCES

1. Bergen, J. T., Carrier, G. F., and Krumhansl, J. A., "Criteria for Mixing and the Mixing Process," *Proceedings*, 14th Antec. Soc. Plastics Engrs., 987 (1958).

2. Bergen, J. T., and Scott, G. W., "Pressure Distribution in the Calendering of Plastic Materials," *J. Appl. Mechanics*, **18,** 101 (1951).

3. Bolen, W. R., and Colwell, R. E., "Intensive Mixing," *Proceedings*, 14th Antec., Soc. Plastics Engrs., 1004 (1958).

4. Bullock, H. L., "Practical Mixing Techniques for Viscous Liquids," *Chem. Eng. Progr.*, **47,** 397 (1951).

5. Bullock, H. L., "Mixing in Muller-Type Mixers," *Chem. Eng. Progr.*, **51,** 243 (1955).

6. Comes, D. A., "Rubber Mixing Machinery. The Banbury," *India Rubber World*, **122,** 178 (1950).

7. Comes, R. N., "High-horsepower Banbury Mixing," *Rubber World*, **135,** 565 (1957).

8. Danckwerts, P. V., "Theory of Mixtures and Mixing," *Research (London)*, **6,** 354 (1953).

9. Eirich, F. R. (Ed.), *Rheology*, New York, Academic Press, Inc., 1957.

10. Finston, M., "Thermal Effects in the Calendering of Plastic Materials," *J. Appl. Mechanics*, **73,** 12 (1951).

11. Gaskell, R. E., "The Calendering of Plastic Materials," *J. Appl. Mechanics*, **17,** 334 (1950).

12. Green, S. J., "Agitation in Process Design," *Trans. Inst. Chem. Engrs., (London)*, **31,** 327 (1953).

13. Havenhill, R. S., "Electrical Contact Potentials in Banbury Mixing," *Ind. Eng. Chem.*, **45,** 1128 (1953).

14. Hulbert, H. M., Katz, S., and Street, L. F., "Extrusion Theory," *Proceedings*, 14th Antec., Soc. Plastics Engrs., 177 (1958).

15. Hummel, C., "Mathematical Considerations of Roll-Mill Operation," *J. Oil & Colour Chemists Assoc.*, **39,** 777 (1956).

16. Jones, H. C., and Snyder, E. G., "Banbury Mixing of Zinc Oxide," *Ind. Eng. Chem.*, **43,** 2602 (1951).

17. Lacey, P. M. C., "Developments in the Theory of Particle Mixing," *J. Appl. Chem. (London)*, **4,** 257 (1954).

18. Lowe, P., "Some Problems in the Dispersion of Pigments for Plastics," *Brit. Plastics*, **27,** 304 (1954).

19. Michaels, A. S., and Puzinauskus, V., "Evaluating Performance of Mechanical Mixing Processes: The Dextrose-Kaolinite-Water System," *Chem. Eng. Progr.*, **50,** 604 (1954).

20. Mohr, W. D., Saxton, R. L., and Jepson, C. H., "Theory of Mixing in the Single-Screw Extruder," *Ind. Eng. Chem.*, **49,** 1857 (1957).
21. Quillen, C. S., "Mixing," *Chem. Eng.*, **61,** 204 (1954).
22. Roth, F. L., Decker, G. E., and Stiehler, R. D., "Temperature Control During Mixing of Rubber Compounds," *Rubber World*, **132,** 482 (1955).
23. Seaman, R. G., and Merrill, A. M., "Machinery and Equipment for Rubber and Plastics," New York, Lenz and Riecker, Inc., 1952.
24. Sell, H. S., and McCutcheon, R. J., "Banbury Dispersion of High-Styrene Copolymer Resins with Rubber," *Rubber Age* (New York), **75,** 841 (1954).
25. Sloane, O. V., "Craft and Science in Linoleum Manufacture," *J. Oil & Colour Chemists Assoc.*, **39,** 733 (1956).
26. Spencer, R. S., and Wiley, R. M., "The Mixing of Very Viscous Liquids," *J. Colloid Sci.*, **6,** 133 (1951).
27. Wack, P. E., Anthony, R. L., and Guth, E., "Electrical Conductivity of GR-S and Natural Rubber Stocks Loaded With Shawinigan and R-49 Blacks," *J. Appl. Phys.*, **18,** 456 (1947).

8. SHEET FORMING

N. Platzer, Ph. D.

Plastics Division
Monsanto Chemical Company

DEFINITION, HISTORY, AND SYNOPSIS

Sheet forming consists of heating a thermoplastic sheet to its softening point and pressing the hot and pliable sheet against the contours of a mold. The required pressure is supplied either mechanically, hydraulically, pneumatically, or by vacuum. The formed sheet is removed from the mold after cooling.

Thermoplastic sheet forming is one of the oldest processes of shaping plastic items. It dates back to the end of the last century, when the celluloid-blowing process was developed. However, sheet forming was restricted to a few applications with acrylics and cellulosics, and was of little importance in comparison to compression or injection molding. The development of vacuum forming, the improvement of machinery, and the introduction of new thermoplastics has made sheet forming the fastest-growing processing method for thermoplastics.[11, 13] Today, four basic methods of sheet forming and more than twenty modifications of these methods are known.

Choice of the sheet-forming process over other plastics processing techniques is usually based on economics. In some cases, where a shape with a large surface area and relatively thin walls is needed, sheet forming is the only process that is technically feasible.

The four basic methods of sheet forming, several modifications of these methods, and various types and elements of vacuum forming machines are described in this chapter. Two of the problems encountered in sheet forming are nonuniform thinning and orientation. Means of overcoming these problems are discussed in an additional section, together with other operating problems.

In addition, this chapter deals with the selection of thermoplastic materials for sheet forming and with the finishing of the formed items.

THE FOUR BASIC METHODS OF SHEET FORMING

Matched-Mold Forming

Matched-mold forming is the process in which a thermoplastic sheet is heated to its softening point and formed between a registering male and female mold section (Fig. 8.1A). It is carried out in a hydraulic or pneumatic press delivering a pressure of 5 to 150 psig. It is the most expensive method of sheet forming, because registering male and female mold sections are required. The molds are made of steel or reinforced aluminum and have vent holes for the escape of air.

This method was originally employed by the metal-stamping industry. The plastics industry has replaced metal with high-impact polystyrene and other resins for many industrial applications.[5]

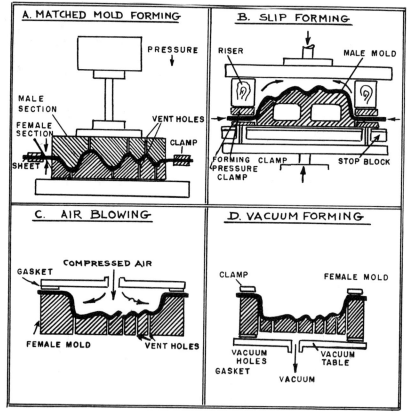

FIG. 8.1. The four basic methods of thermoplastic sheet forming.

Slip Forming

Slip forming is the process wherein a hot thermoplastic sheet is formed mechanically around a male mold. It requires a pneumatic press with an upper and a lower cylinder.

Initially, the thermoplastic sheet is placed on top of the raised pressure clamp and heated to the forming temperature. The heater is removed, and the press is closed. The loosely clamped sheet is allowed to slip between the pressure clamp and the forming clamp and is "wiped" around the mold by the downward movement of the clamps (Fig. 8.1B). The amount of slippage is controlled by the upward pressure of the lower pressure clamp and the area of the sheet between the two clamps. The depth of the draw is determined by the height of the stop blocks in relation to the mold. Various types of clamping methods have been devised to control the slippage and to prevent the clamps from chilling the sheet.

Slip forming is used to avoid excessive thinning when forming articles with deep draws.

Air Blowing

Air blowing is the procedure in which a hot thermoplastic sheet is blown into a female mold. In the basic process the sheet is fastened on top of the mold cavity and heated until it droops slightly (Fig. 8.1C). Compressed and preheated air, up to 150 psig. is applied, blowing the sheet to the required shape. The mold must have vent holes to allow air entrapped below the sheet to escape. This process may be combined with mechanical or vacuum drawing.

Vacuum Forming

The basic method of vacuum forming consists of fastening the thermoplastic sheet on top of a mold (Fig. 8.1D). Radiant heaters are directed on this assembly until the sheet becomes soft and pliable. Vacuum is drawn in the enclosed mold cavity. The sheet, in its rubbery elastic state, is pressed by the normal atmospheric pressure (14.7 psi) against the mold contours in the depressurized space. After a short cooling period, the sheet "sets" in the shape of the mold and can then be removed.

Vacuum forming generally appears to be the least expensive method because the mold can be of light construction and has to withstand only atmospheric pressure. The machinery required can be simple and needs only a heater, a clamping device, and a vacuum pump with reservoir and valve. However, modern sheet-forming machines are semi- or fully automatic and are frequently equipped with both vacuum and pressure equipment.

MODIFIED TECHNIQUES OF SHEET FORMING

Modified Techniques of Matched-Mold Forming

Single-Mold Technique. A modification of matched-mold forming for shallow draws utilizes a rubber blanket operating against the female section of the mold (Fig. 8.2A). The rubber blanket is either filled in the back with a liquid or is inflated by air, pressing the hot sheet into the mold cavity.

Plug-and-Ring Technique. In this technique the plug may or may not resemble the final formed article. The shape is drawn between the plug and the ring. Either the sheet is heated and the plug is forced down into the sheet for a predetermined distance (Fig. 8.2B), or the plug is heated and moved slowly into the cold sheet. In the latter case the plug would have the shape of the formed article.

The latter variation is applied successfully for forming thin thermoplastic sheets to shallow depth. Reduction of the ring diameter, with accompanying increase of the plug size, allows the production of cups or other articles with straight side walls.

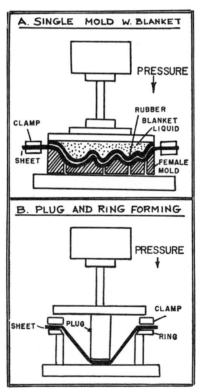

FIG. 8.2. Modified techniques of matched-mold forming.

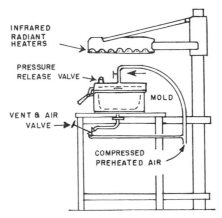

FIG. 8.3. Small air-blowing machine.

Modified Techniques of Air Blowing

Straight Air Blowing. A manually operated blowing machine is sketched in Fig. 8.3. The thermoplastic sheet is clamped on top of the female mold and heated under infrared heaters. The cover is placed over the hot sheet and clamped down. Preheated air at 70 to 115 psig pressure is blown through an inlet in the cover and presses the hot sheet against the contours of the mold. Uniform distribution of the air blast is aided by use of a deflecting disk attached to the inner surface of the cover. Air trapped underneath the sheet escapes through the vent holes, which may also be used for air circulation during the cooling cycle after release of the clamping pressure.[27]

Free Blowing. In this technique, which is commonly used with acrylics, the sheet is heated and clamped over the top of a circular, oval, or rectangular pressure box. Compressed air is applied, blowing the sheet into a large bubble. Air pressure and heat regulate the height of the bubble. Rings, bars, or rods placed on top of the sheet may be used to divide the bubble into several smaller ones. Articles requiring high optical clarity, such as aircraft canopies are formed by this technique.

Plug-Assist Blowing. This technique is performed with the aid of a pneumatic press which operates a cored plug or helper. The plug has sufficient contour and height to push the hot sheet ahead of it (Fig. 8.4A). As the press closes, a gasket forms an airtight seal around the top edges of the cavity. Compressed air is then introduced through the cored plug to form the sheet to the shape of the mold.

Trapped Sheet Forming. This technique is illustrated schematically in Fig. 8.4B, and is generally used to produce transparent covers for food containers, or for other purposes, from circular pieces of thermoplastic

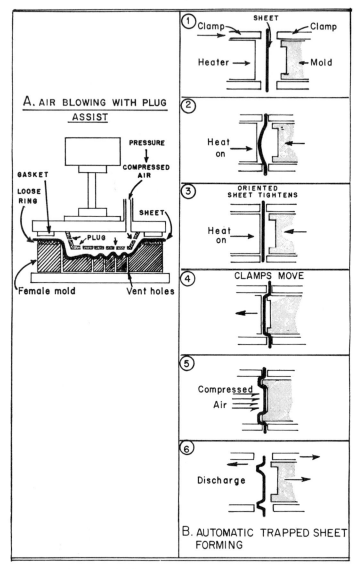

Fig. 8.4. Different techniques of air-blowing.

material.[1] The operation is as follows: A stack of thin plastic disks is placed in a feeding magazine. A single disk is removed at a time by a vacuum cup from the stack and is dropped into the open mold. The mold then closes, and heat is applied to the entire surface of the disk. Automatic temperature regulators are provided to control the proper operating temperature. The clamping ring slides over the mold to form a lip on the plastic cover. Com-

(Courtesy of Emhart Manufacturing Co.)

FIG. 8.4C. Trapped sheet-forming machine. Hydraulically operated machine with 6 forming heads.

pressed air is then introduced to blow the warm plastic into the cooled portion of the mold cavity. After the plastic has solidified, the mold opens, and the formed cover is ejected by a stream of air or knockout plate. The cover falls into an inclined chute in which the finished covers are stacked. A hydraulically operated automatic machine with six forming heads, which can handle disk blanks up to 5 in. in diameter, is illustrated in Fig. 8.4C. The speed of machine operation depends on the type of article being made, on the thickness of the plastic sheet, and on the plastic resin used. For instance, a 16-oz cover made of 10-mil oriented polystyrene sheeting has been satisfactorily produced at a rate of 15 covers per minute per head, or 90 per minute for the six-head machine. An economic analysis has indicated that these plastic covers are generally competitive in price with paper covers of similar design.

An automatic roll-fed machine which forms larger articles of various shapes, such as toys, boxes, blister packs, advertising signs, etc., is illustrated in Fig. 8.4D. It consists of a cam-operated 22-ton forming and blanking press, an automatic feeding device, and a scrap chopper. The plastic film is moved horizontally through the machine and cut, after

(*Courtesy of Emhart Manufacturing Co.*)
Fig. 8.4D. Roll-fed, trapped-sheet forming machine.

forming, while the part is still in the mold. For instance, a tray 5 by 10 in. and 3 in. deep, has been produced from oriented polystyrene film, 10 mil thick, at a rate of 20 pieces per minute. Other non-oriented film or sheeting materials may also be used.

Modified Techniques of Vacuum Forming

Straight Vacuum Forming. This is the oldest and easiest technique of vacuum forming. In a straight vacuum forming machine, the thermoplastic sheet is clamped over a mold or mold box (Fig. 8.5A). The manually operated clamping frame is usually attached to the mold or mold box to prevent air from leaking in between the sheet and the mold. A heater is brought into position above the sheet, and heat is applied for sufficient time to soften the sheet thoroughly. The heater is removed, and the sheet is drawn down instantaneously by pulling a vacuum in the mold.

Straight Vacuum Forming into Female Mold. Drawing sheets into a female mold results in excellent replica of fine details and embossing on the outer surface of the drawn articles.[37] In articles having relatively shallow

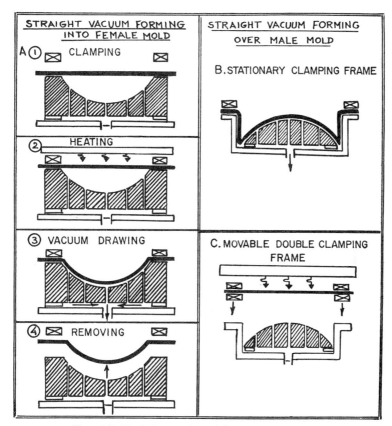

Fig. 8.5. Techniques of straight vacuum forming.

draws, straight vacuum forming has proved excellent; however, with articles having small radii or deeper dimensions, the corners and bottom generally are excessively thinned out.

Employing a female mold with multiple cavities is more economical than forming over a number of male molds, since it permits smaller spacing between cavities, which, in turn, allows more pieces per sheet.

Straight Vacuum Forming over Male Mold. A variation of straight vacuum forming is vacuum forming over a male mold placed into a mold box (Fig. 8.5B). This type of forming produces a formed article with the thickest section on top. However, much waste occurs since the plastic sheet must be drawn down the sides of the mold box sufficiently far to prevent excess thinning at the base of the male mold. In this technique, the sheet is heated while held between two clamping frames at a distance above the mold and is moved down manually or pneumatically on top of the mold box for forming (Fig. 8.5C). This practice is preferred with sheets which droop during heating, since it avoids premature contact of the hot sheet with the top of the cold mold which may lead to "locking" of the sheet on the mold top, with resultant overthickness of this portion of the article.

Straight vacuum forming of thin sheets over a male mold is used for the production of three-dimensional geographical maps, since it gives a greater accuracy of registration owing to restricted shrinkage than occurs when molding into a female mold.

Free Vacuum Forming. The sheet is clamped, as in straight vacuum forming, over a vacuum box without a mold and is heated. When the proper temperature is reached, vacuum is applied, drawing the sheet into the box without touching the walls. When the formed hemisphere is of correct depth, the vacuum is reduced and held until the hemisphere is cold. The vacuum is frequently controlled by an electric-eye circuit, actuated by the drawn hemisphere. This technique is similar to free air blowing and is also employed where perfect optical clarity has to be maintained during the molding of hemispherical shapes. Acrylics are frequently handled by this procedure.

Vacuum Snap-Back Forming. The technique of straight vacuum forming is well suited for most rigid thermoplastic materials. However, difficulties arise when vacuum-forming sheets which possess rubbery or elastic characteristics over a wide temperature range.[17] In such a case the so-called "snap-back" technique is often preferred.

The heated sheet, such as soft polyblends or graft polymers of acrylonitrile-butadiene-styrene (ABS) with a high rubber content or a plasticized vinyl sheet, is drawn by vacuum into the cavity of the vacuum box, as in the free-vacuum-forming technique (Fig. 8.6A). When the sheet has reached a sufficient depth, the male mold is moved by pressure into the vacuum box. When the stop blocks contact the vacuum box, the vacuum is released. The sheet, still hot and elastic, snaps back against the male mold and cools along the contours of the mold. This technique is also employed for forming acrylic sheeting.[31] Some fabricators apply vacuum to the male mold, which results in a better replica of the mold details (Fig. 8.6B). The process is performed in an air press with an overhead piston. Heating is frequently performed outside the press.

Vacuum Drape Forming. Drape forming is a technique which allows deep drawings[13, 24, 25, 34, 39, 40]. The thermoplastic sheet is held in a double frame above an inverted male mold and heated under radiant heaters (Fig. 8.7). When the forming temperature has been reached, the clamped sheet is lowered and pulled over the male mold. After the sheet has covered the entire mold, vacuum is applied, and the prestretched sheet picks up the detailed contours of the mold. The sheet is cooled as soon as it touches the surface of the cold mold during the draping operation.

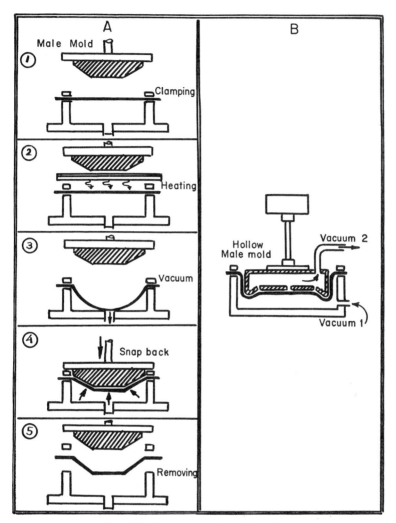

Fig. 8.6. Vacuum snap-back forming.

Thickness control is a problem at deep draws. Acrylic and styrene sheeting slides over the cold mold surface without difficulty, whereas polyethylene sheeting tends to freeze on contact with the mold. In this instance the section of the sheet on top of the mold is nearly as thick as the original sheet, while the sides are thinner, and the areas at the junction of the nearly vertical wall and horizontal base are usually the thinnest.

Vacuum Plug-Assist Forming. To overcome the problem of thinning, a modification of vacuum forming into a female mold has been developed which is called vacuum plug-assist forming, or drop forming (Fig. 8.8).[28] Its principle is to force a heated and clamped sheet into a female mold using a plug before applying the vacuum. The plug approximates the shape of the cavity and prestretches the sheet during its down movement. Immediately after the plug bottoms, vacuum is drawn and stretches the sheet further, to reproduce the mold surface detail. This technique may be considered as a reverse of the snap-back method.

During the downward travel of the plug, the air in the closed mold cavity is compressed. This causes the softened sheet to blow upward away from the mold edges and to press closely around the plug. The sheet is not

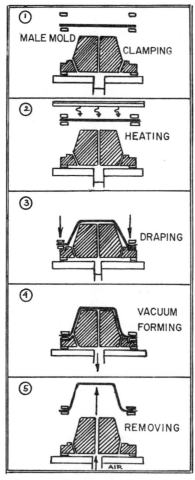

FIG. 8.7. Vacuum drape forming.

chilled and stiffened due to mold-edge contact and is drawn on the horizontal portion uniformly into the cavity. The plug may be heated to avoid chill marks on the sheet. The female mold is generally maintained cold to allow fast cooling. A deep-drawn article of uniform wall thickness and without "mark-off" defects is obtained.

Since the plug fills a large portion of the mold volume, control of the internal air pressure in the cavity by a vacuum bleed or by a sensitive relief valve is required.

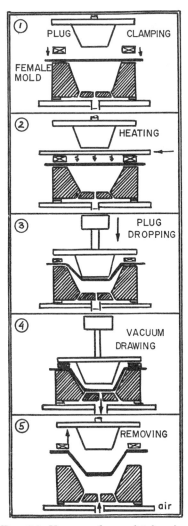

Fig. 8.8. Vacuum plug-assist forming.

(Courtesy of Hydrochemie Co.)

FIG. 8.9. Double-walled article made by combined vacuum drape and plug-assist forming.

Double-walled articles, such as refrigerator cabinets (Fig. 8.9), can be produced by maintaining the clamping frame stationary and moving the plug downward and the mold upward.

Vacuum Air-Slip Forming. This technique is a modification of drape forming over a male mold and is designed to reduce thinning on deep-drawn items.[2, 6, 8] It consists of prestretching the sheet prior to drape forming, just as the plug does prior to plug-assist forming (Fig. 8.10). The thermoplastic sheet is heated to the correct temperature in a stationary clamping frame. The portion of the machine below the clamping frame is enclosed. The male mold is mounted on a table. This table has a rubber gasket around the sides and travels like a square piston in the enclosed portion. An air bubble is formed when the air between the heated sheet and the mold is compressed by raising the table. This air bubble prestretches the sheet uniformly, and the size of the bubble is controlled by one or two automatic bleed valves located in the front enclosure. By evacuating the bubble, the hot sheet collapses around the mold, thus forming the required shape. Very uniform gauge distribution is achieved, because the sheet slips over the corners and edges of the mold. This and the vacuum snap-back forming

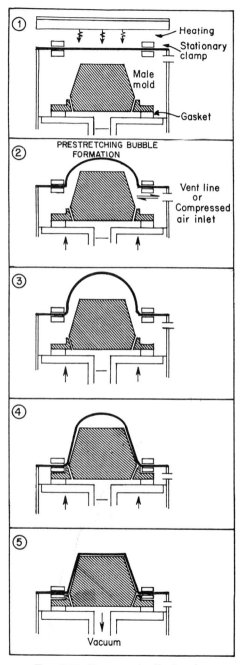

Fɪɢ. 8.10. Vacuum air-slip forming.

technique give the most uniform biaxial orientation of the sheet and reduce cost, because less edge trim may be incorporated.

Generally, the air entrapped below the heated sheet is sufficient to form the air bubble. However, if desired, it is possible to introduce additional compressed preheated air to increase the size of the bubble and obtain further stretching. If too much pressure is encountered, it may be reduced by bleed valves or gates.

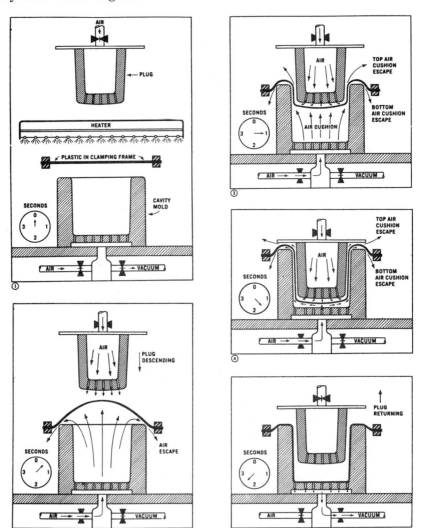

(*Courtesy of Autovac Co.*)

Fig. 8.11. Vacuum air-cushion forming.

Vacuum Air-Cushion Forming. This technique is a modification of plug-assist forming, as well as of air-slip forming. It requires vacuum, air pressure, and a plug with air holes.[37] Its principle consists of prestretching the hot sheet by air (Fig. 8.11).

The thermoplastic sheet is heated to the proper molding temperature. The clamped sheet is lowered to drape slightly around the female mold. Air is introduced into the mold and stretches the sheet into a bubble. Excess air escapes over the mold lip. The heated plug drops into the plastic bubble. Air blowing through the plug holes forms a second air cushion and stretches the sheet to the final general shape, yet maintains highly uniform wall thickness. The hot sheet is supported between the hot plug and the cool female mold by cushions of moving air. Vacuum is drawn as air introduction is stopped, and the hot sheet immediately snaps along the contours of the mold. The hot plug starts withdrawal simultaneously. The formed material chills rapidly in the cold mold, and may be removed quickly by assisting

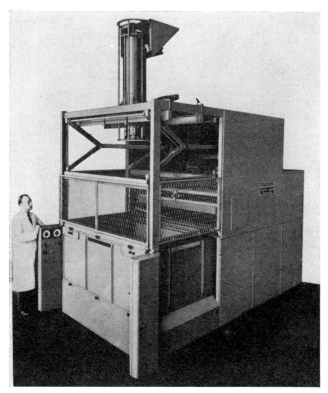

(Courtesy of Hydrochemie Co.)

FIG. 8.12. Universal vacuum forming machine which can be used for all techniques of vacuum forming.

drape lift action and air jets. Air continues to flush the mold of residual heat to ensure fast repeat cycles.

A vacuum forming machine in which a thermoplastic sheet can be formed by all these techniques is illustrated in Fig. 8.12. The upper cylinder for plug-assist, air-cushion, and snap-back forming can be seen, as well as the lower enclosed section for the air-slip technique.

Combined Pressure and Vacuum Forming Technique

This combined technique uses air pressure and vacuum simultaneously and is carried out in a hydraulic press, illustrated in Fig. 8.13. The top platen of the press is flat and electrically heated. The bottom platen carries the female mold. The thermoplastic sheet is clamped between the top platen and the female mold by closing the press, and is heated by conduction. Compressed air at 50 to 250 psi is introduced through fine slots in

(Courtesy of Autovac Co.)

Fig. 8.13. Pressure-vacuum forming machine.

the top platen, and vacuum is drawn simultaneously through the vacuum holes in the female mold. The pressure is released, and the hot top platen is raised. The vacuum is maintained until the formed sheet is cool enough to be blown off.

This technique is well suited for thermoforming oriented films, such as polystyrene or polyester films, or for simultaneously laminating and forming these films with other sheeting materials. The oriented films have the tendency to shrink when heated, tighten up, and maintain an intimate contact with the hot top platen. Difficulties occur when a sheet sags away from the hot top platen and does not get heated uniformly. This can be corrected by applying pressure through vacuum holes during heating.

VACUUM FORMING MACHINES

Manually Operated Machines

In manually operated machines, all operations such as clamping, heating, vacuum drawing, cooling, and removal of the formed sheet are regulated or done by hand.

A basic machine for straight vacuum forming consists of a radiant heater, a clamping frame, and a vacuum pump with reservoir and valve. The female mold rests on a vacuum table which is provided with a vacuum port and connected through large-diameter piping to the valve. Frequently, the formed work is blown from the mold with a reverse air pressure. Auxiliary equipment consists of a temperature controller for the radiant heater, a handwheel connected to a worm-and-pinion gear to adjust the distance between the heater and the sheet, and a vacuum gauge.

Semiautomatic Machines

In semiautomatic machines, clamping and removal of the formed sheet are done manually. All other operations are preset and carried out automatically. The machines are equipped with cycling controls and timers. The control system includes a microswitch assembly, pyrometer in the heater, and solenoid valves wired integrally with four delay timers to regulate the duration of the over-all cycle, heating, forming, and cooling. The control system is usually interlocked, so that each individual operation has to be complete before the following one can start.

Single-Stage Semiautomatic Machines. Most of the vacuum forming machines in use are single-stage semiautomatic machines and have features which permit the use of several of the new techniques as well as straight vacuum forming. One air cylinder is required to move the heater or the sheet-clamping frame horizontally. Another air cylinder is required to move either the frame, plug, or mold vertically in the drape, plug-assist forming, or air-slip techniques. Three air cylinders are required for the universal machine, as illustrated in Fig. 8.12. Plug and mold may be moved simultaneously against each other, and the vacuum may be synchronized with either one or the two motions.

Commercial equipment ranges from a 1- by 1-ft frame size up to 12 by 12 ft. Although the pressure differential in vacuum forming is relatively low, the total force on a large mold can be very high. For example, when using a 48- by 72-in. mold, a force of 48,000 lb is imposed on the mold and also on the table to which the mold is gasketed.

Double-Stage Semiautomatic Machine. To double the output and to utilize electric heating better, several machines are built with two vacuum tables. A single heater bank moves horizontally between the two tables and heats one sheet while the other one is formed and changed.

Multi-station Continuous Semiautomatic Machines. All operations are carried out simultaneously at different stations. A schematic

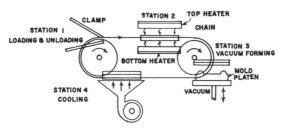

FIG. 8.14a. Four-station, continuous, semiautomatic machine.

(Courtesy of Brown Machine Co.)

FIG. 8.14b. Three-station, continuous, semiautomatic machine.

side view of a four-station machine is illustrated in Fig. 8.14a and is used for forming refrigerator and freezer inner-door liners.[19]

Four frames are fastened to two hydraulically driven precision chains. They stop at the four stations: (1) for unloading the formed liner from the frame and for loading a new sheet, (2) for heating the sheet from both sides, (3) for drape forming, and (4) for cooling in an air stream. The total cycle consists of the time of moving a frame around to all four stations, and of the heating, forming, cooling, and loading period. The machine is automatically controlled by seven timers and is capable of producing 80 to 100 door liners per hour. One operator can load and unload the machine, pierce the liners in an adjacent hydraulic punch press, and hang them on a conveyor.

Three-station machines are more commonly used and these incorporate an indexing table (Fig. 8.14b). The table has three steps 120 deg. apart. One step serves for loading and unloading the sheet, at the second step the sheet is heated, and at the third step the sheet is drawn into the desired shape and cooled.

Automatic Machines

In a fully automatic machine, all operations are automatic and synchronized. These machines were developed for the production of small packaging containers, houseware, and other high-volume items. Figure 8.15 shows a number of undercut containers which were formed by plug assist into split molds.

Roll-Fed Machine. In contrast to the general-purpose machines, where cut sheets are formed, this machine has been developed to handle rolls of flexible materials (Fig. 8.16). Any material of 0.005- to 0.040-in. thickness, and which can be rolled, may be used. It is mechanically drawn across the mold, heated, and formed. A new section is drawn automatically into place while the formed section moves to a second station in the machine for trimming. This machine reduces man power by eliminating costly handling of sheet. Speed of forming is variable, depending upon the type of sheet being used and its thickness. Rigid vinyl film, e.g., of 0.008-in. thickness, can be formed at the rate of three cycles per minute, employing a multi-cavity mold.

Multi-station Machine for Small Containers. An automatic multi-station machine is on the market for forming small packaging containers employing the plug-assist forming technique and the horizontal rotary principle (Fig. 8.17). The machine works as follows: Sheeting is fed into it from a continuous roll or from a stock of precut blanks. Preprinted sheet is accurately indexed by means of a photocell. Following the loading into the clamp frame, the sheet and frame are carried horizontally through

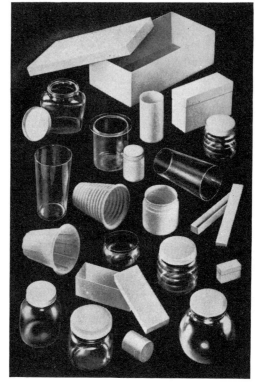

(*Courtesy of Hydrochemie Co.*)

FIG. 8.15. Vacuum-formed containers.

(*Courtesy of Autovac Co.*)

FIG. 8.16. Automatic roll-fed machine.

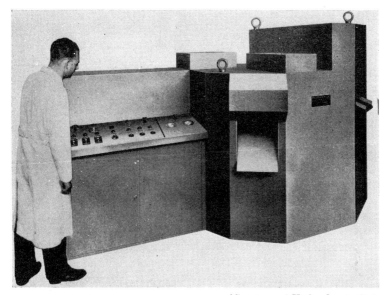

(*Courtesy of Hydrochemie Co.*)

FIG. 8.17. Automatic multi-station forming machine for packaging containers.

several heating stages, each consisting of an upper and a lower radiant heater which can be regulated in temperature. This multi-stage heating principle can deliver sheeting of any color or thickness, up to $\frac{1}{8}$ in., to the forming stage in properly heat-softened condition every 3 sec. The molding area is 10 by 12 in. and allows simultaneous forming of 20 containers, 2 in. in diameter by 3 in. deep, or 24,000 containers per hour. The forming is accomplished by a hot plug and a chilled mold, allowing, generally, 2 sec for cooling. After forming, the sheet with the molded containers can be transported directly to a filling station, then to a sealing station, and finally to a trimming station, where the filled and sealed containers are separated from the base sheet, conveniently ejected, the trim mechanically removed, and the finished work stacked. Another alternative is simply to trim the containers immediately after forming, and to have them ejected, as shown in Fig. 8.17. The latter machine is a six-station machine with six clamping frames which revolve horizontally and stop at each 60 deg of travel.

In another roll-fed machine, a small vinyl closure, e.g., is turned out in a multi-cavity mold at a rate of 60,000 units per hour. The automatic machine feeds the roll of vinyl film into the vacuum section, prints it, cuts out the formed pieces, dries the printed ink, stacks the units, counts them, and packages them into paper tubes.

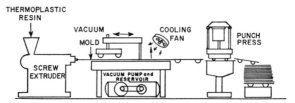

FIG. 8.18. Single-stage continuous machine.

Specialty Machines for Blister, Skin, and Snap Packaging. Roll-fed machines are used in forming transparent thermoplastic packaging film or sheeting for blister, skin, or snap packaging. In blister packaging, the film or sheeting is vacuum-formed over or into a mold of the shape of a hemisphere or of the article to be packaged. The formed "window" is cemented or stapled to a printed cardboard. In skin packaging, no mold is employed, and the transparent packaging film is drawn directly over the article to be packaged. In snap packaging, the thermoplastic sheet is formed with a lip by a sliding ring, so that it can be snapped as a protection above the article.[38]

Combined Extrusion and Vacuum Forming Machine. A number of sheet materials, such as high-impact polystyrene, foam polystyrene, polyethylene, and acrylics, are made by extrusion through a flat die. To utilize the heat in the freshly extruded sheet, the forming equipment may be positioned directly behind the extruder (Fig. 8.18). The machine elements, without heater, are basically the same as for conventional forming.[22] Straight vacuum forming, drape, and plug-assist forming techniques are employed. The process variation exists in that the mold section travels with the moving extruded sheet through the forming cycle, retracts from the formed section, and returns to a recycle position. After forming, the items are trimmed from the extruded sheet. Speed of extruder, vacuum former, and punch press are synchronized.

Frequently, a three-roll take-off finisher is needed between extruder and the forming unit to prevent transmission of vibration from the forming station to the still molten portion of the sheet near the extruder die and/or to polish surfaces of the sheet. With the take-off, a reheating section in the forming machine is required.

The combined extrusion and vacuum forming technique is employed for forming products where large quantities and long runs are required. Its disadvantages are that a high degree of control and synchronization is needed, that hot sheeting cannot be preprinted conveniently, and that the rate of extrusion is generally lower than the capacity of a modern vacuum forming machine. Its advantages are lower heating cost, uniformly heated sheets, reduced materials-handling cost, and, since hot sheet is continuously delivered to the forming zone, elimination of intervals when the mold is idle.

ELEMENTS OF VACUUM FORMING MACHINES

Heating Equipment

Heating of the thermoplastic sheet to the required forming temperature can be brought about either by utilizing the heat from the original manufacturing process (extrusion, calendering, planishing, or laminating) or by separate heating. Conduction heating by steam, hot water, oil, or electricity is generally used when employing matched-mold forming or the combined pressure and vacuum forming technique. Heavier gauge sheeting is usually preheated in air circulating over or under infrared heaters in order to reduce the machine heating cycle. All commercial vaccum forming machines have provisions for infrared radiant heating.

The four factors which affect the heating cycle with infrared heaters are (1) heater temperature, (2) heater density, (3) spacing between heater and sheet, and (4) radiant-energy absorption characteristic of the sheeting material.

Types, Controls, Temperature, and Density of Infrared Heaters. The infrared radiant heaters are either strip-style, rod-type, conducting glass panels, or "Nichrome" resistance wires, open or embedded in glass-fiber mat or tubing. The heating area should extend about 2 in. beyond the clamping frames and should provide a uniform radiation of infrared waves into the material.

Glass-embedded "Nichrome" resistance wires provide a very uniform heat but cannot exceed 700 to 800°F, since the glass fibers would crystallize at higher temperatures. Their heater density, which defines the electrical power input per square foot of heater area, is about 2 to 3 kw at full heater temperature. Their heating cycle is generally slower than that of the strip heaters, as shown in Fig. 8.29. For example, a 0.080-in.-thick white high-impact styrene sheet requires 150 sec to heat, using a mat-type heater of 700°F. Chromalox strip heaters of 1000°F accomplish the same result in approximately 20 sec.

Strip- or rod-type heaters have exceedingly long life, since the elements are not exposed to humidity, dust, or fumes. Their heater density depends on the spacing of the rods or strips in the heater bank. The relationship between heater density and time required to heat to forming temperature is shown in Table 8.1.[20, 33]

Banks of strip- or rod-type infrared heaters are used in almost all commercial vacuum forming machines. The temperature of these banks is generally preset and controlled by an attached surface thermocouple

TABLE 8.1. HEATER DENSITY VS. HEATING TIME

Heater density, kw/sq ft	Heating time, sec
1.7	160
3.4	70

Material, polyethylene, 0.120 in. thick; heater temperature, 1100°F; final sheet temperature, 250°F.

connected to a millivoltmeter as a temperature-indicator and to a regulating on-and-off switch. In a few continuous machines, the temperature is controlled by time-proportioning devices which keep the power on for only part of the time. The temperature of the strip- and rod-type heaters is difficult to maintain uniformly and must be worked out to compensate for cold air flow, heater travel, and edge cooling effect. Heat insulation above the heaters and insulation below the heater in the nonheating cycle reduce radiation heat losses. The strip- and rod-type heaters have the disadvantages that they lose radiation intensity in the course of time. They also require 10 to 15 min to reach full heat before operation can be started.

These deficiencies have been overcome in a recent machine where the heaters consist of small cells, containing several free resistance wires heated to 1800°F. These wires do not alter in intensity of radiation even after hundreds of hours of operation. A second advantage of these heaters is that they save on electric power in so far as they furnish the full power of 6.25 kw/sq ft only when directly over the sheet. The power input drops to one quarter while the heaters are traveling and when in the neutral position.[21] The heaters are, therefore, relatively cool while traveling across the sheet, preventing uneven heating. However, the temperature of the resistance wire can only be varied by means of a transformer, which increases the cost of equipment.

Heater Arrangements, Heat Absorption, Conductivity, and Economy. A handwheel connected to a worm-and-pinion gear is used to adjust the distance between the heater and the sheet.

It is known that, as heater temperature increases, a greater portion of the emitted energy is in the short wave lengths which the sheet will not readily absorb. This means that the electrical energy supplied to the heater bank is utilized less efficiently at maximum heater temperature than at a lower temperature. However, the total energy emitted is proportional to the fourth power of absolute temperature. As heater temperature increases, there is a significant increase in energy emission at all wave lengths. The resultant gain in sheet heating outweighs by far the penalty in heater efficiency.

Operation at maximum heater temperature to obtain rapid heating is both effective and economically sound for all thin thermoplastic sheet (generally less than 0.050 in. thick under a single heater bank) and for thick polyethylene sheets. Heavier sheets of other materials, however, should be heated more slowly at a rate dependent on the material, to avoid overheating of the surface. The poor thermal conductivity of plastic materials requires the adjustment of the heating cycle in conformance with the thickness of the sheet.

To shorten the heating cycle for heavier sheets, several machines are furnished either with a polished and non-tarnishing reflector underneath the heated sheet or with a top and bottom heater bank, so that both sides of the sheet are heated. Frequently, the bottom heater is of lower wattage than the top heater.

On large machines (over 24 by 36 in.) heater turn-off switches are provided so that various sections of the heater bank can be turned off when forming sheets of smaller area or for pattern heating. When large sheets are being formed, zonal control heating is used. This means that a separate temperature-control unit is provided for each zone to ensure controlled heat over the entire sheet.

In most commercial machines the heaters travel horizontally over the clamped sheet which is kept stationary during the heating cycle. This arrangement is relatively simple as long as only one top heater bank is employed. It gets complicated, however, when using a plug-assist forming arrangement or a top and bottom heater. Therefore, several recent machines keep their heaters stationary and move the clamped sheet horizontally underneath or between the heaters.

Sheet Clamping

In all vacuum forming techniques, the sheet is clamped tight during the heating, forming, and cooling cycle.

The sheet-clamping frame is adjustable in size, is pneumatically operated, and features parallel clamping action on the newer machines. An air-driven cam action locks the upper frame against the lower frame with uniform pressure on all edges of the sheet and is self-compensating for all sheet thicknesses. Four cams, giving approximately 12,000 lb total locking force in larger machines, can hold the thickest and toughest sheet firmly in place for any forming operation.

The clamping frame and air-cylinder shafts on the frame are frequently maintained at a uniform temperature by circulating either hot or cold water through them. Polyethylene sheeting, for example, tends to stick to hot frames.

The clamping frame is held stationary during the forming cycle in most vacuum forming techniques, but, it travels vertically in drape forming and horizontally in trapped sheet forming.

(*Courtesy of Autovac Co.*)

FIG. 8.19. Mechanical assist.

Mechanical Assist

Assist rings (Fig. 8.19), bars, or rods are frequently used in drape vacuum forming to avoid "webbing" between male mold sections, and to help produce articles with small taper. Webbing is the folding under of excess material on a mold because of excessive stretching or sagging of the sheet before forming. The ring, bar, or rod is attached to the upper clamping frame above the sheet. During the draping operation, it carries the sheet to the lowest area between the male mold sections and ensures a tight fit of the sheet against the mold surfaces when vacuum is applied.

Assist rings, bars, or rods may also be used in air-slip vacuum drawing (Fig. 8.11) to subdivide the blown bubble into several smaller bubbles when forming several items simultaneously.

Vacuum plug-assist forming (Fig. 8.9) may be combined with the method of slip forming employing assist rings, bars, or rods which are attached to the lower clamping frame. The plastic sheet is held loosely between the two frames. After the sheet is heated, the plug is pushed down into the sheet to draw the work. The loosely held sheet slips under the clamp and draws into the side walls, producing an article with thicker walls than would otherwise be possible. Vacuum is applied to make the final shape and details.

Frequently, a mechanical aid to aid removal of the formed sheet, called a "stripper," is employed. A stripper functions like a drape assist in reverse. It may be made by fastening piano wire to the lower clamp frame. When the clamp frame moves upward, the formed article is pulled from the mold mechanically. In using a stripper, the mold must be grooved to allow the wire to lie flush during the forming operation.

Vacuum Systems

The air between the mold and the sheet has to be evacuated very rapidly. This requires a large vacuum surge tank, large-diameter piping, wide-opening valves, and an effective pump. The pump should be of the high-capacity type rather than the high-vacuum type, and should deliver a vacuum of about 28 in. of mercury. Both rotary- and piston-type vacuum pumps are in use. In the higher capacities, water-cooled pumps are required. When several machines are installed in one plant, a central vacuum system is frequently used and is piped to the individual machines. The vacuum tank should have a larger capacity than the volume to be evacuated and, together with the pump, should be engineered to provide adequate recovery rates for a particular size of machine.

This presents a problem when large articles have to be vacuum-formed. In the standard machines the vacuum pump is arranged behind the vacuum surge tank. One solution to the problem has been found by placing the pump in a side line between the mold and the vacuum surge tank and by installing two electromagnetic valves in the main line, as shown in Fig. 8.20. In operation, Valve A is closed first, and the tank is evacuated through Valve B. Both valves are opened when evacuating the air between the sheet and the mold. The sheet is drawn closely to the mold walls, and Valve B is closed. The pump now has to evacuate only the remaining space left between the mold and the almost formed sheet, which is accomplished within a fraction of a second. Finally, Valve A is closed, Valve B is opened, and the surge tank is evacuated again, till the next sheet is drawn.

Vacuum systems required for two different machine sizes are given in Table 8.2.

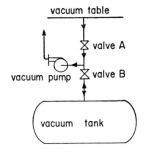

Fig. 8.20. Vacuum system.

TABLE 8.2 VACUUM SYSTEMS

	Mold size	
	16 by 24 in.	40 by 60 in.
Vacuum surge tank	10 gal	25–30 gal
Vacuum pump	30 cu ft/min	150 cu ft/min
Motor on pump	2½ hp	9½ hp
Diameter of vacuum port	2 in.	3 in.

Air Compressor

An air compressor supplying 5 to 10 cu ft/min at 85 to 100 psig is required for the average-sized drape, plug-assist or air-slip machine. More compressed air is required for pressure forming. Compressed air is also used for removal of the formed items from the mold to aid cooling. When several machines are installed together, a central air compressor is usually used.

Molds

The shape and the details of the formed article influence the type of mold and mold materials used.[4, 18]

Female vs. Male Mold. In forming articles with a single mold, the finest details are reproduced on the side which comes in contact with the mold. Therefore, location of fine details often determines whether a male or female mold should be used. Female molds are suitable for the reproduction of the fine details on the outside of the formed article. Male molds, on the other hand, are used for reproduction of fine details on the inside of the formed piece, and are more easily polished than is a female-mold cavity. If high-gloss thermoplastic sheeting is formed so that the glossy side is in contact with the mold, the mold surface has, in most instances, to be highly finished in order to enhance rather than impair the gloss. However, a matte surface is required for polyethylene sheeting to prevent air entrapment. When a multicavity mold is to be used, female molds are preferred, because there is less danger of webbing, and cavities can be more closely spaced.

Depth of Draw. The depth of draw is a prime factor controlling the final wall thickness of the formed article. It indicates which forming technique may best be used. The degree of draw is characterized by the ratio of H to W (where H = height or depth, and W = width), as illustrated in Fig. 8.21. When straight vacuum-forming into a female cavity, the depth of draw should not exceed one half of the cavity's width. For drape forming over a male mold, the height-to-width ratio should be 1:1 or less. With plug-assist or air-slip forming, the ratio may exceed the ratio 1:1.

Vacuum Holes or Slots. Proper air evacuation assists material flow in the desired direction and in uniform wall thickness. In general, deep

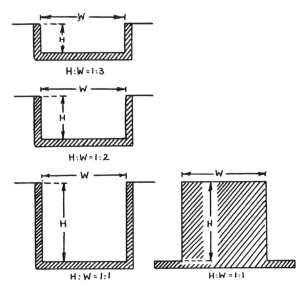

Fig. 8.21. Different drawing ratios.

corners require intensified evacuation to ensure the draw of material into corners. Large, flat surfaces require the least evacuation. The diameter of vacuum holes should be 0.010 to 0.025 in. for polyethylene sheeting, 0.025 to 0.040 in. for other thin-gauge material, and may increase to 0.060 in. for heavier rigid material. These diameters may be used without causing undesirable blemishes in the formed item.

In most materials, the vacuum holes have to be drilled. For easier manufacture, the holes may be counterbored 0.25 in. diameter from the underside of the mold. Piano wire coated with a release agent may be used for getting very small holes in spray metal, cast resin, or plaster molds. The mold material is sprayed or cast around the wires, which are pulled out later. The time of evacuation depends, generally, on the number and diameter of the vacuum holes. For instance, in formed door liners the average evacuation time is between 2 and 5 sec. To ensure very fast venting in the air-slip technique, the vents on the mold are in the form of long slots, approximately 0.015 in. wide for polyethylene and 0.020 in. wide for other rigid materials. The average time of evacuation is less than $\frac{1}{2}$ sec. However, in some special blister or contour-package forming, slow controlled exhausting of the air aids in forming.

Radii and Angles. Items with sharp corners can be formed but should be avoided if possible, and radii should be kept as large as the functional design of the item permits. In most instances a radius should be at least equal to the original sheet thickness or $\frac{1}{8}$ in., and never less than $\frac{1}{16}$ in.

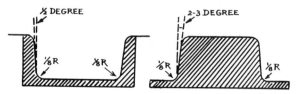

Fig. 8.22. Minimum radii and draft for female and male mold.

Sharp bends, corners, notches, grooves, or other abrupt changes in cross section result in excessive stress concentration and in reduction of strength of the material down to one third of its original value.

Right angles should be avoided. In general, ½ to 1 deg of draft should be allowed in a female mold (Fig. 8.22), since the material will shrink away from the mold. In a male mold, drafts should be 2 to 3 deg, since the material tends to cling to the mold.[26]

Ribbing. Wherever possible, curves or ribs should be designed into the weaker sections of the molded article to increase stiffness. This is important in the case of long, flat surfaces. By proper ribbing (Fig. 8.23), sheet gauge can be reduced, leading to a lower cost and shorter heating cycle.

Undercuts. Undercuts are possible when forming flexible materials, such as polyethylene or plasticized vinyl. They should be avoided with rigid sheeting unless the article is designed to permit angular removal

Fig. 8.23. Adding rigidity by ribbing.

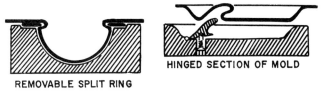

REMOVABLE SPLIT RING   **HINGED SECTION OF MOLD**

Fig. 8.24. Molding undercuts.

Fig. 8.25. Permanent insert.

from the mold, or a mold is used with hinged, cammed, or loose split sections, as illustrated in Fig. 8.24.

Inserts. Structural or functional inserts, such as metal strips or bars, can be made an integral part of the molding by placing them in a recess of the mold and forming the thermoplastic sheet around them (Fig. 8.25). This technique is frequently used in the manufacture of parts, such as refrigerator inner door liners, and is called reinforcing with orphaned inserts.

Cooling and Heating. The forming cycle can be accelerated and maintained uniformly through the use of mold temperature controls. The mold temperature should be low enough to facilitate rapid cooling and, on the other hand, high enough to prevent chill marks. In most vacuum forming operations, it should be between 100°F and 190°F, according to the thermoplastic material used. Circulating water lines are either drilled into the mold, placed in or around a mold, or attached to the hollow side of a mold. They are generally between $3/8$ and $1/2$ in. in diameter. Localized heating of a mold may be achieved by inserting cartridge-type electrical heaters. A typical position for localized mold heating is in the half-round radius on top of a cup mold, as shown in Fig. 8.26. The higher local temperature will allow drape forming without chilling. In vacuum plug-assist forming, the plug should have the temperature of the drawn sheet to avoid

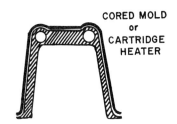

CORED MOLD
or
**CARTRIDGE
HEATER**

Fig. 8.26. Localized mold heating.

chilling. For this reason, the plug should be made of metal and cored for heating. The mold itself is cooled to accelerate the cycle.

Accuracy of Dimensions and Shrinkage. The closest dimensions are held in the side of the sheet which comes in contact with the mold. Variations in sheet thickness, during drawing, cause more dimensional change on the opposite side. A female mold is indicated if the closest dimensions must be held on the outside of the item. A male mold is preferred if the closer dimensions should be on the inside of the item.

When a thermoplastic sheet is vacuum-formed, shrinkage occurs during the cooling cycle. Shrinkage is less in forming over a male mold than in forming into a female mold. This is due to the fact that the material shrinks onto the male mold in the first case, and shrinks away from the mold in the second case. However, the formed item is more difficult to strip from a male mold. Drape or air-slip forming minimizes shrinkage.

Aftermolding shrinkage takes place when the formed article is removed hot from the machine.

Mold Materials. The low pressure involved in vacuum forming permits the use of a large variety of materials in mold construction. The choice of material depends primarily upon the quantity and quality of formed items to be produced.

Molds for Short Runs. For experimental or short runs, wood or plaster molds may be used. Hardwood should be kiln-dried and glued with the grain in parallel direction, since the shrinkage rate of wood across the grain is different from that with the grain. For improved surface finish and wear resistance, wooden molds may be coated with an epoxy resin and then sanded, buffed, and polished. The advantages of plaster are low cost, easy workability, and the fact that it sets at room temperature. Molds constructed from plaster and impregnated with an epoxy resin have produced as many as 50,000 formed articles.

Molds for Medium Runs. Cast phenolic, cast filled epoxy resin, and furan resin molds have been used for medium runs. They are characterized by good dimensional stability and good abrasion resistance, and they may have highly polished surfaces. For added strength, they may be reinforced with glass fibers.

The slow cooling of plaster, wood, plastic, and similar poorly conductive materials requires that such molds be cooled by a cold air blast or similar means when rapid production cycles are desired.

Molds for Permanent Use. Metal or metal-surfaced molds are used for long runs. Molds cast of aluminum or magnesium alloys are most widely used because they can easily be machined and are good heat conductors, and their shrinkage is well known to mold- and patternmakers. They may be cast by gravity or by pressure into sand or plaster. A pressure-cast mold is more expensive but provides a mold requiring less finishing and polishing.[7] The molds are usually cored for water circulation.

Molds may be surface-finished with copper-nickel or chromium plating. Electroplated, sprayed-metal, and metal molds[9] have produced as many as 500,000 molded articles without any evidence of deterioration. The mold itself consists of a metal shell, reinforced with nonferrous alloys or resin-impregnated backing. Precise detail and exceptional surface finish may be obtained with molds of this type. Items such as vinyl or polyethylene place mats with cloth or fiber texture have been vacuum-formed in sprayed-metal molds employing cotton fabric as the pattern.

(Courtesy of Hydrochemie Co.)
FIG. 8.27. Mold temperature regulator.

Molds machined of standard steel stock are satisfactory for simple shapes and single-cavity molds. However, multi-cavity cast molds require less polishing than do molds which are machined individually in single-cavity design.

Temperature Controls and Cooling

The temperature of the molds, as well as of the plugs and clamping frame, may be maintained by circulating water through them. A temperature controller with an electrically heated and thermostatically controlled water tank and a circulating pump is illustrated in Fig. 8.27. A timer is frequently connected to the water tank to start the heater automatically 1 to 2 hours before operating the vacuum forming machine.

Cooling of the formed article is sometimes brought about by forced convection through the use of large-volume air fans (Fig. 8.28). These fans are synchronized with the machine cycle and are running only during the cooling cycle.

Safety Devices

Screens are usually provided to prevent persons from placing hands underneath clamping frames or moving molds, and may only be opened when the machine is not operating. Two-hand controls are installed to make sure operator's hands are out of the way of the mechanism. Inter-

(Courtesy of Autovac Co.)

Fig. 8.28. Cooling fans.

locking circuits between air and electric controls are furnished to prevent the mechanism from moving if air pressure fails.

ANALYSIS OF OPERATING PROBLEMS IN VACUUM FORMING

Heating

Temperature Gradients and Rate of Heating. Heating the sheet to forming temperature accounts for 50 to 80 per cent of the total time required for most forming cycles. Hence, rapid heating is important for high rates and economic production of formed items. Examples 9 and 10 of Chap. 2 show the calculation of the time required to heat or cool a thermoplastic sheet to a certain temperature by conduction and/or convection. The time of heating or cooling is roughly proportional to the specific heat and sheet thickness and varies inversely with the thermal conductivity and surface heat-transfer coefficient.

For best results, thermoplastic sheets should be heated uniformly to prevent internal strains. All thin sheets, 0.001 to 0.040 in. thick, may be heated within a few seconds by an infrared radiant heater, located 3 to 4 in. above the sheet surface. Sheets heavier than 0.060 in. (with the exception of polyethylene) should be heated with less intensive heat, considering the low thermal conductivity of thermoplastics, which is generally in the range between 1×10^{-4} and 8×10^{-4} cal/sq cm/sec/°C/cm.

Commercial vacuum forming machines have no provision to measure the actual temperature in the plastic sheeting. A satisfactory method of measuring this temperature is by embedding several small thermocouples on top, bottom, center, and sides of the sheet and connecting them with a multiple switch to a sensitive potentiometer.

The time required to heat polyethylene sheets of different thickness from room temperature to a forming temperature of 250°F is given in Table 8.3.[20, 33] The increase in heating time is not directly proportional to the increase in thickness.

A high-impact, white, polystyrene sheet, 0.080 in. thick, was chosen for an empirical study of the temperature distribution during the heating cycle. Figure 8.29 illustrates the temperature distribution on top and bot-

TABLE 8.3. HEATING TIME VS. SHEET THICKNESS (POLYETHYLENE)

Sheet thickness, in.	Time to heat to 250°F, sec	Heating time per unit thickness, sec/mil
0.020	18	0.9
0.060	36	0.6
0.100	48	0.5

Experimental conditions: temperature of heater, 950°F; heater input, 4 kw/sq ft; spacing, 5 in. between heater and sheet.

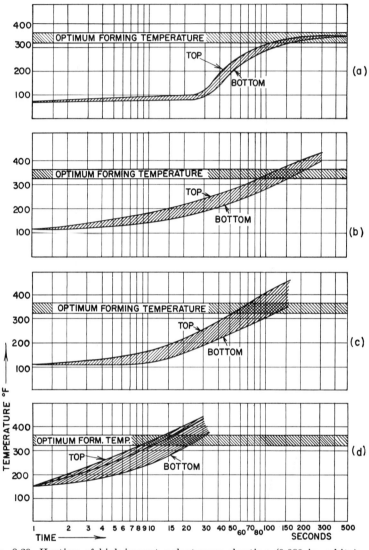

FIG. 8.29. Heating of high-impact polystyrene sheeting (0.080 in. white) under infrared radiant heaters.

    (a) "Pyrex" glass heater—8 in. distance.
    (b) Sill glass-fiber heater—700°F—4½ in. distance.
    (c) Chromalox strip heater—700°F—3½ in. distance.
    (d) Chromalox strip heater—1000°F—3½ in. distance.

tom of the sheet when heated with three different types of heaters—a "Pyrex" glass heater, a glass-fiber heater, and a bank with strip heaters. The heat distribution may also be calculated according to the method of Example 15 of Chap. 2. The heat distributions, measured or calculated, indicate that either a longer heating cycle at lower heater temperature or heating from both sides is required, for most of the materials, to give a fairly uniform heat distribution throughout a heavier-gauged sheet. Two other ways of shortening the machine cycle are by dielectric heating or by preheating the sheet outside the machine.

Pattern Heating. Pattern heating is a technique in which the radiating heat is varied. It is applied to reduce nonuniformity in thickness reduction and is accomplished by shading off areas of the sheet which would otherwise be drawn excessively along sharp contours and corners.

A high-impact, white, polystyrene sheet, 0.082 in. thick, was shaded with several layers of tissue paper, as illustrated in Fig. 8.30.[32] Controlled temperature differences of 70°F could be obtained on the pattern heated sheet, in contrast to 20°F on a blank sheet. Both sheets were vacuum-drawn into a square female mold (7 by 7 by 3 in.). The variation in thickness was 0.002 in. for the shaded drawn sheet and 0.027 in. for the blank drawn sheet.

The formation of strains and the effect of pattern heating on dimensional stability and mechanical properties were investigated. Shaded drawn sheets were dimensionally less stable and had a higher impact strength than the blank drawn sheets. Increase in the over-all forming temperature resulted in less internal strains and better dimensional stability.

Forming Range. Thermoplastic sheet can be vacuum-drawn over a range of temperatures. The lowest forming temperature is that at which a square box with fairly sharp and distinguished corners can be drawn from the sheet without whitening or other visible disadvantage; the highest forming temperature is that at which the sheets either get so soft and fluid that they sag in the clamping frame by their own weight (melt sagging) or change their appearance, or scorch owing to degradation. For example, certain high-impact polystyrene sheet can be heated to 460°F without change in appearance. Sheets of styrene-acrylonitrile-butadiene polyblends may be heated to 450°F before discoloration or a strong odor of burned rubber becomes noticeable.

The heat-distortion temperature (ASTM D 648) and the softening temperature, measured by a simple droop test, were determined for various sheeting materials and are compared with the lowest and optimum forming temperature in Table 8.7. The droop test, which is applicable for rigid sheetings, consists of fastening a $\frac{1}{2}$-in.-wide specimen to a bar with a 1-in. horizontally free overhang and heating in an oven. The temperature is

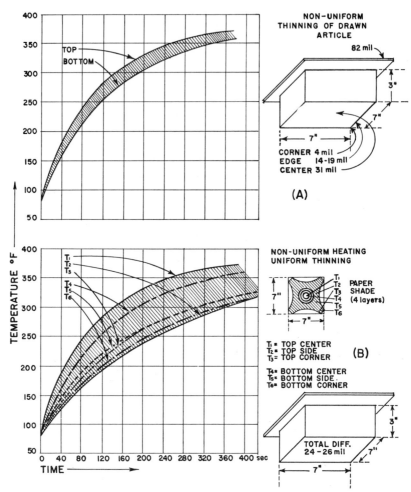

FIG. 8.30. Pattern heating and straight vacuum forming. (A) Without shading; (B) With shading.

raised gradually, 2°C per minute, until the overhang portion deflects ⅛ in., which is reported as the softening temperature. This temperature lies below the lowest forming temperature and corresponds to the temperature dynamically determined by measuring the maximum damping and decrease in torsion modulus.[29] The optimum forming range is dealt with on pp. 499–503.

Sagging. There are two causes for sagging in heated sheets—thermal expansion and melt flow.

Thermal expansion occurs in all non-oriented sheets being heated from

TABLE 8.4. MELT INDEX OF POLYETHYLENE VS. SAG RATE

Resin	Melt index (ASTM D 1238)	Sag rate (% of value for resin A)
A	0.6	100
B	1.0	135
C	7.1	150
D	3.0	300

room temperature to forming temperature, and is in the order of 1 to 2 per cent in all directions. Since the sheet is firmly restrained on all four sides by the clamping frames, this growth must appear as sag.

Melt sagging can occur in a thermoplastic sheet when the viscosity of the resin becomes excessively low at the forming temperature and the sheet begins to droop because of its own weight. It may represent a serious problem with some resins when drawing large sheets into shallow molds. In such cases, sag may exceed the amount of drawing, and webbing of the sheet may be encountered.

Sagging owing to thermal expansion and melting can sometimes be overcome by pre-stretching and orienting the sheet while it is extruded. Sheet made in this manner tends to shrink after it is heated beyond the softening point. If stretch is properly controlled, the shrinkage can compensate for the thermal expansion. Excessive stretching, however, may result in enough stress to interfere with forming.

Sagging of polyethylene sheet can be controlled by employing a resin of low melt index[20, 33] (high melt viscosity) which reduces the rate of sagging, as Table 8.4 indicates.

Drawing of Heated Sheet

Uniformity of Thickness Reduction. Non-uniform thinning of the drawn sheet is the limiting factor of straight vacuum forming. It depends on the ratio of H to W, as well as on the shape, angles, and radii of the mold. Figure 8.31 illustrates the thickness reduction of a rigid vinyl sheeting, 0.008 in. thick, drawn into a circular pot mold of different depths.[30] A more uniform thinning is obtainable by differentiated vacuum draw, i.e., intensified suction in corners and less suction on flat surfaces. A very uniform thinning can be brought about by pattern heating. However, internal strains occur in the formed sheet, influencing dimensional stability.

Good uniformity and dimensional stability are obtained by drape, plug-assist, or air-slip forming. The effect of forming temperature on bottom and wall thickness is shown in Fig. 8.32 for a high-impact polystyrene sheeting, 0.040 in. thick, formed by plug-assist forming into a rectangular box.[28] Another variable which influences the uniformity in thickness reduction is the speed of drawing, affected by the speed of evacuation or the motion of the plug, the clamping frame, or the mold (Fig. 8.33). Slow

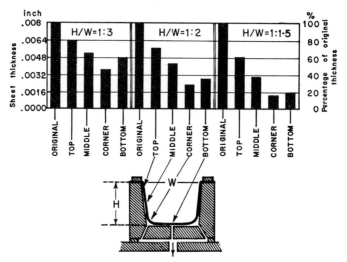

FIG. 8.31. Thinning of a 0.008 in. rigid P.V.C. film drawn at different ratios of H to W.

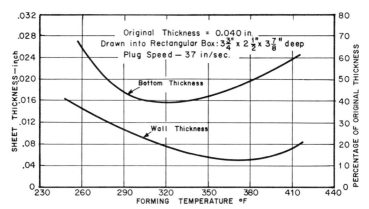

FIG. 8.32. Plug-assist forming. Effect of forming temperature on bottom and wall thickness of a high-impact polystyrene sheet.

drawing may result in crazing owing to early cooling. Very fast drawing may result in too much thinning on corners or undercuts, because the material did not flow fast enough.

The speed is generally governed by the temperature of the material being formed; consequently, thin-gauge material must be drawn faster than heavy-gauge material, since the heat of the former is more rapidly dissipated into the air.

Monoaxial Stretching. It is desirable that stretching be uniform in all directions. For specially shaped articles, however, this may be

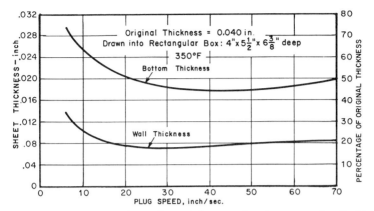

FIG. 8.33. Plug-assist forming. Effect of plug speed on bottom and wall thickness of a high-impact polystyrene sheet.

extremely difficult, or impossible. The extreme would be stretching in one direction only, and would cause the greatest changes in the mechanical properties due to orientation.

High-impact polystyrene sheeting was heated to the optimum forming temperature of 340 to 365°F and drawn to varying degrees in a mono-axial stretching device. The effect of the orientation on the mechanical properties was determined by measuring the impact strength in the length-wise and transverse directions. The slope of the two curves (Fig. 8.34) indicates that the impact strength increases slightly in the direction of draw but decreases more in the transverse direction. These two curves describe the effect of orientation under most extreme drawing conditions. The difference is more distinct at lower forming temperatures and in sheet-ings of the elastomeric type, such as the acrylonitrile-butadiene-styrene (ABS) polymers and the vinyls.[32]

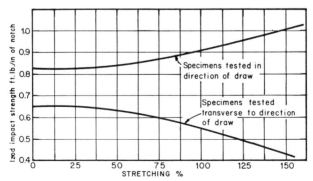

FIG. 8.34. Monoaxial stretching *vs.* impact strength for high-impact polystyrene forming temperature 340 to 365°F.

Straight polystyrene film can be stretched several hundred per cent in one direction, whereby tensile strength, total elongation, and the craze-resistance increase in the direction of stretch.[16] In most forming operations the average draw is less than 60 per cent, and the difference between draws in biaxial stretching is less than 30 per cent. Therefore, no large directional differences in the mechanical properties can be expected in most thermoplastic sheetings drawn at the correct forming temperature.

Biaxial Stretching. The amount of biaxial stretching is frequently expressed as a percentage increase in linear directions—lengthwise and transverse. It may also be defined as an area increase by thickness reduction, according to the formula

$$\text{Per cent stretch} = 100 \left(\sqrt{\frac{t_i}{t_f}} - 1 \right)$$

where

$$t_i = \text{initial thickness}$$

$$t_f = \text{final thickness}$$

A correlation between the thinning out of the sheet during the drawing operation and the biaxial stretching in linear directions may be calculated from the following formula or may be read from Fig. 8.35.[14, 15, 23]

$$t_f = \frac{t_i}{\left(\dfrac{L_F - L_i}{L_i} + 1 \right) \left(\dfrac{W_F - W_i}{W_i} + 1 \right)}$$

where

$$L_F = \text{final length}$$

$$L_i = \text{initial length}$$

$$W_F = \text{final width}$$

$$W_i = \text{initial width}$$

The influence of biaxial stretching on the mechanical and thermal properties has been studied for most of the common rigid sheeting materials. In most experiments the linear stretching was determined by printing a square pattern, subdivided into $\frac{1}{8}$- by $\frac{1}{8}$-in. squares, over the total surface to be drawn, and measuring the dimensions of the extended squares. The sheets were heated on one side to the required forming temperature and stretched 5 to 90 per cent by vacuum forming.[32]

The Effect of Biaxial Stretching on Mechanical Properties. Biaxial stretching increases tensile strength in longitudinal and transverse direction

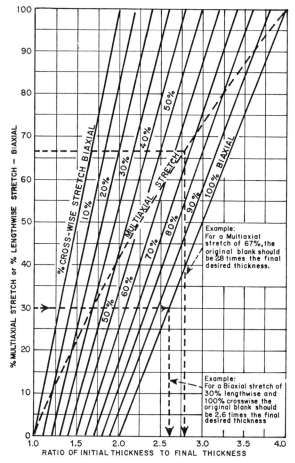

FIG. 8.35. Biaxial stretch *vs.* thickness reduction.

due to orientation. This was observed on straight polystyrene sheeting which was stretched hot 200 per cent longitudinally and transversely.[16] The effect of the stretching ratio was studied on cast polymethyl methacrylate sheeting which was biaxially stretched in a hot oil bath at a low strain rate.[14, 15, 23] The tensile strength remained the same over a wide stretching ratio and increased only 6 to 12 per cent up to a stretching of 150 per cent.

Impact strength increases with percentage of stretch and decreases with increase in forming temperature. Figure 8.36 illustrates these results for high-impact polystyrene sheeting which had been vacuum-formed at temperatures between 250 and 470°F.[32] Similar effects of stretching on impact strength were also observed on acrylic sheeting,[14, 15, 23] as shown in Figs. 8.37a and b.

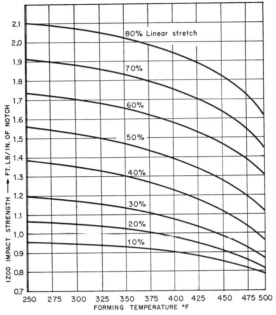

FIG. 8.36. The effect of biaxial stretching at different forming temperatures on the izod impact strength of high-impact polystyrene sheets.

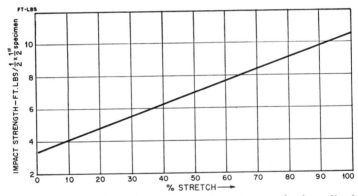

FIG. 8.37a. Effect of stretching on charpy impact strength of acrylic sheet.

The tensile elongation at failure was found higher for stretched polymethyl methacrylate sheeting[16] than the unstretched material, but it decreased as the degree of stretching increased. Polyethylene sheeting which was vacuum-formed at two different temperatures[20, 33] (Table 8.5) showed a higher total elongation at higher temperature owing to less orientation.

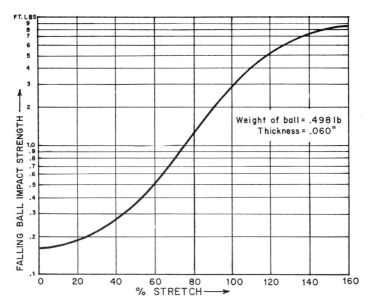

Fig. 8.37b. Effect of stretching on the falling ball impact strength of acrylic sheet.

TABLE 8.5. THE EFFECT OF FORMING TEMPERATURE ON
TENSILE PROPERTIES OF POLYETHYLENE

Forming temperature, °F	Tensile strength, psi		Elongation, %	
	Length direction	Transverse direction	Length direction	Transverse direction
240	2,340	1,850	350	510
315	2,050	1,970	560	

If the tensile test is carried out at a high speed (20 in./min), the total elongation may be taken as a measure of toughness of rigid sheeting. Figure 8.38 illustrates that the total elongation of high-impact styrene sheeting decreases with increase in forming temperature, but decreases with the percentage of draw. Analogous results were also obtained with ABS sheets (acrylonitrile-butadiene-styrene polyblends), as shown in Fig. 8.39.[32]

The Effect of Biaxial Stretching on Dimensional Stability. The dimensional stability of drawn sheets was determined after 100 hr exposure at elevated temperature. Sheets formed at higher temperature have less orientation and are, therefore, dimensionally more stable than sheets formed at lower temperature.

Three different rigid vinyl sheetings were drawn 20 to 25 per cent at various temperatures in the forming range and exposed for 100 hr to 165°F.[32]

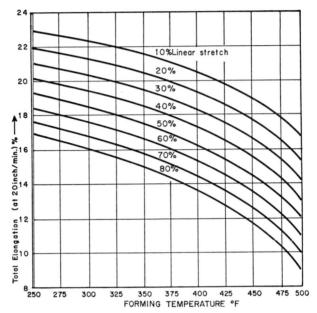

FIG. 8.38. The effect of biaxial stretching at different forming temperatures on the total elongation of high-impact polystyrene sheets.

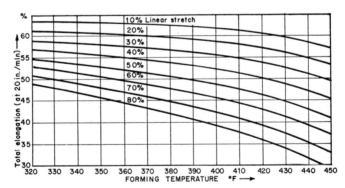

FIG. 8.39. The effect of biaxial stretching at different forming temperatures on the total elongation of ABS (Acrylonitrile-Butadiene-Styrene) polyblend-sheets.

The unplasticized polyvinyl chloride sheeting developed less shrinkage than the unplasticized copolymer (vinyl chloride–vinyl acetate) sheeting (Fig. 8.40). The addition of 5 to 10 per cent plasticizer (dioctyl phthalate) to polyvinyl chloride allowed the sheet to be drawn at temperatures as low as 165°F but made it less dimensionally stable.

The heat exposure resulted also in warping of the sheets. Sheets which

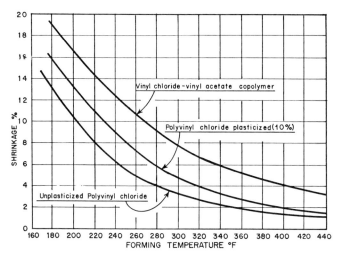

Fig. 8-40. The effect of biaxial stretching (20 to 25 per cent) on the dimensional stability of rigid vinyl sheetings. Shrinkage after 100 hours exposure at 165°F.

were drawn at a medium forming temperature warped most, whereas sheets which were drawn at a lower or higher forming temperature bent only slightly or remained flat.

Polyethylene sheeting which was formed at higher temperature was dimensionally more stable when exposed to a temperature above 150°F.

Two grades of high-impact polystyrene sheeting were evaluated—standard and heat-resistant.[32] The drawn specimens of the heat-resistant grade did not shrink after exposure at 165°F, whereas the specimens of the standard grade shrank significantly, as shown in Fig. 8.41. For example, the shrinkage was almost 21 per cent at a drawing ratio of 80 per cent and a forming temperature of 250°F, but only 6 to 7 per cent at a forming temperature of 320°F. By increasing the temperature of heat exposure from 165 to 185°F, the heat-resistant grade started to shrink too, as shown in Fig. 8.41b. The percentage of shrinkage at this higher temperature corresponds to the shrinkage of the standard type at the lower exposure temperature. To maintain optimum strength, a low forming temperature is preferred; whereas to avoid excessive shrinkage, a high forming temperature appears to be desirable. A compromise has to be made between these two properties. Drawn acrylonitrile-butadiene-styrene sheeting does not shrink when exposed at 165°F for 100 hr. At 185°F and a longer exposure, discoloration and degradation of the rubber portion occur.

The Effect of Biaxial Stretching on Craze Resistance. Biaxial stretching improves craze resistance. Stretched polymethyl methacrylate sheeting does not craze in short-time tensile tests.[14, 15, 23] The threshold stress for stress-

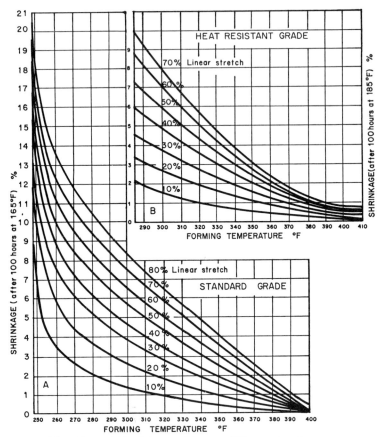

FIG. 8.41. The effect of biaxial stretching at different forming temperatures on the dimensional stability of high-impact polystyrene sheetings.

A. Shrinkage of standard sheeting after 100 hours exposure at 165°F.

B. Shrinkage of heat-resistant sheeting after 100 hours exposure at 185°F.

solvent crazing with benzene is equal to approximately three quarters of the ultimate strength for the 100 per cent stretched material, as compared with a threshold stress equal to approximately one quarter of the ultimate strength for unstretched material. Crazing decreases markedly with increasing stretching ratio. However, abrasion resistance of the stretched material was found to be appreciably less than that of the unstretched material.

The Effect of Forming Speed on Orientation. Reduction in speed has been found to be another method of reducing orientation.[20, 33] Table 8.6 compares data from tests on polyethylene sheeting formed at drape speeds of 8 and 4 in./sec. At the higher drape speed, elongation in the direction of maximum draw was reduced owing to a higher degree of orientation in that direction.

TABLE 8.6. THE EFFECT OF DRAPE SPEED ON
TENSILE PROPERTIES OF POLYETHYLENE

Forming temperature, °F	Drape speed, in./sec	Tensile strength, psi		Elongation, %	
		Direction of maximum draw	Transverse to maximum draw	Direction of maximum draw	Transverse to maximum draw
240	8	2,340	1,850	350	510
240	4	2,180	1,810	505	500

Maximum Stretching. A testing apparatus is on the market to measure how far a thermoplastic sheet will stretch at various temperatures (Fig. 8.42).[10, 36] Its principle consists of drawing a sheet, heated to a certain forming temperature, over an annular frame. The amount of stretch can be regulated. For a given sheet material and forming temperature, the amount of stretch which ruptures the sheet is determined first, and then test pieces are drawn to a point just short of the rupture point. After drawing, the sheet is cooled, and the thickness of the sheet section stretched within the ring is measured. The amount of biaxial stretching is calculated from the reduction in thickness. The dependence of maximum stretching from the forming temperature is illustrated in Fig. 8.43 for a high-impact polystyrene sheet.

(Courtesy of Hydrochemie Co.)

FIG. 8.42. Testing apparatus for maximum biaxial stretching.

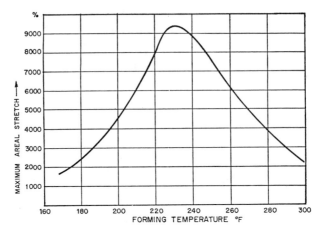

Fɪɢ. 8.43. The effect of forming temperature on maximum stretching of a high-impact polystyrene sheet.

Cooling

Proper cooling of the formed piece of work is an important factor of the sheet-forming process. Difficulties have occurred with the use of male molds when cooling thin rigid sheeting which could not be stripped without cracking. The temperature of the mold or of the plug should be maintained, at the ranges stated in Table 8.7, by the circulation of water or by electrical heating.

In plug-assist forming, the female mold is generally maintained cold. Chill marks may occur on drawn products when the mold is too cold. Warping of the drawn item is caused when the mold is too hot or the article is removed too early. The rate of cooling depends on the thermal conductivity and thickness of the sheet. Cooling may be accelerated by blowing or circulating cool air over the formed item and mold.

SHEET MATERIALS

The ideal sheet material should be strong and tough at low as well as at elevated use temperatures; it should not deform under load; should not deteriorate with aging; should have a high heat-distortion temperature; should resist water, oil, and grease; should have a low residual strain, a good caliper control, an adequate melt viscosity to resist sagging, and a high gloss; and, finally, should be inexpensive. None of the presently used thermoplastic sheeting fulfills all of these requirements. The five groups of thermoplastic sheeting which account for the major share of the sheet-forming business are the styrenes, the acrylics, the vinyls, the polyolefins, and the cellulosics. A sixth group of increasing importance consists of the polycondensation products, such as polesters, polyamides, polyoxymethyl-ene, and polycarbonates. The forming temperatures and other thermal properties of various sheeting materials are summarized in Table 8.7. Trade names are omitted and may be found in "Modern Plastics Encyclopedia" or in recent publications.

Styrene Sheeting

High-Impact Polystyrene Sheeting. High-impact polystyrene sheets are either polyblends of polystyrene resin with styrene-butadiene rubber, or graft polymers in which styrene has been polymerized onto polybutadiene chains. Their sale amounted to 40,000,000 lb in 1956. High-impact polystyrene is a low-cost resin and can readily be processed into sheets by flat-die extrusion. About 75 per cent of the produced sheets were formed into refrigerator parts.[12]

An optimum forming temperature of 340 to 365°F is recommended. This temperature is obtainable for an 0.080-in.-thick white sheet in a standard forming machine after 70 sec at a heater distance of 3 to 4 in. To obtain a high surface gloss, some sheets are laminated with a straight oriented polystyrene film. A modified sheet, impregnated on its surface with an ultra-violet-light-absorbent material, was developed to improve light stability. "Mylar" polyester film, laminated to high impact polystyrene sheets, provides a highly abrasion-resistant surface which is useful in furniture, appliances, and wall coverings.

Acrylonitrile-Butadiene-Styrene (ABS) Sheeting. Sheets of styrene-acrylonitrile copolymer (SAN) are more brittle than high-impact polystyrene sheeting. However, by blending or grafting this copolymer in different ratios with butadiene-acrylonitrile copolymer, very tough sheeting of stiff to leatherlike rigidity is obtainable. Its impact strength at room temperature is significantly higher than that of high-impact polystyrene material. At low temperatures the impact strength of both materials is of the same magnitude. Because of their rubber content, the mechanical properties are affected by heat and light aging. The optimum forming temperature is 300 to 350°F. Thermoformed ABS sheets are finding increasing applications in the automotive and airplane industry—for head liners, dashboards, post covers, and side and inner door panels—amounting to an annual volume of 12,000,000 lb.

Oriented Polystyrene Film. Straight, biaxially oriented polystyrene film requires a close control of the heating cycle. It can be vacuum-formed by using shallow draws into hot female molds, but it is more frequently drawn by either the trapped-sheet-forming technique or by combined pressure and vacuum forming. Most of it is fabricated into small transparent packaging containers.

TABLE 8.7. FORMING TEMPERATURES AND OTHER THERMAL PROPERTIES OF VARIOUS SHEET MATERIALS

Material	Forming conditions				Softening temperature droop test, °F	Heat-distortion temperature, °F		Deformation under load % per day at 122°F 2,000 psi load	Linear thermal expansion % at 122°F 10^{-5} in./in./°C	Thermal conductivity cal/cm²/sec/°C/cm × 10^{-4}
	Forming temperature		Mold temperature, °F	Plug temperature °F		at 66 psi	at 264 psi			
	°F optimum	°F lowest								
						ASTM D 648	ASTM D 648	ASTM D 621	ASTM D 696	
	—	—	—	—	—					—
Styrenes:										
High-impact polystyrene	285–350	248	120–150	175–250	223–230	180–190	155–180	2.1–2.8	7.8–9.1	1.0–3.0
	340–365	285	125–150	175–250	245–257	—	193–198	2.0–2.5	7.8–9.1	1.0–3.0
Biaxially stretched polystyrene	360–380	—	120–140	240–250	—	—	175–195	—	6–8	2.4–3.3
SAN copolymer	430–450	—	—	—	—	—	203	0.6	6.4	3–4
ABS polyblend	300–350	285–320	—	—	189–263	170–190	148–215	34.0–4.8	4.8–11.2	
ABS graft polymer	310–340	—	—	212–220	215	—	183–190	—	—	
Acrylics:										
cast	290–360	—	—	—	—	210	205	—	—	4–6
extruded	230–320	—	—	—	—	175–216	166–202	4.5	7.5–9.0	4–6
Vinyls:										
P.V.C. unplasticized	285–355	200–260	105–115	140–300	230–239	166	158–172	2.5	6.6–8.0	3–4
P.V.C.Ac. unplasticized	255–320	195–240	100–110	—	162–167	—	140–146	1.6–4.0	6.9	4–5
Polyolefins:										
Polyethylene branched	250–375	225	120–170	300	194	120	—	0.6 @ 100 psi	15–30	8
linear	275–375	250	150–200	300	—	145–175	—		15–30	8
Polypropylene	300–395	—	—	—	284	—	—		11	3.3

Cellulosics:										
Cellulose acetate	270–325	210–250	125–140	—	—	180–230	130–160	45	8–16	4–8
Cellulose acetate-butyrate	265–320	210	—	—	250–310	170–180	150–170	—	11–17	4–8
Ethyl cellulose	255–290	—	—	—	245–280	—	120–160	—	10–20	3.8–7
Polycondensation products:										
Acetal (polyoxymethylene)	365–390	365	150–170	—	354	338	212	0.5	4.5	5.5
Polyamides										
polycaprolactam	420–430	410	—	—	413–421	—	137–253	1.7	10	5.8
polyhexamethylene adipamide	430–480	—	—	—	425–477	300–360	135–150	—	10	5.8
Polyethylene glycol terephthalate										
oriented	380–490	—	—	—	380–480					
nonoriented	350–400	—	—	—	350					
Polycarbonate, (polybisphenol-A carbonate)	440–475	420	170–200	525–600	427–445	282–293	280–290	—	7	4.6

Polystyrene Foam Sheeting. Thin sheets, 0.010 to 0.025 in. thick, of extruded polystyrene foam are vacuum-formed into picnic plates, ice-cream containers, and disposable cups for vending machines. Due to their excellent insulating properties, polystyrene-foam containers are well suited for hot drinks as well as for ice cream. The density of the foam sheets is generally 1.5 to 4 lb/cu ft. The heater temperature has to be lowered (e.g., from 1000 to 650°F) in vacuum-forming these sheets, and length of the heating cycle has to be increased correspondingly. Combined extrusion and vacuum forming machines are frequently employed to avoid reheating of the foam sheet. Foam sheets have a greater tendency to web than high-impact sheets, because they expand further under the influence of heat.

Acrylic Sheeting

Cast and Extruded Acrylic Sheeting. Acrylic sheeting stands second after the high-impact polystyrene sheeting, with a total of 20,000,000 lb sold for sheet-formed articles in 1956. Polymethyl methacrylate sheeting, cast and extruded, can be formed by the same techniques. Owing to their excellent outdoor weatherability, optical clarity, and toughness, arcylic sheets find use in airplane canopies, car taillights, signs, displays, and light fixtures. A less expensive sheeting material is a copolymer of styrene–methacrylate with excellent transparency but reduced weather resistance. A more impact-resistant sheeting material is the translucent polyblend of methyl methacrylate with rubber.

Oriented Acrylic Film. Oriented acrylic film is an extruded, biaxially stretched material of high clarity and strength. Its main use has been for lighting panels and ceilings.

Vinyl Sheeting

Rigid Polyvinyl Chloride Sheeting. The impact strength of rigid polyvinyl chloride is of the same magnitude as that of high-impact polystyrene and does not decrease significantly down to −40°F. Most polyvinyl chloride sheet darkens, but is little affected mechanically by heat and light aging. Rigid polyvinyl chloride sheeting can be drawn over a wide temperature range (175 to 455°F) when stretched only 5 to 25 per cent. Higher draws require close temperature control, otherwise the draws are incomplete at low forming temperature, or holes are torn when the temperature is too high. Small packaging containers and three-dimensional contour maps are sheet-formed from rigid vinyl sheetings.

Rigid Vinyl Copolymer Sheeting. Rigid sheets made of vinyl chloride–vinyl acetate copolymer have better flow and are easier to draw into female vacuum molds. But, their heat-distortion point is so low that these sheets cannot be considered for many applications, e.g., in the automotive or building industry. Transparent packaging containers, signs, and displays are vacuum-formed from this copolymer.

Plasticized Vinyl Sheeting. Plasticized vinyl sheeting is difficult to form when deep embossed details are required. Excellent results are obtainable with heated molds of low depth. Place mats, Halloween masks, and wallets are drawn from plasticized vinyl sheeting.

Polyolefin Sheeting

Polyethylene Sheeting. Polyethylene sheeting may be thermoformed at temperatures of from 10 to 100°F above their crystalline melting point. A higher forming temperature results in higher dimensional stability owing to less orientation. The problem of sagging can be overcome by the use of a resin with a low melt index. Many household articles and packaging containers are thermoformed from thin- and medium-gauge branched polyethylene. These uses amounted to over 5,000,000 lb in 1956. Further end-use development work will open new fields of applications, such as laboratory equipment, boilable kitchen utensils, toys, and packages for food, hardware, and chemicals. In cases where higher stiffness is required, linear polyethylene sheeting may be employed. The polyethylenes combine a high degree of toughness, even at low temperatures, with complete freedom from toxicity and resistance to a wide variety of chemicals.

Higher Polyolefin Sheeting. Polypropylene sheeting is presently available only in semi-commercial quantities and can be formed under similar conditions as linear polyethylene.

Cellulosic Sheeting

Cellulose acetate and cellulose acetate–butyrate sheeting are sheet-formed into transparent packaging containers and display articles. An optimum forming temperature of 270 to 325°F was established for cellulose acetate and of 265 to 320°F for cellulose acetate–butyrate. At higher temperatures, blisters occur. During the heating cycle, plasticizer and/or residual solvent may evaporate and can condense inside a female mold. Venting of the female mold or the use of a male mold has overcome this difficulty. Plasticizer and/or solvent evaporation may also cause the formation of micro-bubbles in the heated sheet and result in loss of clarity. Practice has shown that it is better to heat cellulose acetate and acetate-butyrate sheet as fast as possible. Whitening or blushing of the drawn sheet can be avoided by maintaining the mold at 100 to 150°F.

Ethyl cellulose sheeting has a brilliant clarity and can be easily formed. Its resistance to acids and alkalies is satisfactory to allow its use for food packaging.

Polyamide and Polyester Films

Polyamide films have been tested for their sheet-forming characteristic and found to form fairly easy. Polycaprolactam film is in use for fish packaging.

Oriented polyethylene terephthalate film is characterized by a very high strength and sharp softening range. It has been successfully formed, employing either the trapped-sheet-forming technique or the combined pressure- and vacuum-forming technique. Due to their excellent electrical properties, polyester films are suitable for industrial applications, such as liners or covers for TV tubes, diaphragms for radio speakers, and other insulating applications.

FINISHING

Trimming

After the item has been formed, it must be separated from the remainder of the sheet.

Trimming of Thin-Walled Articles. Items formed from thin-gauge sheets can be trimmed either while still hot or after cooling. In short experimental runs, trimming is done by hand with a linoleum knife or a pair of shears.

Mechanical trimming is carried out with a steel die punch which consists of a sharpened rule, $\frac{1}{16}$ to $\frac{3}{32}$ in. thick and 1 to 2 in. high. The rules are shaped to fit single or multiple cavities and may also be used to punch out holes or slots. They are mounted on wooden or nonferrous metal frames and operated against a cutting surface made of end-grained wooden blocks, fiberboards, hard rubber, or rigid, tough plastic sheetings. The die punch can be built up if it is necessary to trim articles with draws deeper than 1 or 2 in. Clicker machines and small air- or hydraulic-operated presses have been used for thin-gauged materials. The principle of a combined trimming and vacuum forming machine is illustrated in Fig. 8.44a.

A planetary trimmer has been brought on the market to separate vacuum-formed items or group of items from the base sheet, provided that the line of separation lies in a plane. The principle of operation involves a stationary positive cutting die, against which is blocked the portion of sheet to be trimmed, and a movable negative cutting die which, by describing a circular path along the entire edge of the positive die, shears the formed article from the sheet. The principle is illustrated in Fig. 8.45, and the motion of the negative cutting die is shown by arrows. Mechanization is achieved by pneumatic means (Fig. 8.46). Automatic trimming devices have been incorporated in several recent automatic packaging-forming machines.

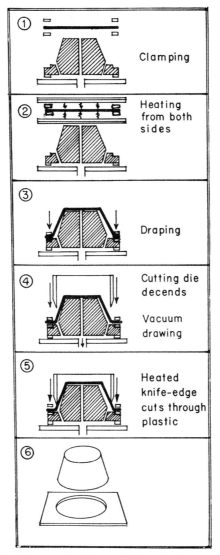

① Clamping

② Heating from both sides

③ Draping

④ Cutting die decends

Vacuum drawing

⑤ Heated knife-edge cuts through plastic

⑥

Fig. 8.44a. Vacuum drawing and trimming in one operation.

Trimming of Thick-Walled Articles. Heavy-gauge items should be trimmed only after cooling. Trimming by hand is done either by shearing with a guillotine knife or by sawing with a band saw (using buttress-type teeth or a rocker-type blade). Mechanical trimming is carried out by punching or shearing.

Clicker dies, high dies, and Walker dies are different types of cutting-

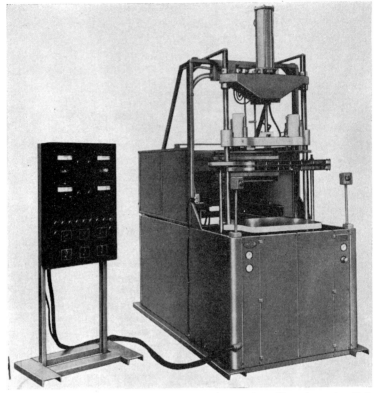

(*Courtesy of Emhart Manufacturing Co.*)

FIG. 8.44b. Combined vacuum forming and trimming machine.

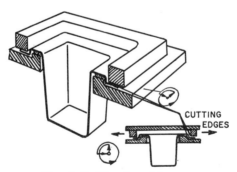

FIG. 8.45. Planetary trimmer.

edge punches. Clicker dies are either forged or bent from $\frac{1}{8}$- to $\frac{1}{4}$-in. steel strips and are provided with a sharp cutting edge. They are used for punching formed parts with a draw less than $2\frac{1}{2}$ in. High dies and Walker dies are built up and afford clearance for items between $2\frac{1}{2}$ and 7 in. deep.

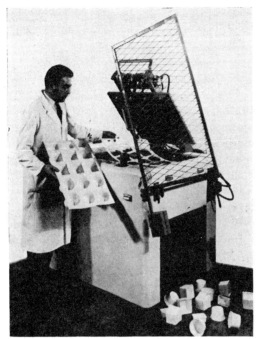

(Courtesy of Hydrochemie Co.)

Fig. 8.46. Planetary trimming machine.

The item to be trimmed can be supported by incorporating a nest or fixture into the cutting surface to form a single plate. The dies are installed in regular metal-cutting presses, such as open side crank presses, guided platen crank presses, heavy-duty air or hydraulic presses. Large items, such as refrigerator doors, are cut with the aid of 150-ton hydraulic presses with a stroke of 20 in.

In order to avoid going to extremely heavy presses, hot die cutting is frequently employed. The die half cuts and half melts its way through the thermoplastic sheet. Heating of the die is accomplished either by electricity or by circulating hot oil through copper tubing around the die. For accurate work, blanking or shearing dies with matched male and female sections are employed and are frequently furnished with leader and guide pins. A planetary trimmer may be used where the line of shearing lies in one plane. In some instances the use of cam-actuated dies permits punching in more than one plane of the formed item. However, this type of die is expensive and limited to large-volume operation.

Decorating and Processing

Preprinting. It is relatively simple to decorate formed articles by preprinting the flat sheet before the forming operation.[3] Precise and multicolor preprinting may be attained through silk screening, lithography, roto-gravure, letter press, spray painting, or decalcomania. Silk screening, being the least expensive method, is the most widely used for large production runs of single-sheet stock, and rotogravure for roll plastic stock.

When designing a preprinted article, a white sheet is first sheet-formed, hand painted, and flattened out again by reheating and pressing, whereby the required distorted image is produced. This is then copied, and a silk-screen stencil or printing plate is made.

Surface Finishing. Sheet-formed items may be spray-coated with varnishes or lacquers for protection of the print or with certain conductive materials to prevent static dust attraction. They may be covered with many different lay-ups, such as films, fabrics, paper, or foams, or may be flocked with short fibers, or laminated to other materials. Caution has to be taken to avoid plasticizer migration or solvent attack.

Machining. The trimmed edges of heavy-gauged formed articles may be finished with sanding belts or spindle shapers. The formed items can also be drilled, tapped, punched, swaged, etc., with ordinary hand or power tools designed for these operations. Care must be taken to minimize the occurrence of localized heating, which may set up strains in the formed articles.

SUGGESTIONS FOR FUTURE STUDIES

Because of the rapid development of the sheet-forming technique in recent years, most of the progress has come from empirical approach rather than through a fundamental engineering analysis. Little is known regarding the quantitative interrelationship of process variables. Some of the important objectives for future studies are: (1) to determine and predict radiant heating rates from the properties of the thermoplastic sheet; (2) to estimate cooling cycles based on heat-transfer and stress-relaxation data; (3) to determine the degree of thinning out of a sheet in relation to mold design and forming conditions; and (4) to design the item and the mold for optimum final strength, dimensional stability, and other desirable properties.

REFERENCES

1. Aldington, E. T., *et al.*, "Trapped Sheet Forming," *Modern Plastics*, **33**, 7, 117 (Mar. 1956).
2. Anonymous, "The Air-Slip Method of Vacuum Forming," *Plastics (London)* 158 (July 1954).
3. Anonymous, "From Design to 3-D Display," *Modern Plastics*, **33**, 3, 101 (Nov. 1955).
4. Anonymous, "Engineering a New Case," *Modern Plastics*, **32**, 11, 113 (July 1955).
5. Anonymous, "Formed Sheet Styrene Copolymers Invade Metal Stamping Field," *Modern Plastics*, **33**, 4, 108 (Dec. 1955).

6. Anonymous, "Formvac-Airslip Process," *Kunststoffe*, **47**, 23 (1957).
7. Anonymous, "Machine for Thermoplastics," *Modern Plastics*, **34**, 5, 142 (Jan. 1957).
8. Anonymous, "Modified Vacuum Forming Technique," *Brit. Plastics*, **29**, 252 (1956).
9. Anonymous, "Molds for Vacuum Forming," *Modern Plastics*, **32**, 7, 124 (Mar. 1955).
10. Anonymous, "A New Test of Sheet Formability," *Modern Plastics*, **35**, 3, 145 (Nov. 1957).
11. Anonymous, "Plastics' Junior Giant," *Modern Plastics*, **32**, 8, 87 (Apr. 1955).
12. Anonymous, "Progress Report on Sheet Thermoforming," *Modern Plastics*, **34**, 9, 107 (May 1957).
13. Anonymous, "Shape a Sheet," *Modern Plastics*, **31**, 9, 87 (May 1954).
14. Axilrod, B. M., "Effects of Biaxial Stretch Forming," *Modern Plastics*, **30**, 4, 117 (Dec. 1952).
15. Axilrod, B. M., *et al.*, "Biaxial Stretch Forming of Acrylic," *Modern Plastics*, **31**, 1, 128 (Sept. 1953).
16. Baily, J., "Stretch Orientation of Polystyrene and Its Interesting Results," *India Rubber World*, **118**, 225 (May 1948).
17. Blom, A. V., "Graphical Characterization of Plastics," *Kunststoffe*, **43**, 294 (1953).
18. Davenport, R. C., "Forming of Rigid Thermoplastic Sheet," *Plastics Technol.*, **2**, 232 (1956).
19. Davis, D. A., "Automatic Sheet Forming," *Modern Plastics*, **33**, 12, 119 (Aug. 1956).
20. du Pont (E. I. du Pont de Nemours & Co., Inc.), *Information Bulletin*, X-92 "Alathon" Polyethylene Resin-Thermoforming.
21. Escales, E., "Combined Vacuum and Thermoforming Machine," *Kunststoffe*, **47**, 543 (1957).
22. Anonymous, "Picnic Plates Vacuum Formed," *Modern Plastics*, **29**, 12, 92 (Aug., 1952).
23. Hiltner, J. R., "Recent Progress in the Development of Multiaxially Stretched Acrylics," paper presented at 5th Transparent Material Conference, Sept. 15, 1953.
24. Howell, G. H., "When and Why to Use Drape Forming," *Modern Plastics*, **32**, 2, 138 (Oct. 1954).
25. Hoy, J. M., "Vacuum Forming of Polystyrene Sheet," *SPE Journal*, **10**, 1, 9 (Jan. 1954).
26. Hrudka, R. F., "Techniques for Designing Vacuum Formed Plastics Parts," *Machine Design*, **28**, 114 (Mar. 2, 1956).
27. Matulat, G., "Progress in Forming Thermoplastic Materials," *Kunststoffe*, **47**, 291 (1957).
28. Mighton, J. W., "Plug-Assist Forming," *SPE Journal*, **12**, 6, 83 (June 1956).
29. Moritz, H., and Ewald, R., "Chemical and Physical Questions at the Manufacture and Forming of Thermoplastic Sheets and Films," *Kunststoffe*, **46**, 195 (1956).
30. Oelze, H., "Processing of Rigid P.V.C. Films," *Kunststoffe*, **47**, 93 (1957).
31. Pierson, O. L., "Forming Sharper Thicker Corners," *Modern Plastics*, **35**, 3, 152 (Nov. 1957).
32. Platzer, N., "Rigid Thermoplastic Sheeting," *Modern Plastics*, **31**, 3, 144 (Nov. 1954).

33. Rowe, A. G., "Thermoforming of Polyethylene Sheeting," paper presented at ACS meeting Sept. 1957.
34. Sauter, P. A., "Vacuum Forming and Drape Moulding," *Brit. Plastics*, **27**, 420 (1954).
35. Schmieder, K., and Wolf, K., "The Temperature and Frequency Dependance of the Mechanical Properties of High Polymeric Materials," *Kolloid-Z*, **127**, 65 (1952).
36. Siatem Co., "Testing apparatus," *Italian Patent* 41165 (1956).
37. Stratton, B., "Deep-Draw Vacuum Forming," *Plastics World*, (New York), **16**, 1, 1 (Jan. 1958).
38. Stratton, B., "Blister, Skin and Snap Packaging," *Kunststoffe*, **48**, 68 (1958).
39. Zimmermann, S. S., "Vacuum Forming of Thermoplastic Sheet," *India Rubber World*, **129**, 216 (Nov. 1953).
40. Zimmermann, S. S., "Vacuum Forming of Thermoplastic Sheet," *Can. Plastics*, 99 (Mar. 1954).

9. FORMING OF HOLLOW ARTICLES

G. P. Kovach, Dipl. Ing.

Foster Grant Co., Inc.

INTRODUCTION

Definition

For the purpose of this chapter, hollow articles are defined as those hollow objects that have either no external opening or a single opening smaller than their largest diameter. Examples of the first group are ping-pong balls, baby rattles, etc. The second group—hollow bodies with a single opening smaller than their largest diameter—comprises all sorts of bottles, etc.

History of the Hollow-Body Forming Industry

The desire to form hollow bodies from thermoplastics is as old as the appearance of the first truly thermoplastic material—celluloid. Probably the first hollow body formed commercially was the baby rattle, an item, which is still manufactured in essentially the same way as it was 70 years ago.

As long as celluloid was the only available thermoplastic material, the items fabricated therefrom had limited usefulness because of the high flammability of the material, and they were relegated mostly to the class of "novelties."

With the advent of injection molding and the parallel development of compounds suitable for this new fabricating technique in the early 1930's, the opportunity arose for the development of new techniques.

The predominant material available at that time was cellulose acetate. This could be made into sheeting and tubing, could be obtained in glass-clear form, and provided a wide latitude in processing conditions.

An extruded tube of clear cellulose acetate resembles in appearance the glass parison pulled from a glass melt with a blowing stick or emerging from the orifice of a glass-bottle machine. The main difference lies in the melt viscosity of the two materials. Whereas glass is so fluid that it will flow by gravity through a reasonably large orifice, cellulose acetate must be pushed by external pressure.

Nevertheless, this similarity fostered the idea of producing a container from cellulose acetate similar to a glass bottle. First attempts followed very closely the known glass techniques and departed from these only gradually as the peculiarities and different behavior of the available thermoplastic materials were recognized.

Interestingly, the forming of hollow bodies has received its biggest impetus so far not from the development of new methods but from the advent of a new material—polyethylene.

This dependence of the bottle-blowing and, generally, the hollow-body forming industry on polyethylene emphasizes the fact that the commercial history of this branch of the plastics industry is one of the shortest, and this product has caught the public fancy faster and has developed more rapidly than any other segment of this fast-growing industry.

The advantages of polyethylene, especially when used as a container for liquid, are obvious—nonbreakability, light weight, chemical resistance, and, most important, flexibility, which allows the manufacture of a squeezable bottle.

BASIC METHODS FOR FORMING HOLLOW ARTICLES

Blowing of Sheet

In the early industrial phases of thermoplastics fabrication, the plastic materials were available only in the form of sheets, and the first attempts in forming hollow bodies were necessarily restricted to these. The technique developed involved putting two sheets in a press (low pressure), followed by steam blowing through a small opening in the mold between the two sheets. The heat of the steam softened the sheets, and the steam pressure stretched them to conform with the mold faces which were normally cooled. The pressure of the mold halves was sufficient to fuse the edges of the two formed sheets.

Before long, the concept of forming hollow bodies from tubes made in a prior operation was patented. An application was filed May 28, 1880, and a patent was issued Feb. 1, 1881, to the Celluloid Novelty Company and Celluloid Manufacturing Company of New York describing "an improved process for molding hollow articles from a blank tube of any substance that is rendered plastic by heat, as celluloid or similar plastic material. . . ."

The methods described above were very suitable for the available materials, namely cellulose nitrate and cellulose acetate. These two materials are also easy to join by cementing methods, and most of the articles which could be made by a hollow-forming technique could also easily be made by forming halves separately by a swedging technique, followed by joining and cementing to form a hollow body

It is interesting to note that recent work in forming hollow bodies indicates a return to the original concept of forming from two sheets. One of the modern methods involves simultaneous extrusion of two sheets, followed by clamping and blowing of the warm sheets. This is particularly suitable for the manufacture of very large or very flat articles, where the uniformity of wall thickness from a tubular parison would not be adequate.

Injection and Assembly

As the injection-molding method became well established, efforts were made to manufacture hollow articles of all types by injection-molding the article in two or three parts and assembling the molded parts by cementing or welding. This method has the advantage over blowing methods of greater accuracy and better surface finish.

A modification of this method, which has been speeded up by automation of the assembly operation, has gained considerable commercial significance, particularly for the manufacture of cylindrical and other simple shapes. The actual body section is made by extrusion of a continuous tube, whereas the neck and bottom are injection-molded, and the three parts are then automatically assembled. This method has gained particular importance for the manufacture of tubes for packaging creams, glues, etc., which are too viscous to be dispensed from a bottle. A further modification of this basic method is the use of the extruded tubular body as an insert in the injection mold. By this method a container can be made without any manual assembly or heat-sealing operations. This process still maintains the advantages of the greater dimensional accuracy and better surface finish typical of injection molding. Another advantage of this method is the ease of printing on the extruded body section, on either a mandrel or a flat, before assembly.

Molding by Transfer

A well-known method in this category has been developed in England. A parison is injection-molded around a hollow mandrel, and the whole assembly is then rapidly removed from the mold to prevent cooling. This warm assembly is transferred to a bottle mold, and air is introduced through the hollow handle of the mandrel. The advantage of this method lies in the accuracy of final dimensions, which approaches that of injection moldings. The items made by this method are naturally limited in size by injection capacity and mold area. The movement of the core or mandrel from injection cavity to blowing cavity can be automated. This process is in use today both in the United States and abroad.

The injection-and-assembly method described previously results in products of greater accuracy. On the other hand, it requires some taper and imposes limitations in shape and wall thickness, characteristic of an injection-molding process. The injection-transfer process permits considerable variation in shape and wall thickness, more characteristic of a blowing process. The principal difficulty is in increased tooling cost. This can be offset to some extent by elimination of finishing operations.

Centrifugal Casting

Centrifugal casting was developed specifically for the forming of hollow bodies from polyvinyl plastisols and has led to large-scale replacement of the familiar hollow-rubber childhood toys by vinyl plastisol toys. The new synthetics can be compounded into a variety of bright colors, can allow variations in hardness, are free from odor, and possess better aging properties.

A number of modifications to the casting method exist:

The simplest and oldest method is known as "slush molding." This is still used to a large extent for the manufacture of open hollow items. A plastisol is poured into a one-piece or split mold, usually made by copper electroforming or aluminum casting. The surplus plastisol is then removed, leaving a coating on the inside of the mold. This coating is fused by heating and subsequently cooled to facilitate its removal from the mold.

In practice, a single-pour or two-pour method can be used. The single-pour system consists of a filling station and a spinning or vibrating step to eliminate air bubbles. After this, the filled molds are heated by hot water or infrared radiation to jell the contact layer. The surplus plastisol is now drained, the coating fused, and the mold cooled. The two-pour method differs in that surplus plastisol is removed by draining before heating, leaving only a very thin coat, the thickness of which depends only on the viscosity of the plastisol. The film is now fused or thoroughly jelled by heating. The mold is then filled a second time. The residual heat in the mold determines the thickness of the second coat. Surplus is again drained, and the second coat is fused by the application of additional heat. This method guarantees better reproduction of mold detail and improved removal of bubbles due to the thin wall of the first coat.

Both of the above methods have been automated to a large extent.

Rotational or centrifugal casting is an improved process based on the slush-molding technique. The same type of molds are used as in slush molding, but they are completely closed. This method is therefore particularly suitable for closed hollow bodies such as balls, collapsible toys, bathware, etc. The split molds are filled with a predetermined amount of plastisol, the two halves are closed, and, by centrifugal spinning in at least two planes, the plastisol is evenly distributed over the inside walls of the mold. This coating is now fused by heat, the mold cooled, and the finished work removed.

Blowing of Tubular Parisons

The forming of tubular parisons by fluid pressure is the preferred modern method for manufacture of polyethylene bottles and other hollow bodies. An unending number of modifications of the basic process are in use, many being described in patent claims and an equal number practiced as a secret art.

The basic principle is extremely simple: a tubular parison is made by known methods—screw-extrusion, injection, ram-extrusion, or a combination of these. This parison is immediately surrounded by the two halves of a mold or is transferred by other means into a mold. As the mold closes (or before), either one or both ends of the tube are pinched, and pressure (usually air) is introduced either through the open end of the tube or, if both ends are closed, through a needle or some other injection device.

The above description encompasses all readily known commercial methods for the manufacture of plastic bottles or other hollow bodies by blowing of a tube. Proper design of equipment to carry out the process can make the difference between success or failure in this highly competitive field.

DEVELOPMENT OF BLOW-MOLDING TECHNIQUES

Historical Development of Process and Resins

As mentioned at the beginning of this chapter, the early hollow-body forming techniques developed from glass processes.

This can probably be best illustrated by citing a claim from a patent on the forming of glass bottles, U.S. Patent 1,592,299, filed July 8, 1921, issued July 13, 1926:

Claim 1 reads as follows: "The method of making blown glassware that comprises directing fluid under pressure into the interior of a mass of molten glass contained in a receptacle, thereby forcing a bubble of glass to issue from the said receptacle, and enclosing said bubble of glass in a mold."

Claim 48 of the same patent reads: "Apparatus for making glassware, comprising a support for a supply of molten glass, the said support having a downwardly opening orifice for the issue of glass from said supply, a conveyor movable beneath said orifice, a mold carried by said conveyor for enclosing glass issuing from said orifice and a blowpipe for blowing air through the said orifice into the interior of the issued glass while said glass is enclosed in said mold."

Anybody familiar with the processing of plastics can see in the above claims a good starting point for the design of a machine to blow hollow bodies from thermoplastic materials. This statement is not meant to slight the first workers in this field. They made the adaptation at a time when familiarity with processing conditions and equipment for thermoplastics was not widespread, and available materials and methods were not as advanced as today.

Indeed, the timing of one of the earliest patents in the field is amazing. Most textbooks disclose that the first thermoplastic melt extruder went into production in 1937. Yet on Feb. 25, 1933, Enoch T. Ferngren applied for a patent, U.S. Patent 2,128,239 issued Aug. 30, 1938, to Plax Corporation, which contains the following statement in its third paragraph:

" . . . The method is partly an extrusion procedure and partly a synchronized distending operation on the extruding material while the same is received in, or is caused to cover the walls of a mold element, or is otherwise formatively restrained, or caused to assume a given shape. . . . "

The straight-line development of this process from the previously quoted glass-blowing process is obvious. Since this application was filed 25 years ago, many improvements in mechanical operations have been developed and disclosed. But the basic process for the forming of thermoplastic hollow bodies still fits within the description of the above patent.

The above comprises but a sketchy history of the process. Despite this ingenious application of a new processing technique, large-scale commercial development of the thermoplastic-bottle industry had to await the appearance of a suitable material. Cellulose acetate, one of the earliest available thermoplastics, is clear, transparent, and tough but has serious shortcomings as a bottle material. It has high water absorption and relatively poor dimensional stability, and it tends to lose plasticizer and become brittle, particularly when fabricated into a thin-walled article. The next thermoplastic to become available in substantial quantity was polystyrene. This material had a substantial weight advantage over glass but did not have other compensating advantages, particularly in price, strength, and functional properties. Thermoplastic bottles became commercially acceptable only with the advent of polyethylene, which added a "squeezability" feature and thus an ideal dispensing characteristic which glass containers could not match without cumbersome and expensive pumping and spraying devices.

More recently, the adaptation of plastics has been augmented by other factors. During the last 15 years thermoplastics have become large tonnage items, and their prices, therefore, have substantially declined. In addition, they have been adapted for automatic and fast processing and can compete with glass on a more favorable basis. Their light weight and correspondingly low shipping cost make plastic bottles more competitive as general packaging materials.

The obvious advantages of polyethylene as a plastic bottle material are to some extent offset by the following disadvantages:

(1) Lack of rigidity

(2) Environmental stress cracking

(3) Low melting point

(4) Lack of transparency

(5) Permeability, especially to essential oils

(6) High mold shrinkage

Despite these shortcomings and the appearance of many new materials on the market during the last few years, low-density (branched) polyethylene still occupies a dominant position in this application.

Medium- and high-density (linear) polyethylenes are gradually making their appearance in the field, and polyamides are being evaluated for aerosol pressure containers. But the important feature of "squeezability" and ease of processing will maintain low-density polyethylene as the most important material for bottles for some time to come.

During the last 2 years, numerous attempts have been made to overcome or reduce the permeability of polyethylene containers by coating the inside or outside of the hollow body with less permeable materials. It is too early to say whether this method will have commercial success, or whether improvements in the basic material will make these coatings unnecessary.

Extensive studies on the permeability of polyethylene have been published in recent years.[6, 7, 8]

Modern Techniques

The blowing of tubular parisons, described earlier in this chapter, forms the basis for the majority of the modern methods for the manufacture of plastic bottles. The first step is the creation of a tubular parison. This parison has to be sufficiently hot to allow complete welding when pinched in order to form a closed hollow body which can be expanded against the walls of a mold by application of pressure. The viscosity of the material in the parison has to be sufficiently high for the parison to keep its shape while the mold halves close around it or while it is being transferred into the mold. This problem will be treated later in a more quantitative manner.

The tube has to be of controlled length, diameter, and wall thickness. In one basic process this accuracy in dimensions is achieved by continuous extrusion and precisely timed removal of the tube, when it has reached the proper length, by mechanical movement of the mold or by other means. The continuous extrusion in this process precludes the introduction of the pressure medium (compressed air) through the extrusion die from which the tube emerges. Therefore there always is a time lag between the clamping of the parison by the mold and the expansion toward the mold walls. This time lag can be kept at a minimum by mechanical means.

A second extrusion process involves continuous extrusion into a multiorifice manifold, where timing and valving mechanisms open only one or two orifices at a time. A third approach is by intermittent extrusion with a conventional screw extruder fitted with a timed start-stop device or by means of a ram extruder (viz., an injection-molding cylinder and plunger) or a combination of both where plasticated material is extruded into the injection cylinder. There are few variations of the blowing step itself. The parison is pinched either at the bottom or at both ends. When only the bottom is pinched, the pressure medium can be introduced directly through the mandrel of the extrusion die, or the parison can be severed from the die and the air introduced through a separate mandrel or pin. If both ends of the parison are pinched, the pressure medium has to be introduced by piercing the wall of the parison. In all cases a mold consisting of two halves is involved, and in some cases the bottom may be a separate third part. The greatest variations are in the mechanization of this basic operation. In order to utilize the full plasticating capacity of the equipment, it should function during the cooling cycle of the blown item. This can be achieved either by moving the molds away from the extrusion orifice (rotary table or reciprocating arrangement) or the plasticating equipment can be equipped with valves on multiple orifices through which parisons are extruded one or two at a time. Another way of utilizing the capacity of the equipment, especially when small or short items have to be blown, is the vertical arrangement of multiple (usually double) cavities, where the two bottles are arranged neck to neck, and the pressure medium is introduced between the two necks. Some of these variations are described in the following patents.

A patent applied for on Dec. 3, 1930, U.S. Patent 2,099,055, issued to Plax Corporation on Nov. 16, 1937, refers to the manufacture of a plastic bottle by flowing a cellulosic solution (dope) into a mold and using internal pressure or external vacuum to get accurate reproduction of the mold surface.

A later application by the same inventor (application Feb. 25, 1933, U.S. Patent 2,128,239, issued Aug. 30, 1938) contains the first mention of the extrusion of a thermoplastic tube by heat and pressure. The bottle in this process is formed by inserting the extrusion die into the bottom of the mold, at which point the emerging tube is sealed by contact with the bottom of the mold, and gradually withdrawing the die while simultaneously extruding material and expanding it by fluid pressure.

A later patent (U.S. Patent 2,230,190) details mechanical means for carrying out the above invention and gives an alternate method for closing the tube before extruding it. The extrusion die has a mandrel shorter than the outside forming member where the plastic material, by a short application of vacuum, can be sucked to the inside and sealed. This patent also contains the first mention of a rotary arrangement of a number of molds which move toward the extrusion orifice to receive the tubular parison.

The die itself performs a vertical motion to make contact with the mold as it moves into position.

After this patent, a number of improvements and process details were patented without any major modification of the basic process (U.S. Patents 2,260,750, 2,283,751, and 2,285,150).

On Oct. 12, 1943, a patent was issued which contained a new element (U.S. Patent 2,331,702). Here a parison is manufactured by the standard injection-molding technique. The core is pulled out of the parison, and this parison, hanging from a holding ring, is transferred to the blow-molding cavity. In a modification of this technique, parison is transferred on the core and is blown in the finishing mold by a pressure medium introduced through the core.

Both of these injection-molding methods claim greater accuracy of dimensions, more uniformity, and better finish compared with extruded blown bottles. A detailed discussion is found in the literature, where these processes are also described in detail.[9]

Almost all the blowing methods described so far start with the extrusion of a tubular parison which is closed at its leading end, usually at the start of extrusion. It is apparent to one familiar with the behavior of thermoplastic melts that this closing operation will not always lead to a very neat and uniform bottom section. On May 16, 1944, a patent was issued to Plax Corporation (U.S. Patent 2,349,177) describing a process which still begins extrusion by closing the tube, but the mold is designed in such a manner that its lower end (away from the extrusion orifice) has a pinching blade which removes the usually unsightly and heavy bottom portion and results in a new, cleaner bottom. By building the mold with a similar pinching mechanism on the top side, a blown article is manufactured which is completely closed and contains the gas which was used to blow it. This method is particularly adaptable to the manufacture of Christmas ornaments, toilet floats, and similar spherical objects.

An entirely different approach is described in a patent issued July 11, 1950 (U.S. Patent 2,515,093). According to this disclosure, a continuous tube is extruded by a conventional method. A rotary table containing a large number of molds with opening and closing mechanisms is located in front of the extruder die. The mold which moves up to receive the tubing from the die is, at that point, coaxial with the extruder die. It does not matter whether the tube as deposited in the mold has open or closed ends. As the mold closes, it pinches both ends of the tube and, at the same time, introduces the pressure medium through a small opening containing a puncturing tool above the neck section of the bottle. This method is fast and efficient but requires a large number of molds in order to utilize it properly.

Most of the methods for the manufacture of plastic bottles described in the foregoing paragraphs have one drawback in common: The bottle, as released from the machine, has to go through a number of finishing steps which frequently double labor requirements. The "tail" formed by pinching the tube at the bottle bottom has to be separated. The neck, which is usually formed longer than required, has to be trimmed, and, finally, the inside diameter of the neck frequently has to be drilled in order to conform to specifications.

Two recent patents (U.S. Patents 2,787,023 and 2,810,934) describe processes to achieve a partially finished bottle by extending the mandrel of the extrusion die into the neck of the bottle and having the top of the mold cut the length of the neck.

The most basic methods covered by U.S. patents have now been described. A recent publication[9] gives a list of British patents issued in the field of forming hollow bodies. An excellent description of a typical up-to-date bottle-blowing operation can also be found in an article published in 1950.[2]

Other recent articles on the subject are to be found in refs. 1, 3, 4, and 10.

ANALYSIS OF PROCESS VARIABLES

Operating Variables

In most of the bottle-blowing processes described above, a short but definite length of tubing is extruded through a die orifice into the atmosphere. Sufficiently accurate control of stock temperature has to be maintained so that the extruded parison retains its shape and does not flow and thin out by gravity as the mold closes around it. Control of this operation obviously requires an understanding of material characteristics, which will be discussed later. But, independent of these, control of stock temperature is a most important consideration. This is stressed, because in the case of most bottle-blowing equipment, two factors exist which make this control difficult: (1) intermittent operation, in which a large part of the volume stored in the crosshead is extruded with each stroke and replaced with fresh material which often must be thermally equilibrated in a short period of time; and (2) the generally recognized difficulty encountered in crosshead dies where the section farthest from the feed port requires longer material travel (around the mandrel) than do closer sections. Crosshead die design and the problem of heat equalization in crossheads require considerable attention. This problem becomes even more important on machines of the Shipton type,[4] where the material travels a considerable distance between the extruder and the crosshead and die.

Polymer Variables

The one most important property required in a resin for bottle blowing employing the downward vertical-extrusion technique is a definite minimum melt viscosity which allows the extruded tubing to hold its shape for sufficient time to be blown against the mold.

A simple equation has been derived[5] which relates the melt viscosity required to some of the other variables which enter into consideration in this process, such as melt density, required length of tubing, and velocity at the die. The equation given below has been verified fairly well by experience with more than eight resins.

$$M = \frac{622L^2d}{V}$$

where

M = apparent melt viscosity, poises

d = melt density, gm/cc

L = length of parison required, in.

V = extrusion velocity at the die exit, in./sec

By examining each variable in this equation, it is noted that the arrangement of terms is reasonable and logical. For example, a high-melt-density resin requires a high-melt viscosity to accommodate itself to extrusion at the same velocity. The longer the tubing to be extruded, the higher the required viscosity, since the tubing not only is heavier but also takes longer to extrude, thus allowing more time for drawdown. With higher extrusion velocity, a lower viscosity is adequate.

This equation is only a first attempt at trying to grasp the relationships involved in this fabricating method. In reality, the relationships are more involved, because the diameter and wall thickness of the extruded tube, which influence in turn the cooling rate, should also be considered. However, for simply comparing the suitability of two resins for a bottle-blowing application, this equation will be very helpful.

A hypothetical example will show how this equation is applied:

A resin is being extruded at 310°F. The melt viscosity at 310°F has been determined to be 3.8×10^5 poises at a shear stress approaching zero. The melt density at 310°F is 0.79 gm/cc.

The bottle to be blown requires a parison 11 in. long. The best extrusion velocity for the available machine and tubing-die setup is 1.5 in./sec.

The problem is to determine if resin viscosity is high enough for this application. The equation is solved for the required viscosity, and this is compared with the viscosity of the available resin:

$$M = \frac{622L^2d}{V} = \frac{(622)(11)^2(0.79)}{1.5} = 39,600 = 4 \times 10^4 \text{ poises.}$$

Since the melt viscosity of the selected resin is 3.8×10^5 poises, it is more than adequate for the job at hand. But melt viscosity is not the only consideration in a resin for forming hollow bodies. In addition to the requirement for a high viscosity because of the vertical extrusion and required shape-retaining characteristics, a high melt extensibility is also required in order to allow the parison to expand or flow under air pressure and to conform with the faces of the mold. Another important requirement is the weld strength obtained at the end of the parison which forms the bottom of the bottle. This can be the top or the bottom of the parison, depending on the method chosen. If the bottom of the parison forms the bottom of the bottle, this part is the one which emerges from the die earliest and therefore cools first. In blowing bottles of larger sizes, premature cooling of the parison bottom becomes an important problem, as this affects extensibility under air pressure and welding of the bottom seam.

FUTURE OUTLOOK

The continued growth in the application of hollow plastic articles, particularly as basic packaging units, will be accelerated by two current trends: (1) development of more efficient processing machinery and fabricating techniques through the increased application of fundamental theories in the design of bottle-blowing equipment and through a less restrictive patent situation, and (2) improvement of existing resins and the development of new thermoplastic materials particularly designed for packaging applications. Among the new materials is high-melt-viscosity polyamide which is superior to polyethylene in impermeability toward essential oils, in rigidity, and in suitability as a pressure container for aerosol packages. Clarity, as available in some nylon copolymers and in the polycarbonates, will also create new markets. Other materials now on the horizon for thermoplastic bottles are polypropylene and polyformaldehyde.

REFERENCES

1. Anonymous, "Blow-Moulding of Polythene Bottles," *Brit. Plastics*, **26**, 375 (1953).
2. Anonymous, "Extrusion-Blowing of Bottles," *Brit. Plastics*, **23**, 98 (1950).
3. Anonymous, "New Manufacturing Techniques for Polythene Bottles," *Brit. Plastics*, **26**, 1950 (1953).
4. Anonymous, "Progress in Polythene Bottle Manufacture," *Plastics (London)*, **19**, 250 (1954).
5. du Pont (E. I. du Pont de Nemours & Co., Inc.), Information Release, Polychemicals Department, "Bottle Blowing Resins—Application of Mathematical Equation to Describe Minimum Viscosity Requirements," Dec. 12, 1955.
6. Huscher, J. L., "Polyethylene Permeability," *Chem. Eng.*, **59**, 260 (1952).
7. Parliman, J. H., "Polyethylene Permeability," *Modern Packaging*, **21**, 198 (1948).
8. Pinsky, J., Nielsen, A. R., and Parliman, J. H., "Shelf Life in Polyethylene," *Modern Packaging*, **27**, 145 (1954).
9. Renfrew, A. and Morgan, P., "Polythene," p. 420, London, Illife & Sons, Ltd.
10. Spies, H., "The Production of Blown Plastics Articles," *Plastics (London)*, **20**, 114 (1955).

10. SEALING AND WELDING OF THERMOPLASTICS

B. P. Rouse, Jr., Ph.D.
and
T. M. Hearst, B.S.

Tennessee Eastman Company
A Division of Eastman Kodak Company

INTRODUCTION

Sealing and welding are processes for joining plastic parts. There is no rigorous distinction between the two terms, but in many instances "welding" refers to the joining together of parts of relatively heavy cross section, whereas the term "sealing" is more frequently applied to the joining of films and other thin structures. For the purpose of this chapter, no distinction will be made between the terms "sealing" and "welding."

The importance of sealing and welding operations is easily illustrated. For example, in the packaging industry, nearly 200 million pounds of polyethylene film were converted into bags for vegetables, dry goods, hardware, toys, etc. in 1957.[2] This represents an estimate of 10 billion bags, each of which contains at least one heat seal.

Almost everybody is familiar with the raincoats made from heat-sealed vinyl film. The assembly of pipes and ductwork, corrosion-resistant vessels, or tank linings for the chemical industry, and the fabrication of assemblies, such as valves, from thermoplastic materials represent other areas where sealing and welding are important. It will be seen from these examples that sealing or welding processes differ from the other thermoplastics processes in that they are performed on a semifinished article.

The technology applied in the sealing and welding operations described in this chapter is relatively new and developed largely through empirical experimentation.

TYPES OF SEALS AND WELDS

Two pieces of a thermoplastic may be joined through heat and pressure, or through the use of a solvent or adhesive. This chapter will not include a discussion of seals made with solvents or adhesives, since such operations do not fall within the definition of "thermoplastics processes."

In this chapter seven types of sealing and welding operations will be discussed:

(1) Heated-bar sealing
(2) Dielectric, or high-frequency sealing
(3) Hot-gas welding
(4) Heated-tool welding
(5) Induction welding and other encapsulating methods
(6) Extruded-bead sealing
(7) Spin welding

HEATED-BAR SEALING

Heated-bar sealing is the most widely used method for sealing thermoplastics. In this method of sealing, two pieces of thermoplastic film are joined in a lap weld. Fusion of the surfaces at the interface is effected under heat and pressure applied by the sealing bars. A typical arrangement for producing heated-bar seals is illustrated schematically in Fig. 10.1.

It will be noted that all of the heat has to reach the site of the seal by heat transfer through one of the layers of film. Since thermoplastic resins are notoriously poor heat conductors, it becomes obvious that heated-bar seals will be practical only in applications where at least one of the layers of thermoplastic to be joined is very thin.

The largest applications of heated-bar seals are in the manufacture of bags from polyethylene and in the sealing of polyethylene containers.

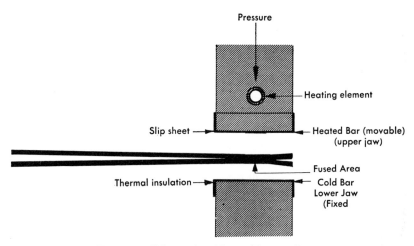

Fig. 10.1. Schematic of heated-bar sealing.

Types of Heated Bars

There are two types of heated bars—hot bars and impulse-heated bars. Hot bars are characterized by the fact that they remain at a steady and, controlled temperature throughout the sealing operation. This temperature is usually maintained by mounting a resistance heater in the core of the bar. Hot bars usually are made of a very good thermal conductor, so that a uniform temperature can be achieved over the entire working surface. The temperature of the bar may be measured by thermocouples attached to the bar, and the current supply may be controlled by automatic instruments or manually through a variable transformer. Other temperature-control systems employ simple bi-metallic thermo-regulators to govern the current flow to the heaters.

Impulse-heated bars differ from hot bars in that their temperature does not stay constant during the sealing cycle. Impulse-heated bars contain a small resistance element on the sealing surface which is heated for only a small portion of the total cycle. The body of the bar may actually be cooled by internal circulation of a coolant. Temperature control of impulse-heated bars is maintained by governing the period of the current impulse through an electronic timer and by regulating the voltage supplied to the resistance heater by means of a variable transformer.

The sequence of an impulse-sealing operation may be described as follows: (1) The two pieces to be joined are placed together between the jaws of the sealer. (2) The jaws are pressed together at a set pressure, and an impulse of electrical current is applied to the heating element. (3) After the impulse, the jaws remain closed while the coolant lowers the temperature of the bar and the seal.

Impulse sealing makes it possible to remove heat very rapidly after a seal has been produced. This is advantageous in sealing partly crystalline polymers, because the rapid cooling lowers the crystallinity at the seal and consequently produces a tougher joint.[5] In addition, impulse seals are widely used in operations where this consequence is not of primary importance, such as in the manufacture of bags from polyethylene.

With either the heated bar or the impulse sealer, a heat-stable resilient material may be substituted for the lower metal jaw. Sufficient heat is then supplied from the single jaw to produce the seal. The resilient material permits compensation for thickness variations and sealing over wrinkles, splices, and gussets.

Controllable Variables

The interrelationship of the three controllable variables (temperature, time cycle and pressure) in the heated-bar sealing operation is discussed in the following paragraphs.

Temperature. In Table 10.1 the thermal conductivities, specific heats, and heat-distortion temperatures for the most widely used thermoplastics are given. It can be seen from this table that the heat requirements to seal different thermoplastic materials vary considerably. There is also a wide variation in the heat requirements within a given thermoplastic. It is because of these differences and to allow for sealing different thicknesses that commercial sealers are equipped with high-capacity heaters. There is a definite range over which a good seal can be made when any one of the three variables is held constant.[13]

Figure 10.2 illustrates this point. This graph, reproduced from the article by Knight and Funk,[13] shows the temperature range and time-cycle range over which satisfactory seals can be obtained with the pressure held constant. These data are for a specific polyethylene film, but the same principle would be true of other thermoplastic materials. Figure 10.3 shows the same relationship but at two different pressures.[13] In this case it is shown that as the pressure is increased the time cycle is reduced, but the temperature range is also reduced. The reduced temperature range is due to the fact

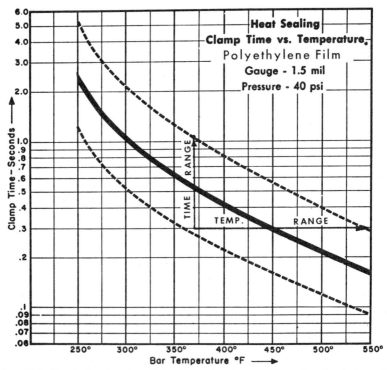

Fig. 10.2. Typical operating "map" for hot-bar sealing of polyethylene film. Broken lines enclose operating range within which satisfactory seals can be made.

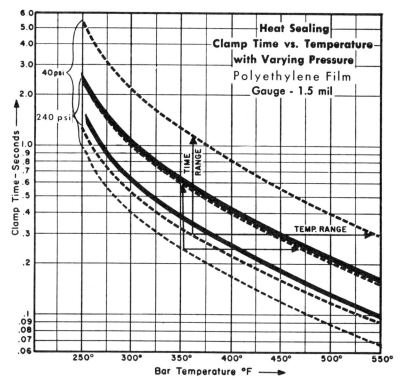

Fig. 10.3. Time-temperature maps at two different sealing pressures for same film as in Fig. 10.2. Raising pressure shortens cycle but pinches operating range.

that, at the higher pressure, the flow of the material increases more sharply with time.

The thickness of the film being sealed has a large effect on the heat requirements. With any thermoplastic a maximum thickness will be reached at which it is impossible to effect a true seal by the hot-bar method. The sealing of thick sections within reasonable time periods requires such high bar temperatures that excessive flow of the plastic results near the heated bar under the applied pressure. Thus, if two materials have essentially equivalent softening temperatures, the material with the lower specific heat and/or higher thermal conductivity can be sealed in the greater thickness.

Time Cycle. Heated-bar sealers are usually equipped with electric timers having fractional-second scales. The time can be set to any desired clamping time, and at the end of this interval the pressure is automatically released, allowing the jaws to open. In the case of the impulse sealer, the pressure cycle and the heat impulse are triggered simultaneously. When a film is being sealed, it is necessary to allow adequate time for the heat to be conducted from the bar through the thermoplastic film to the interface and bring the temperature of the surfaces at the interface to the softening point. From a commercial standpoint, if the time cycle is too long, productivity will be low. For this reason the desired time cycle is established, and the pressure and temperature are balanced to give satisfactory seals. Short time cycles necessitate high temperatures. High temperatures and low pressures, as illustrated, increase the probability of effecting good seals.

Pressure. It is necessary to provide pressure when sealing two thermoplastic films in order to ensure intimate contact at the interface and to supply the force necessary to fuse the softened thermoplastic. Pneumatic devices are the most commonly used sources of pressure for heated-bar sealers. Most commercial sealers are equipped with a reduction valve and a pressure gauge so that the system can be connected directly to a compressed-air source.

If the softening temperature of the film has been reached, the film can be sealed over a very wide pressure range. The pressure is adjusted to the point at which the seals can be made in the shortest period of time but without excessive flow of material from the site of the seal. This means that relatively low pressures should be used for most thermoplastics films. Low pressures have the effect of widening the temperature range over which satisfactory seals can be made (Figs. 10.2 and 10.3). The allowable pressure range for a particular thermoplastic film is largely dependent on the viscosity of the material at its softening temperature. For example, polyethylene has a relatively low viscosity at its softening temperature and can be sealed at pressures as low as 10 to 20 psi, whereas cellulose acetate has a relatively high viscosity at its softening temperature and requires pressures as high as 200 psi to effect a seal.

Slip Sheets and Other Methods to Prevent Adhesion to Sealing Bars

Many thermoplastic materials tend to adhere to metallic sealing bars at the temperatures required for practical operation. Various methods may be used to keep the hot resin from contacting the jaws directly. A slip sheet consisting of a piece of cellophane or thin paper may be used for this purpose. The slip sheet is usually stripped off after the seal has been made, but it may be left in place and utilized as a saddle label. Other slip sheets may be made from glass cloth impregnated with "Teflon"* (TFE—fluorocarbon resin). The edges of such sheets may be attached permanently to the heat sealer, acting as re-useable slip sheets between the source of heat and the film being sealed. (Further information on glass cloth impregnated with "Teflon" is contained in "New Product Technical Bulletin No. 3,"

---

* Registered U.S. Patent Office.

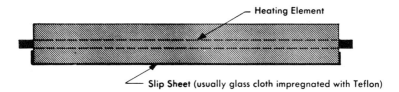

Hot Bar (showing attachment of slip sheet)

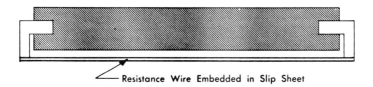

Impulse Heated Bar (showing attachment of slip sheet)

Fig. 10.4. Attachment of slip sheets.

available from the Fabrics Division, Fabrics and Finishes Department, E. I. du Pont de Nemours & Co., Inc., Fairfield, Conn.)

Silicone rubber has also been used, particularly to give resilience to the surface of the unheated jaw. Another effective anti-sticking agent is silicone grease. A thin coating of this lubricant over the jaws will prevent sticking, but it must be replaced frequently, since a small part of it adheres to each seal. (Figure 10.4 illustrates a cross section through each type of bar showing attachment of a "Teflon" slip sheet.)

Continuous Sealers

There are other heated-bar sealing techniques in commercial use which utilize the same principles but differ in operation. The most widely used is the rotary or continuous sealer. Figures 10.5, 10.6, and 10.7 illustrate this type sealer.[14] In this unit the film is held firmly between two narrow, endless belts and is passed through a heating zone and then a cooling zone. In the heating zone the temperature of the belts is brought to the level needed for sealing through contact with the resistance-heated shoe. In the cooling zone the temperature is lowered by an air blast or by an internally circulating coolant. Pressure on the sealed area is usually applied by means of small guide wheels which are located between the heating zone and the cooling zone. Other models have guide wheels ahead of the heating zone, between the heating and cooling zones, and after the cooling zones. The pressure on these wheels is maintained by spring tension or by means of air pressure.

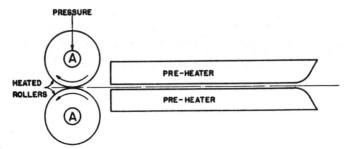

(*Drawings Courtesy Supply Engineering Div., U. S. Naval
Supply Research & Development Facility.*)

Fig. 10.5. Rotary sealer with fixed pre-heater followed by contacting rollers, sometimes powered to draw material past pre-heaters. If rollers are hand-fed, material is pulled through the pre-heaters and rollers. Pre-heaters soften material or coatings; then rollers apply bond pressure. This type of heat sealer is frequently used for cellophane and the surface of the rollers is sometimes crimped. Special models have been developed for sealing some coated or laminated materials.

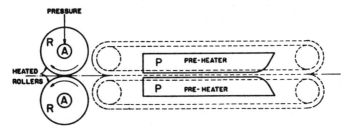

(*Drawings Courtesy Supply Engineering Div., U. S. Naval
Supply Research & Development Facility.*)

Fig. 10.6. Rotary-sealer, belt intake. Endless belts (usually rubber, fiber or chain) grasp material to carry it through pre-heaters to pressure rollers, which are sometimes heated. Sometimes a second set of belts carries the material past cooling area to permit "set." Purpose of the belts is to transport material through sealers at uniform rate. Used for cellophane and some coated or laminated materials. Special models have been developed for sealing of unsupported films.

The belt tension is controlled by spring pressure on the shoes. The belt may be permanently coated with a "Teflon" lacquer. The cooling zone reduces the tendency for the film to stick to the metal belt, however, so that surface treatment is optional.

A second continuous sealer is the rotating sealing-wheel,[9] or drum, which is usually made of aluminum and has suitable heating elements and a thermostatic control. The surface of the wheel is about $\frac{1}{8}$ in. in width, with smooth, rounded edges. After being coated with "Teflon," the wheel is mounted in the conventional position on a standard heat-sealing machine.

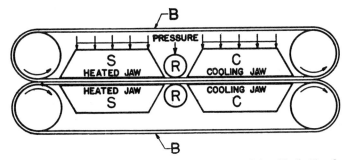

(*Drawings Courtesy Supply Engineering Div., U. S. Naval Supply Research & Development Facility.*)

FIG. 10.7. Band rotary sealer. Endless metal bands (B) carry material between heating jaws, pressure rollers (R) and cooling jaws. Bands are thin, transmit heat quickly; hold material under uninterrupted contact while transmitting heat to seal material and cooling to "set" seal. Models with rollers to apply pressure between heating and cooling operations used for heavier work, including barrier materials. Used for unsupported thermoplastic films, coated and laminated barrier materials.

The wheel rolls on a table called a forming plate, and the film passes between the wheel and the forming plate. The wheel is counterbalanced with an adjustable weight, and the speed is regulated to the rate at which the film travels over the plate. Tape of "Teflon" covers the plate at the point of contact with the sealing wheel. The recommended force exerted by the wheel against the forming plate is about $1\frac{1}{4}$ lb.

It has been found possible to seal polyethylene in tubular form at speeds ranging from a very few feet per minute up to 100 ft/min. Temperatures should be high enough to effect a good seal, but extremely accurate temperature controls are not necessary. At a speed of 65 ft/min, it is possible to make satisfactory seals of 2-mil film at temperatures ranging from 350 to 450°F.

Tests show that seals made under these conditions approach the strength of the body of the material itself. Sealers of this type were designed for use with packaging materials such as polyethylene, polyvinyl chloride, polyvinylidene chloride, etc.

DIELECTRIC, OR HIGH-FREQUENCY, SEALING

The dielectric method of sealing plastics is a comparatively recent development. The principles of dielectric heating are well explained in a number of references. One of the best is the chapter on "The Electrical Properties of High Polymers" by R. M. Fuoss.[4] Two comprehensive articles in *Modern Plastics* review the more recent applications of dielectric heat sealing.[1, 10]

As the name "dielectric sealing" implies, the thermoplastic to be sealed is placed in the position of a dielectric between two electrodes (sealing bars). The electrodes transmit a high-frequency current to the thermoplastic and at the same time exert the necessary pressure on it.

When polar plastic materials are exposed to this high-frequency current, heat is generated throughout the material owing to the friction between the molecules shifting back and forth in response to the electromagnetic field. With this combination of heat and pressure, a seal is effected.

Resin Properties

A polar material is one in which electrons have been borrowed from one atom to help fill the outer electron ring of another, thus creating ionic valence bonds within the molecules. The formation of such a bond causes the donor atom to become positively charged and the borrower to become negatively charged. Pairs of charges of opposite sign, called dipoles, are set up. If a dipole is placed in an electric field, it will tend to align itself with the positive portion toward the negative electrode and the negative portion toward the positive electrode. In the case of an alternating potential, this process is reversed many times a second, depending upon the frequency. The greater the viscosity of the material, the greater will be the resistance to realignment and the more work will be done. This work is converted to heat and is called the dielectric loss.

The electrical properties which are of importance from a dielectric sealing standpoint are dielectric strength and the dielectric constant, the power factor, and the loss factor.

Dielectric strength is the ability of an insulating material to resist the passage of a disruptive discharge produced by an electrical stress. When thermoplastics are exposed to an electrical potential they are stressed, just as mechanical pressure puts them under stress. There is a certain point for every thermoplastic sheet at which the electrical stress becomes so great that the material is ruptured. The voltage at which this occurs for a specified thickness is called the dielectric strength. This property is dependent on many variables such as the rate of application and increase in voltage, surface effects, etc. It is evident that this property is of great importance when considering conditions for sealing a material on a dielectric sealer.

Thermal conductivity is of little importance in this method of sealing because the heat is generated equally throughout the thermoplastic material itself and does not have to be conducted through it.

The dielectric constant is primarily an indication of the capacitance, but secondarily it is indicative of the relaxation time of the material.[15] The relaxation time is the time required for the molecules of a resin to regain their random arrangement after the removal of an applied d-c electrical field. A short relaxation time corresponds to a low dielectric constant. Materials with very short relaxation times can be sealed in a shorter time if higher frequencies are used.[10]

The power factor is defined as the ratio of total power loss (watts) in the material to the product of the voltage and current in a capacitor in which that material is a dielectric. In dielectric sealing it can be seen that materials with the highest power factors would be most adaptable to this type of heating. As a general rule, when the power factor of a material in the frequency range of the dielectric sealer is 10^{-4} or less, it can be assumed that it would be impractical to attempt to seal this material by the dielectric method.

The dielectric loss factor is the product of the dielectric constant and the power factor. This property is probably the best indication of how a material will react to dielectric heating. When attempting to predict the behavior of a thermoplastic material on a dielectric sealer, it can be assumed that the lower the loss factor the more power will be required to heat it sufficiently for sealing.

It should be pointed out that the relationship of these properties (dielectric constant, power factor, and loss factor) with frequency is not linear. For this reason it is important that these properties be determined at a frequency near the one being used on the dielectric sealer, if they are to be used as indications of the behavior of that material.

The following thermoplastics are suitable for high-frequency sealing: cellulose acetate, cellulose propionate, cellulose acetate butyrate, nylon, polymethyl methacrylate, polyvinyl chloride, and polyvinylidene chloride. This list is not complete, but it covers the materials which are used in the largest quantities. Some of the best examples of dielectric seals are, perhaps, in raincoats and shower curtains made of polyvinyl chloride film. Polyethylene and polystyrene, which are nonpolar materials and have very low power factors (on the order of 10^{-4}), cannot be sealed efficiently by a dielectric sealer.

Table 10.1 gives the dielectric constant, power factor, and dielectric strength for the thermoplastic materials which are used in the largest quantities.

Principles of Operation

Dielectric heat-sealing equipment is similar in construction to the heated-bar sealer previously discussed. The main difference is that in a dielectric heat sealer the jaws function as electrodes and do not supply heat by conduction. It is necessary, therefore, that these electrodes be made from a conductive metal to prevent resistance heating which might cause the mate-

TABLE 10.1

Thermal properties:	Thermal conductivity, 10^{-4} Btu/sec/ sq ft/°F/in. ASTM C 177	Specific heat Btu/lb/°F	Heat-distortion* temperature, °F ASTM D 648
Cellulose acetate	4.96–9.92	0.3–0.42	110–205
Cellulose propionate	6.55–6.67	0.38–0.40	110–180
Cellulose acetate butyrate	4.96–9.92	0.3–0.4	115–200
Nylon	6.45–7.19	0.4	300–360 (66 psi)
Polymethyl methacrylate	5.71	0.35	160–195
Polyvinyl chloride			
Plasticized	3.72–4.96	0.3–0.5	
Unplasticized	3.72–8.68	0.2–0.3	130–170
Polyvinylidene chloride	3.72	0.32	130–150
Polyethylene	9.92	0.55	105–121
Polystyrene	2.98–4.09	0.32	160–210

Electrical properties:	Dielectric constant ASTM D 150		Power factor ASTM D 150		Dielectric strength, in volts per mil ASTM D 149	
	10^3 (cycles)	10^6 (cycles)	10^3 (cycles)	10^6 (cycles)	Short time	Step by step
Cellulose acetate	3.5–7.0	3.2–7.0	0.01–0.06	0.01–0.10	250–365	200–300
Cellulose propionate	3.6	3.0–3.6	0.006–0.01	0.02–0.03	300–450	
Cellulose acetate butyrate	—	3.2–6.2	—	0.01–0.04	250–400	
Nylon	4.0–4.5	3.4–3.5	0.02–0.04	0.03–0.04	385–470	340–410
Polymethyl methacrylate	3.0–3.5	2.2–3.2	0.03–0.05	0.02–0.03	450–550	350–400
Polyvinyl chloride						
Plasticized	4.0–8.0	3.3–4.5	0.07–0.16	0.04–0.14	300–1,000	275–900
Unplasticized	3.0–3.3	2.8–3.1	0.009–0.017	0.006–0.019	425–1,300	375–750
Polyvinylidene chloride	3.5–5.0	3.0–4.0	0.06–0.075	0.05–0.08	350	300
Polyethylene	2.3	2.3	<0.0005	<0.0005	460	420
Polystyrene	2.4–2.65	2.4–2.65	0.0001–0.0004	0.0001–0.0004	500–700	400–600

* The heat-distortion temperature is a standard test used in the plastics industry, which gives the temperature at which a material will distort a given amount under a given applied load, usually 264 psi.

Values reproduced from Plastics Properties Chart. Courtesy of *Modern Plastics Encyclopedia Issue, 1957*.

rial being sealed to stick to the electrodes. As with the heated-bar sealers, there are many variations in the design of dielectric sealers. For practical purposes, many of the dielectric sealers are built so that electrodes of various shapes may be employed. Manufacturers also provide electrodes with internal channels for water cooling to remove the small amount of heat picked up from the material being sealed and from the unavoidable resistance heating in any electrode.

The jaws are usually made of a brass strip from $\frac{1}{2}$ to 4 in. wide and up to $\frac{1}{8}$ in. thick, backed up with brass, aluminum, or steel. Thicknesses over $\frac{1}{8}$ in. do not appreciably increase the strength of the seal. All surfaces that contact the work must be smooth, and the edge must be rounded to avoid a concentration of energy that would result in arcing or burning. Conversely, tear seals are accomplished by sharpening the electrode on one side. This weakens the film at the sharp edge and allows subsequent tearing by hand.

There are also continuous dielectric sealers or so-called electronic sewing machines. In this type of unit, the upper electrode is in the form of a wheel. This wheel is powered so that it pulls the material to be sealed under it. The operation of the unit is similar to that of a conventional sewing machine. Sealers of this design are ideally suited and widely used for the manufacture of raincoats, tobacco pouches, and food packages.

The electronic equipment necessary to produce the radio-frequency energy necessary for the seal consists of a power supply, an oscillator, and control circuitry.

The power supply converts the 60-cycle line voltage to a high-level d-c potential required by the oscillator tube. The hazard of this high potential requires suitable safety devices such as interlocked doors. In the oscillator tube, the high-voltage direct current is converted to alternating current in the frequency range of 10 to 40 megacycles. (The hazard is no longer great at this point because of the high frequency of the current.) Sufficient current must be available at the output terminals to generate heat in materials of low power factor. The output ratings of the equipment are usually in the range of $\frac{1}{4}$ to 100 kw. The frequency most widely used is 27.18 megacycles. This frequency is allotted by the Federal Communications Commission for this use; however, if adequately shielded equipment is used, any frequency attainable may be employed. In actual usage, the room where the sealing is being done is usually shielded with unlacquered galvanized iron. Shielding the room has economic advantages over buying several different shielded units. The Federal Communications Commission has definite radiation requirements for shielded rooms.

The control circuitry ties together the action of the die and generator as a whole. It must facilitate warm-up of the tubes, protect the components, and provide operator safety. Primarily, it must control the time of radio-frequency application and the cooling time.

Modern generators are equipped with an arc anticipator that protects the dies and trays. Should the leakage resistance fall below a pre-set value, the anticipator will instantly cut off the oscillators. The resistance might fall as a result of dirt, metallic particles, or arcing around the material.

The size of the generator determines the capacity of the sealer, i.e., the volume of material which can be heated to the temperature required for fusion at a given pressure and within the given time period. A simplified calculation to determine the power requirements to seal a thermoplastic in a certain thickness is offered by Curtis in "High Frequency Induction Heating."[8]

$$W \times S \times T = \text{Btu}$$

where

$$W = \text{weight of material (lb)}$$

$$S = \text{specific heat (Btu/lb/°F)}$$

$$T = \text{temperature rise desired (°F)}$$

The power requirements can be easily converted to kilowatts (1 Btu/min = 0.0177 kw).

Of course, this calculation does not take into consideration the electrical properties of the material to be heated. A more detailed calculation also given by Curtis is

$$H = CFL \frac{E^2}{T}$$

where

$$H = \text{coefficient of specific heat (Btu/lb/°F)}$$

$$C = \text{dielectric constant}$$

$$F = \text{frequency (megacycles)}$$

$$L = \text{loss factor}$$

$$E = \text{voltage (volts)}$$

$$T = \text{thickness of part (in.)}$$

Typical Cycles

Typical settings for sealing various thermoplastics are difficult to give, since power and time requirements will vary with each change in thickness and length and width of the seal. Sealing units have a set power capacity and frequency so that the time required to effect a seal is the only variable. The typical cycle is less than 4 sec., usually arrived at by trial and error. If longer periods are required, a larger generator is needed. In actual practice it will be found that thick sections can be heated more quickly than thinner sections, because the heat generated in thin sections is carried away by the electrodes so much more quickly than in thicker sections.

In general, materials containing plasticizers require less power to heat. This can be seen by the higher values for dielectric constant and power factor for the plasticized polyvinyl chloride when compared to the unplasticized polyvinyl chloride.

The initial cost of dielectric sealing equipment is high when compared to heated-bar sealers, but in many cases it is the only type of sealer which will do a satisfactory job. For heat-sensitive materials, dielectric heating offers particular advantages, because the heat is generated rapidly and uniformly within the resins, without a large temperature gradient.

HOT-GAS WELDING

Hot-gas welding[1] is a method of welding thermoplastic materials in which the material is heated by a jet of hot air or inert gas directed from a welding torch on the area of contact of the surfaces which are being welded. Welding operations to which the method is applied usually require a filler rod (Fig. 10.8).

The gas is heated in the torch. It may be passed either over an electric heating element or through a coil heated by a gas flame. The electrically heated torches are more compact and light, and for this reason they are more widely used than gas-heated torches. The gas-heated torch has advantages for use in the field, however, since it can be operated more readily

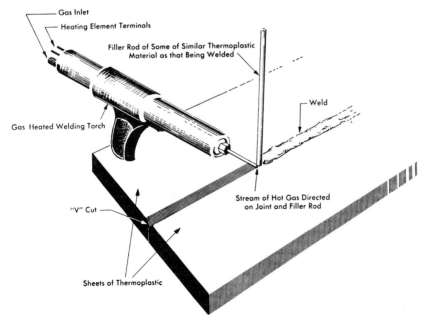

FIG. 10.8. Schematic diagram of hot-gas welding operation.

as a portable unit. The welding torches usually have replaceable tips so that the orifice size can be varied. Common orifice sizes are from $\frac{1}{8}$ to $\frac{1}{4}$ in.

The gas welding torch permits the regulation of the temperature of the stream of hot gas by varying the flame which heats the coil. The power input to the electric torch is regulated by a variable transformer. The temperature of the stream of hot gas may be further regulated by varying the distance between the tip of the torch and the piece to be welded. For polyethylene, the temperature at the orifice should be approximately 540°F. The working temperature of the gas will be about 360°F, since there is a loss of about 180°F between the nozzle and the work. It has been found that polyethylene suffers some deterioration when welded by a blast of hot air. This is evidenced by an impairment of its elongation. Since difficulty is attributed to the oxidation of the plastic, inert gases, such as nitrogen and carbon dioxide, have been tried. Nitrogen had been found satisfactory and is the gas most commonly used at present.

The pressure regulator should permit a continuous flow of nitrogen at a constant pressure of 5 to 10 psi. Approximately 0.2 to 1.0 cu ft of heated gas is used per minute of welding time. Welding speeds are usually slow (averaging from 1 to $2\frac{1}{2}$ in./min).

As in the gas welding of metals, the filler rods are of a composition similar to that of the material to be welded. For welding polyethylene the most satisfactory results have been obtained by using filler rods of polyethylene containing up to 5 per cent of polyisobutylene. This composition gives improved stress-crack resistance and a lower softening point which facilitates rapid welding. Diameter of the filler rod varies from $\frac{1}{16}$ to $\frac{3}{16}$ in., the size depending on the size of the gun. A round rod is preferred, since it produces a smooth and even deposit.[12]

HEATED-TOOL WELDING

In heated-tool welding, the surfaces to be joined are brought to the temperature required for welding by contacting them with a heated metal tool. When the surfaces have reached the required temperature, the heating tool is removed, and the surfaces to be joined are quickly pressed together. Upon cooling, the pressure is removed, and the weld is complete. This method of welding is applied in the assembly of polyethylene ductwork and in the manufacture of toys and household articles from a variety of resins.

INDUCTION WELDING AND OTHER ENCAPSULATING METHODS

There are at least two welding techniques in which heat generated within a wire, which is to become a permanent part of the assembly, is used to melt and weld adjacent plastic surfaces. One system employs a current induced in a closed wire loop (induction welding) and the other applies an imposed current across a resistance wire (resistance welding).

Induction Welding

Induction welding utilizes heat generated by a high-frequency electrodynamic field in a resistance circuit.[6] A typical induction-welding operation involves the following steps: (1) A conductive metallic insert is placed on the interface of two sections to be joined. (2) The sections are placed within the field of a high-frequency generator. (3) Pressure is applied to the sections and the field is energized. (4) Current is induced in the metallic circuit, generating heat which, in turn, melts the surrounding plastic material. (5) The field is de-energized and the fused area cools to form a strong and durable joint.

Power input governs the heat-up time of the insert. The energy and time required to heat the loop to the desired temperature can be calculated:[8]

$$W \times S \langle T = \text{Btu required}$$

where

W = weight of material (lb)

S = specific heat (Btu/lb/°F)

T = temperature rise desired (F°)

By converting the Btu required into kw of energy and dividing by the capacity of the generator in kw/min. the time necessary to heat the loop can be determined.

Induction welding of thick sections requires the application of considerable force on the parts to be joined. In such applications a minimum of 100 lb of force per linear inch of weld is required.

Heat input to the insert is a direct function of cycle time for a given power setting. More melt and, consequently, stronger welds will be obtained with longer cycles. However, cycle time should be only long enough to ensure adequate welding, as too long a cycle may cause overheating and consequent degrading of the material. Typical applications require from 3 to 10 sec of cycle time.

The joint of a mating part should be designed so that pressure is distributed uniformly throughout and over the metal insert. For efficient energy transfer, the metal insert should be located as close as possible to the generator coil. A tongue-and-groove joint, or similar configuration, may be desirable to locate and hold the metal insert. In all cases the insert must be located between the plastic-material faces so that no portion of the insert is exposed to air, as rapid heating and subsequent disintegration of the insert may otherwise occur.

Inserts. Successful welds have been achieved by use of stamped-foil inserts, standard metallic shapes such as wire screen, and various configurations of conductive wire. The insert is not limited to the normal closed-resistance-circuit pattern. It may, in fact, be made in the shape of a star, letter, or other decorative shape. When wire is used, diameters ranging from 0.010 to 0.030 in. will be found most effective.

Precautions should be taken to assure that the insert contacts the resin over its entire length to avoid localized overheating. It is advantageous to locate the insert in a retaining groove in one of the surfaces to be joined.

Fixtures. A clamping jig is required to obtain reproducible clamping pressures and to distribute the pressure evenly over the entire joint and insert. The jig must be in place during heating and cooling. It should be designed for rapid assembly and removal.

Safety. The energized coil of induction-welding equipment should be treated with caution. Any metallic object placed within or near the field of the coil may heat suddenly. Thus, persons wearing rings or other metallic jewelry should be cautioned about the potential burning hazard, and operators should not be allowed to wear articles that are subject to inductive heating.

Induction welding is particularly suited to the joining of thick sections. For example, it has been used in the assembly of nylon battery cases.

Resistance Welding

Resistance welding is very closely related to induction welding. It differs only in that the heat is generated in a resistance wire by imposing a current across it. The most widely used resistance-welding application is in joining pipe fittings. Special fittings with the resistance wire embedded at the joining surface have been used commercially. The fitting is press-fitted on the pipe to which it is to be joined, and a current is applied to the exposed terminals of the resistance wire. This system is particularly useful in field assembly where a portable current source can be employed.

EXTRUDED-BEAD SEALING

In extruded-bead sealing, two sections of a thermoplastic are joined by extruding a bead of the same material between them. The extruded bead contains sufficient heat to cause the surfaces adjacent to the bead to fuse A homogeneous structure results as the thermoplastic cools.[7]

The advantage of extruded-bead sealing lies in the method by which the required heat is generated. The extruded bead supplies all of the heat for the sealing operation. The generation of the heat in the bead is accomplished largely by mechanical work in the extruder, which is a particularly efficient processing device for heating thermoplastics. This method of sealing has been applied to the joining of polyethylene films by a technique shown in Fig. 10.9. It is also applicable for welding heavy sections, but the problem of guiding the molten bead into the weld is difficult.

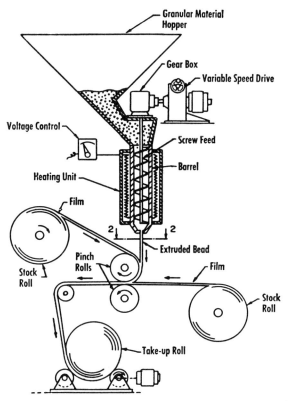

Granular Material Hopper

Gear Box

Variable Speed Drive

Voltage Control

Screw Feed

Barrel

Heating Unit

Film

2   2

Pinch Rolls

Extruded Bead

Film

Stock Roll

Stock Roll

Take-up Roll

(*Drawing by Supply Engineering Division, U. S. Naval Supply Research and Development Facility, Reproduced Courtesy Modern Packaging Encyclopedia.*)

FIG. 10.9. The molten bead sealer.

SPIN WELDING

Spin welding employs frictional heat that is generated by the rotational rubbing of two contacting surfaces to produce a joint.[6, 9] Specifically, the spin-welding process involves rotating one section to be welded in a powered spindle against another part which is held stationary. Rubbing contact is maintained at a speed and pressure which generate frictional heat and melt the adjacent surfaces. When sufficient melt is obtained, pressure is increased to squeeze out all bubbles and to flow the melt uniformly between the weld faces. The stationary part is then released, or the powered spindle stopped, halting the rubbing action and allowing the weld to cool under pressure. A typical application is illustrated in Fig. 10.10.

Spin welding offers economic advantages through speed and simplicity of operation. With the aid of jigs and fixtures, standard lathes and drill presses may be converted to spin-welding units.

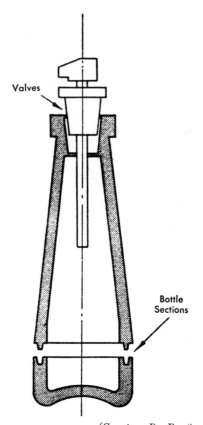

(Courtesy Du Pont)

FIG. 10.10. Typical application for spin welding.

The frictional heat generated by spin welding produces surface melting, while the temperature of the material immediately beneath the surface remains relatively unchanged. For many applications no surface preparation is necessary. A rough saw finish, in fact, can be welded into a joint of similar quality to that obtained from a machined surface.

One disadvantage of this technique is in the limitation of joint shape. The required circular shape may, however, be designed into a noncircular part, and the spin-welding apparatus may be indexed to align the non-uniform part into the required final position.

A possible second disadvantage is flashing, which is sometimes necessary to ensure complete welding. However, joint design may be regulated to minimize this flash or to trap it in internal recesses. Another possible disadvantage of spin-welded joints is that some orientation and sealed-in stresses are unavoidable. Therefore, it is often necessary to anneal spin-welded joints.

Operating Variables

The heat generated between two rotating, rubbing surfaces is a function of the relative surface velocity, of the contact pressure, and of the duration of contact. It is also a variable of material properties such as the coefficient of friction and the heat-transfer capacity.

Pressure must be applied uniformly to the surfaces to be welded. In many applications best results are obtained with an increase in pressure after initial melting. Pressure control is best obtained by use of a pneumatic feed unit.

The time cycle should be only long enough to ensure complete welding. A short time cycle minimizes flash and internal stresses. In many applications, 1 or 2 sec. may be sufficient for welding. The total cycle time, including insertion and removal of the part to be welded, is greatly influenced by the effectiveness of the jigs and adapter.

The axial spindle motion may be governed by a limit switch or stop, which ensures that a given amount of material is melted and displaced by each cycle. The limit switch is normally used with an automatic feed unit and an automatically disengaging adaptor. When production volume does not merit an automatic setup, visual control may be sufficient, and the rubbing may be stopped simply by shutting off the spindle drive.

Braking (stopping the relative motion of the contacting surfaces) may be critical with some plastics. Nylon, and other rigid thermoplastics with a low-viscosity melt and a relatively "sharp" melt-to-solid transition, must be braked almost instantaneously. When welding materials of this description, it is impossible to maintain more than a very thin film of melt between the contacting surfaces. If braking is slow, this thin film will solidify before the relative motion can be stopped, and the weld will be sheared.

Surface velocities of 5 to 60 ft/sec and initial pressures from 10 to 150 psi cover the range of values which have been used successfully.

Spin welding is not a widely used technique but has been employed for the assembly of nylon bottles and of thermoplastic dowels into assemblies of the same resin.

FUTURE STUDIES

A quantitative analysis of the various sealing and welding operations is still lacking. The problems of heat transfer and conduction, and the viscous and dielectric properties of polymers in sealing and welding operations have been examined only superficially. For example, the calculation of the temperature gradients in a film and the temperature at the interface during a hot-bar sealing operation have not been found in the literature. A definition of the viscous properties of the resin at the seal during the fusion process could contribute considerably to the understanding of these operations.

Similarly, dielectric sealing has been limited to materials of high dielectric constants. There is scant knowledge in the field of relaxation times, and the effects of molecular weight distribution and the size of crystallites on relaxation times have yet to be studied.

There is also need for more concrete knowledge about the change in the electrical properties of the materials during the sealing operation. It is known that the power factor and the dielectric constant of thermoplastics vary with temperature and pressure, but the extent of these variations and the effect which they have on the sealing operation are not known.

It is likely that a more quantitative approach, applying the available thermodynamic and flow theories, will lead to important improvements and a better understanding in all of the sealing and welding processes described in this chapter.

REFERENCES

1. Anonymous, "Hot Subject-Heat Sealing," *Modern Plastics*, p. 85, April, 1958.
2. Anonymous, "Markets for Materials—1957," *Modern Plastics*, p. 102, January, 1958.
3. Brown, George H., Hoyler, Cyril N., and Bierwirth, Rudolph A., "Theory and Application of Radio-Frequency Heating," Princeton, N. J., D. Van Nostrand Company, Inc., 1947.
4. Burk, R. E., and Grummitt, Oliver, "The Chemistry of Large Molecules," in "The Electrical Properties of High Polymers," by Fuoss, Raymond M., pp. 191–217, New York, Interscience Publishers, Inc., 1943.
5. Burk, R. E., and Grummitt, Oliver, "The Chemistry of Large Molecules," in "The Investigation of High Polymers with X-Rays," by Mark, H., pp. 33–67, New York, Interscience Publishers, Inc., 1943.
6. Cheney, A. J., and Ebeling, W. E., "Methods for Joining Plastics Parts," *SPE Journal*, p. 31, March, 1958.
7. Chinn, H. G., "The Molten Bead Sealer," *Modern Packaging*, p. 153, December, 1956.
8. Curtis, Frank W., "High Frequency Induction Heating," New York, McGraw-Hill Book Company, Inc., 1944.
9. du Pont (E. I. du Pont de Nemours & Co., Inc.) *Information Bulletin* X-5, "Alathon" Polyethylene Resin-Methods of Sealing.
10. Farkus, R. D., "Electronic Heat Sealing," *Modern Plastics*, p. 109, March, 1958.
11. Haim, G., and Newmann, J. A., "Manual for Plastic Welding," "Polyethylene," Vol. II, Cleveland, Industrial Publishing Company, 1954.
12. Haim, G., and Zade, H. P., "Welding of Plastics," London, Crosby Lockwood & Sons Ltd., 1947.
13. Knight, R. M., and Funk, W. U., "Heat Sealing of Polyethylene Film," *Modern Plastics*, p. 133, December, 1957.
14. Rohdin, H., "Heat Sealing Equipment," in "Modern Packaging Encyclopedia," Vol. 31, pp. 93–96, Packaging Catalogue Corp., 1958.
15. Van Beek, L. K. H., and Hermans, J. J., "Dielectric Relaxation in Dilute Solutions of Polar Chain Molecules," *J. Polymer Sci.*, Vol. XXIII, Symposium on Macromolecules, 1956, Part 2, New York, Interscience Publishers, Inc., 1956.

Section III

Processing Properties

PROCESSING PROPERTIES

R. F. Westover, M.S.E.

Bell Telephone Laboratories

The quantitative analyses of the previous chapters can be applied only if the processing properties of polymers, in the ranges of practical operating conditions, are known. Very little information describing the processing properties of thermoplastics in the molten state has been assembled heretofore. It is the purpose of this section to compile the available information in this area for use by the processing engineer.

In compiling this section, material suppliers were requested to contribute processing data, transposed into a standard set of units and plotted on standard graphs. An English system of units was selected which is in agreement with the standards of the chemical engineering field. The following data are the latest and most complete information available, as supplied directly by the respective resin manufacturers. The sample data form and the sample graphs shown on the following four pages indicate what information was sought.

Because of the lack of standardization of test equipment and methods commonly employed in procuring this information, instruments and techniques used must be specified to make meaningful interpretations of the data possible. Caution should be used in comparing data from different sources. All flow data reported here were obtained from capillary rheometers, loaded with granules. No entrance corrections were applied.

It is hoped that in future editions many of the gaps evident in the present collection of data may be filled. Revisions and additions will also be required to keep abreast of the changes in resin compositions. Eventually, as the demand for this type of information increases, it is hoped that data on "Processing Properties" may be included in readily available handbooks, obviating the need for this section in this book.

The support of the companies who have contributed these processing data is gratefully acknowledged. Without their participation, this section of the book could not have been published.

DATA FORM

RESIN DESIGNATION AND MANUFACTURER _____

RESIN SPECIFICATIONS: _____

1. Polymer or Copolymer? _____ % Composition _____
2. Chemical Name or Formula _____
3. Density at 23°C (lb_M/ft^3) _____
4. Molecular Weight
   Weight Average _____ Number Average _____
   How Determined? _____   _____
5. Plasticizers: Kinds _____ Amounts _____
6. Lubricants: Kinds _____ Amounts _____
7. Additives (Antioxidants, etc.):
   Kinds _____ Amounts _____
8. Fillers: Kinds _____ Amounts _____

FLOW BEHAVIOR: _____

9. Melt Index or Flow Rate Index (gm/10 min.) _____
   (ASTM-D1238-52T)
10. Graph: Maximum shear stress ($\Delta pR/2L$, $lb_F/in.^2$) *vs.* apparent shear rate ($4q/\pi R^3$, sec^{-1}) at several temperatures (°F) (show plotted points on curves)
11. If rotational viscometers are used, define shear stress and shear rate.
12. Describe briefly the type of test equipment used—capillary, rotating drum, rotating cone, etc.
13. For capillary tubes give: Dimensions of tubes (inches), including entrance geometry (flat entry die preferred) and chamber size.
    Was chamber loaded with granules or preforms? _____
    For rotation viscometers give: Cup and bob dimensions (inches), including clearance at bottom; or other pertinent data.
14. Were corrections made for entrance or end effects? If so, how were corrections made?
15. What temperature (°F) is referred to (melt, die, chamber, etc.) and how is it measured?
16. Locate inception of extrudate roughness on graphs. (Use arrow as shown on sample graph.)
17. Graph: Apparent viscosity (lb_F-sec/in.^{2}) *vs.* temperature (°F) at several apparent shear rates ($4q/\pi R^3$, sec^{-1}). Apparent viscosity is defined as maximum shear stress ($\Delta pR/2L$, $lb_F/in.^2$) Appar-

548

ent shear rate $(4q/\pi R^3,\ \text{sec}^{-1})$. This is the slope of the line from the *origin* to the specific apparent shear rate on the maximum shear stress *vs.* apparent shear rate curve plotted on rectangular coordinates. (Show plotted points on curves)

18. Graph: Apparent viscosity (lb$_F$-sec/in.^{2}) *vs.* apparent shear rate $(4q/\pi R^3,\ \text{sec}^{-1})$ at several temperatures (°F). (Show plotted points on curves)

19. From: Maximum shear stress $(\Delta pR/2L,\ \text{lb}_F/\text{in.}^2)\ =\ K'$ [apparent shear rate $(4q/\pi R^3,\ \text{sec}^{-1})]^{n'}$
give a table of values of K' and n' at several temperatures (°F) and give the range of apparent shear rates over which the n' value is valid. (n' will be less than 1)

20. Graph: Per cent increase in extrudate diameter *vs.* apparent shear rate $(4q/\pi R^3,\ \text{sec}^{-1})$ at several temperatures (°F) and various die dimensions (inches).

21. Miscellaneous test data (examples—thixotropy, bulk modulus, elasticity, etc.)

PV/T DATA:

22. Graph: Density (lb$_M$/ft^3) *vs.* temperatures (°F) at several pressures (lb$_F$/in.^{2})

23. Give constants for equation of state, $(P + \pi_i)(V - \omega) = R'T$
Reference: R. S. Spencer & G. D. Gilmore, *Journal Appl. Phys.*, **21**: 523–526, 1950.

$\pi_i = $ _____ $\omega = $ _____ R' _____

ELECTRICAL PROPERTIES:

24. Dielectric loss factor at heat sealing frequencies.

THERMAL PROPERTIES:

25. Graph: Enthalpy (Btu/lb$_M$) *vs.* temperature (°F) up to maximum processing temperature.

26. Graph: Thermal conductivity (Btu/hr-ft − °F) *vs.* temperature (°F) at several pressures for solid and liquid states.

27. Graph: Thermal diffusivity (ft^2/hr) *vs.* temperature (°F) for both solid and liquid states.

28. Graph: Specific heat (Btu/lb$_M$ − °F) *vs.* temperature (°F) for solid and liquid states.

29. Table: Latent heats (Btu/lb$_M$) of all phase changes with the temperature (°F) or temperature range at which these phase changes occur.

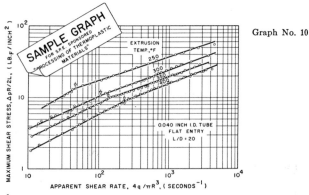

Graph No. 10

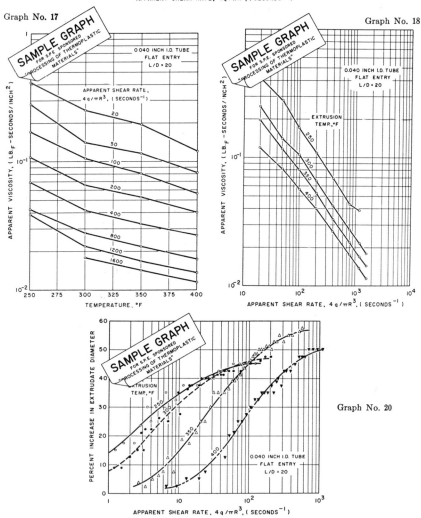

Graph No. 17

Graph No. 18

Graph No. 20

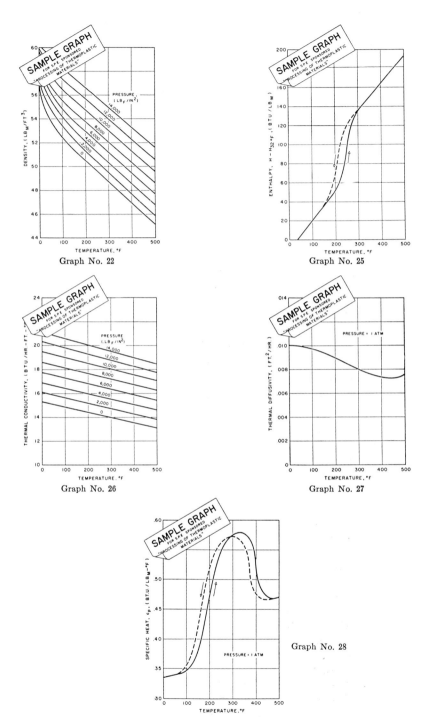

Graph No. 22

Graph No. 25

Graph No. 26

Graph No. 27

Graph No. 28

551

The resins for which processing data are presented are arranged in the following order:

ACRYLIC RESINS

E. I. DU PONT DE NEMOURS & CO., INC.
Lucite® 129
Lucite® 130
Lucite® 140

ROHM AND HAAS COMPANY
Plexiglas® V100
Plexiglas® VM100
Plexiglas® VS100
Implex® A

CELLULOSIC RESINS

THE DOW CHEMICAL COMPANY
Ethocel® 856

EASTMAN CHEMICAL PRODUCTS, INC.
Tenite® Acetate 036-H2
Tenite® Acetate 036-MS
Tenite® Butyrate 205-H2
Tenite® Butyrate 205-MS
Tenite® Propionate 307-H
Tenite® Propionate 307-H5

NYLON RESINS

ALLIED CHEMICAL AND DYE CORP.
Plaskon® Nylon 8201
Plaskon® Nylon 8205

E. I. DU PONT DE NEMOURS & CO., INC.
Zytel® 42NC10
Zytel® 101NC10

POLYETHYLENE RESINS

CANADIAN INDUSTRIES LIMITED
204E Polyethylene
1200H Polyethylene

THE DOW CHEMICAL COMPANY
Dow Polyethylene M.1.2
Dow Polyethylene M.1.20
Dow Polyethylene M.1.7

E. I. DU PONT DE NEMOURS & CO., INC.
Alathon® 3
Alathon® 10
Alathon® 17
Alathon® 34

EASTMAN CHEMICAL PRODUCTS, INC.
Tenite® Polyethylene 854
Tenite® Polyethylene 856

HERCULES POWDER COMPANY
Hi-Fax® 1400
Hi-Fax® 1700
PHILLIPS CHEMICAL COMPANY
Marlex® 50 Polyethylene, Type 9
Marlex®, 50 Polyethylene, Type 15
Marlex® 50 Polyethylene, Type 35
Marlex® 50 Polyethylene, Type 50
UNION CARBIDE CORPORATION
DYNH Polyethylene
DYNK Polyethylene

STYRENE RESINS

THE DOW CHEMICAL COMPANY
Styron® 475
Styron® 666
Styron® 683
Styron® 700
Tyril® 767
MONSANTO CHEMICAL COMPANY
Lustrex® HF55-2020
Luxtrex® HF77-2020
Lustrex® HH-99A-5-2020
Lustrex® LHA-1000
Lustrex® LSA-843-411
Lustrex® HT-88B-1000
UNION CARBIDE CORPORATION
Copolymer RMD 4511
TMD-2155, TGDA-2001

VINYL RESINS

B. F. GOODRICH CHEMICAL COMPANY
Geon® 8700A
Geon® 8750
MONSANTO CHEMICAL COMPANY
Opalon® 1028
Opalon® 1038
Opalon® 1406
Opalon® 1706
Opalon® 71329
UNION CARBIDE CORPORATION
Vinyl Chloride Copolymer VYNW, 30% plasticizer
Vinyl Chloride Copolymer VYNW, 35% plasticizer
Vinyl Chloride Copolymer VYNW, 40% plasticizer
Vinyl Chloride Copolymer VYNW, 45% plasticizer
Vinyl Chloride-Acetate Copolymer VYHH
Vinyl Chloride-Acetate Copolymer VYNS

E. I. DU PONT DE NEMOURS & CO., INC.

LUCITE® 129

(Polymethyl Methacrylate, ASTM Grade 6)

Density at 23°C: 73.5 lb$_M$/ft³

Melt Index or Flow Rate Index (gm/10 min.): 15; ASTM-D1238-52T using 230°C, 3800 gm wt, and 7 min. from start of charging to start of measured flow.

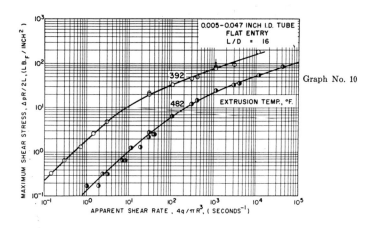

Graph No. 10

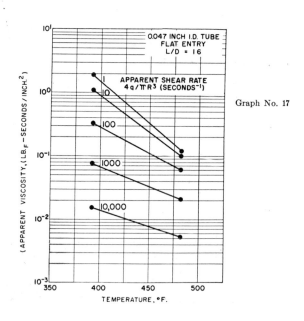

Graph No. 17

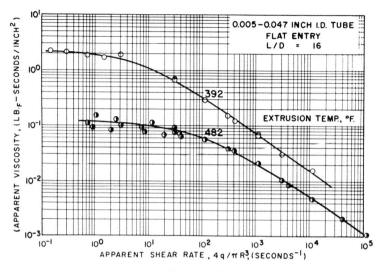

Graph No. 18

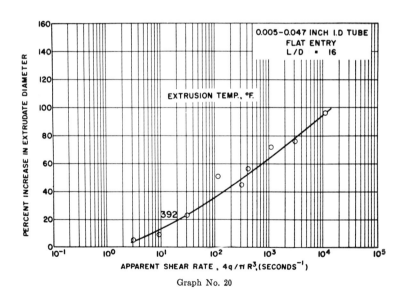

Graph No. 20

E. I. DU PONT DE NEMOURS & CO., INC.

LUCITE® 130

(Polymethyl Methacrylate, ASTM Grade 5)

Density at 23°C: 73.5 lb_M/ft^3

Melt Index or Flow Rate Index (gm/10 min.): 30; ASTM-D1238-52T using 230°C, 3800 gm wt, and 7 min. from start of charging to start of measured flow.

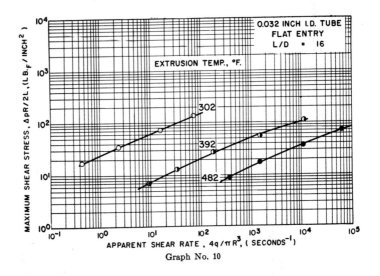

Graph No. 10

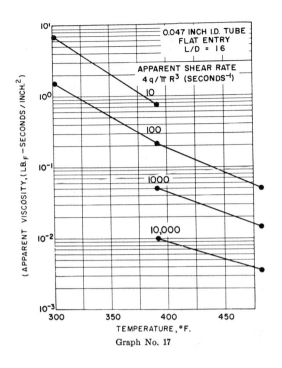

Graph No. 17

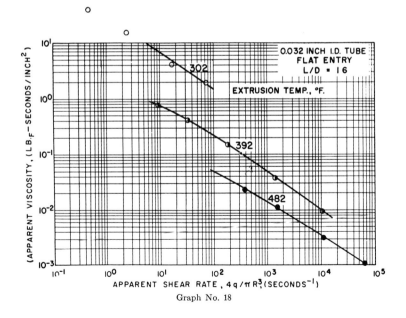

Graph No. 18

ACRYLIC RESINS

E. I. DU PONT DE NEMOURS & CO., INC.

LUCITE® 140 ACRYLIC RESIN

(Polymethyl Methacrylate, ASTM Grade 8)

Density at 23°C: 74.1 lb_M/ft^3

Melt Index or Flow Rate Index (gm/10 min.): 5; ASTM-D1238-52T using 230°C, 3800 gm wt, and 7 min. from start of charging to start of measured flow.

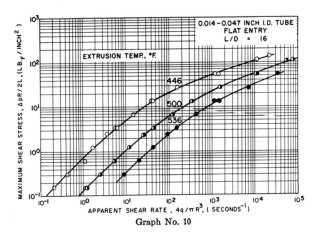

Graph No. 10

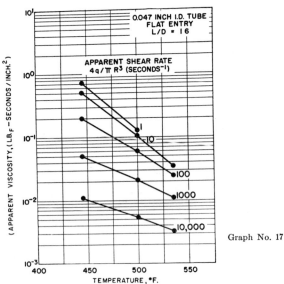

Graph No. 17

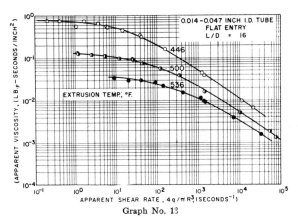

Graph No. 13

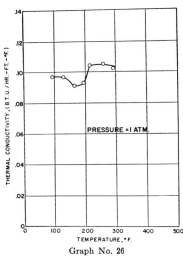

Graph No. 26

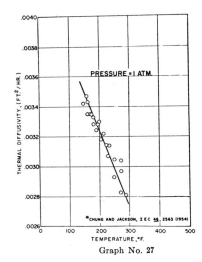

Graph No. 27

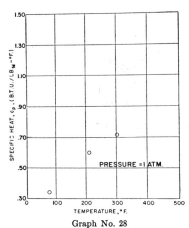

Graph No. 28

559

ROHM AND HAAS COMPANY

PLEXIGLAS® V100

(Methyl Methacrylate)

Density at 23°C: 74.2 lb_M/ft^3
No Plasticizers or Fillers
Table of K' and n' at Various Temperatures

Temp. (°F)	K'	n'	Range of Validity (Sec. $^{-1}$)
302	289.0	0.251	2–80
338	56.5	0.370	2–80
374	13.2	0.441	2–80
410	4.1	0.451	2–80
446	0.660	0.654	2–80

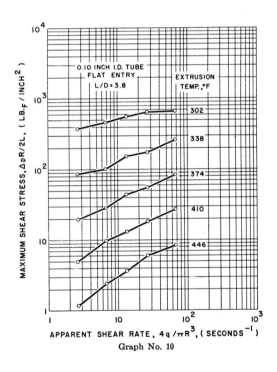

Graph No. 10

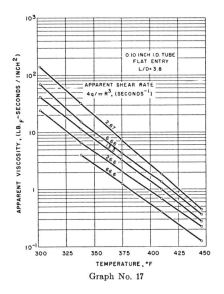

Graph No. 17

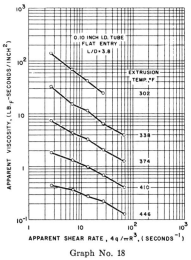

Graph No. 18

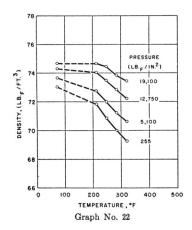

Graph No. 22

561

ROHM AND HAAS COMPANY

PLEXIGLAS® VM100
(Copolymer, Methyl Methacrylate Base)

Density at 23°C: 74.2 lb_M/ft^3
No Plasticizers or Fillers
Table of K' and n' at Various Temperatures

Temp. (°F)	K'	n'	Range of Validity (Sec.$^{-1}$)
302	63.0	0.376	2–80
338	16.7	0.411	2–80
374	4.15	0.500	2–80
410	1.08	0.570	2–80

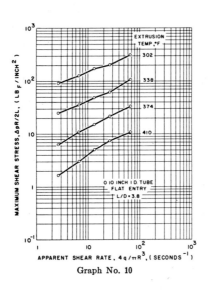

Graph No. 10

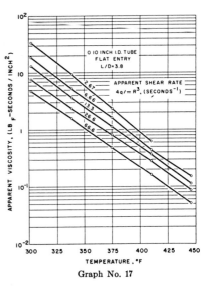

Graph No. 17

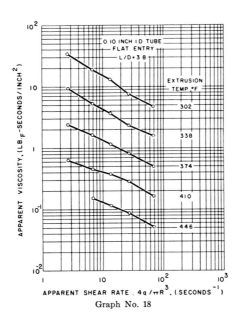

Graph No. 18

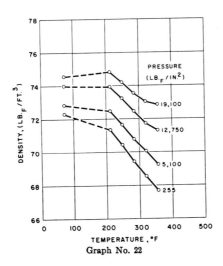

Graph No. 22

563

ROHM AND HAAS COMPANY

PLEXIGLAS® VS100

(Copolymer, Methyl Methacrylate Base)

Density at 23°C: 74.2 lb_M/ft^3
No Plasticizers or Fillers
Table of K' and n' at Various Temperatures

Temp (°F)	K'	n'	Range of Validity (Sec.⁻¹)
302	41.6	0.335	2–80
338	9.7	0.430	2–80
374	2.36	0.514	2–80
410	0.410	0.722	2–80

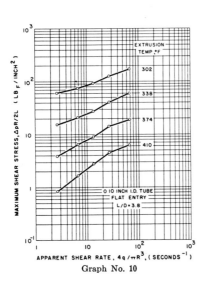

Graph No. 10

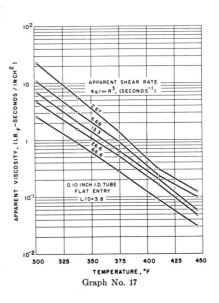

Graph No. 17

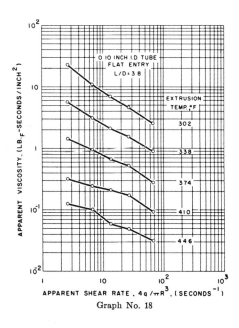

Graph No. 18

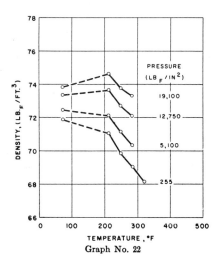

Graph No. 22

565

ROHM AND HAAS COMPANY

IMPLEX® A

(Modified Methyl Methacrylate)

Density at 23°C: 69.6 lb$_M$/ft^3
No Plasticizers or Fillers
Table of K' and n' at Various Temperatures

Temp (°F)	K'	n'	Range of Validity (Sec.$^{-1}$)
302	178.0	0.378	2–80
338	52.0	0.343	2–80
374	22.0	0.351	2–80
410	11.3	0.343	2–80
446	6.8	0.392	2–80

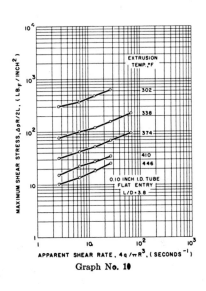

Graph No. 10

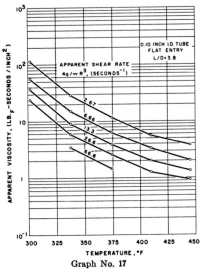

Graph No. 17

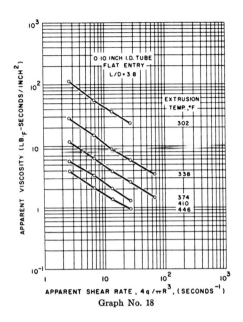

Graph No. 18

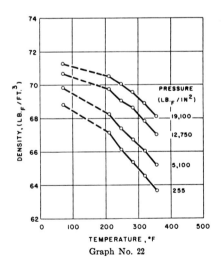

Graph No. 22

567

CELLULOSIC RESINS

THE DOW CHEMICAL COMPANY

ETHOCEL® 856

(Ethyl Cellulose)

Thermal Diffusivity for the Temperature Range from 325 to 500°F: 3.68×10^{-3} ft²/hr

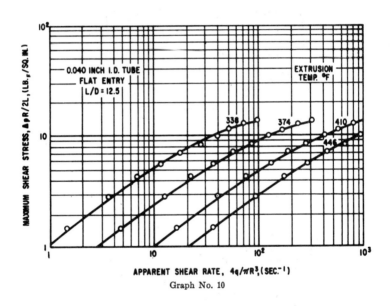

Graph No. 10

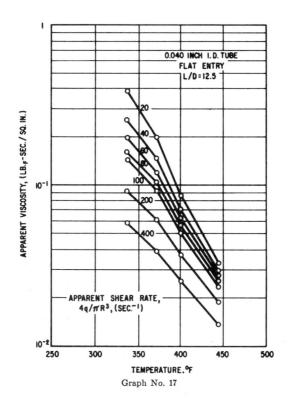

Graph No. 17

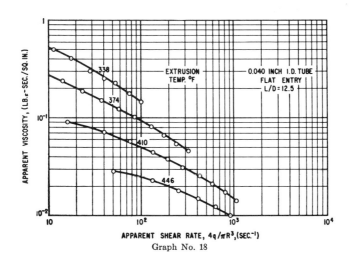

Graph No. 18

569

EASTMAN CHEMICAL PRODUCTS, INC.

TENITE® ACETATE 036-H2

(Cellulose Acetate)

Density at 23°C: 79.9 lb_M/ft^3
Organic Ester Plasticizer
Melt Index or Flow Rate Index (gm/10 min.): 0.7; ASTM-D1238-52T

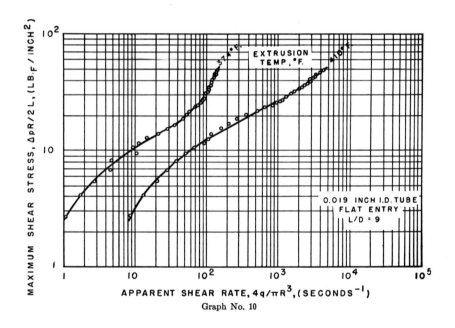

Graph No. 10

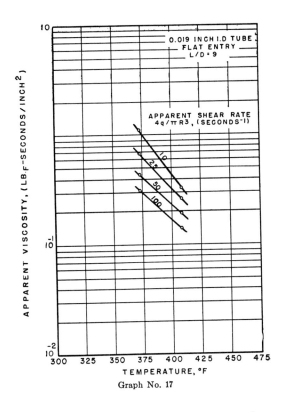

Graph No. 17

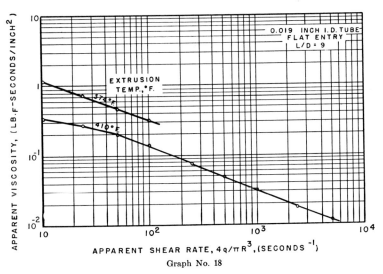

Graph No. 18

571

EASTMAN CHEMICAL PRODUCTS, INC.

TENITE® ACETATE 036-MS

(Cellulose Acetate)

Density at 23°C: 78.7 lb_M/ft^3
Organic Ester Plasticizer
Melt Index or Flow Rate Index (gm/10 min.): 4.8; ASTM-D1238-52T

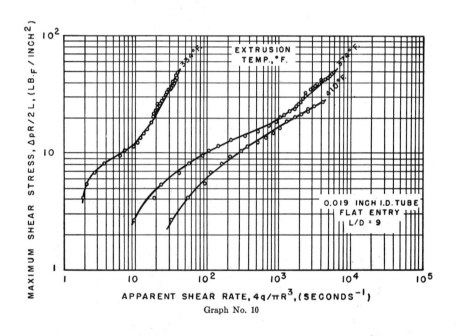

Graph No. 10

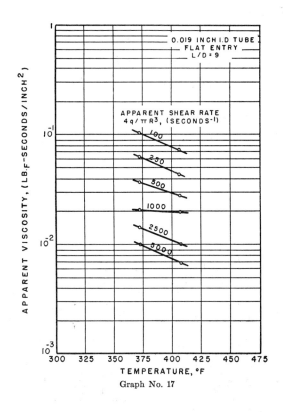

Graph No. 17

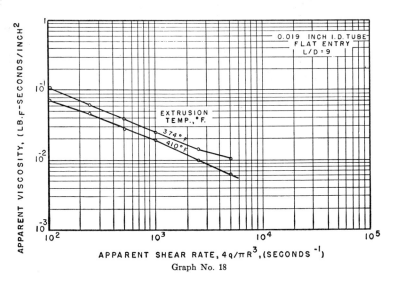

Graph No. 18

EASTMAN CHEMICAL PRODUCTS, INC.

TENITE® BUTYRATE 205-H2

(Cellulose Acetate Butyrate)

Density at 23°C: 75.5 lb_M/ft^3
Organic Ester Plasticizer
Melt Index or Flow Rate Index (gm/10 min.): 0.25; ASTM-D1238-52T

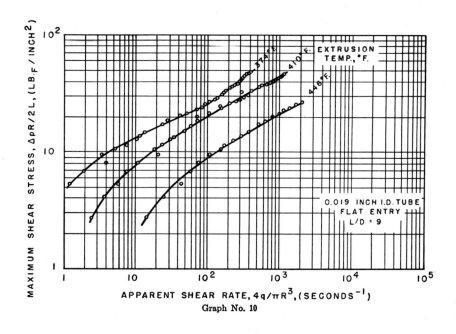

Graph No. 10

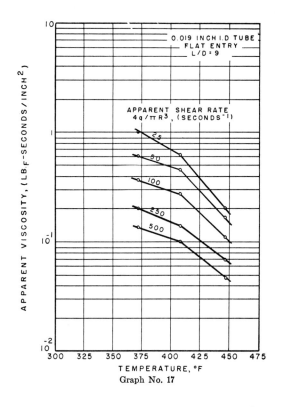

Graph No. 17

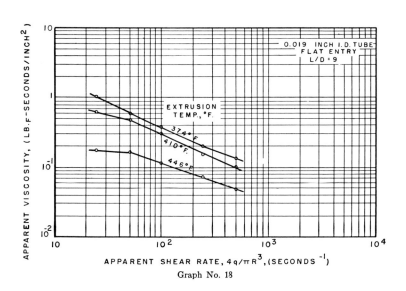

Graph No. 18

EASTMAN CHEMICAL PRODUCTS, INC.

TENITE® BUTYRATE 205-MS

(Cellulose Acetate Butyrate)

Density at 23°C: 73.8 $lb_M/ft.^3$
Organic Ester Plasticizer
Melt Index or Flow Rate Index (gm/10 min.): 2.5; ASTM-D1238-52T

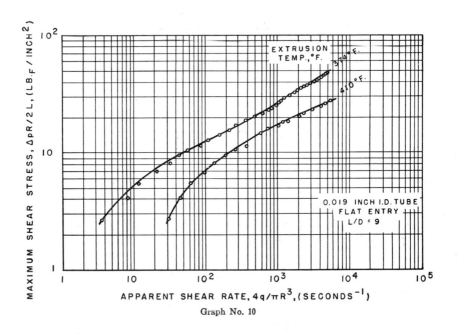

Graph No. 10

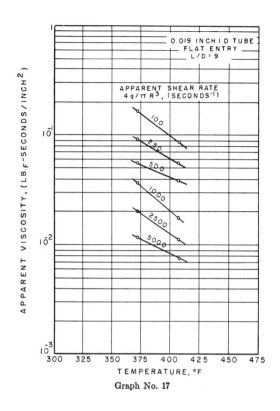

Graph No. 17

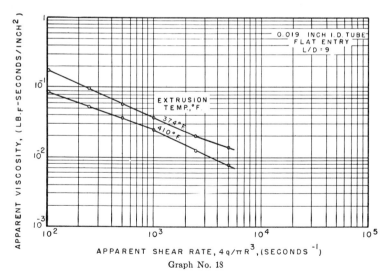

Graph No. 18

EASTMAN CHEMICAL PRODUCTS, INC.

TENITE® PROPIONATE 307-H

(Cellulose Propionate)

Density at 23°C: 74.9 lb_M/ft^3
Organic Ester Plasticizer
Melt Index or Flow Rate Index (gm/10 min.): 3.7; ASTM-D1238-52T

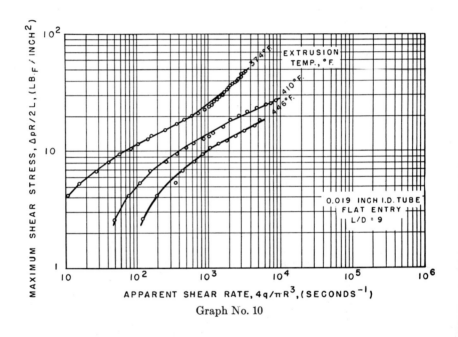

Graph No. 10

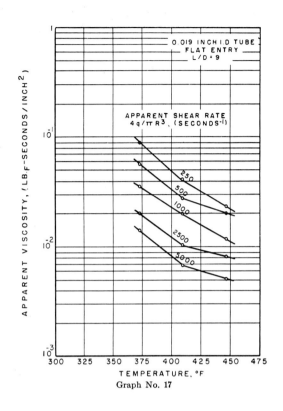

Graph No. 17

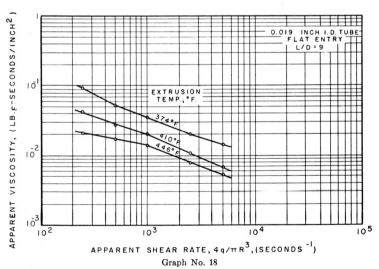

Graph No. 18

579

EASTMAN CHEMICAL PRODUCTS, INC.

TENITE® PROPIONATE 307-H5

(Cellulose Propionate)

Density at 23°C: 76.2 lb_M/ft^3
Organic Ester Plasticizer
Melt Index or Flow Rate Index (gm/10 min.): 0.25; ASTM-D1238-52T

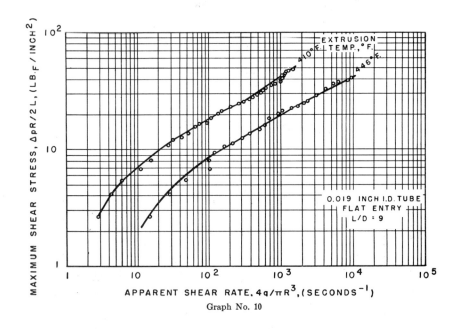

Graph No. 10

580

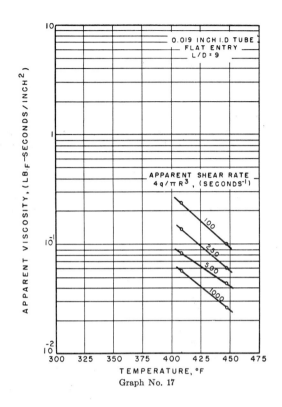

Graph No. 17

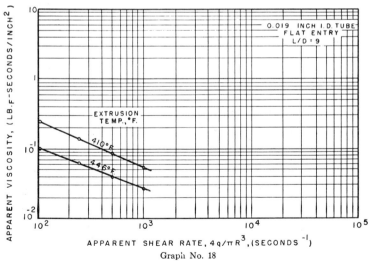

Graph No. 18

581

ALLIED CHEMICAL AND DYE CORP.

PLASKON® NYLON 8201

(Polycaprolactam, Nylon "Type 6")

Density at 23°C: 70.4 lb_M/ft^3

Weight Average Molecular Weight (light scattering): 34,000 to 40,000

Number Average Molecular Weight (intrinsic viscosity and end-group titration):
18,000 to 22,000

No Plasticizers, Lubricants, Additives or Fillers

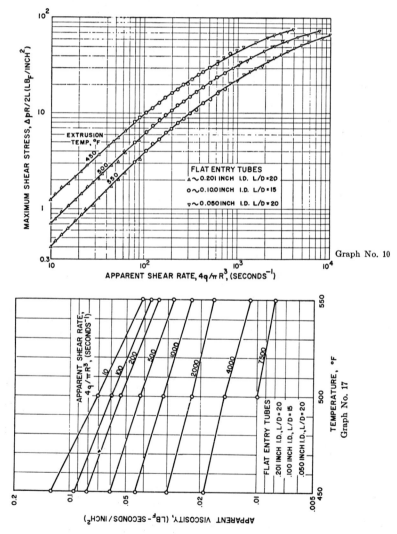

Graph No. 10

Graph No. 17

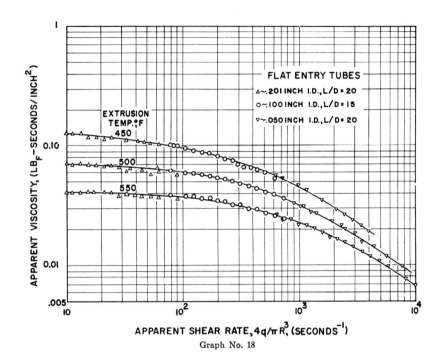

Graph No. 18

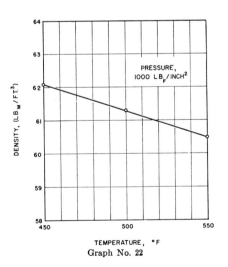

Graph No. 22

NYLON RESINS

ALLIED CHEMICAL AND DYE CORP.

PLASKON® NYLON 8205

(Polycaprolactam, Nylon "Type 6")

Density at 23°C: 70.4 lb_M/ft^3

Weight Average Molecular Weight (light scattering): 70,000 to 80,000

Number Average Molecular Weight (intrinsic viscosity and end-group titration): 35,000 to 40,000

No Plasticizers, Lubricants, Additives or Fillers

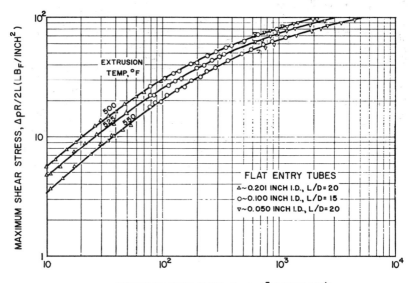

Graph No. 10

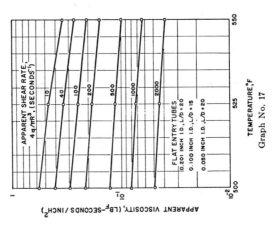

584

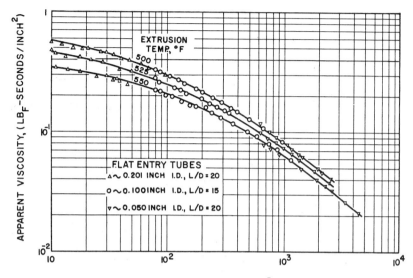

APPARENT SHEAR RATE, $4q/\pi R^3$, (SECONDS^{-1})

Graph No. 18

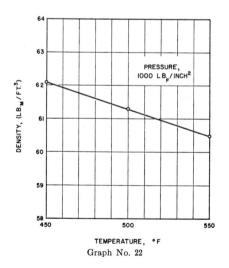

TEMPERATURE, °F

Graph No. 22

585

E. I. DU PONT DE NEMOURS & CO., INC.

ZYTEL® 42 NC10

(Hexamethyleneadipamide Polymer)

Density at 23°C: 71.2 lb$_M$/ft³
Number Average Molecular Weight (end group analysis): 34,000 ± 1,000
No Plasticizer or Filler
Melt Index or Flow Rate Index (gm/10 min.): 2; ASTM-D1238-57T (Condition K except 2160 gm wt)

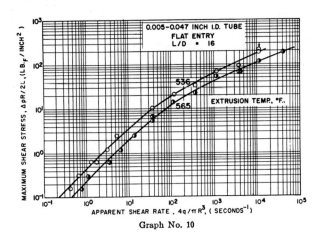

Graph No. 10

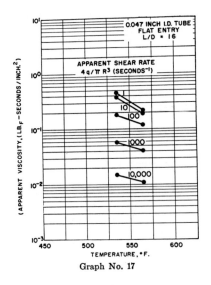

Graph No. 17

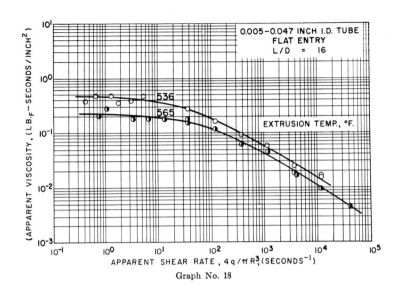

Graph No. 18

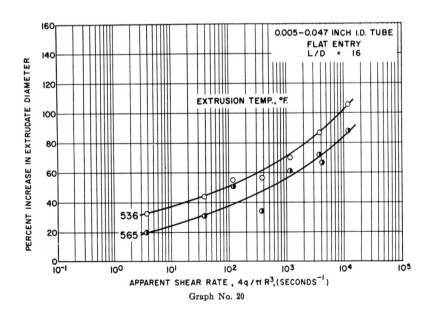

Graph No. 20

E. I. DU PONT DE NEMOURS & CO., INC.

ZYTEL® 101 NC10

(Hexamethyleneadipamide Polymer)

Density at 23°C: 71.2 lb_M/ft^3
Weight Average Molecular Weight (light scattering): 39,000
Number Average Molecular Weight (end group analysis): 18,000 ± 500
No Plasticizer or Filler
Melt Index or Flow Rate Index (gm/10 min.): 5; ASTM-D1238-57T (Condition K)

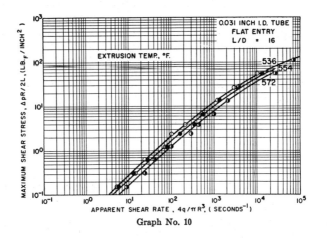

Graph No. 10

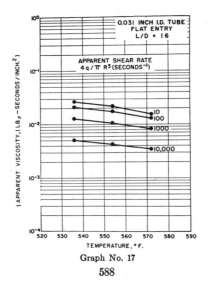

Graph No. 17

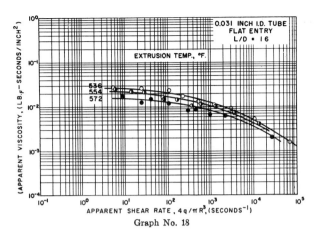

Graph No. 18

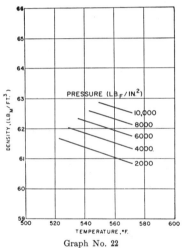

Graph No. 22

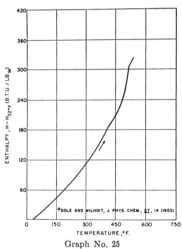

Graph No. 25

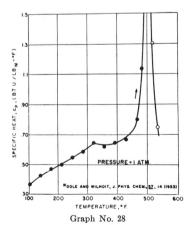

Graph No. 28

589

POLYETHYLENE RESINS

CANADIAN INDUSTRIES LIMITED

POLYETHYLENE 204 E

(Polyethylene)

Density at 23°C: 57.1 lb$_M$/ft³
Melt Index or Flow Rate Index (gm/10 min.): 0.35; ASTM-D1238-52T
Table of K' and n' at Various Temperatures

Temp. (°F)	K'	n'	Range of Validity (Sec.$^{-1}$)
250	11.0	0.280	94–630
300	8.3	0.288	200–1140
350	6.8	0.288	440–1400
374	5.9	0.298	490–3700
400	5.2	0.306	545–2200
428	4.2	0.320	990–2300
455	4.37	0.303	1160–4150

Note: The arrows on the graphs indicate the graphical break points and do not in this case coincide with the onset of roughness.

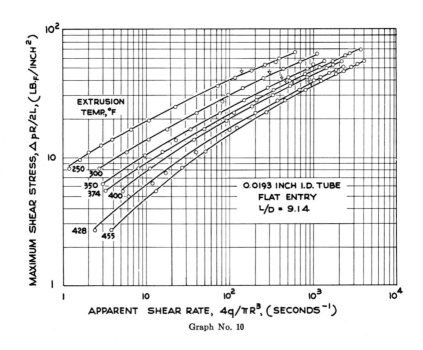

Graph No. 10

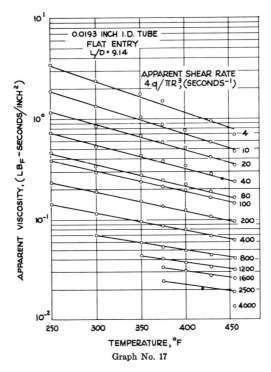

Graph No. 17

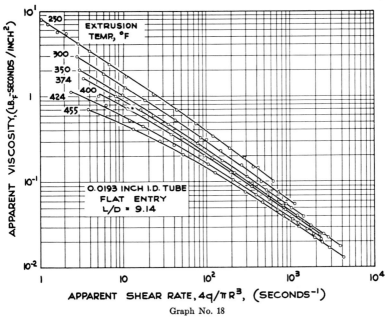

Graph No. 18

591

CANADIAN INDUSTRIES LIMITED

POLYETHYLENE 1200 H

(Polyethylene)

Density at 23°C: 57.2 lb$_M$/ft^3
Melt Index or Flow Rate Index (gm/10 min.): 16.56; ASTM-D1238-52T
Table of K' and n' at Various Temperatures

Temp. (°F)	K'	n'	Range of Validity (Sec.$^{-1}$)
250	3.7	0.355	930–2600
300	2.95	0.354	2900–6000
350	2.35	0.354	6700–10,000
374	3.06	0.317	9000–19,000
400	2.7	0.321	13,500–26,000
428	2.24	0.329	21,000–30,000

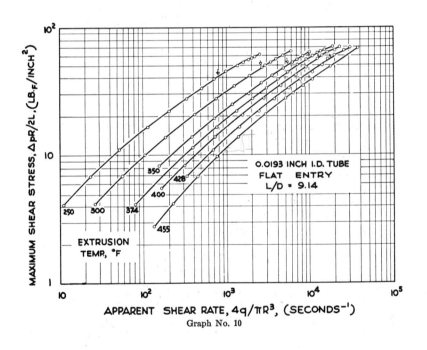

Graph No. 10

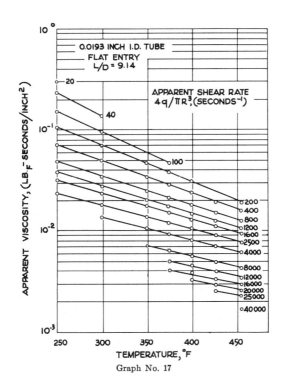

Graph No. 17

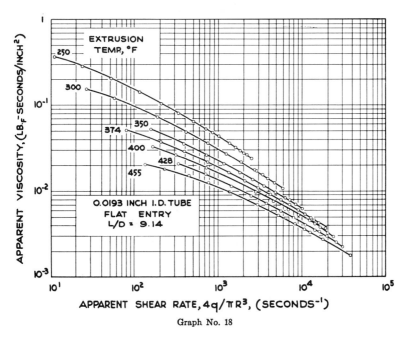

Graph No. 18

THE DOW CHEMICAL COMPANY

DOW POLYETHYLENE M.I. 2

(Polyethylene)

Density at 23°C: 57.16 lb_M/ft^3
Constants for Equation of State, $(P + \pi_i)(V - \omega) = R'T$

$$\pi_i = 47600 \qquad \omega = 0.875 \qquad R' = 43.0$$

Thermal Diffusivity for the Temperature Range from 325 to 500°F: $4.50 \times 10^{-3} ft^2/hr$

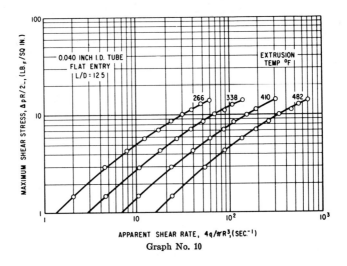

Graph No. 10

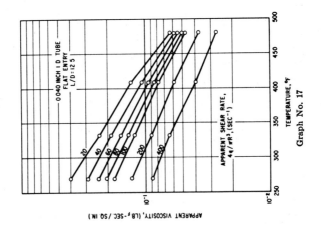

Graph No. 17

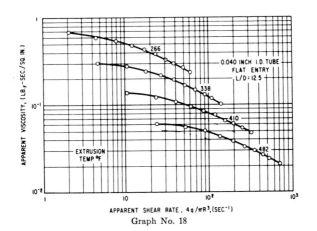

Graph No. 18

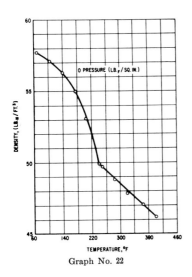

Graph No. 22

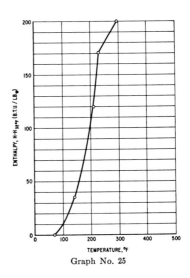

Graph No. 25

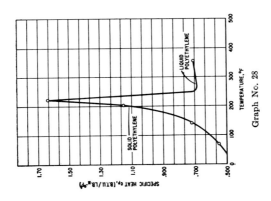

Graph No. 28

595

POLYETHYLENE RESINS

DOW POLYETHYLENE M.I. 7

(Polyethylene)

Density at 23°C: 57.16 lb_M/ft^3

Constants for Equation of State, $(P + \pi_i)\,(V - \omega) = R'T$

$$\pi_i = 47600 \qquad \omega = 0.875 \qquad R' = 43.0$$

Thermal Diffusivity for the Temperature Range from 325 to 500°F: $4.50 \times 10^{-3}\ ft^2/hr$

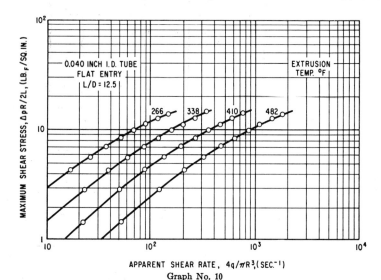

APPARENT SHEAR RATE, $4q/\pi R^3$, (SEC.$^{-1}$)

Graph No. 10

APPARENT VISCOSITY, (LB._F-SEC./ SQ. IN.)

Graph No. 17

596

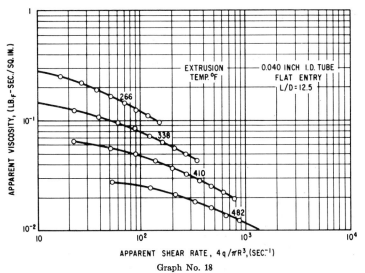

Graph No. 18

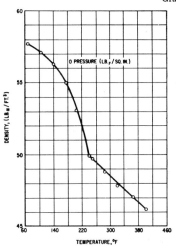

Graph No. 22

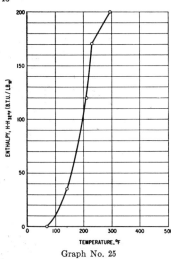

Graph No. 25

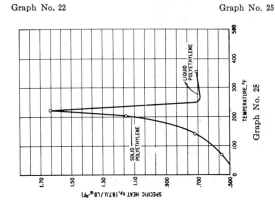

597

THE DOW CHEMICAL COMPANY

DOW POLYETHYLENE M.I. 20

(Polyethylene)

Density at 23°C: 57.10 lb_M/ft^3

Constants for Equation of State, $(P + \pi_i)(V - \omega) = R'T$

$$\pi_i = 47,600 \qquad \omega = 0.875 \qquad R' = 43.0$$

Thermal Diffusivity for the Temperature Range from 325 to 500°F: 4.50×10^{-3} ft²/hr

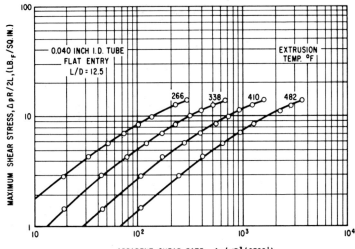

Graph No. 10

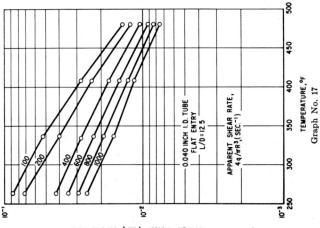

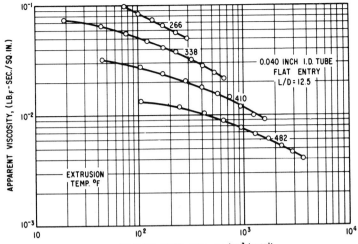

Graph No. 18

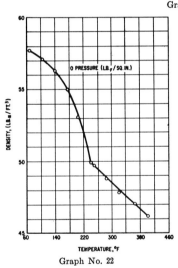

Graph No. 22

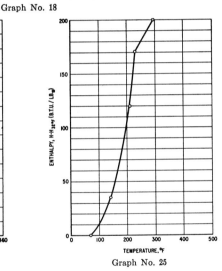

Graph No. 25

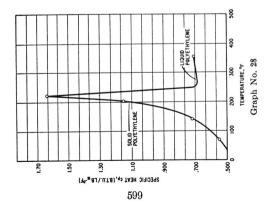

Graph No. 28

POLYETHYLENE RESINS

E. I. DU PONT DE NEMOURS & CO., INC.

ALATHON® 3

(Polyethylene)

Density at 23°C: 57.5 lb$_M$/ft³
Weight Average Molecular Weight (light scattering):   525,000
Number Average Molecular Weight (osmotic pressure):   30,000
Melt Index or Flow Rate Index (gm/10 min.):   0.2;   ASTM-D1238-52T

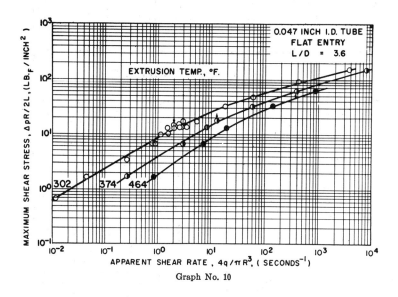

Graph No. 10

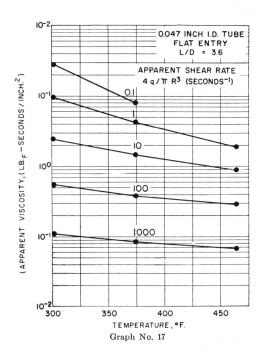

Graph No. 17

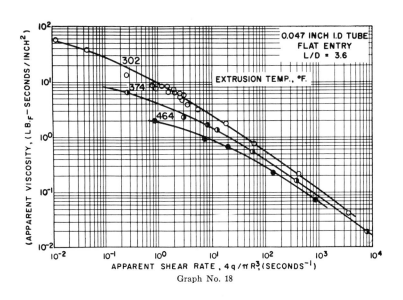

Graph No. 18

601

E. I. DU PONT DE NEMOURS & CO., INC.

ALATHON® 10

(Polyethylene)

Density at 23°C: 57.6 lb$_M$/ft^3
Weight Average Molecular Weight (light scattering): 300,000
Number Average Molecular Weight (osmotic pressure): 26,000
Melt Index or Flow Rate Index (gm/10 min.): 2.1; ASTM-D1238-52T

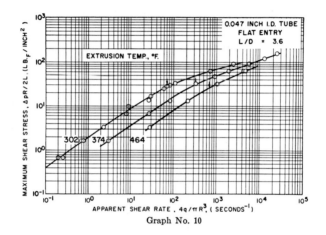

Graph No. 10

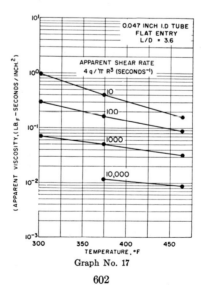

Graph No. 17

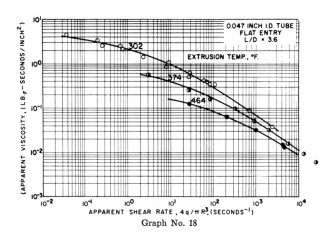

Graph No. 18

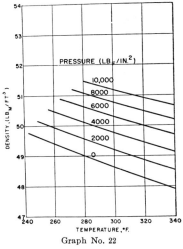

Graph No. 22

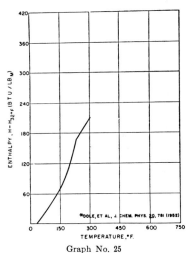

Graph No. 25

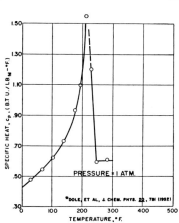

Graph No. 28

603

E. I. DU PONT DE NEMOURS & CO., INC.

ALATHON® 17

(Polyethylene)

Density at 23°C: 57.6 lb$_M$/ft³
Weight Average Molecular Weight (light scattering): 225,000
Number Average Molecular Weight (Estimated): 16,000
Melt Index or Flow Rate Index (gm/10 min.): 20; ASTM-D1238-52T

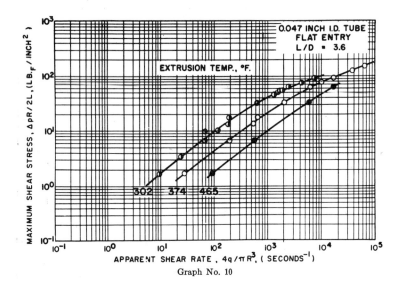

Graph No. 10

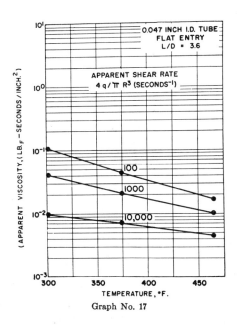

Graph No. 17

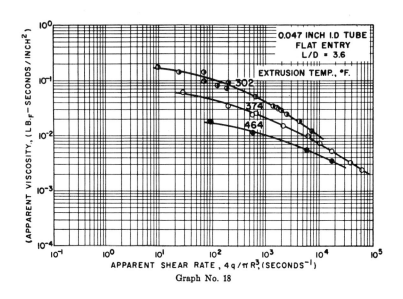

Graph No. 18

605

E. I. DU PONT DE NEMOURS & CO., INC.

ALATHON® 34

(Polyethylene)

Density at 23°C: 58.0 lb$_M$/ft³
Weight Average Molecular Weight (Newtonian viscosity): 175,000
Number Average Molecular Weight (estimated): 15,000
Melt Index or Flow Rate Index (gm/10 min.): 3.0; ASTM-D1238-52T

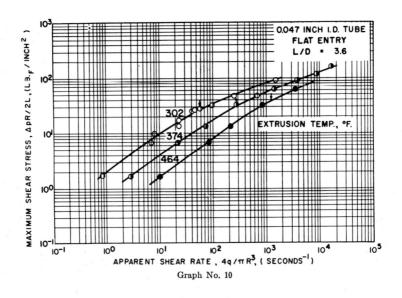

Graph No. 10

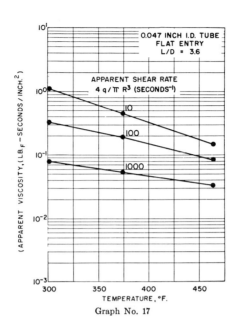

Graph No. 17

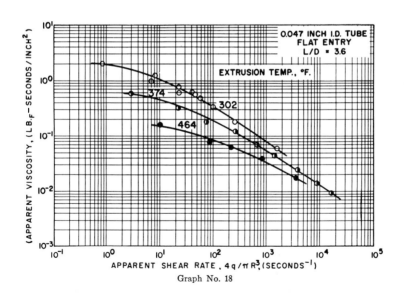

Graph No. 18

EASTMAN CHEMICAL PRODUCTS, INC.

TENITE® POLYETHYLENE 854

(Polyethylene)

Density at 23°C: 57.4 lb$_M$/ft³
Number Average Molecular Weight (inherent viscosity): 30,000
Melt Index or Flow Rate Index (gm/10 min.): 1.7; ASTM-D1238-52T

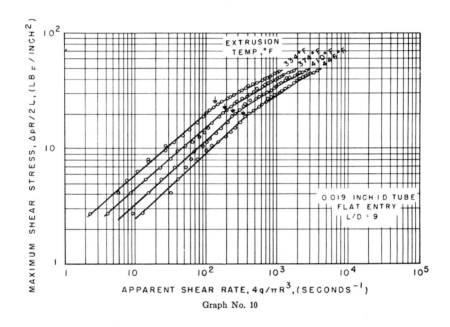

Graph No. 10

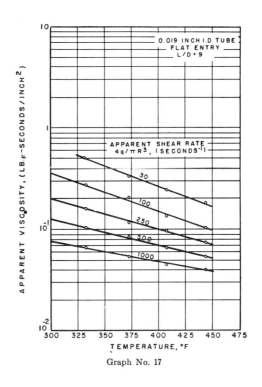

Graph No. 17

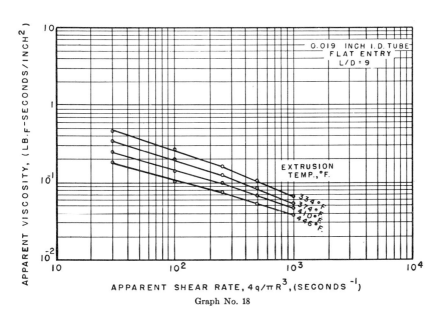

Graph No. 18

609

POLYETHYLENE RESINS

EASTMAN CHEMICAL PRODUCTS, INC.

TENITE® POLYETHYLENE 856

(Polyethylene)

Density at 23°C: 57.4 lb$_M$/ft³
Number Average Molecular Weight (inherent viscosity): 38,000
Melt Index or Flow Rate Index (gm/10 min.): 0.3; ASTM-D1238-52T

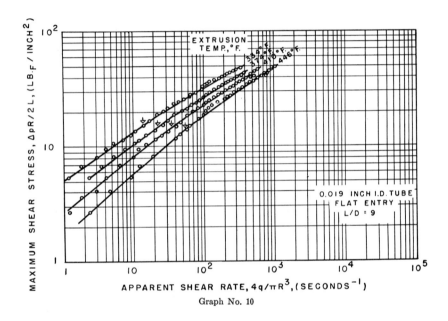

Graph No. 10

610

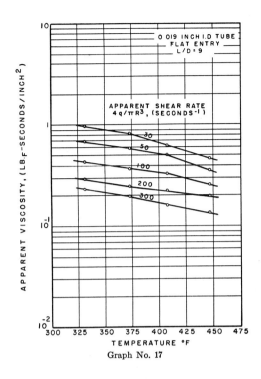

Graph No. 17

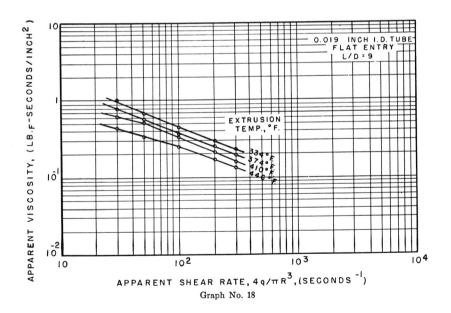

Graph No. 18

611

POLYETHYLENE RESINS

HI-FAX® 1400

(Polyethylene)

Density at 23°C: 59 lb$_M$/ft³

Weight Average Molecular Weight (light scattering): 160,000

No Plasticizers, Lubricants, or Fillers; contains 0.15% alkaline earth salt of fatty acid as additive

Melt Index or Flow Rate Index (gm/10 min.): 0.8; ASTM-D1238-52T

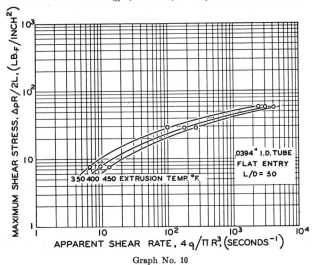

Graph No. 10

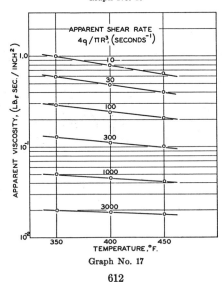

Graph No. 17

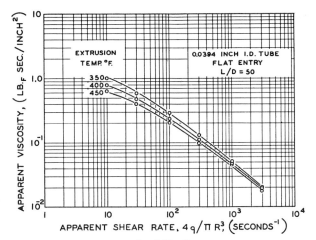

Graph No. 18

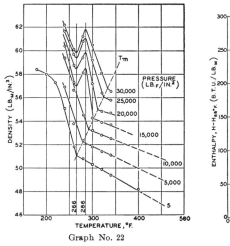

Graph No. 22

Graph No. 25

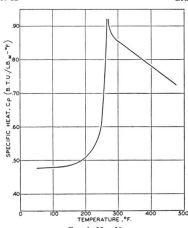

Graph No. 28

613

HERCULES POWDER COMPANY

HI-FAX® 1700

(Polyethylene)

Density at 23°C: 59 lb_M/ft^3
Weight Average Molecular Weight (light scattering): 340,000
No Plasticizers, Lubricants, or Fillers; contains 0.15% alkaline earth salt of fatty acid as additive
Melt Index or Flow Rate Index (gm/10 min.): *ca.* 0.1; ASTM-D1238-52T

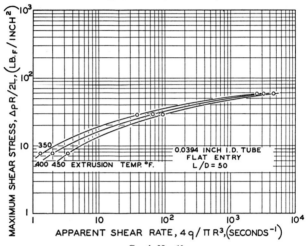

Graph No. 10

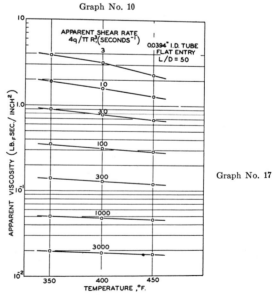

Graph No. 17

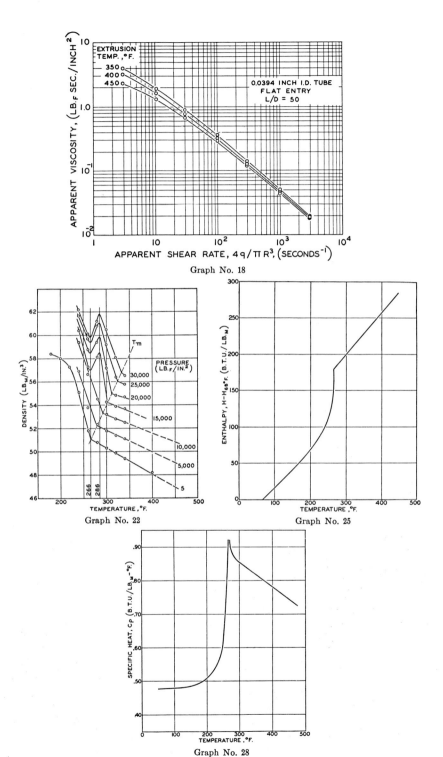

Graph No. 18

Graph No. 22

Graph No. 25

Graph No. 28

615

PHILLIPS CHEMICAL COMPANY

MARLEX® 50 POLYETHYLENE, TYPE 9

(Polyethylene)

Density at 23°C: 59.9 lb_M/ft^3
Weight Average Molecular Weight (light scattering): 126,000
Number Average Molecular Weight (boiling point elevation): 8,700
No Plasticizers, Lubricants or Fillers; contains 0.015% Ionol as additive
Melt Index or Flow Rate Index (gm/10 min.): 0.9; ASTM-D1238-52T

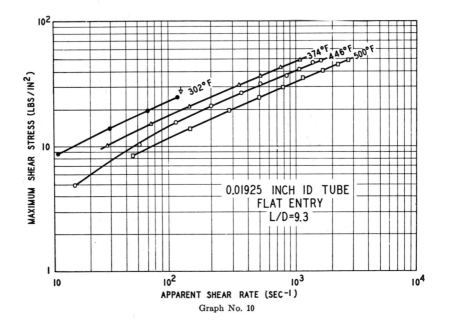

Graph No. 10

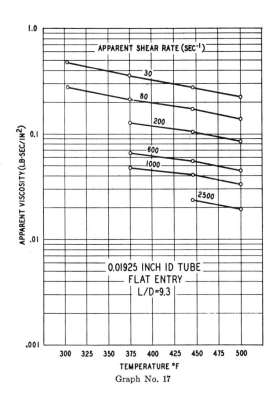

Graph No. 17

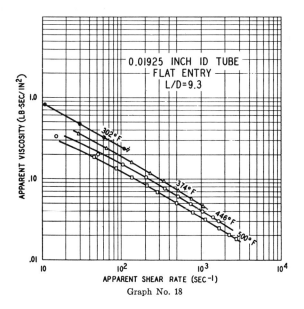

Graph No. 18

617

PHILLIPS CHEMICAL COMPANY

MARLEX® POLYETHYLENE, TYPE 15

(Polyethylene)

Density at 23°C: 59.9 lb_M/ft^3
No Plasticizers, Lubricants or Fillers; contains 0.015% Ionol as additive
Melt Index or Flow Rate Index (gm/10 min.):   1.5;   ASTM-D1238-52T

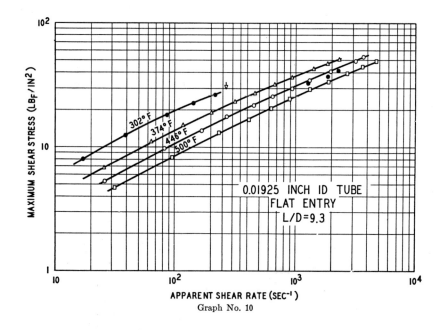

Graph No. 10

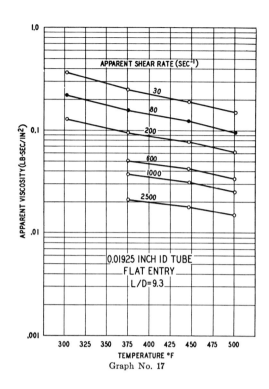

Graph No. 17

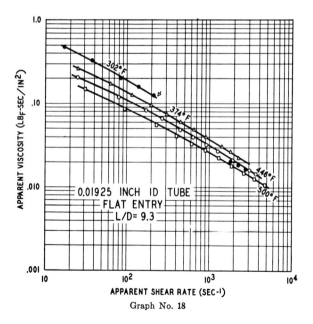

Graph No. 18

619

POLYETHYLENE RESINS

PHILLIPS CHEMICAL COMPANY

MARLEX® 50 POLYETHYLENE, TYPE 35

(Polyethylene)

Density at 23°C: 59.9 lb_M/ft^3
No Plasticizers, Lubricants or Fillers; contains 0.015% Ionol as additive
Melt Index or Flow Rate Index (gm/10 min.): 3.5;   ASTM-D1238-52T

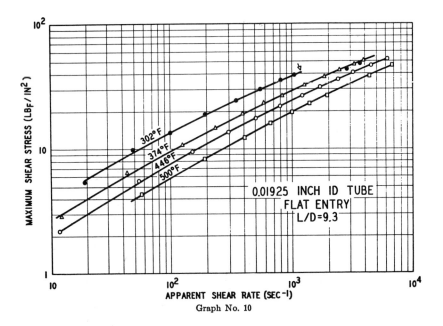

Graph No. 10

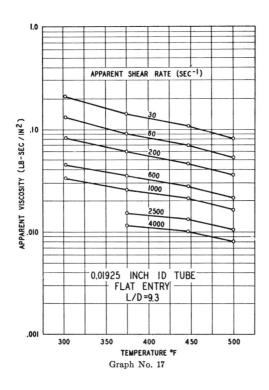

Graph No. 17

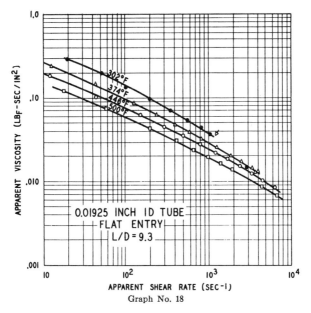

Graph No. 18

POLYETHYLENE RESINS

PHILLIPS CHEMICAL COMPANY

MARLEX® 50 POLYETHYLENE, TYPE 50

(Polyethylene)

Density at 23°C: 59.9 lb_M/ft^3
No Plasticizers, Lubricants or Fillers; contains 0.015% Ionol as additive
Melt Index or Flow Rate Index (gm/10 min.): 5.0; ASTM-D1238-52T

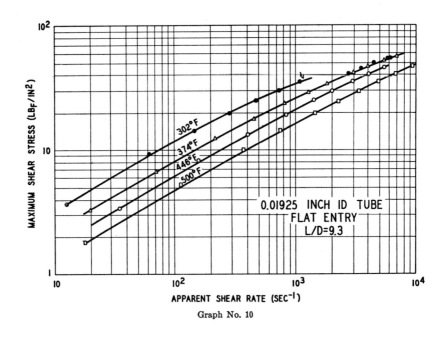

Graph No. 10

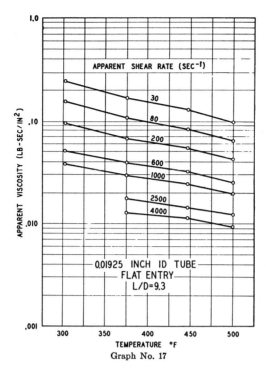

Graph No. 17

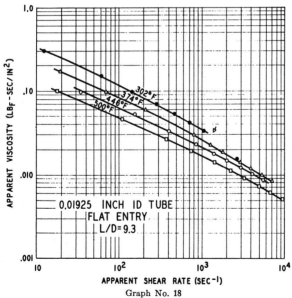

Graph No. 18

POLYETHYLENE RESINS

UNION CARBIDE CORPORATION

POLYETHYLENE DYNH

(Polyethylene)

Density at 23°C: 57.4 lb$_M$/ft³
Melt Index or Flow Rate Index (gm/10 min.): 2.1; ASTM-D1238-52T

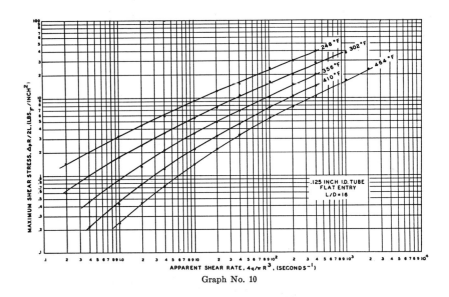

Graph No. 10

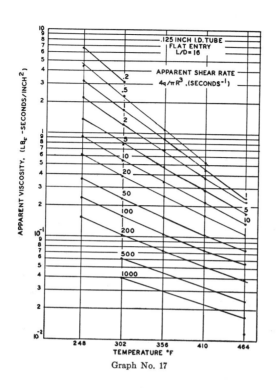

Graph No. 17

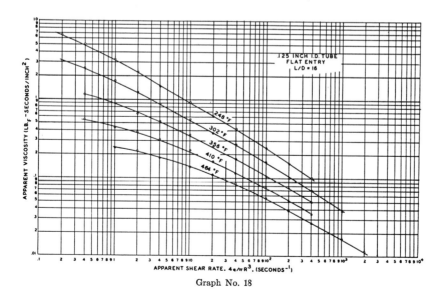

Graph No. 18

625

POLYETHYLENE RESINS

UNION CARBIDE CORPORATION

POLYETHYLENE DYNK

(Polyethylene)

Density at 23°C: 57.4 lb_M/ft^3
Melt Index or Flow Rate Index (gm/10 min.): 0.30; ASTM-D1238-52T

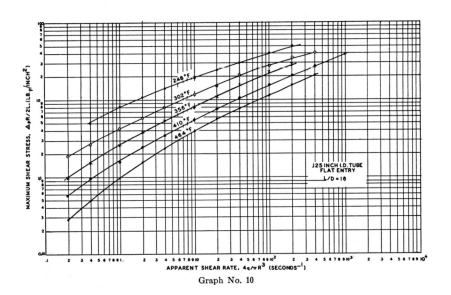

Graph No. 10

626

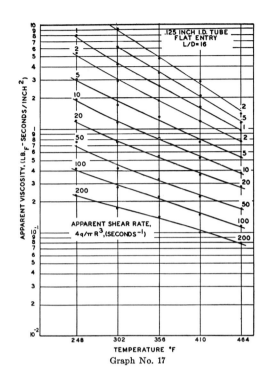

Graph No. 17

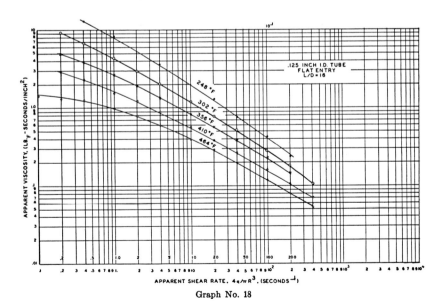

Graph No. 18

627

THE DOW CHEMICAL COMPANY

STYRON® 475

(Hi-impact Polystyrene)

Density at 23°C: 65.9 lb$_M$/ft³
Weight Average Molecular Weight (light scattering): 230,000
Number Average Molecular Weight (osmotic pressure): 130,000
Thermal Diffusivity for the Temperature Range from 25 to 450°F: 3.71 × 10⁻³ ft²/hr

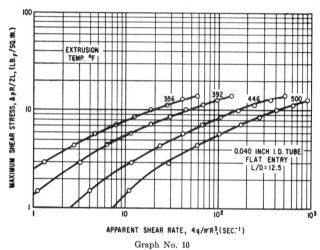

Graph No. 10

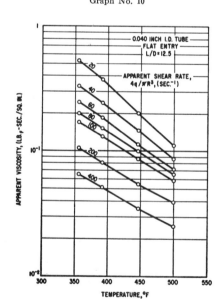

Graph No. 17

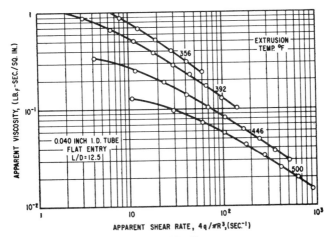

Graph No. 18

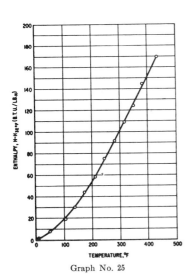

Graph No. 25

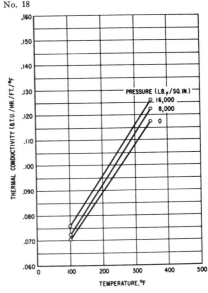

Graph No. 26

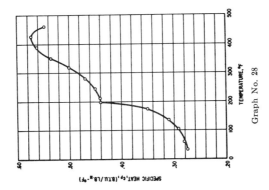

Graph No. 28

629

THE DOW CHEMICAL COMPANY

STYRON® 666

(Polystyrene)

Density at 23°C: 65.9 lb$_M$/ft³
Weight Average Molecular Weight (light scattering): 375,000
Number Average Molecular Weight (osmotic pressure): 230,000
Constants for Equation of State, $(P + \pi_i)\,(V - \omega) = R'T$

$$\pi_i = 27000 \qquad \omega = 0.822 \qquad R' = 11.6$$

Thermal Diffusivity for the Temperature Range from 25 to 450°F: 5.03×10^{-3} ft²/hr

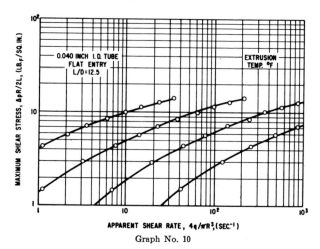

Graph No. 10

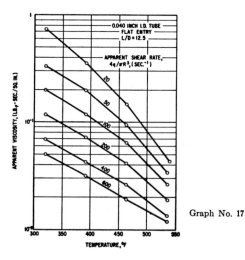

Graph No. 17

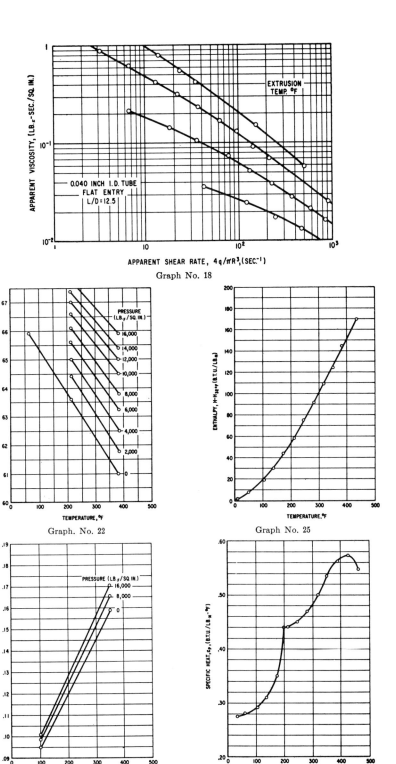

Graph No. 18

APPARENT VISCOSITY, (LB.ₑ-SEC./SQ. IN.)

EXTRUSION TEMP. °F

0.040 INCH I.D. TUBE
FLAT ENTRY
L/D = 12.5

APPARENT SHEAR RATE, 4q/πR³, (SEC.⁻¹)

Graph. No. 22

DENSITY, (LBₘ/FT.³)

PRESSURE (LBₓ/SQ. IN.)

16,000
14,000
12,000
10,000
8,000
6,000
4,000
2,000
0

TEMPERATURE, °F

Graph No. 25

ENTHALPY, H-H₃₂°F (B.T.U./LBₘ)

TEMPERATURE, °F

Graph No. 26

THERMAL CONDUCTIVITY (B.T.U./HR.-FT.-°F)

PRESSURE (LBₓ/SQ. IN.)
16,000
8,000
0

TEMPERATURE, °F

Graph No. 28

SPECIFIC HEAT, cₚ, (B.T.U./LBₘ-°F)

TEMPERATURE, °F

631

THE DOW CHEMICAL COMPANY

STYRON® 683

(Polystyrene)

Density at 23°C: 65.9 lb$_M$/ft³
Weight Average Molecular Weight (light scattering): 225,000
Number Average Molecular Weight (osmotic pressure): 130,000
Constants for Equation of State, $(P + \pi_i)\,(V - \omega) = R'T$

$$\pi_i = 27,000 \qquad \omega = 0.822 \qquad R' = 11.6$$

Thermal Diffusivity for the Temperature Range from 25 to 450°F: 5.03×10^{-3} ft²/hr

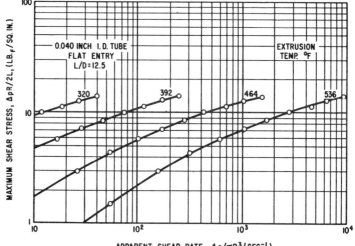

Graph No. 10

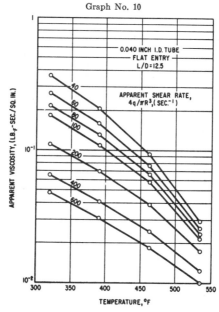

Graph No. 17

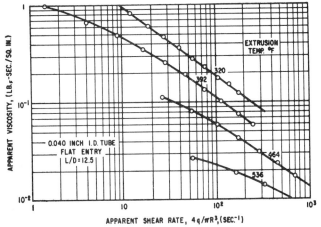

Graph No. 18

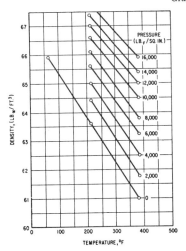

Graph. No. 22

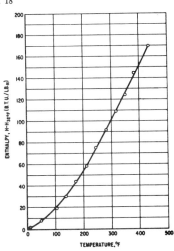

Graph No. 25

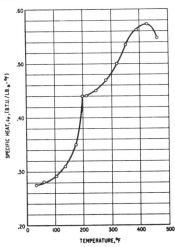

Graph No. 28

THE DOW CHEMICAL COMPANY

STYRON® 700

(Polystyrene)

Density at 23°C: 65.9 lb_M/ft^3
Weight Average Molecular Weight (light scattering): 220,000
Number Average Molecular Weight (osmotic pressure): 76,500

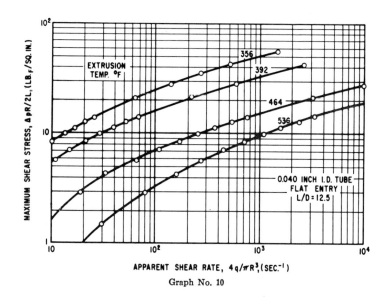

APPARENT SHEAR RATE, $4q/\pi R^3$, (SEC.$^{-1}$)

Graph No. 10

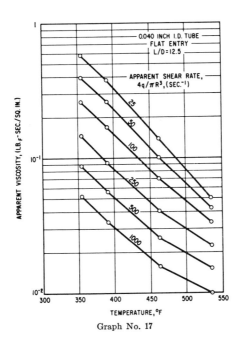

Graph No. 17

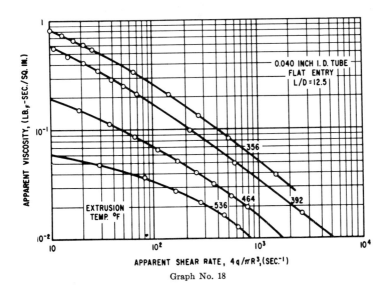

Graph No. 18

THE DOW CHEMICAL COMPANY

TYRIL® 767

(30% Acrylonitrile—70% Styrene Copolymer)

Density at 23°C: 65.9 lb$_M$/ft^3

Weight Average Molecular Weight (light scattering): 177,000

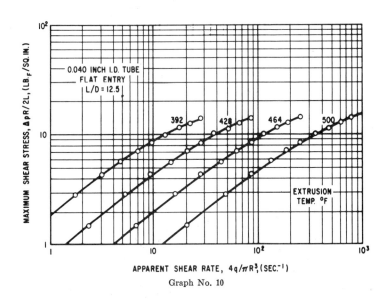

APPARENT SHEAR RATE, $4q/\pi R^3$, (SEC.$^{-1}$)

Graph No. 10

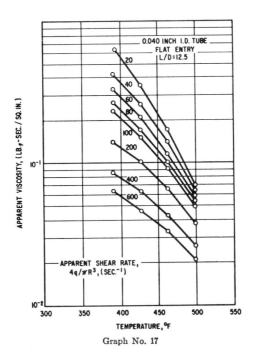

Graph No. 17

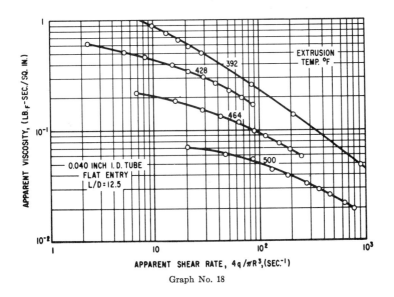

Graph No. 18

MONSANTO CHEMICAL COMPANY

LUSTREX® HF 55-2020

(Polystyrene)

Density at 23°C: 65.6 lb$_M$/ft³

Melt Index or Flow Rate Index (gm/10 min.): 1.87; ASTM-D1238-52T

Table of K' and n' at Two Temperatures

Temp. (°F)	K'	n'	Range of Validity (Sec.⁻¹)
400	0.80	0.52	1–30
400	1.6	0.33	30–10⁴
500	0.05	0.86	1–70
500	0.25	0.48	70–10⁴

Dielectric Loss Factor at Heat Sealing Frequencies: 0.002

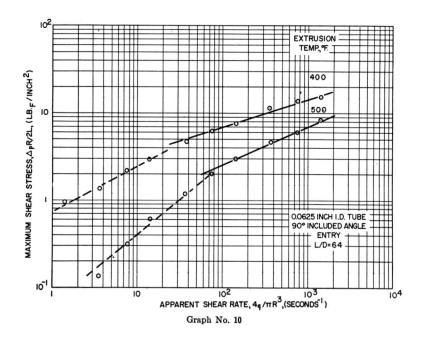

Graph No. 10

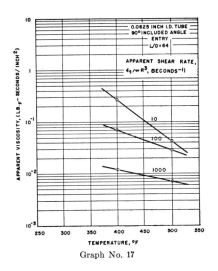

Graph No. 17

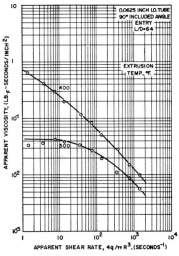

Graph No. 18

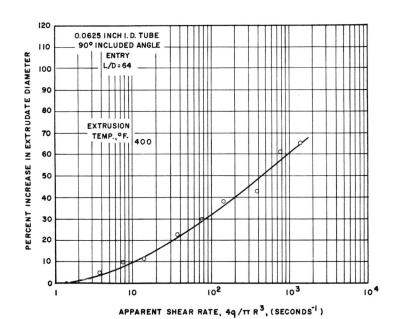

Graph No. 20

639

MONSANTO CHEMICAL COMPANY

LUSTREX® HF 77-2020

(Polystyrene)

Density at 23°C: 65.6 lb$_M$/ft³
Melt Index or Flow Rate Index (gm/10 min.): 0.34; ASTM-D1238-52T
Table of K' and n' at Two Temperatures

Temp. (°F)	K'	n'	Range of Validity (Sec.⁻¹)
400	2.1	0.31	1–10⁴
500	0.26	0.54	1–10⁴

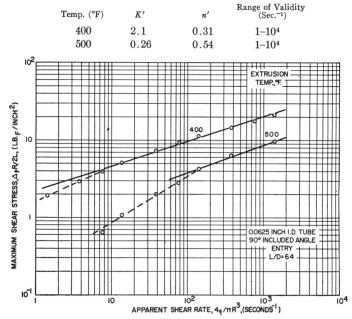

Graph No. 10

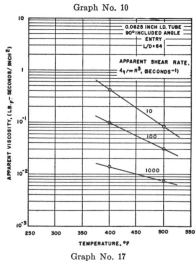

Graph No. 17

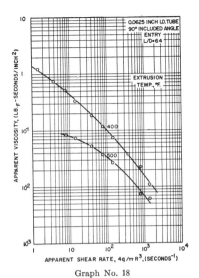

Graph No. 18

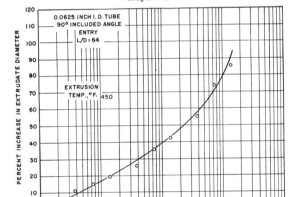

Graph No. 20

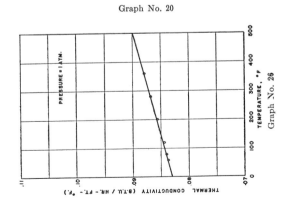

641

MONSANTO CHEMICAL COMPANY

LUSTREX® HH 99A-5-2020

(Polystyrene)

Density at 23°C: 65.6 lb$_M$/ft³
Melt Index or Flow Rate Index (gm/10 min.): 0.53; ASTM-D1238-52T
Table of K' and n' at Two Temperatures

Temp. (°F)	K'	n'	Range of Validity (Sec.⁻¹)
400	1.5	0.5	1–20
400	2.5	0.31	20–10⁴
500	0.20	0.66	1–50
500	0.58	0.41	50–10⁴

Dielectric Loss Factor at Heat Sealing Frequencies: 0.001

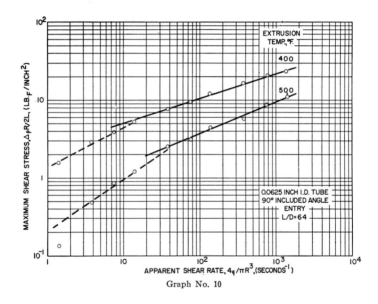

Graph No. 10

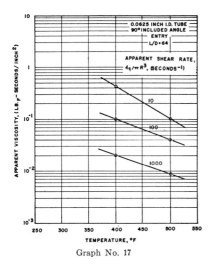

Graph No. 17

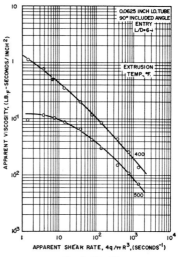

Graph No. 18

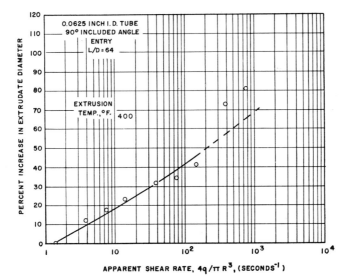

Graph No. 20

643

MONSANTO CHEMICAL COMPANY

LUSTREX® LHA-1000

(Polystyrene—Rubber Polyblend)

Density at 23°C: 66.3 lb$_M$/ft³
Melt Index or Flow Rate Index (gm/10 min.): 1.35; ASTM-D1238-52T
Table of K' and n' at Three Temperatures

Temp. (°F)	K'	n'	Range of Validity (Sec.⁻¹)
400	0.50	0.68	1–30
400	1.6	0.33	30–10⁴
450	0.15	0.82	1–40
450	0.73	0.39	40–10⁴
500	0.10	0.71	1–100
500	0.29	0.48	100–10⁴

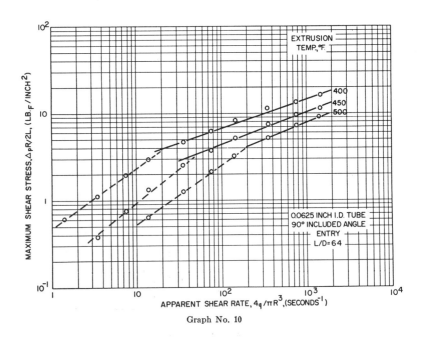

Graph No. 10

644

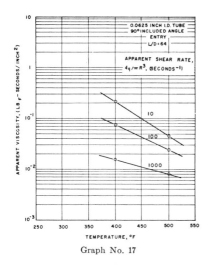

Graph No. 17

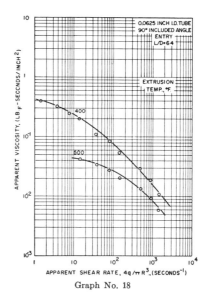

Graph No. 18

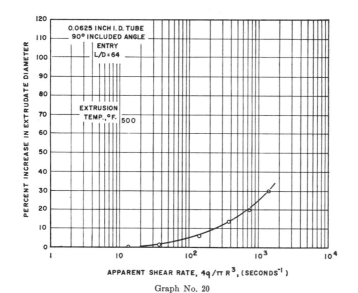

Graph No. 20

645

MONSANTO CHEMICAL COMPANY

LUSTREX® LSA 843-411

(Polystyrene)

Density at 23°C: 65.6 lb_M/ft^3
Melt Index or Flow Rate Index (gm/10 min.): 1.33; ASTM-D1238-52T
Table of K' and n' at Several Temperatures

Temp. (°F)	K'	n'	Range of Validity (Sec.$^{-1}$)
275	9.5	0.48	$1-10^4$
300	3.6	0.46	$1-10^4$
325	2.3	0.40	$1-10^4$
350	1.3	0.42	$1-10^4$

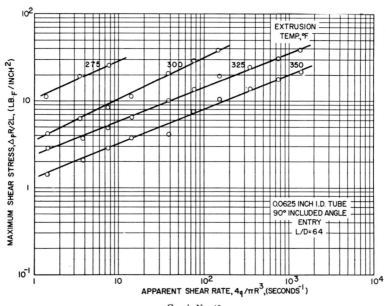

Graph No. 10

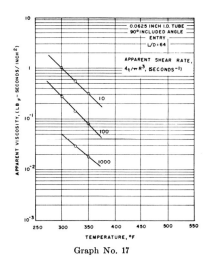

Graph No. 17

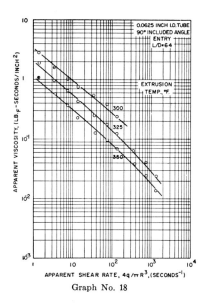

Graph No. 18

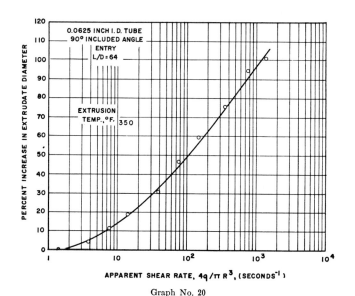

Graph No. 20

647

MONSANTO CHEMICAL COMPANY

LUSTREX® HT 88B-1000

(Polystyrene—Rubber Polyblend)

Density at 23°C: 66.9 lb$_M$/ft³
Melt Index or Flow Rate Index (gm/10 min.): 0.86; ASTM-D1238-52T
Table of K' and n' at Three Temperatures

Temp. (°F)	K'	n'	Range of Validity (Sec.$^{-1}$)
400	1.2	0.42	1–10
400	1.7	0.35	10–10⁴
450	0.34	0.53	1–25
450	0.90	0.38	25–10⁴
500	0.22	0.52	1–10²
500	0.60	0.40	10²–10⁴

Dielectric Loss Factor at Heat Sealing Frequencies: 0.003

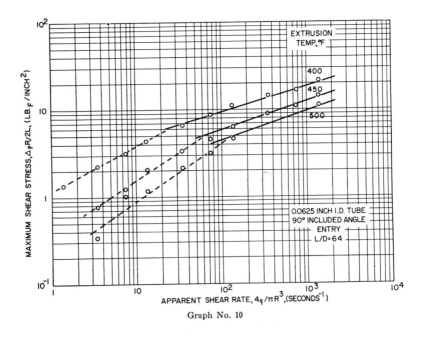

Graph No. 10

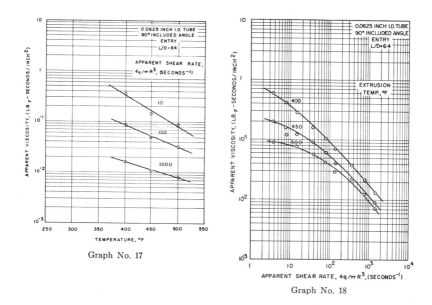

Graph No. 17

Graph No. 18

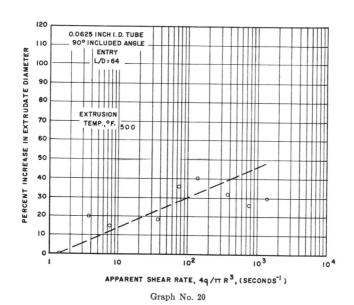

Graph No. 20

649

UNION CARBIDE CORPORATION

COPOLYMER RMD 4511

(Polystyrene Acrylonitrile Copolymer)

Density at 23°C: 67.0 lb$_M$/ft³

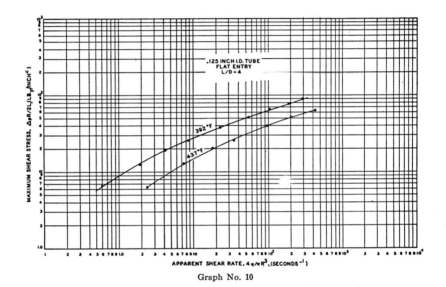

Graph No. 10

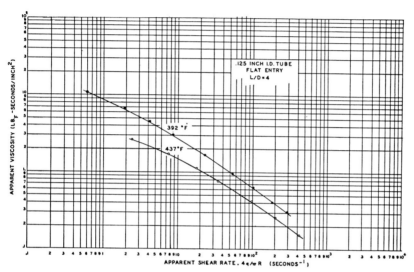

Graph No. 18

651

UNION CARBIDE CORPORATION

TMD-2155, TGDA-2001—EXTRA HIGH-IMPACT POLYSTYRENE

(Modified Polystyrene)

Density at 23°C: 64.3 lb$_M$/ft³

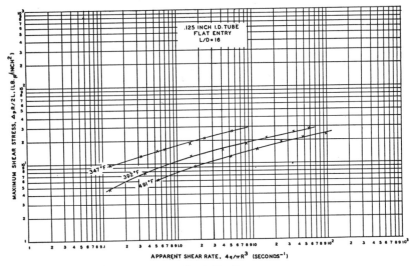

Graph No. 10

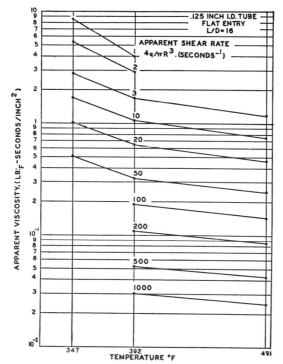

Graph No. 17

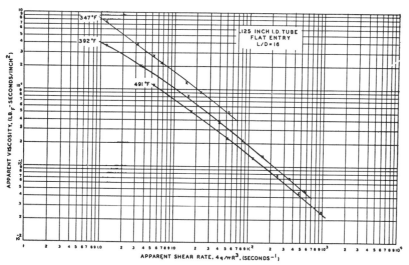

Graph No. 18

653

B. F. GOODRICH CHEMICAL COMPANY

GEON® 8700A

(Rigid Polyvinyl Chloride)

No Plasticizer

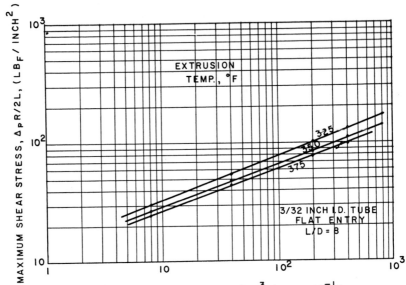

Graph No. 10

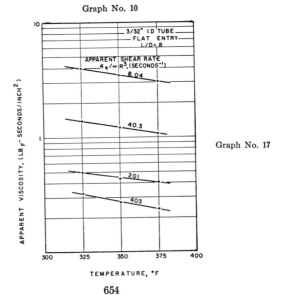

Graph No. 17

654

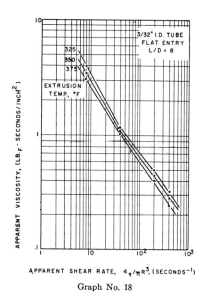

Graph No. 18

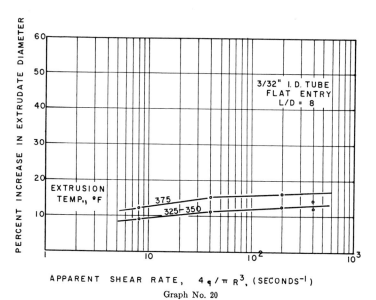

Graph No. 20

B.F. GOODRICH CHEMICAL COMPANY

GEON® 8750

(Rigid Polyvinyl Chloride)

No Plasticizer

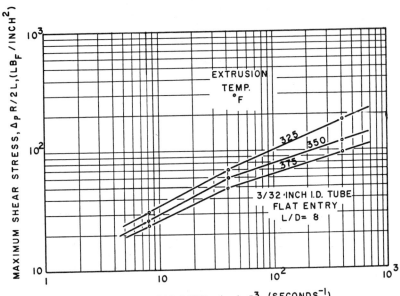

Graph No. 10

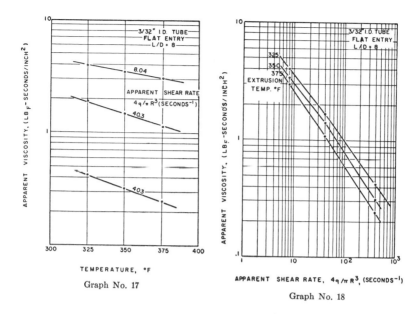

Graph No. 17

Graph No. 18

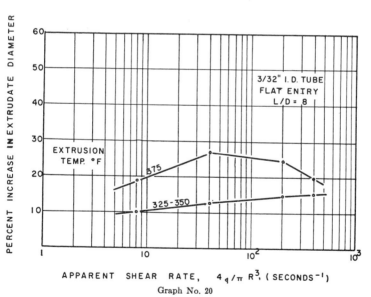

Graph No. 20

MONSANTO CHEMICAL COMPANY

OPALON® 1028 (NATURAL)

(Polyvinyl Chloride)

Density at 23°C: 85.6 lb$_M$/ft³
Melt Index or Flow Rate Index (gm/10 min.): 4.59; ASTM-D1238-52T
Table of K' and n' at Two Temperatures

Temp. (°F)	K'	n'	Range of Validity (Sec.⁻¹)
300	7.0	0.24	1–10⁴
350	1.8	0.38	1–10⁴

Plasticized Compound

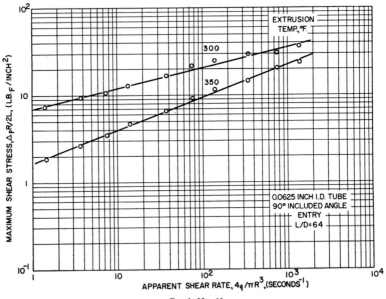

Graph No. 10

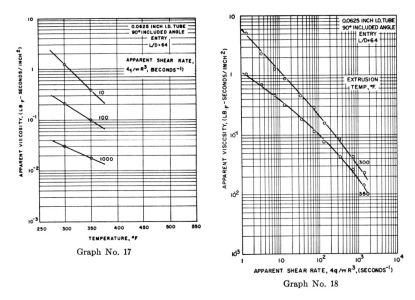

Graph No. 17

Graph No. 18

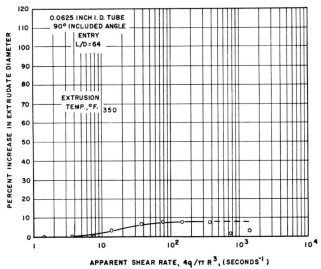

Graph No. 20

MONSANTO CHEMICAL COMPANY

OPALON® 1038 (NATURAL)

(Polyvinyl Chloride)

Density at 23°C: 86.2 lb_M/ft^3
Melt Index or Flow Rate Index (gm/10 min.): 0.12; ASTM-D1238-52T
Plasticized Compound
Table of K' and n' at Two Temperatures

Temp. (°F)	K'	n'	Range of Validity (Sec.$^{-1}$)
300	11.	0.27	1–10⁴
350	4.6	0.31	1–10⁴

Dielectric Loss Factor at Heat Sealing Frequencies: 0.200

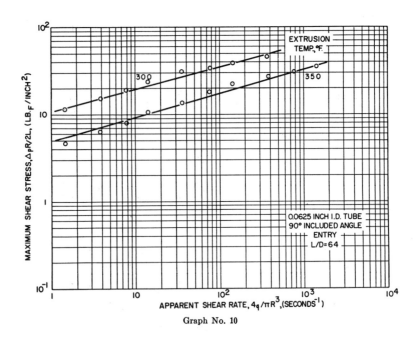

Graph No. 10

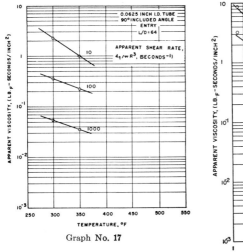

Graph No. 17

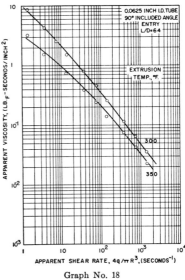

Graph No. 18

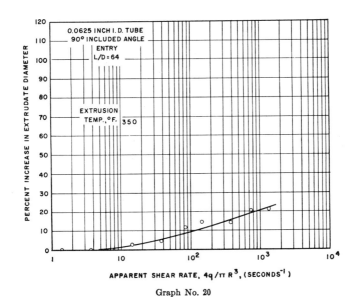

Graph No. 20

661

MONSANTO CHEMICAL COMPANY

OPALON® 1406 (NATURAL)

(Polyvinyl Chloride)

Density at 23°C: 85.6 lb_M/ft^3
Melt Index or Flow Rate Index (gm/10 min.): 0.09; ASTM-D1238-52T
Plasticized Compound
Table of K' and n' at Two Temperatures

Temp. (°F)	K'	n'	Range of Validity (Sec.$^{-1}$)
300	5.5	0.26	$1-10^4$
350	1.8	0.21	$1-10^4$

Dielectric Loss Factor at Heat Sealing Frequencies: 0.180

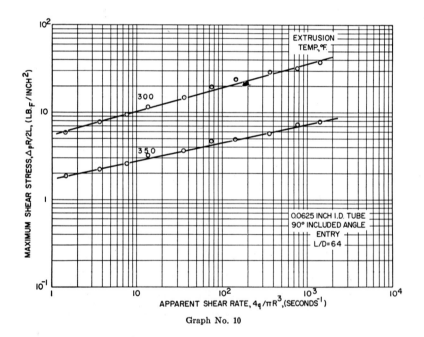

Graph No. 10

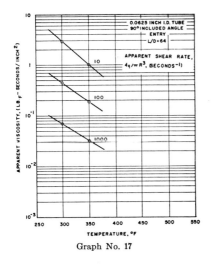

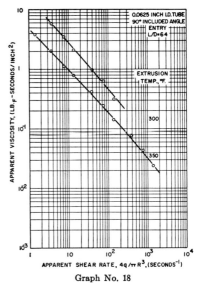

Graph No. 17

Graph No. 18

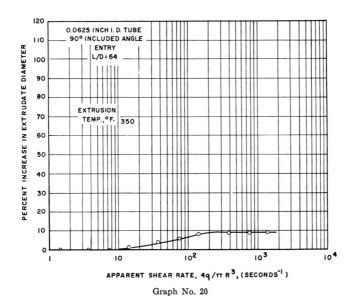

Graph No. 20

663

MONSANTO CHEMICAL COMPANY

OPALON® 1706 (NATURAL)

(Polyvinyl Chloride)

Density at 23°C: 83.7 lb$_M$/ft³
Melt Index or Flow Rate Index (gm/10 min.): 0.07; ASTM-D1238-52T
Plasticized Compound
Table of K' and n' at Two Temperatures

Temp. (°F)	K'	n'	Range of Validity (Sec.⁻¹)
300	25.0	0.24	1–10³
350	7.7	0.31	1–10³

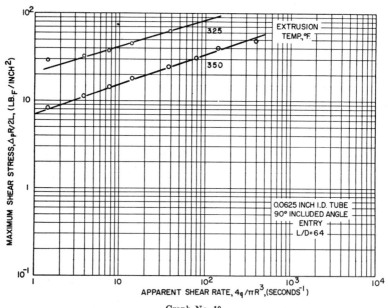

Graph No. 10

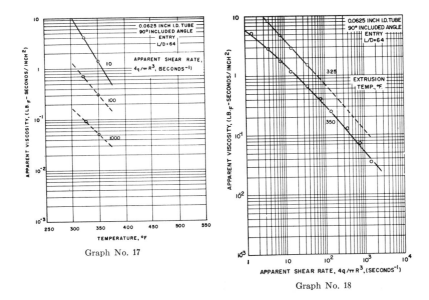

Graph No. 17

Graph No. 18

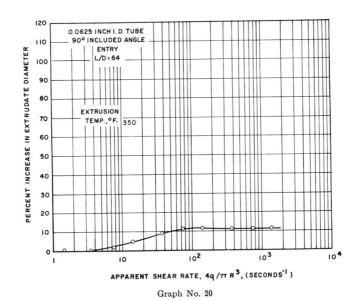

Graph No. 20

665

MONSANTO CHEMICAL COMPANY

OPALON® 71329 (NATURAL)

(Polyvinyl Chloride)

Density at 23°C: 85.6 lb$_M$/ft³
Melt Index or Flow Rate Index (gm/10 min.): 8.05; ASTM-D1238-52T
Plasticized Compound
Table of K' and n' at Two Temperatures

Temp. (°F)	K'	n'	Range of Validity (Sec.⁻¹)
300	6.9	0.23	1–10⁴
350	1.2	0.42	1–10⁴

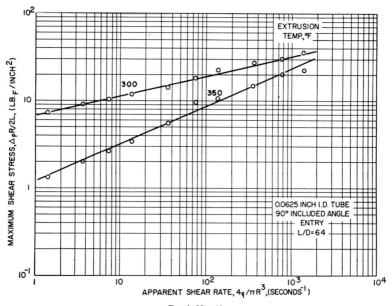

Graph No. 10

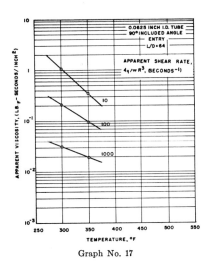

Graph No. 17

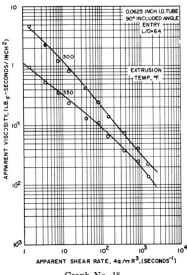

Graph No. 18

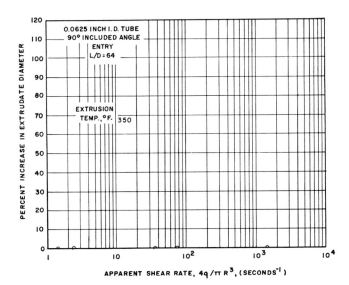

Graph No. 20

UNION CARBIDE CORPORATION

VINYL CHLORIDE COPOLYMER VYNW, 30% PLASTICIZER

(3 % Vinyl Acetate—97 % Vinyl Chloride Copolymer)

Density at 23°C: 79.8 lb$_M$/ft³
30% By Weight of Di-2-ethylhexylphthalate Plasticizer

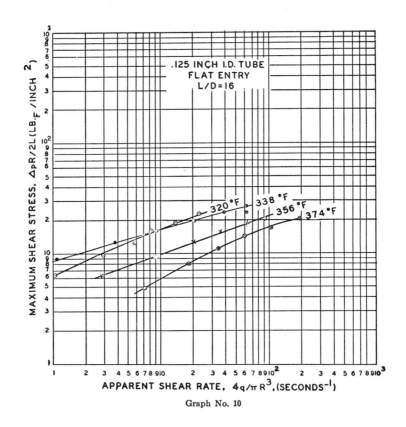

Graph No. 10

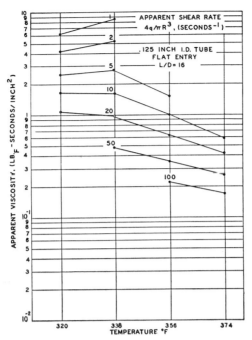

Graph No. 17

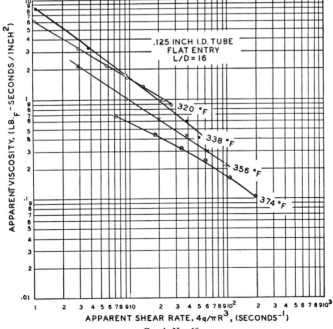

Graph No. 18

UNION CARBIDE CORPORATION

VINYL CHLORIDE COPOLYMER VYNW, 35% PLASTICIZER

(3 % Vinyl Acetate—97 % Vinyl Chloride Copolymer)

Density at 23°C: 78.3 lb_M/ft^3
35% By Weight of Di-2-ethylhexylphthalate Plasticizer

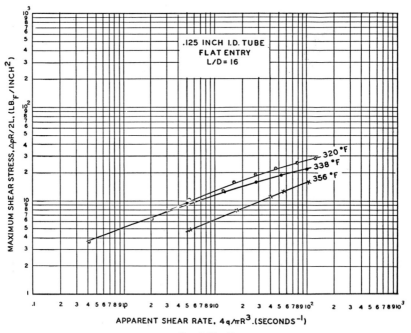

.125 INCH I.D. TUBE
FLAT ENTRY
L/D = 16

320 °F
338 °F
356 °F

MAXIMUM SHEAR STRESS, $\Delta pR/2L$, $(LB_F/INCH^2)$

APPARENT SHEAR RATE, $4q/\pi R^3$. (SECONDS^{-1})

Graph No. 10

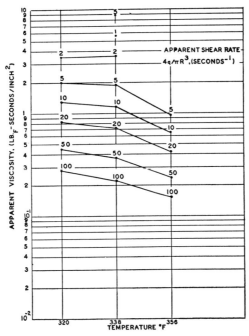

Graph No. 17

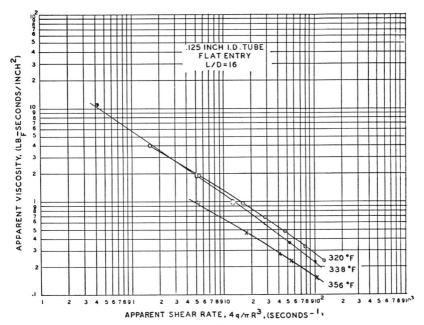

Graph No. 18

671

UNION CARBIDE CORPORATION

VINYL CHLORIDE COPOLYMER VYNW, 40% PLASTICIZER

(3 % Vinyl Acetate—97 % Vinyl Chloride Copolymer)

Density at 23°C: 76.9 lb_M/ft^3
40% By Weight of Di-2-ethylhexylphthalate Plasticizer

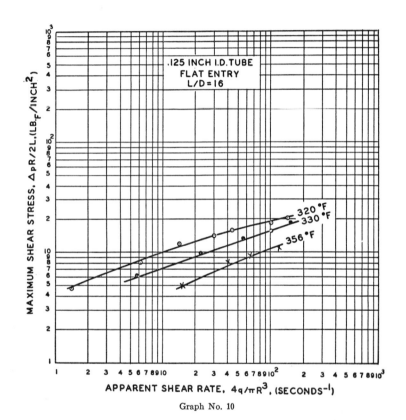

Graph No. 10

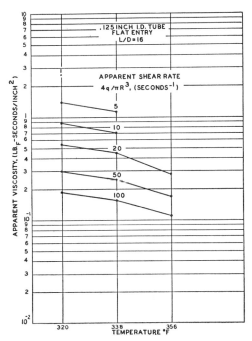

Graph No. 17

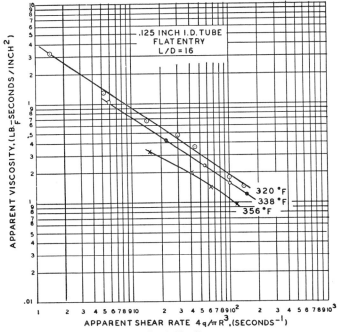

Graph No. 18

673

UNION CARBIDE CORPORATION

VINYL CHLORIDE COPOLYMER VYNW, 45% PLASTICIZER

(3% Vinyl Acetate—97% Vinyl Chloride Copolymer)

Density at 23°C: 75.5 lb_M/ft^3
45% By Weight of Di-2-ethylhexylphthalate Plasticizer

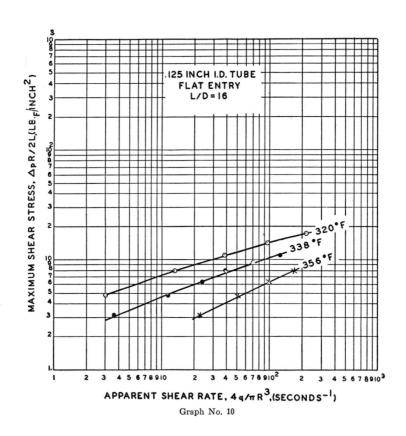

Graph No. 10

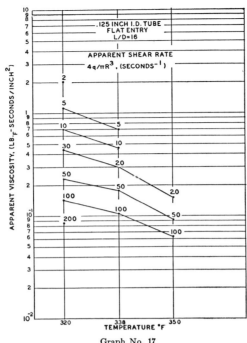

Graph No. 17

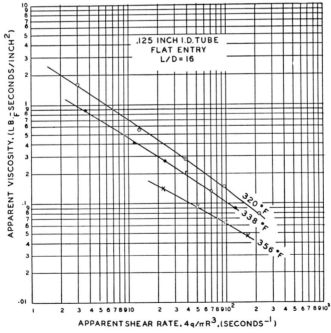

Graph No. 18

675

UNION CARBIDE CORPORATION

VINYL CHLORIDE—ACETATE COPOLYMER VYHH

(13 % Vinyl Acetate—90 % Vinyl Chloride Copolymer)

Density at 23°C: 84.8 lb$_M$/ft³

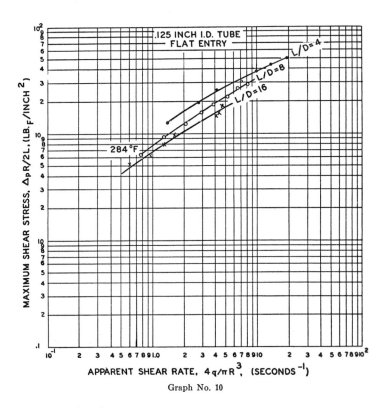

Graph No. 10

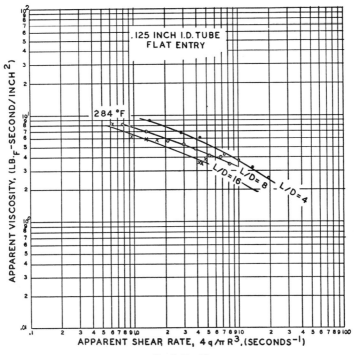

Graph No. 18

677

UNION CARBIDE CORPORATION

VINYL CHLORIDE—ACETATE COPOLYMER VYNS

(10 % Vinyl Acetate—90 % Vinyl Chloride Copolymer)

Density at 23°C: 84.9 lb_M/ft^3

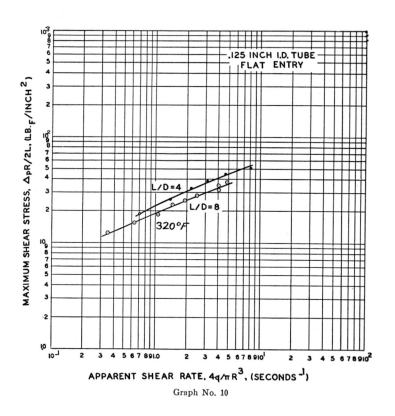

Graph No. 10

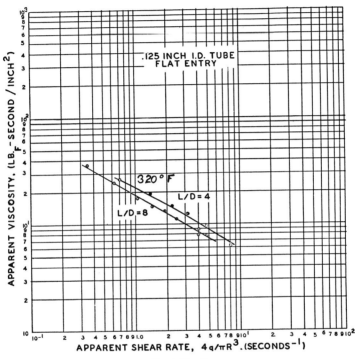

Graph No. 17

679